BASIC PRINCIPLES AND LAWS OF

Mechanics

D. C. HEATH AND COMPANY

Boston   Englewood   Atlanta
Chicago   Dallas   San Francisco

BASIC PRINCIPLES AND LAWS OF

Mechanics

Alfred Zając

ADELPHI UNIVERSITY

TO *Dorothy, Mark, and Andrew*

THIS BOOK IS PUBLISHED IN ASSOCIATION WITH TEXTBOOK ASSOCIATES, INC., NEW YORK

Library of Congress Catalog Card Number 66–12390

Printed February 1966

COVER DESIGN BY GAIL B. FINE   DIAGRAMS BY R. F. C. STUDIO

PREFACE

This book was written for advanced undergraduate and first-year graduate students. Early chapters review aspects of elementary mechanics so that the book can well be used by students who have not taken the usual intermediate mechanics course. Although a previous course in mechanics is not assumed, it is assumed that the reader has acquired a degree of sophistication acquired by pursuing a two or three year undergraduate curriculum in science, including a course in differential and integral calculus.

All the basic definitions, concepts, and principles of elementary mechanics are introduced in Chapters 1 and 2. This is followed by a brief chapter on equilibrium, one on oscillations, one on the motion of a particle in a central force field, and another on the motion of a system of particles.

With Chapter 7 we begin the three main parts of this discourse on mechanics: the Lagrangian and Hamiltonian formalisms, rigid body motion, and small oscillations.

The studies of the Lagrangian mechanics are preceded by a discussion of generalized coordinates and contain a treatment of unconstrained motion of a single particle and the motion of a particle, and motion of a system of particles under holonomic and nonholonomic constraints. The problem of constraints receives more attention than is usual in comparable texts. The Hamiltonian theory, including the Routhian procedure, follows. This part closes with a discussion of variational and integral principles and with some very general considerations of the integration of equations of motion of a system of particles.

The rigid body motion is presented in three chapters consisting of a discussion of the kinematical principles, the general dynamical principles, and some applications to special cases. Of these, the kinematics of rigid body motion is presented in greater detail and with more care than is usually done.

The theory of small oscillations constitutes the last of the three main parts of mechanics presented in this book. The discussions contained in these three parts by no means exhaust the subjects covered but these parts are presented in considerable detail. In the Lagrangian formulation a repetitive presentation was purposely used in order to introduce the more complicated systems smoothly.

For many purposes natural phenomena are best described by use of the theories of relativity and wave mechanics. Two chapters are devoted to the theory of relativity: one discusses the evidence for the necessity of the theory, with some particularly careful presentation of fundamental experiments, and the other contains elementary exposition of relativistic kinematics. The discussion of wave mechanics is preceded by the presentation of some of the mathematics of "eigenphysics." In the chapter on wave mechanics the classical picture of nature is discussed first. Evidence is cited to show that in certain cases pure classical physics can be applied successfully to the submicroscopic domain, but that in other cases classical physics fails. The Schrodinger equation is then introduced and solved for two cases, some postulates of wave mechanics are discussed, and the quantum mechanical picture of nature is offered.

In writing a book, as in preparing a lecture, an author must decide how much detail to include in explanation and how much explanation, search, and thought should be left to the student. Although a student may profit greatly by participating in rediscovery of the various laws of science, this procedure is time consuming. An effort has been made here to present a dissertation on introductory mechanics which can, in general, be understood on first reading. The reasoning is that through such a presentation the student can acquire a rudimentary knowledge of mechanics in a comparatively short time and in a comparatively painless manner. With this background he is equipped to venture further.

By its very nature, this text cannot be original in content. Although it is original in certain of its presentations, the author has profited from many other presentations. He wishes especially to acknowledge the lectures on mechanics by D. R. Rutherford given at St. Andrews University in Scotland. A considerable portion of this book, namely Lagrange's formulation and rigid body motion, is based in many parts on the two volumes of *Lectures on Theoretical Mechanics* by A. Przeborski (Wykłady Mechaniki Teoretycznej, Warszawa, 1935). Other sources are mentioned in the list of references.

In preparation of the manuscript the author is deeply indebted to Jeffrey Bindell from the Polytechnic Institute of Brooklyn for reading the entire manuscript critically and for suggesting many changes and revisions. The entire manuscript was also read by Riet de Beuss, to whom sincere thanks are given. Parts of the manuscript were read by Alexander Harvey of Queens College in New York and by Terry O'Dwyer from Nassau Community College; their suggestions and criticism are gratefully acknowledged here. Thanks are also offered to Anthony Lemos of Adelphi University and Bruce Keyes of Polytechnic Institute of Brooklyn for helpful criticism.

It is impossible to acknowledge all the discussions with friends and students on various parts of mechanics and various problems. The results of a great many of these discussions are incorporated here. The author will consider it a compliment if suggestions and criticism are forwarded to him.

Special appreciation and thanks are conveyed to the editorial staff of D. C. Heath and Company, especially to Richard T. Wareham and Paul P. Bryant. Finally, praise is given to the fine work of the designer, the printer, and the artist, who are responsible for the appearance of the book.

Alfred Zając
Adelphi University

CONTENTS

BASIC PRINCIPLES AND LAWS OF

Mechanics

1

INTRODUCTION

1-1 *The Role of Classical Mechanics*

The first subject which one must master when studying physics is mechanics, for it is this subject which formulates the laws and physical concepts which enter into the whole domain of physics.

Even more, it so happens that we approach all parts of physics with an outlook based on our knowledge of mechanical phenomena. This is simply the way we have been trained. We apply this knowledge of mechanics to all other branches of physics (optics, acoustics, kinetic theory, statistical mechanics, electricity, magnetism and even modern physics). At least, this is the first thing that, in general, we would do. The reason for such an approach to physics is that we are constantly confronted with mechanical phenomena and constantly verifying a multitude of laws from mechanics. Thus, for instance, being able to set up the laws of motion of the planets about the sun, and verifying them experimentally, we are tempted to transplant all the results to the motion of electrons about the nucleus of an atom. However, in such cases our knowledge of mechanical phenomena is sometimes a hindrance to proper understanding of atomic phenomena. Nevertheless it is true, and it appears that it will be so for some time, that the mechanical laws will lead us in constructing new theories. In many instances their guiding principles have produced useful results.

The proper description of the behavior of atoms is provided by quantum mechanics. In one of its methods, the mathematical form of the basic differential equation—which describes the behavior of an atomic system—is something like that describing the wave in a string. In order to set up this equation we start with concepts taken from mechanics.

Classical mechanics formulate the laws of motion of macroscopic systems. These laws predict the motion with absolute accuracy. The last statement perhaps requires some explanation. Consider, for instance, the case of the uniform motion of a point mass along a straight line. Let the x-axis be the line along which the particle moves. On this line choose an origin O (a mathematical point) and establish the positive and negative directions. The uniform motion of the point is completely described by the equation

$$\mathbf{x} = \mathbf{x}_o + \mathbf{v}t \tag{1.1}$$

where $\mathbf{v}$ (the velocity of the particle) is constant and $\mathbf{x}_o$ is given. This equation describes the past and the future kinematical history of the particle with absolute accuracy in the same sense that the mathematical analysis locates a point on a straight line. The same applies to all other laws of classical mechanics. In many cases (e.g., the three body problem) it is not possible to construct analytical expressions which will predict the required physical quantities in such a manner as was the case in the above example. Even in such cases, however, the classical physicist would say that by a series of successive approximations or otherwise one could arrive at the absolute values of the physical quantities. That all cases could be solved as accurately as desired was the belief of the classical physicist. Modern physics has modified this view entirely, even in the simplest cases.

1–2 The Concept of a Field

The concept of a field is basic in physics and should be used as soon as one attempts to study the various branches of physics in a serious manner. The field always pertains to a particular physical quantity in the sense that one speaks about the field of this quantity. Actually we can speak of the field of any physical quantity, e.g., temperature field, force field, the field of the electric intensity, potential field, the field of velocity, of position of material particles, and so on.

In the mathematical sense *the field of a given physical quantity is given if this quantity is specified as a mathematical function of space and of time.* Thus for instance, a particular field of force $\mathbf{F}$ is given if we are given the function

$$\mathbf{F} = \mathbf{F}(t, x, y, z) \tag{1.2}$$

Here the independent variables are the time and the space coordinates x, y, z. As we see, the mathematical description of a field is straightforward.

The physical description of a field depends on the particular case. Usually there are sources, the nature of which is not always clear, but which create some special physical situation. *The physical situation is the field,* and the sources are the sources of the field. Often, to picture things better, one identifies with the field the region of space in which the particular physical situation exists. But *it is really this physical situation created by the sources which constitutes the field.*

Given the field of a physical quantity, we investigate its properties and formulate laws which describe their behavior. We refer to the mathematical form of these laws as *field equations.*

1–3 Scalar and Vector Description

There will be two main categories of fields with which we shall deal namely *scalar* and *vector fields.* These do not exhaust all possible types but they will fulfill our main purpose. By their nature, scalar fields are simpler; this follows from the definition of a scalar as a quantity which is completely specified by its magnitude. A vector quantity is more complicated which, again, can be seen from the definition of the vector.*

Certain physical situations can be described by both a scalar and a vector field; in that case the two should be related. We will see that such a double description of the same field permits us to understand its properties more fully.

1-4 Newton's Laws

Consider the Euclidean space E connected with some Cartesian frame of reference K, and let the variable t denote the time. We may call the four-dimensional continuum (x, y, z, t) the Newtonian world N or the Newtonian space-time N. We will examine the motion of *kinematical points*** in E. The collection of kinematical points will be called a set of *material points* in N if certain conditions to be specified presently are satisfied.

If we postulate that apart from a certain system of the material points no other points are present in E then we will call such a system a *closed system*. A closed system, consisting of one point only, will be called an *isolated point*.

The collection of kinematical points will constitute a set of material points if the following two conditions are satisfied:

1. *With every material point there is associated a certain positive number called its mass.****

2. *The motion of the material points in E is governed by certain laws, called Newton's laws*, which will now be stated.

At this time we will state Newton's laws for very simple systems only, namely for an isolated point and for a closed system consisting of only two points.† In later chapters these laws will be formulated for closed systems consisting of any number of material points. These laws will then be extended to the case of a closed system which is under the influence of external forces. All these laws will apply to the case when the motion of the system occurs in the Newtonian world defined above. As we will see, Newton's laws will have to be extended further still to the case when another Newtonian world N_1 exists which has the time common with N and when the space E_1 belonging

---

* Appendix A.
** A kinematical point is a point function $A(x, y, z)$ (or depending on some other set of coordinates), specified in Euclidean space, which also depends on time.
*** There is more than one way to achieve a passage from kinematics to dynamics, and one of them is to introduce, as a postulate, the concept of mass. That such a postulate is necessary is suggested by experiments which demonstrate that every object offers a resistance against motion. This resistance is termed inertia, and its quantitative measure is the mass. It is possible to devise an experiment, the result of which will be the assignment of mass to every particle of a system. Such an experiment can only assign relative masses to all the components of the system. Some unit of mass must be chosen, and this can be done in an arbitrary way.
† In formulating these laws we will assume that neither the isolated point nor the system of two points is subjected to any external influence.

to N_1 moves in a prescribed manner in the space E. We will thus examine motions of material points occuring simultaneously in N and N_1.*

First Law (The Law of Inertia). *An isolated point in E remains in a state of rest or uniform motion, i.e., the acceleration of an isolated point is at all times zero.*

Such an isolated moving point could serve as a most precise clock, for it would take the same time to traverse equal lengths at all points of its path.

This and all other laws of mechanics are the results of observations and certain idealized experiments. Let us now suppose that we have a closed system consisting of two material points P_1 and P_2 only. Let the masses of the two points be m_1 and m_2 respectively. The results of observations and experiments performed on such a system lead to the conclusion that the motion of the system proceeds in such a way that the accelerations a_1 and a_2 of the two points are at all times different than zero and satisfy the condition

$$\mathbf{r}_1 \times m_1\mathbf{a}_1 + \mathbf{r}_2 \times m_2\mathbf{a}_2 = \mathbf{0} \tag{1.3}$$

where $\mathbf{r}_1$ and $\mathbf{r}_2$ are the position vectors drawn from an arbitrary point O in E, i.e., $\mathbf{r}_1 = \overrightarrow{OP_1}$ and $\mathbf{r}_2 = \overrightarrow{OP_2}$. From the result stated in the above form we can make certain deductions. Choose another arbitrary point O_1 of E, and let $\overrightarrow{O_1P_1} = \mathbf{r}_1'$ and $\overrightarrow{O_1P_2} = \mathbf{r}_2'$. Then

$$\mathbf{r}_1' \times m_1\mathbf{a}_1 + \mathbf{r}_2' \times m_2\mathbf{a}_2 = \mathbf{0} \tag{1.4}$$

Subtracting Eq. (1.4) from (1.3) we obtain

$$\overrightarrow{OO_1} \times (m_1\mathbf{a}_1 + m_2\mathbf{a}_2) = \mathbf{0}$$

and since the vector $\overrightarrow{OO_1}$ is arbitrary

$$m_1\mathbf{a}_1 + m_2\mathbf{a}_2 = \mathbf{0}$$

which in turn means that the direction of the acceleration $\mathbf{a}_1$ is opposite to that of $\mathbf{a}_2$. If a_1 and a_2 denote the magnitudes of these accelerations then

$$\frac{a_1}{a_2} = \frac{m_2}{m_1}$$

If O be at the position of P_1 then Eq. (1.3) takes the form

$$\overrightarrow{P_1P_2} \times m_2\mathbf{a}_2 = \mathbf{0}$$

which indicates that the acceleration $\mathbf{a}_2$, and therefore also $\mathbf{a}_1$, have the direction of the vector $\overrightarrow{P_1P_2}$ which joins the two material points.

---

* In other words we will describe the possibility of viewing the same physical events from different coordinate systems.

It follows from the above considerations that in the motion of a closed system consisting of two material points P_1 and P_2 of masses m_1 and m_2 the vectors

$$\mathbf{F}_{12} = -m_2\mathbf{a}_2, \quad \mathbf{F}_{21} = -m_1\mathbf{a}_1$$

are determined as functions of relative position $\mathbf{r}_1 - \mathbf{r}_2$ of the two points and their relative velocity $\mathbf{v}_1 - \mathbf{v}_2$. The vector $\mathbf{F}_{12}$ lying along the line P_1P_2 is called *the geometrical representation of the force acting on P_1; the source of this force is the material point P_2.* Similarly the vector $\mathbf{F}_{21}$, lying along the same line is called the geometrical representation of the force acting on the point P_2. We shall simply call $\mathbf{F}_{12}$ and $\mathbf{F}_{21}$ forces. If, for some reason, we focus our attention on the point P_1 then force $\mathbf{F}_{12}$ is termed the action of P_2 on P_1, and the force $\mathbf{F}_{21}$ is called the reaction of P_1 on P_2. It has to be stressed that the action and reaction are forces acting on different points.

We are now in position to state the remaining two laws of Newton.

The Second Law. *In a closed system consisting of two material points, the force acting on every point is equal to the product of its mass and acceleration.* Thus

$$m_1\mathbf{a}_1 = \mathbf{F}_{12}, \quad m_2\mathbf{a}_2 = \mathbf{F}_{21}$$

We say that the acceleration $\mathbf{a}_1$ of the point P_1 is caused by the force $\mathbf{F}_{12}$, and the acceleration of P_2 by the force $\mathbf{F}_{21}$.

The Third Law. *The action and reaction of two material points are at every instant represented by two opposite vectors lying along the straight line joining the two points at that instant.* We usually say that "the action is equal to the reaction."*

1–5 The Role of Differential Equations in Physics

Physics and, for that matter, all the other exact sciences do not really have their own language. When it comes to the enunciation of a precise law they all use the same language, namely that of mathematics. It is actually a happy situation that such a well-developed medium exists because without it precise knowledge of the outside world would be almost impossible.

* As stated above, we will extend Newton's laws to other systems. Here we might want to state Newton's laws in a manner very roughly resembling Newton's own statements (formulated in *Philosophiae Naturalis Principia Mathematica*, London (1687)):
  I. Every body remains in a state of rest or uniform motion unless acted upon by an unbalanced force.
  II. The force acting on a body is equal to the time rate of change of the linear momentum of the body, (momentum being the product of the mass of the body and its velocity).
  III. When one body exerts a force on another, the second body reacts on the first with a force equal in magnitude to the original force but opposite in direction.
  In formulating the second law, Newton did not speak about "the time rate of change of momentum" but instead used the expression "change of motion."

The relation between the physical phenomena and their mathematical description should be carefully studied. In certain branches of physics, this will have to be done more extensively than in others. In classical mechanics such a relation between the appropriate physical problem and its mathematical description should either be obvious or, in general, should easily be obtained. (The last sentence was purposely retained in its conditional form.)

When a particular phenomenon is being investigated, one chooses a number of quantities which describe the system at hand. The choice at first may be arbitrary, but eventually one should arrive at a set of quantities which are well suited to describe the system. A good set need not be unique but should consist of independent quantities only. This means that any other quantity which is of interest can be expressed in terms of this set.

A functional relationship between the quantity of interest and the independent set will constitute a physical law. Such functional relationships almost invariably contain derivatives; therefore, *they are differential equations. In practically all cases a physical law is stated in the form of one or more differential equations.* Their solutions will produce quantities which can be subjected to experimental test.

2

REVIEW OF ELEMENTARY MECHANICS

Considerable insight into mechanics can be obtained from the study of the motion of a point mass in a plane. Most of the concepts used in mechanics can be introduced here and their physical significance clearly seen. All the laws governing such motion have lucid meaning, and the various principles can be derived readily. For this reason, the study of this type of simple motion will be emphasized in this review of elementary mechanics.

2-1 Displacement, Velocity, and Acceleration

There are several aspects of motion which can be studied without admitting the existence of any forces. In such a case one studies the purely *kinematical aspects of motion*. The physical quantities which one needs in this case are the displacement vector **r**, the velocity vector **v** and the acceleration vector **a**.

Consider a particle of mass m which moves in a plane. The *displacement vector* is the position vector of the particle at any time (Fig. 2.1). The locus of the tip of the displacement vector is the path of the particle.

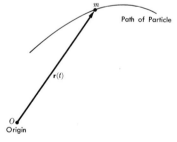

Fig. 2.1
Position vector.

The *velocity vector* is defined as

$$\mathbf{v} = \lim_{\Delta t \to 0} \frac{[\mathbf{r}(t) + \Delta\mathbf{r}(t)] - \mathbf{r}(t)}{\Delta t}$$

$$= \lim_{\Delta t \to 0} \frac{\Delta\mathbf{r}(t)}{\Delta t} \tag{2.1}$$

Thus
$$\mathbf{v} = \frac{d\mathbf{r}}{dt} \tag{2.2}$$

The direction of the velocity vector is always tangential to the path of the

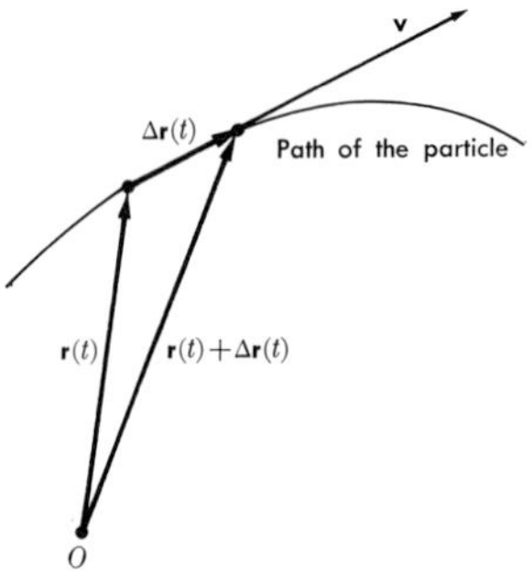

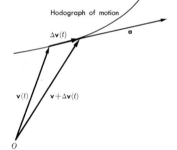

Fig. 2.2
Change of
position vector.

particle as can be seen from the definition of **v** and from Figure 2.2. The direction of the velocity vector is given by the differential element $d\mathbf{r}$ which is an element of the path and which is the only vector entering in the definition of the velocity.

Starting from the same point O let us now draw vectors $\mathbf{v}(t)$ at different times which represent the velocity in magnitude and direction. The locus of the tip of the vector $\mathbf{v}(t)$ will be a curve which is called the *hodograph of the motion* (Fig. 2.3). The *acceleration vector* is defined as

$$\mathbf{a} = \lim_{\Delta t \to 0} \frac{\Delta \mathbf{v}(t)}{\Delta t}$$

or

$$\mathbf{a} = \frac{d\mathbf{v}}{dt} \tag{2.3}$$

The acceleration will be tangential to the hodograph as can be seen from the definition and from Figure 2.3.

Fig. 2.3
Hodograph
of motion.

With reference to the path of the particle, the acceleration can, in general, assume any direction.

Since

$$\mathbf{v} = \frac{d\mathbf{r}}{dt}$$

therefore

$$\mathbf{a} = \frac{d^2\mathbf{r}}{dt^2} \tag{2.4}$$

In the case of one-dimensional motion all the quantities can be written in the scalar form. If the motion is along the x-axis, for instance, then, choosing

2–1 Displacement, velocity, and acceleration

an origin and assigning a direction to the axis, the displacement is given by x and the velocity and acceleration are given by

$$v = \frac{dx}{dt}$$

and

$$a = \frac{dv}{dt}$$

From these

$$dx = v\, dt$$

and

$$x = \int v\, dt \qquad (2.5)$$

and similarly

$$v = \int a\, dt \qquad (2.6)$$

The last two expressions can be used without any change of the variable of integration when

$$v = v(t) \quad \text{and} \quad a = a(t)$$

i.e., when both v and a are functions of time. When the integrals are indefinite, the first integral gives the functional dependence of x on t and the second gives v as a function of time. When the motion takes place between two given instants of time, the integrals become definite, so that

$$x = \int_{t_1}^{t_2} v\, dt \qquad (2.7)$$

and similarly

$$v = \int_{t_1}^{t_2} a\, dt \qquad (2.8)$$

The graphical interpretation of the various expressions should not be over-looked. Let us plot three graphs, namely x versus t, v versus t and the acceleration a versus t. The slopes of the graphs of x and v furnish the values of the velocity and acceleration respectively at any time t; the areas under the graphs of v and a give the displacement and the velocity respectively in any time interval (t_1, t_2).

Often the acceleration and velocity are given as well-behaved functions of position. Thus, for acceleration, we will have

$$a = a(x) \qquad (2.9)$$

Now

$$a = \frac{d\dot{x}}{dt}$$

$$= \frac{d\dot{x}}{dt}\frac{dx}{dx}$$

The order of differentiation does not affect the result, and so we can write

$$a = \frac{dx}{dt}\frac{d\dot{x}}{dx}$$

2-1 Displacement, velocity, and acceleration

9

or
$$a(x) = \dot{x}\,\frac{d\dot{x}}{dx} \tag{2.10}$$

This expression is useful in two cases. When the velocity is given as a function of position, i.e., when
$$\dot{x} = \dot{x}(x)$$

the last expression can be used to evaluate the acceleration. If the acceleration is given as a function of position, then the last relation can be written as
$$a(x)\,dx = \dot{x}\,d\dot{x} \tag{2.11}$$

in which the variables are separated and therefore integration can be performed readily.

When
$$\dot{x} = \dot{x}(x)$$

is given, and it is required to obtain x, then we substitute
$$\dot{x} = \frac{dx}{dt}$$

in the expression for the velocity and obtain
$$\frac{dx}{dt} = \dot{x}(x)$$

from which
$$\frac{dx}{\dot{x}(x)} = dt \tag{2.12}$$

Again the variables are separated and the integration can be carried out. The resulting expression will really give the time as a function of x. In principle this relation can be untangled so that x is on one side and everything else is on the other side of the equation.

2-2   Absolute and Relative Motion

Every motion is relative.* It is relative to other bodies or systems. We may choose some particular frame of reference which appears to us to be fixed, and refer the motion of a system of particles to it. Motion referred to such a frame may be termed absolute.** We then say that the motion of every particle referred to the fixed system will be governed by the laws of absolute motion.

* This fact was independently discovered by the son of the author when the boy was two years old. Travelling in an elevated train he observed that the windows of the nearby houses were *moving* past him.
** We are on slippery ground here. Actually, no motion is absolute and there is no experiment which will prove that some particular frame is fixed. This, however, does not affect the kinematical laws of relative motion which are presented here.

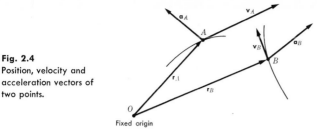

Fig. 2.4
Position, velocity and
acceleration vectors of
two points.

Consider two such particles A and B (Fig. 2.4). Their absolute displacements will be given by the vectors $\mathbf{r}_A$ and $\mathbf{r}_B$. Their velocities and accelerations referred to the same fixed space will be given by vectors $\mathbf{v}_A$, $\mathbf{v}_B$ and $\mathbf{a}_A$, $\mathbf{a}_B$.

Now, we may consider the motion of one particle with respect to the other, for instance that of B with respect to A. This relative motion can best be investigated by constructing appropriate vector diagrams as shown in Figures 2.5 (a), (b), and (c). These diagrams can be termed the *displacement diagram*, the *velocity diagram* and the *acceleration diagram* respectively. These are simply diagrams of the respective vectors, drawn to scale and in the proper direction from a common origin. The quantities describing the relative motion will be the vector differences shown in Figure 2.5. Thus, for instance, the relative

(a)
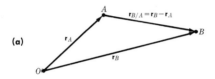

Fig. 2.5
Relative displacement,
relative velocity and
relative acceleration.

(b)
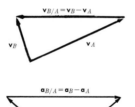

(c)

velocity of B with respect to A, $\mathbf{v}_{B/A}$, will be given by

$$\mathbf{v}_{B/A} = \mathbf{v}_B - \mathbf{v}_A \qquad (2.13)$$

where the vector $\mathbf{v}_{B/A}$ will start at the tip of the vector $\mathbf{v}_A$ and end at the tip of the vector $\mathbf{v}_B$.

This analysis can be extended to any number of moving points.

2-3 Dynamics of the Linear Motion of a Point Mass

The motion of a particle is governed by Newton's second law, viz.

$$\mathbf{F} = \dot{\mathbf{p}} \tag{2.14}$$

where $\mathbf{F}$ is the net force acting on the particle and

$$\mathbf{p} = m\mathbf{v} \tag{2.15}$$

is the *linear momentum* of the particle. In cases when m is constant, Eq. (2.15) reduces to

$$\mathbf{F} = m\mathbf{a} \tag{2.16}$$

From Eq. (2.16) we have

$$\mathbf{F} = m\,\frac{d\mathbf{v}}{dt} \tag{2.17}$$

or

$$\mathbf{F}\,dt = m\,d\mathbf{v}$$

from which

$$\int_{t_1}^{t_2} \mathbf{F}\,dt = \int_{\mathbf{v}_1}^{\mathbf{v}_2} m\,d\mathbf{v} \tag{2.18}$$

The quantity

$$\mathbf{J} = \int_{t_1}^{t_2} \mathbf{F}\,dt \tag{2.19}$$

is called the *impulse* acting between the times t_1 and t_2. Thus, performing the integration on the right-hand side of Eq. (2.18) we obtain

$$\mathbf{J} = m\mathbf{v}_2 - m\mathbf{v}_1 \tag{2.20}$$

This relation embodies the *principle of linear impulse and linear momentum* which states that *the total impulse exerted on the particle is equal to the change of its linear momentum.*

When

$$\mathbf{J} = \mathbf{0}$$

then

$$m\mathbf{v}_2 = m\mathbf{v}_1 \tag{2.21}$$

This is *the principle of conservation of linear momentum.* It applies to the case when the linear impulse is zero, i.e., in general when no force acts on the particle. In such a case the particle is an example of a *closed system.* The principle of conservation of linear momentum states that *for a closed system its total linear momentum is conserved.*

All the above equations are vector equations and, in our case of the motion of a particle in a plane, each is equivalent to two scalar equations. Thus Eq. (2.21) is equivalent to

$$m(v_1)_x = m(v_2)_x$$

and

$$m(v_1)_y = m(v_2)_y \tag{2.22}$$

The same holds for Eq. (2.20) which gives

$$J_x = m(v_2)_x - m(v_1)_x$$

and

$$J_y = m(v_2)_y - m(v_1)_y$$

(2.23)

In some cases $J_x = 0$ and $J_y \neq 0$; then only the x-component of the linear momentum is conserved and the y-component is not.

2–4 Expressing the Motion in Terms of Components

A vector is a directed quantity; therefore, in the two-dimensional case, one needs two coordinates to describe it completely. This can be seen immediately if we place the beginning of the vector at the origin. Then the vector will be specified uniquely if the coordinates of its endpoint are given. The simplest such coordinates are obtained when referred to the Cartesian rectangular frame of reference. In this system the displacement vector **r** can be written as

$$\mathbf{r} = \mathbf{r}_x + \mathbf{r}_y$$

where $\mathbf{r}_x$ and $\mathbf{r}_y$ are termed the *rectangular components of the vector* **r** (Fig. 2.6).

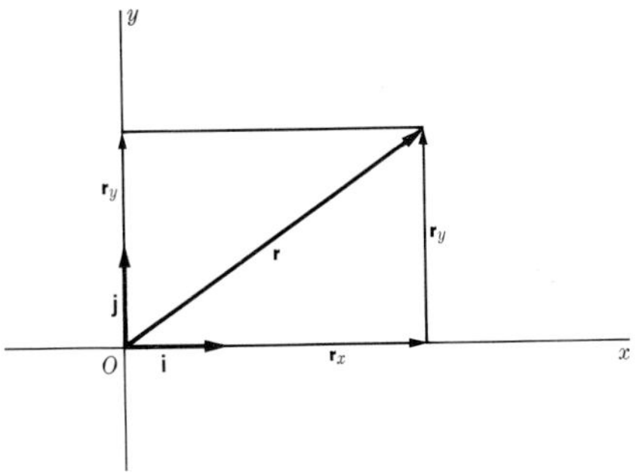

Fig. 2.6
Rectangular components
of the position vector.

Introducing unit vectors **i** and **j**, one can write

$$\mathbf{r}_x = r_x \mathbf{i} \qquad \mathbf{r}_y = r_y \mathbf{j}$$

(2.24)

therefore

$$\mathbf{r} = r_x \mathbf{i} + r_y \mathbf{j}$$

(2.25)

Thus, actually a non-localized vector is completely specified by a pair of numbers (r_x, r_y).

For the velocity and the acceleration vectors we have

$$\mathbf{v} = v_x \mathbf{i} + v_y \mathbf{j}$$

(2.26)

and

$$\mathbf{a} = a_x \mathbf{i} + a_y \mathbf{j}$$

(2.27)

It follows that every vector equation

$$\mathbf{A} = \mathbf{f}(\mathbf{B})$$

(2.28)

is equivalent to two scalar equations. When solving practical problems one always makes use of this fact. Before replacing a vector equation by two scalar equations, a proper choice of components should be made.

Besides the rectangular components mentioned above, the ones used most often are:

(1) *the normal and tangential components*, and

(2) *the radial and transverse components*.

The normal and tangential components are only used for the acceleration vector. This vector is resolved into two components along the tangent and the normal to the path of motion of the particle (Fig. 2.7). Thus the resultant

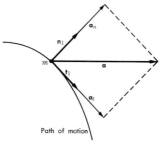

Fig. 2.7
Normal and tangential components of the acceleration vector.

acceleration vector is given by

$$\mathbf{a} = \mathbf{a}_t + \mathbf{a}_n \tag{2.29}$$

where $\mathbf{a}_t$ and $\mathbf{a}_n$ are the tangential and normal components respectively. If unit vectors $\mathbf{t}_1$ and $\mathbf{n}_1$ along the tangent and the normal are used then

$$\mathbf{a} = a_t \mathbf{t}_1 + a_n \mathbf{n}_1 \tag{2.30}$$

The velocity vector is always tangential to the path. The two components of the acceleration can be expressed in terms of the velocity vector. Consider two neighboring positions P_1 and P_2 of the moving particle (Fig. 2.8a) at which the velocities are $\mathbf{v}_1$ and $\mathbf{v}_2$ respectively. The normals at P_1 and P_2

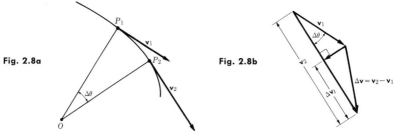

Fig. 2.8a

Fig. 2.8b

to the path will meet at a point O and will be inclined at an angle $\Delta\theta$ to each other. Draw the two vectors $\mathbf{v}_1$ and $\mathbf{v}_2$ from a common point (Fig. 2.8b). The inclination of the two velocity vectors will also be $\Delta\theta$. The change of velocity is

$$\Delta\mathbf{v} = \mathbf{v}_2 - \mathbf{v}_1 \tag{2.31}$$

Resolve the $\Delta\mathbf{v}$ into two components as shown. Then

$$\Delta\mathbf{v} = \Delta\mathbf{v}_n + \Delta\mathbf{v}_t \tag{2.32}$$

2-4 Expressing the motion in terms of components

From this
$$\frac{\Delta \mathbf{v}}{\Delta t} = \frac{\Delta \mathbf{v}_n}{\Delta t} + \frac{\Delta \mathbf{v}_t}{\Delta t} \qquad (2.33)$$

and
$$\lim_{\Delta t \to 0} \frac{\Delta \mathbf{v}}{\Delta t} = \lim_{\Delta t \to 0} \frac{\Delta \mathbf{v}_n}{\Delta t} + \lim_{\Delta t \to 0} \frac{\Delta \mathbf{v}_t}{\Delta t} \qquad (2.34)$$

In the limit as $\Delta t \to 0$, or as $P_2 \to P_1$, $\Delta \mathbf{v}_n$ will be in the normal direction and $\Delta \mathbf{v}_t$ in the tangential direction. Therefore the last relation becomes

$$\mathbf{a} = \mathbf{a}_n + \mathbf{a}_t \qquad (2.35)$$

Now
$$\frac{\Delta \mathbf{v}_n}{\Delta t} = v_1 \frac{\Delta \theta}{\Delta t} \qquad (2.36)$$

In the limit, as $\Delta t \to 0$, $\mathbf{v}_1 \to \mathbf{v}$, where $\mathbf{v}$ is the velocity of the particle at P_1.

Thus
$$\mathbf{a}_n = v \frac{d\theta}{dt} \mathbf{n}_1 \qquad (2.37)$$

For the other component we simply get

$$\mathbf{a}_t = \frac{dv}{dt} \mathbf{t}_1 \qquad (2.38)$$

Thus
$$\mathbf{a} = v \frac{d\theta}{dt} \mathbf{n}_1 + \frac{dv}{dt} \mathbf{t}_1 \qquad (2.39)$$

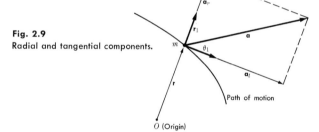

Fig. 2.9
Radial and tangential components.

To define *the radial and transverse components* we draw from a fixed origin O (Fig. 2.9) the position vector $\mathbf{r}$ of the particle. The direction along $\mathbf{r}$, given by the unit vector $\mathbf{r}_1$, is called the *radial direction*, and the direction perpendicular to it, denoted by the unit vector $\boldsymbol{\theta}_1$ is called the *transverse direction*. The acceleration vector $\mathbf{a}$ may then be resolved along these two directions. Thus

$$\mathbf{a} = \mathbf{a}_r + \mathbf{a}_t \qquad (2.40)$$
or
$$\mathbf{a} = a_r \mathbf{r}_1 + a_t \boldsymbol{\theta}_1 \qquad (2.41)$$

Similarly we may write the velocity vector in the form

$$\mathbf{v} = v_r \mathbf{r}_1 + v_t \boldsymbol{\theta}_1 \qquad (2.42)$$

These components can be expressed in terms of the time rate of change of the position vector $\mathbf{r}$ and the time rate of change of an angle θ that $\mathbf{r}$ makes with

2–4 Expressing the motion in terms of components

some fixed direction. The following elegant method* will be used to obtain the components. Consider a rotating frame of reference $O'x'y'$. Attached to the axes are unit vectors $\mathbf{i}'$ and $\mathbf{j}'$ (Fig. 2.10). During the time interval Δt

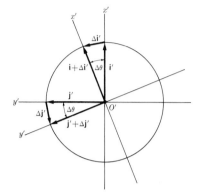

Fig. 2.10
Rotating unit vectors.

the system will rotate through an angle $\Delta\theta$. The vector $\mathbf{i}'$ will move into a new position $\mathbf{i}' + \Delta\mathbf{i}'$. The change of the vector is given by $\Delta\mathbf{i}'$. We notice that the magnitude of this vector, $\Delta\mathbf{i}'$, is $\Delta\theta$ and the direction is that of the y' axis and is therefore given by the unit vector $\mathbf{j}'$. Thus

$$\Delta\mathbf{i}' = \Delta\theta\mathbf{j}'$$

Dividing by Δt and going to the limit as Δt tends to zero we obtain

$$\lim_{\Delta t \to 0} \frac{\Delta\mathbf{i}'}{\Delta t} = \mathbf{j}' \lim_{\Delta t \to 0} \frac{\Delta\theta}{\Delta t}$$

or

$$\frac{d\mathbf{i}'}{dt} = \frac{d\theta}{dt}\mathbf{j}' \tag{2.43}$$

In a similar way

$$\Delta\mathbf{j}' = -\Delta\theta\mathbf{i}'$$

Here the vector $\Delta\mathbf{j}'$ points in the negative direction of the x' axis. Again

$$\lim \frac{\Delta\mathbf{j}'}{\Delta t} = -\mathbf{i}' \lim_{\Delta t \to 0} \frac{\Delta\theta}{\Delta t}$$

or

$$\frac{d\mathbf{j}'}{dt} = -\frac{d\theta}{dt}\mathbf{i}' \tag{2.44}$$

We have thus obtained the time rate of change of rotating unit vectors. Denoting the differentiation with respect to time by a dot above the differentiated quantity, the two respective expressions can be written as

$$\dot{\mathbf{i}}' = \dot{\theta}\mathbf{j}'$$

and

$$\dot{\mathbf{j}}' = -\dot{\theta}\mathbf{i}' \tag{2.45}$$

Now let a particle O' describe a certain path in the fixed xy plane (Fig. 2.11).

* D. E. Rutherford, *Classical Mechanics*, Oliver and Boyd, Edinburgh and London, New York: Interscience Publishers (1951).

2–4 Expressing the motion in terms of components

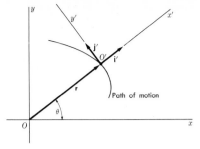

Fig. 2.11
Rotating frame
of reference.

From the fixed origin O draw the position vector

$$\overrightarrow{OO'} = \mathbf{r}$$

Introduce the radial and transverse directions $O'x'$ and $O'y'$. These can be denoted by unit vectors $\mathbf{i}'$ and $\mathbf{j}'$ respectively. Notice that in effect we have introduced a new coordinate system $O'x'y'$ which, as the particle O' describes its path, rotates in the xy plane. The angle between Ox and $OO'x'$ is θ (Fig. 2.11), thus the angular velocity of $O'x'y'$ with respect to Oxy is given by $\dot{\theta}$.

The position vector $\mathbf{r}$ can be written as

$$\mathbf{r} = r\mathbf{i}'$$

Differentiating with respect to time we obtain

$$\dot{\mathbf{r}} = \dot{r}\mathbf{i}' + r\dot{\mathbf{i}}'$$

or, using the expression for $\dot{\mathbf{i}}'$ $\quad \dot{\mathbf{r}} = \dot{r}\mathbf{i}' + r\dot{\theta}\mathbf{j}'$ (2.46)

$\dot{\mathbf{r}}$ is the total velocity vector of the particle O' and the coefficients of the unit vectors $\mathbf{i}'$ and $\mathbf{j}'$ are its radial and transverse components respectively.

Differentiating $\dot{\mathbf{r}}$ we obtain

$$\ddot{\mathbf{r}} = \ddot{r}\mathbf{i}' + \dot{r}\dot{\mathbf{i}}' + \dot{r}\dot{\theta}\mathbf{j}' + r\ddot{\theta}\mathbf{j}' + r\dot{\theta}\dot{\mathbf{j}}'$$
$$= \ddot{r}\mathbf{i}' + \dot{r}\dot{\theta}\mathbf{j}' + \dot{r}\dot{\theta}\mathbf{j}' + r\ddot{\theta}\mathbf{j}' - r\dot{\theta}^2\mathbf{i}'$$

or $\quad \ddot{\mathbf{r}} = (\ddot{r} - r\dot{\theta}^2)\mathbf{i}' + (r\ddot{\theta} + 2\dot{r}\dot{\theta})\mathbf{j}'$ (2.47)

The radial and transverse components of the acceleration vector $\ddot{\mathbf{r}}$ are the coefficients of the unit vectors $\mathbf{i}'$ and $\mathbf{j}'$ respectively.

The transverse component of acceleration can be written in a different form. In order to obtain this new form let us differentiate with respect to time the expression $r^2\dot{\theta}$ and obtain

$$\frac{d}{dt}(r^2\dot{\theta}) = 2r\dot{r}\dot{\theta} + r^2\ddot{\theta}$$

Therefore $\quad \dfrac{1}{r}\dfrac{d}{dt}(r^2\dot{\theta}) = 2\dot{r}\dot{\theta} + r\ddot{\theta}$ (2.48)

which gives the other form of the transverse component of acceleration.

The following table summarizes the above results:

	Radial component	Transverse component
Velocity	$\dot{r}$	$r\dot{\theta}$
Acceleration	$\ddot{r} - r\dot{\theta}^2$	$r\ddot{\theta} + 2\dot{r}\dot{\theta} = \dfrac{1}{r}\dfrac{d}{dt}(r^2\dot{\theta})$

Three types of components were considered above: rectangular, normal and tangential, and radial and transverse. The nature of the problem to be solved will determine which type of component is to be used. Some thought should be given to an appropriate choice. Thus, if a particle moves in such a way that its acceleration is parallel to a fixed direction, then the rectangular components will always be chosen. Two examples illustrating this case can be cited. The first deals with a projectile moving in the gravitational field of earth. Here the acceleration is always directed in the vertical direction. The second example is that of an electron moving between the plates of a parallel plate capacitor. In this case the acceleration acts perpendicular to the capacitor plates.

The radial and transverse components can be used in a variety of problems, but they will definitely be preferable in cases when the transverse acceleration is zero. There is a vast category of physical problems to be solved, when this is the case. The common feature of all of them is just the fact that the resultant acceleration is always directed towards a single point, and therefore there is no transverse acceleration. The motion of planets in the solar system and the motion of satellites in the gravitational field of earth belong to this category, as do also some problems in atomic physics (Rutherford's scattering, Section 5–5).*

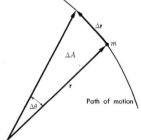

Fig. 2.12
Element of area
swept out by the
position vector.

Let a particle of mass m describe the path shown in Figure 2.12, and let **r** denote the position vector of m at a certain time t. At time $t + \Delta t$ the position vector will change to $\mathbf{r} + \Delta \mathbf{r}$ and will sweep out the area ΔA. This area is given by

$$\Delta A = \tfrac{1}{2} r \, \Delta r$$
$$= \tfrac{1}{2} r^2 \, \Delta \theta$$

Therefore

$$\frac{\Delta A}{\Delta t} = \frac{1}{2} r^2 \frac{\Delta \theta}{\Delta t}$$

* The whole Chapter 5 deals with central forces, and radial and transverse components of velocity and acceleration are used throughout.

Proceeding to the limit we get

$$\lim_{\Delta t \to 0} \frac{\Delta A}{\Delta t} = \frac{1}{2} r^2 \dot{\theta}$$

We define

$$\dot{A} = \lim_{\Delta t \to 0} \frac{\Delta A}{\Delta t}$$

as the areal velocity of m; it gives the time rate of change of the area swept out by $\mathbf{r}$. We see that

$$\dot{A} = \tfrac{1}{2} r^2 \dot{\theta}$$

We notice that if the transverse acceleration is zero then the areal velocity is constant [see Eq. (2.48)].

2–5 *Rotation of a Point Mass about a Fixed Axis*

When a body rotates about a fixed axis every point of it describes a circle. We therefore expect that the analytical description of such motion will not be too difficult. At this time we will just study the circular motion of particle of mass m which may be considered as one of the particles making up the rotating body. Such motion could be studied by the use of previous methods because it is motion along a circular path. We shall, however, consider it as rotational motion about an axis through O (Fig. 2.13), which is perpendicular

Fig. 2.13

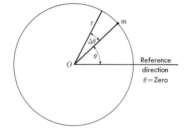

to the plane of the paper. The particle will at all times be on the circle of radius r and its position at any time will be represented by an angle θ. The angular velocity and the angular acceleration are defined as

$$\omega = \lim_{\Delta t \to 0} \frac{\Delta \theta}{\Delta t}$$

or

$$\omega = \frac{d\theta}{dt} \tag{2.49}$$

and

$$\alpha = \lim_{\Delta t \to 0} \frac{\Delta \omega}{\Delta t}$$

or

$$\alpha = \frac{d\omega}{dt} \tag{2.50}$$

We notice an exact *parallelism between the set x, v, a and θ, ω, α.* Therefore *all the kinematical relations for linear motion can at once be written down for this type of motion.* The mathematical formalism is exactly the same. This parallelism between the rotational motion about a fixed axis and the linear motion can be extended considerably as we shall see presently.

We first introduce a quantity which plays a great role in the study of rotational motion, namely the *angular momentum.* It *is defined as the moment of linear momentum about a given axis.* In our case of circular motion, the moment will be taken about the point O. In an elementary definition the moment of a vector, say the force, is given as the product of the vector and the perpendicular distance from the axis to the line of action of the vector. Actually the definition of the moment of a vector should be more general.

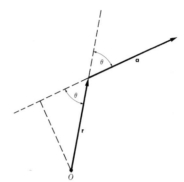

Fig. 2.14

Consider a vector **a** which starts at the end of the vector **r** (Fig. 2.14). *The moment of* **a** *about O is defined as*

$$\mathbf{h} = \mathbf{r} \times \mathbf{a} \tag{2.51}$$

It can be seen that this definition conforms to the more elementary one. In addition, the general definition of the moment also contains its direction.

The angular momentum **h** can now be written as

$$\mathbf{h} = \mathbf{r} \times m\dot{\mathbf{r}} \tag{2.52}$$

In our case
$$h = rmv$$
$$= rm\omega r \tag{2.53}$$

or
$$h = mr^2\omega \tag{2.54}$$

The quantity
$$I = mr^2 \tag{2.55}$$

is called *the moment of inertia of m about the axis of rotation.* This *moment of inertia plays the same role in rotational motion as does the mass m in linear motion.* It will therefore represent a quantitative measure of the resistance of the particle towards rotational acceleration. In terms of the moment of inertia

$$h = I\omega \tag{2.56}$$

In this form the relation for the angular momentum is of the same structure as that of the linear momentum

$$p = mv$$

In order to obtain an expression for the kinetic energy* T in the form used in rotational motion, we first write

$$T = \tfrac{1}{2}mv^2$$

Now

$$v = r\omega$$

therefore

$$T = \tfrac{1}{2}mr^2\omega^2$$

or

$$T = \tfrac{1}{2}I\omega^2 \tag{2.57}$$

We next introduce *the torque which is the moment of the resultant force about the axis of rotation.* Let the resultant force be **F**. We can resolve it into

Fig. 2.15

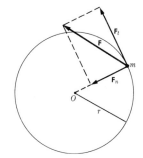

normal and tangential components (Fig. 2.15). Then

$$\mathbf{F} = \mathbf{F}_n + \mathbf{F}_t$$

For the circular motion the torque will be

$$G = rF_t \tag{2.58}$$

Now

$$F_t = m\,\frac{dv}{dt}$$

$$= m\,\frac{d}{dt}\,(r\omega)$$

$$= mr\,\frac{d\omega}{dt}$$

$$= mr\alpha$$

Therefore

$$G = mr^2\alpha$$

In terms of the moment of inertia I

$$G = I\alpha \tag{2.59}$$

* The kinetic energy is introduced in the next section. At present we will only make use of the fact that when a particle of mass m moves with the linear velocity v then its kinetic energy is given by $T = \tfrac{1}{2}mv^2$. In the following section we will see how this expression arises in Newtonian mechanics when work performed by a force is calculated.

This law, derived here for the rotational motion about a fixed axis, is identical in form with Newton's second law for linear motion if angular quantities replace the linear quantities.

Now again
$$\alpha = \frac{d\omega}{dt}$$

therefore
$$G = I \frac{d\omega}{dt}$$

$$= \frac{d(I\omega)}{dt}$$

or
$$G = \frac{dh}{dt} \tag{2.60}$$

This states that *the torque acting is the time rate of change of the angular momentum.* In this form the torque equation is similar in form to

$$F = \frac{dp}{dt}$$

where p is the linear momentum.

The quantity which in angular motion corresponds to the linear impulse is the *angular impulse.* It *is defined as the moment of the linear impulse.* Thus the angular impulse is defined as

$$d\mathbf{M} = \mathbf{r} \times d\mathbf{J} \tag{2.61}$$

For our circular motion of the particle m under the action of the force $\mathbf{F}$,

$$d\mathbf{J} = \mathbf{F} \, dt$$

The direction of $d\mathbf{M}$ is perpendicular to the plane of the motion and its magnitude is given by

$$dM = rF_t \, dt \tag{2.62}$$

and so
$$M = r \int F_t \, dt \tag{2.63}$$

Now
$$F_t = m \frac{dv}{dt}$$

therefore
$$M = rm \int \frac{dv}{dt} \, dt$$

or
$$M = rm \int dv$$

$$= rm \int d(r\omega)$$

$$= r^2 m \int_{\omega_1}^{\omega_2} d\omega$$

$$= r^2 m (\omega_1 - \omega_0)$$

Thus, finally

$$M = I\omega_1 - I\omega_0 \qquad (2.64)$$

This relation contains *the principle of angular impulse and angular momentum;* it states that *the angular impulse is equal to the change of angular momentum.*
When conditions exist that

$$M = 0$$

then

$$I\omega_0 = I\omega_1 \qquad (2.65)$$

i.e., the angular momentum is constant.*

The parallelism between the linear motion and the angular motion about a fixed axis is summarized as

Linear motion $\quad x \ v \ a \ m \ p \ F \quad \ldots$
Angular motion $\quad \theta \ \omega \ \alpha \ I \ h \ G \quad \ldots$

2–6 Work, Energy and Conservation of Mechanical Energy

Consider again a particle of mass m on which a force **F** is acting. Let the

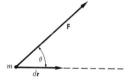

Fig. 2.16

force displace the particle an amount $d\mathbf{r}$ (Fig. 2.16). We say that the *force performed* an amount of *work* given by

$$dW = \mathbf{F} \cdot d\mathbf{r} \qquad (2.66)$$

If the force displaced the particle from an initial position $\mathbf{r}_0$ to a final position $\mathbf{r}_1$ then the total work done will be

$$W = \int_{\mathbf{r}_0}^{\mathbf{r}_1} \mathbf{F} \cdot d\mathbf{r} \qquad (2.67)$$

The force will in general be a function of $\mathbf{r}$, its time derivatives and the time. Thus in order to evaluate this integral all the details of the motion would have to be known.

When a physical system is in such a state that it can perform work on other systems, we say that it has energy; in other words, energy is the capacity of a

---

* Consider a cat tossed out of the window. The resultant torque about his center of gravity is zero and therefore the angular impulse is zero also. Thus during his descent the angular momentum is conserved. The clever cat realizes this fact and always lands on his feet. The angular momentum is $I\omega$. By redistribution of his mass with respect to his center of gravity he changes his moment of inertia and this he does with the purpose to acquire the proper angular velocity at the crucial moment. The principle of conservation of angular momentum which the cat applies is actually of a more advanced nature than the one derived above. It applies to the case of moving systems rotating about an axis passing through their center of gravity.

system to do work. This capacity is manifold in nature but in mechanics it is twofold only. Systems can do work merely by virtue of being in motion. The energy that they then possess is termed *kinetic energy*. Also, systems may have potentialities to perform work simply because they are in special positions. In that case we say that *potential energy* is stored in them.

Purely mechanical systems have only these two types of energy. The sum of the kinetic and the potential energy is called the *total mechanical energy*.

In order to understand the physical significance of work and energy consider the motion of a particle m along the x axis under the action of a force F. By Newton's second law

$$m\ddot{x} = F$$

or

$$\ddot{x} = \frac{F}{m}$$

By Eq. (2.10)

$$\ddot{x} = \dot{x}\,\frac{d\dot{x}}{dx}$$

Therefore

$$\dot{x}\,\frac{d\dot{x}}{dx} = \frac{F}{m}$$

or

$$m\dot{x}\,d\dot{x} = F\,dx$$

If at x_0 and x_1 the velocities are $\dot{x}_0$ and $\dot{x}_1$ respectively, then

$$\int_{\dot{x}_0}^{\dot{x}_1} m\dot{x}\,d\dot{x} = \int_{x_0}^{x_1} F\,dx$$

from which

$$\tfrac{1}{2}m\dot{x}_1{}^2 - \tfrac{1}{2}m\dot{x}_0{}^2 = \int_{x_0}^{x_1} F\,dx \qquad (2.68)$$

The right hand side represents the work performed by the force F when the particle m is moved from x_0 to x_1. It is seen that this work is equal to the change of the quantity $\tfrac{1}{2}mx^2$. This is the kinetic energy of the particle.

We have derived above an important general principle called *the principle of work and kinetic energy*. When applied to a number of forces acting on a system, this principle states that the *total work done by all the forces acting on the system is equal to the change of kinetic energy of the system*. It is important to realize that the force can be of any nature. The independent variables on which the force may depend have no bearing on the derivation of the principle. Thus there could be a case when only a frictional force acts on the system; work performed by this force will then be equal to the change of the kinetic energy. When the body moves under the action of several forces in the gravitational field of earth then, of course, the work done by the gravitational attraction must be included in the total work done by all the forces.

We shall now introduce the concept of potential energy. In order to define this concept at all, certain restrictions will have to be imposed on the forces acting. Consider the case of two-dimensional motion of a particle. Let there be a field of force **F** acting in this two-dimensional space. Suppose that the particle is moved from point A to point B along an arbitrary path 1 (Fig. 2.17)

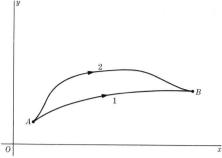

Fig. 2.17

and then again from A to B along a different path 2, and it is found in both cases (and, for that matter, for any number of trials along different paths) that the work is the same. Obviously this work depends only on the positions of A and B. Let us also determine that similar results hold for different points of the plane. The outcome of such experiments clearly points out the fact that the force field $\mathbf{F}$ is of a special kind. It is called a *conservative field of force.*

From the fact that *the work done between any two points is independent of the path,* we deduce that *the field can also be described by a new function.* Choose the origin of the coordinates as the point from which the particle will be moved to various points of the field. Then in the case which we are considering the work done will depend only on the coordinates of the other point, and, in the two-dimensional case, we can write

$$W = W(x, y) \tag{2.69}$$

i.e., W is a function of x and y only. $W(x, y)$ could therefore be used to describe the properties of the conservative field of force.* By convention, however, the function

$$V(x, y) = -W(x, y) \tag{2.70}$$

is used. $V(x, y)$ is called *the potential energy* and, as can be seen, *is defined as the negative of the work done by the force field.*

In defining the potential energy the origin has been chosen as a reference point. It should be obvious that any other point could have been chosen as the reference point. If this be denoted by the vector $\mathbf{r}_0$ then the potential energy will have to be written as

$$V(\mathbf{r}) - V(\mathbf{r}_0) = V(\mathbf{r}')$$

where
$$\mathbf{r}' = \mathbf{r} - \mathbf{r}_0$$

Thus *all that we really define is the potential energy difference.*

The potential energy is a scalar function of position. The designation $V(\mathbf{r})$ signifies that the potential energy is evaluated at the tip of the vector $\mathbf{r}$. (If a quantity F were a vector and we would evaluate it at the point $\mathbf{r}$, then it would be denoted by $\mathbf{F}(\mathbf{r})$.)

* Some engineering books indeed use this function for such a description and call it the work function.

In the case of one-dimensional motion

$$V(x) - V(x_0) = -\int_{x_0}^{x} F \, dx \qquad (2.71)$$

Now, for this to be true it is obvious that F must be a function of position only. For if we assume that there is another independent variable on which F could depend, say t, then an independent variation of t would produce various amounts of work when the particle would move from x_0 to x. In such a case we could not define the function $V(x)$.

For an infinitessimal process

$$dV = -F \, dx \qquad (2.72)$$

and therefore

$$F = -\frac{dV}{dx} \qquad (2.73)$$

We have seen earlier that

$$\int_{x_0}^{x} F \, dx = \tfrac{1}{2}m\dot{x}^2 - \tfrac{1}{2}m\dot{x}_0{}^2$$

Therefore $\qquad \tfrac{1}{2}m\dot{x}^2 - \tfrac{1}{2}m\dot{x}_0{}^2 = V(x_0) - V(x)$

or $\qquad \tfrac{1}{2}m\dot{x}_0{}^2 + V(x_0) = \tfrac{1}{2}m\dot{x}^2 + V(x) \qquad (2.74)$

This embodies *the theorem of conservation of mechanical energy* which states that *for a conservative field the total mechanical energy is constant.*

2–7 The Double Description of Conservative Fields

In the last section we have considered a special field of force, viz., one in which the work done by the force field on a particle is independent of the path along which the particle is taken. We call such a field conservative. We have seen that in such a case there exists a potential V which—in the one-dimensional case—satisfies Eq. (2.73). In the three-dimensional case the relation between **F** and V is

$$\mathbf{F} = -\mathbf{grad}\ V \qquad (2.75)$$

also written as $\qquad \mathbf{F} = -\nabla V$

where $\qquad \mathbf{grad} \equiv \nabla \equiv \dfrac{\partial}{\partial x}\,\mathbf{i} + \dfrac{\partial}{\partial y}\,\mathbf{j} + \dfrac{\partial}{\partial z}\,\mathbf{k}$

In such a case we say that the force is the negative of the gradient of the potential. (The gradient operator "grad" is identical with ∇, pronounced "del" or "nabla".)*

We see that *a conservative field of force is described by a vector function* **F** *and also by a scalar function V*. Both specify the field at any point. **F** can stand

---

* See Appendix A–5 in which the gradient is introduced. The conservative field is also discussed in Appendix A–7.

for the actual force exerted on the system; then V stands for the potential energy of the system. More often we describe the field by the field intensity vector (force per unit mass, force per unit charge, etc.). Let $\mathfrak{F}$ denote such a field intensity. The scalar description is then given in terms of the potential of the field (defined as the negative of the work per unit mass, work per unit charge, etc.). For the potential we will use the symbol ϕ. This double description of a field (in terms of a vector field and a scalar field) is very useful for understanding the characteristic properties of the field.

The scalar potential function

$$\phi = \phi(x, y, z) \tag{2.76}$$

will be defined in the domain of our field. If we set

$$\phi(x, y, z) = \phi_0 \tag{2.77}$$

where ϕ_0 is a constant, then we have obtained the equation of a surface for every point of which the potential is constant. We call such a surface an *equipotential surface*. If we assign to ϕ_0 different constants then we obtain different equipotential surfaces. The family of equipotential surfaces gives a complete description of the field in terms of the potential.

Given the potential function we can obtain the corresponding force field intensity. From Eq. (2.75) we obtain

$$\mathfrak{F} = -\frac{\partial \phi}{\partial x}\, \mathbf{i} - \frac{\partial \phi}{\partial y}\, \mathbf{j} - \frac{\partial \phi}{\partial z}\, \mathbf{k} \tag{2.78}$$

Therefore
$$\mathfrak{F}_x = -\frac{\partial \phi}{\partial x}, \quad \mathfrak{F}_y = -\frac{\partial \phi}{\partial y}, \quad \mathfrak{F}_z = -\frac{\partial \phi}{\partial z} \tag{2.79}$$

We have obtained the components of the force intensity vector at any point of the field. The magnitude of the resultant force intensity is given by

$$\mathfrak{F} = \sqrt{\left(\frac{\partial \phi}{\partial x}\right)^2 + \left(\frac{\partial \phi}{\partial y}\right)^2 + \left(\frac{\partial \phi}{\partial z}\right)^2} \tag{2.80}$$

From Eq. (2.75) we see that the *lines of force will be perpendicular to the equipotential surfaces*. In order to map out the lines of force consider first the xy plane. Let the curve shown in Figure 2.18 represent a line of force passing

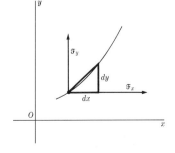

Fig. 2.18
Components of the field intensity.

through the point (x, y). We know that its slope is dy/dx which is also given by $\mathfrak{F}_y/\mathfrak{F}_x$. Thus

$$\frac{dy}{dx} = \frac{\mathfrak{F}_y}{\mathfrak{F}_x}$$

from which

$$\frac{dx}{\mathfrak{F}_x} = \frac{dy}{\mathfrak{F}_y}$$

We can extend this to other coordinate planes, and thus obtain

$$\frac{dx}{\mathfrak{F}_x} = \frac{dy}{\mathfrak{F}_y} = \frac{dz}{\mathfrak{F}_z} \tag{2.81}$$

These are *the differential equations of the lines of force. Upon integration, the equations of the lines of force are obtained.*

Example: The potential of a certain conservative field is given by

$$\phi = c(x^2 + y^2)$$

We see that the equipotentials are circles the equations of which are given by

$$x^2 + y^2 = \phi_0/c$$

Now

$$\mathfrak{F}_x = -\frac{\partial \phi}{\partial x}, \ \mathfrak{F}_y = -\frac{\partial \phi}{\partial y}$$

thus in our case

$$\mathfrak{F}_x = -2cx, \ \mathfrak{F}_y = -2cy$$

We find, therefore, that at any point in the xy-plane the magnitude of the force field is

$$\mathfrak{F} = 2c(x^2 + y^2)^{\frac{1}{2}}$$

The differential equations of the lines of force are

$$\frac{dx}{-2cx} = \frac{dy}{-2cy}$$

or

$$\frac{dx}{x} = \frac{dy}{y}$$

from which

$$\ell n \ y - \ell n \ m = \ell n \ x$$

where we have denoted by $-\ell n \ m$ the constant of integration. The last equation can be transformed into

$$y = mx$$

The equipotentials, therefore, are concentric circles with the center at the origin and the lines of force are straight lines of slope m radiating from the origin.

If the force field is given, then the potential is obtained by integration.

Using the same example as before, let the force field be given by

$$F = 2c(x^2 + y^2)^{\frac{1}{2}}$$

Transforming to polar coordinates we obtain

$$F = 2cr$$

Now
$$V = \int F \, dr \qquad (2.82)$$

or, in our case
$$V = \int 2cr \, dr$$

$$= cr^2$$

or
$$V = c(x^2 + y^2)$$

2-8 The Potential Energy Function

In the case of a conservative field, the potential energy function gives a complete description of the field. We will illustrate the importance of the potential energy function in some detail. Consider the case when the potential energy is a function of only one variable, i.e.

$$V = V(x)$$

The total mechanical energy is

$$E = T + V$$

where T is the kinetic energy.

In a conservative field the total energy is conserved and thus in a particular problem E will be a constant of motion. Solving the above equation for the kinetic energy $T = \frac{1}{2}mv^2$, we get

$$\tfrac{1}{2}mv^2 = E - V(x)$$

from which
$$v = \sqrt{\frac{2[E - V(x)]}{m}} \qquad (2.83)$$

Thus the velocity of a particle moving in a conservative field is a function of the potential.

Let us assume that the form of the potential energy is that shown in Figure 2.19. Let a particle of mass m move in such a potential energy field. The motion of the particle will depend on the total energy of the particle. In Figure 2.19 we have illustrated four separate cases. In the first case, $E = E_1$, and we see that for all x, $E > V(x)$. Thus by Eq. (2.83) v will assume a real value for all positive x. If we restrict our space to positive x, we may say that the particle has complete freedom of motion.

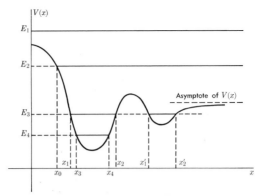

Fig. 2.19
An example of a potential energy curve.

When $E = E_2$ we notice that at $x = x_0$, $E = V(x)$ and the particle has to stop there. The region $0 < x < x_0$ is inaccessible to the particle. In a similar way we can analyze the remaining two cases. When $E = E_4$, the particle can only move in the region (x_3, x_4), and when $E = E_3$, the particle may be in two regions, either in (x_1, x_2) or in (x'_1, x'_2). In this latter case, once the particle is in one of the two regions, it cannot pass to the other.*

2–9   The Energy Integral

If we have a particle moving along the x-axis under the action of a force $F = F(x)$, then, as we have seen, the equation $m\ddot{x} = F(x)$ has the first integral

$$\tfrac{1}{2}m\dot{x}^2 = \int_0^x F(x)\,dx$$

This is known as the *energy integral*. Using Eq. (2.74) we can simply write it as

$$T + V = d \tag{2.84}$$

where d is a constant.

In the case of three-dimensional motion we start with

$$m\ddot{\mathbf{r}} = \mathbf{F} \tag{2.85}$$

Scalar-multiplying both sides by $\dot{\mathbf{r}}\,dt$ and integrating we get

$$\tfrac{1}{2}mv^2 - \tfrac{1}{2}mv_0^2 = \int_{t_0}^{t} \mathbf{F}\cdot\dot{\mathbf{r}}\,dt \tag{2.86}$$

where the integral gives the work done. The integrand $\mathbf{F}\cdot\dot{\mathbf{r}}$ is the power delivered by the force $\mathbf{F}$.

We can also write the same result as

$$\frac{dT}{dt} = \mathbf{F}\cdot\dot{\mathbf{r}} \tag{2.87}$$

* These purely classical results seem obvious to us and hardly necessary of mentioning. They were, however, modified by quantum mechanics. Thus, for instance, in the case when $E = E_3$ there is a finite probability that a particle may penetrate the potential barrier between the two classically permitted regions.

If the power can be expressed as the total time derivative of a function $V = V(x, y, z, t)$, i.e., if

$$\mathbf{F} \cdot \dot{\mathbf{r}} = -\frac{dV}{dt} \tag{2.88}$$

then the above equations yield the energy integral

$$T + V = d$$

where d is constant. V, of course, is the potential energy.

When the power is zero then the energy integral becomes

$$T = d \tag{2.89}$$

It sometimes happens that $\mathbf{F} \cdot \dot{\mathbf{r}}$ cannot be expressed as $-\dfrac{dV}{dt}$ but $\mathbf{F}$ can be split into two forces $\mathbf{F}_c$ and $\mathbf{F}_f$ such that $\mathbf{F} = \mathbf{F}_c + \mathbf{F}_f$ and

$$\mathbf{F}_c \cdot \dot{\mathbf{r}} = -\frac{dV}{dt}$$

Thus
$$\frac{d}{dt}(T + V) = \mathbf{F}_f \cdot \dot{\mathbf{r}}$$

This can be integrated to yield

$$T + V = \int \mathbf{F}_f \cdot \dot{\mathbf{r}} \, dt$$

In this case, therefore, the increase of the mechanical energy $T + V$ is equal to the work done by the force $\mathbf{F}_f$. We realize that $\mathbf{F}_c$ is the conservative part of $\mathbf{F}$, and $\mathbf{F}_f$ is non-conservative; the latter can for instance be a frictional force.

2–10 Fictitious Forces

Consider any vector $\mathbf{H}$ which in the fixed axes can be written as

$$\mathbf{H} = H_x \mathbf{i} + H_y \mathbf{j} + H_z \mathbf{k} \tag{2.90}$$

and when referred to some moving axes it becomes

$$\mathbf{H} = H_{x'} \mathbf{i}' + H_{y'} \mathbf{j}' + H_{z'} \mathbf{k}' \tag{2.91}$$

Differentiating Eq. (2.90) with respect to time, we get

$$\frac{d\mathbf{H}}{dt} = \frac{dH_x}{dt}\mathbf{i} + \frac{dH_y}{dt}\mathbf{j} + \frac{dH_z}{dt}\mathbf{k}$$

and from Eq. (2.91) we get

$$\frac{d\mathbf{H}}{dt} = \frac{dH_{x'}}{dt}\mathbf{i}' + \frac{dH_{y'}}{dt}\mathbf{j}' + \frac{dH_{z'}}{dt}\mathbf{k}' + H_{x'}\dot{\mathbf{i}}' + H_{y'}\dot{\mathbf{j}}' + H_{z'}\dot{\mathbf{k}}'$$

We will denote

$$\frac{dH_{x'}}{dt}\,\mathbf{i'} + \frac{dH_{y'}}{dt}\,\mathbf{j'} + \frac{dH_{z'}}{dt}\,\mathbf{k'} = \frac{d_r}{dt}\,\mathbf{H}$$

where d_r/dt denotes time differentiation performed by an observer fixed in the rotating frame.

It is now necessary to obtain the time derivatives of the unit vectors $\mathbf{i'}, \mathbf{j'}, \mathbf{k'}$. Consider the unit vector $\mathbf{i'}$ which rotates with angular velocity $\boldsymbol{\omega}$ about a certain axis (Fig. 2.20). Choose a point O on this axis and let the position vectors of the beginning and end points of $\mathbf{i'}$ with respect to O be denoted by $\mathbf{r}_1$ and $\mathbf{r}_2$.

Fig. 2.20
A rotating unit vector.

Then
$$\mathbf{i'} = \mathbf{r}_2 - \mathbf{r}_1$$
and
$$\dot{\mathbf{i}}' = \dot{\mathbf{r}}_2 - \dot{\mathbf{r}}_1$$
$$= \boldsymbol{\omega} \times \mathbf{r}_2 - \boldsymbol{\omega} \times \mathbf{r}_1$$
$$= \boldsymbol{\omega} \times (\mathbf{r}_2 - \mathbf{r}_1)$$
or
$$\dot{\mathbf{i}}' = \boldsymbol{\omega} \times \mathbf{i'}$$

In a similar way we can show that

$$\dot{\mathbf{j}}' = \boldsymbol{\omega} \times \mathbf{j'}$$
and
$$\dot{\mathbf{k}}' = \boldsymbol{\omega} \times \mathbf{k'}$$

Making use of these relations we obtain

$$\frac{d_s\mathbf{H}}{dt} = \frac{d_r\mathbf{H}}{dt} + \boldsymbol{\omega} \times \mathbf{H} \qquad (2.92)$$

where the subscripts denote the fact that the differentiations are performed in the two respective frames. Eq. (2.92) is valid for any vector $\mathbf{H}$.

Let K_r denote a system which rotates with angular velocity $\boldsymbol{\omega}$ with respect to a fixed system K_s, and suppose that the origins of K_s and K_r coincide. We will first apply Eq. (2.92) to the case when $\mathbf{H}$ is the position vector $\mathbf{r}$ of a particle P. Then

$$\frac{d_s\mathbf{r}}{dt} = \frac{d_r\mathbf{r}}{dt} + \boldsymbol{\omega} \times \mathbf{r} \qquad (2.93)$$
or
$$\mathbf{v}_s = \mathbf{v}_r + \boldsymbol{\omega} \times \mathbf{r}$$

In this expression $\mathbf{v}_s$ is the velocity of P as measured by an observer in K_s, and $\mathbf{v}_r$ is the velocity of P measured by an observer in K_r.

32

Now apply Eq. (2.92) to $\mathbf{v}_s$. (Thus we are identifying $\mathbf{H}$ with $\mathbf{v}_s$.) We obtain

$$\frac{d_s\mathbf{v}_s}{dt} = \frac{d_r}{dt}\,\mathbf{v}_s + \boldsymbol{\omega} \times \mathbf{v}_s$$

$$= \frac{d_r}{dt}\,(\mathbf{v}_r + \boldsymbol{\omega} \times \mathbf{r}) + \boldsymbol{\omega} \times (\mathbf{v}_r + \boldsymbol{\omega} \times \mathbf{r})$$

$$= \frac{d_r\mathbf{v}_r}{dt} + \frac{d_r}{dt}\,(\boldsymbol{\omega} \times \mathbf{r}) + \boldsymbol{\omega} \times \mathbf{v}_r + \boldsymbol{\omega} \times (\boldsymbol{\omega} \times \mathbf{r})$$

$$= \frac{d_r\mathbf{v}_r}{dt} + \frac{d_r\boldsymbol{\omega}}{dt} \times \mathbf{r} + \boldsymbol{\omega} \times \frac{d_r\mathbf{r}}{dt} + \boldsymbol{\omega} \times \mathbf{v}_r + \boldsymbol{\omega} \times (\boldsymbol{\omega} \times \mathbf{r})$$

or
$$\frac{d_s\mathbf{v}_s}{dt} = \frac{d_r\mathbf{v}_r}{dt} + 2\boldsymbol{\omega} \times \mathbf{v}_r + \frac{d_r\boldsymbol{\omega}}{dt} \times \mathbf{r} + \boldsymbol{\omega} \times (\boldsymbol{\omega} \times \mathbf{r}) \tag{2.94}$$

This can be written as

$$\mathbf{a}_s = \mathbf{a}_r + \mathbf{a}_c + \mathbf{a}_e, \tag{2.95}$$

where
$$\mathbf{a}_c = 2\boldsymbol{\omega} \times \mathbf{v}_r \tag{2.96}$$

and
$$\mathbf{a}_e = \frac{d\boldsymbol{\omega}}{dt} \times \mathbf{r} + \boldsymbol{\omega} \times (\boldsymbol{\omega} \times \mathbf{r}) \tag{2.97}$$

In Eq. (2.95), $\mathbf{a}_s$ is the acceleration measured by an observer in the K_s frame, and $\mathbf{a}_r$ is the acceleration measured by an observer in the K_r frame. Let us assume that K_s is a Newtonian frame, i.e., one in which Newton's laws are valid. Thus the actual force acting on P will be obtained by multiplying $\mathbf{a}_s$ by the mass of P. Then we may write

$$\mathbf{F}_s = m\mathbf{a}_s \tag{2.98}$$

Now, let the observer in K_r multiply the acceleration $\mathbf{a}_r$, which he has determined, by m. He will call this product the force $\mathbf{F}_r$, for he will say that

$$\mathbf{F}_r = m\mathbf{a}_r \tag{2.99}$$

When the two systems are rotating with respect to each other, then $\mathbf{F}_s \neq \mathbf{F}_r$. Actually the observer in K_r finds that

$$\mathbf{F}_r = \mathbf{F}_s + \mathbf{F}_c + \mathbf{F}_e \tag{2.100}$$

where
$$\mathbf{F}_c = -m\mathbf{a}_c \tag{2.101}$$

and
$$\mathbf{F}_e = -m\mathbf{a}_e \tag{2.102}$$

$\mathbf{F}_c$ is called the *Coriolis force*, and $\mathbf{F}_e$ may be called the *lifting force*.*
  If $d\boldsymbol{\omega}/dt = \mathbf{0}$ then

$$\mathbf{a}_e = \boldsymbol{\omega} \times (\boldsymbol{\omega} \times \mathbf{r}) \tag{2.103}$$

and in this case $\mathbf{F}_e$ is in the nature of a centripetal force. Both $\mathbf{F}_c$ and $\mathbf{F}_e$ are fictitious forces, where we are using the word fictitious as opposite to "actual." The forces $\mathbf{F}_c$ and $\mathbf{F}_e$ are the forces resulting from the rotation of one system with respect to the other. If the rotation stops, both $\mathbf{F}_c$ and $\mathbf{F}_e$ become zero.

* French designation is "entrainé."

To illustrate the existence of a fictitious force, imagine that we are firing a projectile at the North Pole parallel to the earth's surface. If somehow we could insert a screen that did not rotate with the earth, then—with respect to the screen—the projectile would travel along a straight line. With respect to an observer on the earth, however, the trajectory of the projectile will be curved. The observer on the earth could attribute this curving to some force, but actually it is only the result of the earth's rotation.*

PROBLEMS

2.1 Given that $\ddot{x} = x^3$ and $x_{t=0} = a$, $\dot{x}_{t=0} = a^2/\sqrt{2}$, find $t_{x=\infty}$.

2.2 Given $\ddot{x} = -k\dot{x}^2$ and $x_{t=0} = 0$, $\dot{x}_{t=0} = u$, determine $\dot{x}$ and t.

2.3 Solve $\ddot{x} = \dot{x}x$, given that $\dot{x}_{t=0} = x_{t=0} = 1$.

2.4 A wheel of radius r is rolling to the left without slipping. If the velocity of the center is v_0, determine the velocity of any point on the wheel. (A general point which does not lie on the rim of the wheel has to be chosen.)

2.5 A particle of mass m at rest at the origin has a force applied to it with components: $F_x = at$, $F_y = bt^2$. What is the magnitude and the direction of the velocity two seconds after its application?

2.6 A 2-gm point mass moves towards point O which is the center of an inverse square repulsive field, the intensity of which has the magnitude $10^{-6}/r^2$ dyne/gm. When at infinity, the point mass has the velocity of 100 cm/sec. The particle comes to rest at A (Fig. 2.21). Find the impulse, in dyne-sec, exerted on the particle, when the particle travels the distance $BA = 3 \times 10^{-10}$ cm.

Fig. 2.21

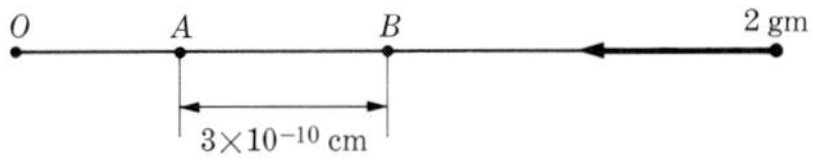

2.7 A string whose upper end is fixed is wound around a circular disc of radius r. The disc is released from rest. Find the acceleration of the disc assuming the axis to remain horizontal during the motion.

2.8 A particle of mass m is moving with constant speed v on the parabola $y = \frac{1}{2}x^2$ so that the x-component of its velocity is positive. At the point where

---

* When you visit the United Nations in New York, go and see Foucault's pendulum. This is a very long pendulum of practically frictionless suspension. It starts oscillating in a given plane, but the plane of oscillations continuously changes. The rotation of the earth is responsible for it.

There are also other institutions which show Foucault's pendulum. As a matter of fact, if you have a staircase some three or more flights high, you can construct such a pendulum yourself.

$x = \frac{3}{4}$, what is:

(a) the x component and the y component of its velocity?

(b) the magnitude of the tangential component of the acceleration?

(c) the direction of the total acceleration vector?

2.9 Boric acid, H_3BO_3, is a planar molecule. Its structure is roughly as shown in Figure 2.22. Find the moment of inertia of the molecule about an axis passing through the boron atom and perpendicular to the plane of the molecule. (The mass of the hydrogen atom is 1.56×10^{-24} gm; for the mass of the oxygen atom take a mass sixteen times as large as that of the hydrogen atom.)

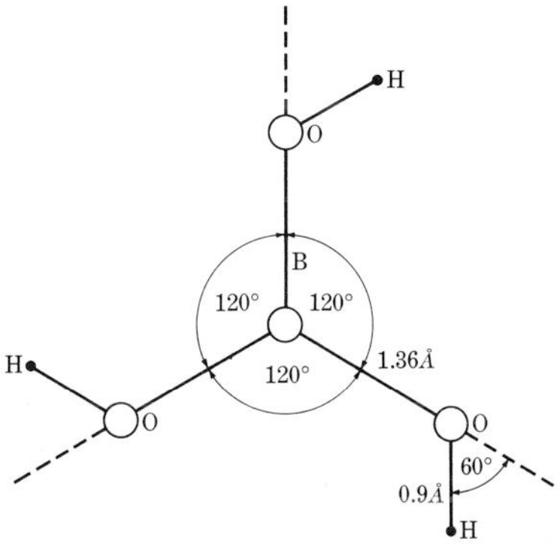

Fig. 2.22
B(OH)₃ molecule.

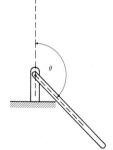

2.10 The motion of a rotating element in a mechanism is controlled so that the rate of change of the angular velocity ω with angular displacement θ is a constant k. When $\theta = 0$ and $t = 0$ then $\omega = \omega_o$. Determine θ, ω and the angular acceleration α as a function of t.

2.11 A thin uniform rod is 4 ft. long, weighs 8 lbs. and is free to rotate in a vertical plane about a fixed, smooth pin joint through one end of the rod. (Fig. 2.23). The rod is released from rest, with its free end vertically above the pin-jointed end. When the rod has rotated through an angle of 120° clockwise from the vertical position, find:

(a) its angular velocity,

(b) its angular acceleration,

(c) the components of force on the rod due to the pin-joint.

Fig. 2.23

2.12 Find the potential due to a thin uniform spherical shell. Show that inside the sphere there is a zero gravitational force.

2.13 A ball of weight 1 lb. is attached to a cord of length 4 ft, pivoted at point O, as shown in Figure 2.24. The ball is released from rest at point A, swings down and collides with the block B and rebounds to point C. The block B weighs 10 lbs. and is initially at rest. Neglect the friction between the block and the horizontal surface.

   (a) Determine the velocity of the ball just before it collides with the block.
   (b) Find the velocity of the ball after the collision with the block.
   (c) Obtain the velocity acquired by the block.
   (d) Find the coefficient of restitution of the collision between the ball and the block.

   (The coefficient of restitution is defined as the ratio of the relative velocity of departure of the two colliding bodies and their relative velocity of approach.)

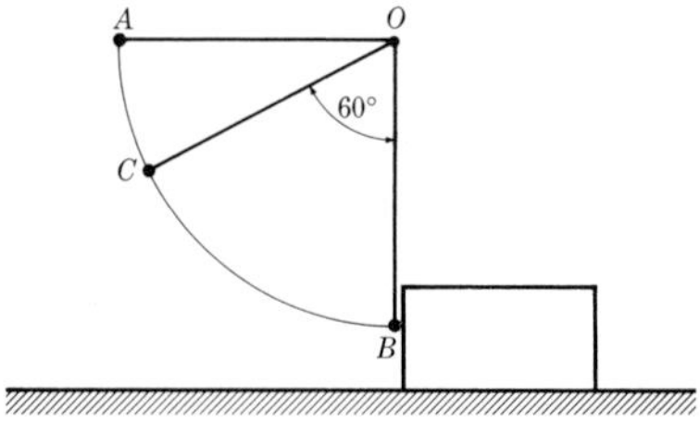

Fig. 2.24

2.14 Find the magnitude of the difference between the gravitational field intensity vectors on the two sides of an infinite plane sheet of mass. The surface mass density is σ.

2.15 If the attraction between two particles of masses m_1 and m_2 is $\gamma m_1 m_2 r^n$, show that the attraction on a particle of unit mass at distance $R(>a)$ from the center of a uniform spherical shell of radius a and mass M is

$$ F = \frac{\gamma M}{4aR^2} \int_{R-a}^{R+a} (u^2 - a^2 + R^2)u^n \, du $$

where u is the distance from the unit mass to any ring of the spherical shell, perpendicular to the line joining the center of the shell and the unit mass.

2.16 Show that the field lines of $\nabla(x^2 - y^2)$ are rectangular hyperbolae.

2.17 Show that the field lines of $\nabla(\tan^{-1} y/x)$ are circles.

2.18 Draw equipotential surfaces for $\phi_1 = \text{const.} = y$ and $\phi_2 = (10/\pi) \tan^{-1} (y/x)$.

2.19 (a) Consider a slim rod of finite length and uniform line density. Find the x and y components, the resultant, and the direction of the resultant

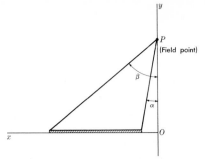

Fig. 2.25

gravitational field intensity at any point due to this rod. (You may place the system of axes in the manner shown in Figure 2.25.)

(b) Find the gravitational field intensity and gravitational potential due to an infinite slim rod.

2.20 Consider a central field of force F, i.e., one in which the force at any point of the field depends only on the distance between the field point and a certain fixed point O (called the center of force). Show that the corresponding potential field is given by $V = -\int F\, dr$. [Thus you are to show explicitly that $F_x = -\partial V/\partial x$, $F_y = -\partial V/\partial y$, $F_z = -\partial V/\partial z$ (Fig. 2.26).]

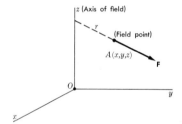

Fig. 2.26
Axial field force.

2.21 An axial field of force $F(x, y, z)$ is a field for which the force acting at any point of the field depends only on the distance r between the field point and a fixed axis (Fig. 2.27). Prove that the potential of this field is $V = -\int F\, dr$.

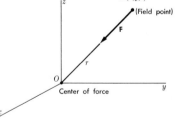

Fig. 2.27
Radial field force.

2.22 (a) Let $F_1, F_2, \ldots, F_n$ be conservative fields, the potential fields of which are $V_1, V_2, \ldots, V_n$ respectively. Prove that the field

$$\mathbf{F} = \mathbf{F}_1 + \mathbf{F}_2 + \cdots + \mathbf{F}_n$$

is also conservative and the potential of $\mathbf{F}$ is $V = V_1 + V_2 + \cdots + V_n$.

(b) The helium atom consists of a nucleus of charge $+2e$ and two electrons of charge $-e$ each. Let the distances of the electrons from the nucleus be r_1 and r_2 respectively, and that between the two electrons be r_{12}. Assuming the inverse square Coulomb field between all the constituents of the atom, write down the electrical potential energy of the helium atom.

2.23 The flux $d\psi$ of a vector $\mathbf{a}$ across an area $d\mathbf{S}$ (Fig. 2.28) is defined as $d\psi = \mathbf{a} \cdot d\mathbf{S}$. Let $\mathbf{a}$ be a vector field caused by a continuous distribution of source of density $\rho(x, y, z)$. Gauss' flux theorem states that the total flux out of a closed surface S is equal to the total strength of the source enclosed by S; thus $\oiint \mathbf{a} \cdot d\mathbf{S} = \iiint \rho \, dV$. When applied to the gravitational field, Gauss' theorem would state that the total flux of the gravitational field intensity out of a closed surface is equal to the total mass enclosed in the surface. Prove the equivalence of this statement to Newton's law of universal attraction for a spherical distribution of mass acting on a unit point mass.

Fig. 2.28

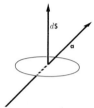

2.24 Prove that the necessary and sufficient condition that for given functions F_x, F_y, F_z there exists a function V satisfying the relations

$$F_x = -\frac{\partial V}{\partial x}, \quad F_y = -\frac{\partial V}{\partial y}, \quad F_z = -\frac{\partial V}{\partial z}$$

is that the following equations will be satisfied

$$\frac{\partial F_x}{\partial y} = \frac{\partial F_y}{\partial x}, \quad \frac{\partial F_y}{\partial z} = \frac{\partial F_z}{\partial y}, \quad \frac{\partial F_z}{\partial x} = \frac{\partial F_x}{\partial z}$$

2.25 Consider a coordinate system fixed with respect to the earth. Assume a perfectly spherical uniform earth, and choose the z axis towards the center of the earth, the x axis north and the y axis east. The x and y axes define a plane tangent to the earth surface; the plane is smooth. Derive the equations of motion for a point mass moving in this plane. The origin of the coordinate system is at the latitude λ. Consider only motion very close to the origin.

2.26 A truck of mass M moves with a linear acceleration a along a horizontal road. On the truck, a horizontal turntable rotates at angular velocity ω. A small object of mass m rests on the turntable at a distance r from its center of rotation. The coefficient of static friction between the object and the surface of the turntable is μ. What is the maximum value which ω may have before the object will start to move?

3 EQUILIBRIUM

    A system is in equilibrium when the resultant of all forces acting on it is zero. It is usually implied that in this case the system is at rest, but according to the definition, a system in uniform motion is also in equilibrium. For simplicity we will consider a system at rest.

    There are *three different types of equilibrium: stable, unstable, and neutral.* We will discuss the conditions under which a system will be in equilibrium and what type of equilibrium we are dealing with. There are several methods by which these conditions can be ascertained. Thus we can elaborate the definition of equilibrium given above and obtain the necessary conditions. This will have to be preceded by a discussion of the resultant of a system of forces. In another method we consider the potential energy function of the system. In addition there is another, quite refined, method based on the principle of virtual work. All these procedures will be discussed in turn.

    The branch of mechanics which deals with systems in equilibrium is called *statics.* This is quite an important and extensive subject. Only some aspects of statics will be considered here.

3-1 The Resultant of a System of Forces

Given a number of forces acting on a body, *the resultant is defined as the simplest possible system which will produce the same action as all the original forces. There are three such resultant systems, namely*
    a single force, a couple, and a force plus a couple.

A single force will always be the resultant of a system of concurrent forces. A single force may also be the resultant of a coplanar nonconcurrent system, and a system of parallel forces. However, in the two latter cases the resultant may also be a couple. The resultant of a system of couples will be a single couple. A nonconcurrent, three-dimensional system of forces will in general have as a resultant a force plus a couple. The simplest form of this latter resultant system is called the wrench (or the screw). The wrench consists of a couple plus a force perpendicular to the plane of the couple. Of course, there may be situations when the resultant of the most general system of forces acting on a body will be single force or a couple.

    A couple produces rotation and therefore its action is completely specified by the moment **G** of the couple. As long as the moment remains the same the action of the couple will be the same. The values of the forces constituting the couple can therefore be changed provided that the perpendicular distance between them is changed appropriately so as to preserve the moment. Also, since the moment of the couple is the same about any axis perpendicular to the plane of the couple, the couple can be shifted in its plane or to any parallel plane.

3–2 *Translational and Rotational Equilibrium. The Number of Independent Conditions to Ensure Equilibrium*

In order that a body be at equilibrium the resultant of all the forces acting on the body must be zero. Here the concept of the resultant is used in the sense discussed above. In the most general case the resultant consists of a force and a couple. Thus, for equilibrium, the resultant force *and* the torque must be zero. In that case the body will be in translational and rotational equilibrium. We may consider these two types of equilibrium separately; in doing so the number of independent conditions which are necessary for equilibrium can be obtained. Consider the most general case of a nonconcurrent system of forces acting on a body. Let the resultant force be denoted by **F**. For equilibrium

$$\mathbf{F} = \mathbf{0} \tag{3.1}$$

Now,
$$\mathbf{F} = F_x\mathbf{i} + F_y\mathbf{j} + F_z\mathbf{k} \tag{3.2}$$

therefore **F** will vanish if

$$F_x = 0, \; F_y = 0, \; F_z = 0 \tag{3.3}$$

Even if these conditions are fulfilled, the body may still rotate because there may be a resultant torque **G**. Since again

$$\mathbf{G} = G_x\mathbf{i} + G_y\mathbf{j} + G_z\mathbf{k} \tag{3.4}$$

therefore, for a vanishing torque

$$G_x = 0, \; G_y = 0, \; G_z = 0 \tag{3.5}$$

Thus, *to ensure equilibrium, six independent conditions must be fulfilled in this most general case.*

The number of conditions necessary for equilibrium in other cases can be obtained in the same manner. In the case of coplanar nonconcurrent forces the resultant force will be of the form

$$\mathbf{F} = F_x\mathbf{i} + F_y\mathbf{j} \tag{3.6}$$

and the resultant moment of the force will be

$$\mathbf{G} = G_z\mathbf{k} \tag{3.7}$$

Three conditions for equilibrium thus obtain, viz.

$$F_x = 0, \; F_y = 0, \; G_z = 0 \tag{3.8}$$

A set of conditions like that is not unique. Any of the first two equations can be replaced by a moment equation about arbitrary axes A and B parallel to the z axis. Thus a set of equations

$$G_A = 0, \; G_B = 0, \; G_C = 0 \tag{3.9}$$

will be an equivalent set of independent conditions for equilibrium. The three points, A, B, and C about which the moments are taken cannot be collinear. To see this consider the somewhat simplified situation shown in

Fig. 3.1

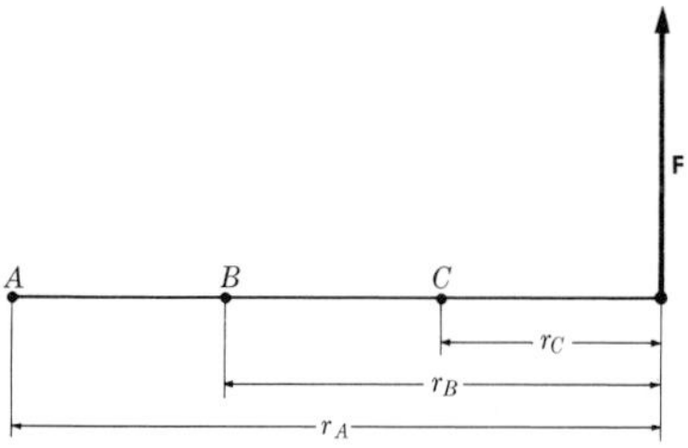

Figure 3.1. The points A, B, and C are collinear. The magnitudes of moments of the force **F** about these points are

$$G_A = r_A F, \; G_B = r_B F, \; G_C = r_C F \tag{3.10}$$

Now, r_A can be written as linear combination of r_B and r_C, viz.

$$r_A = b r_B + c r_C$$

and so, $\qquad\qquad G_A = (b r_B + c r_C)F$

If the three moments are to be zero, then

$$(b r_B + c r_C)F = 0$$
$$r_B F = 0$$
$$r_C F = 0$$

This is not an independent set of conditions because the first follows from the other two.

In other cases the procedure is similar.

3–3   The Three Types of Equilibrium. The Potential Energy Method

The equilibrium of a body can be stable, unstable or neutral. *The type of equilibrium present in a given physical situation is determined by the behavior of the body when it is slightly displaced from its position of equilibrium and then left alone.* If the body returns to its original position then the system is in stable equilibrium. When it moves away from its original position, then the original position was one of unstable equilibrium, and when the body neither returns to its original position nor moves away from it but simply remains in the new position then its equilibrium is neutral. Visual illustrations of the three cases are given in Figures 3.2(a), (b), and (c).

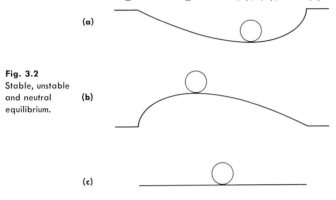

(a)

Fig. 3.2
Stable, unstable
and neutral   (b)
equilibrium.

(c)

Let us consider the mechanics of the various situations in some detail. We start with the assumption that the body is some force field. This *force field will be responsible for the motion of the body towards or away from the position of equilibrium*, after the body has been displaced from this position and left alone. The different types of equilibrium can always be described in terms of the action of the force field for any type of the field. However, a much simpler and more detailed *description of the equilibrium* can be obtained *in terms of the potential energy of the body*.

The potential energy is defined as the negative of the work done by the force field, when the body is moved in it by external forces. Taking the equilibrium position as the zero level for the potential energy, we see that when the body is displaced from stable equilibrium its potential energy is positive, and when displaced from non-stable equilibrium its potential energy is negative. *At the equilibrium position the potential energy is at a minimum, in relation to local surroundings, when the equilibrium is stable, and maximum, when the equilibrium is unstable.* For neutral equilibrium the potential energy is the same in the original and displaced position.

Let the potential energy of the body be a function of one coordinate only, ie.

$$V = V(r)$$

If equilibrium occurs at the point $r = r_0$, then in all cases the potential energy function will have an extremum at this point. Thus

$$\left[\frac{dV}{dr}\right]_{r=r_0} = 0 \qquad (3.11)$$

This relation will determine the position of equilibrium. To find the type of equilibrium we investigate the sign of the second derivative of the potential energy function, evaluated at $r = r_0$. When

$$\left[\frac{d^2V}{dr^2}\right]_{r=r_0} > 0 \tag{3.12}$$

the equilibrium is stable and when

$$\left[\frac{d^2V}{dr^2}\right]_{r=r_0} < 0 \tag{3.13}$$

then the equilibrium is unstable.

Example (A) A homogeneous sphere of mass M and of diameter R rests on the top of a fixed hemisphere of radius R (Fig. 3.3).

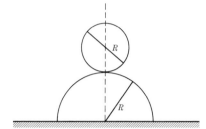

This is a simple example of unstable equilibrium but it may serve as an illustration of the procedure used to determine the position and the type of equilibrium. We first construct the potential energy function. To do this we place the sphere in a general position as shown in Figure 3.4. The potential

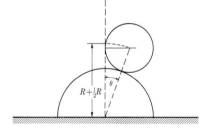

energy is the gravitational potential energy and, in the displaced position, it is negative with respect to the original position. Thus

$$V(\theta) = -(R + \tfrac{1}{2}R)Mg + (R + \tfrac{1}{2}R)Mg\cos\theta$$

or

$$V(\theta) = -(R + \tfrac{1}{2}R)Mg(1 - \cos\theta)$$

To obtain the position of equilibrium we evaluate the first derivative of this function. We get

$$\frac{dV}{d\theta} = \frac{-3\,RMg}{2}\sin\theta$$

3–3 The three types of equilibrium. The potential energy method

43

and we see that
$$\frac{dV}{d\theta} = 0$$

for
$$\theta = 0$$

The position of equilibrium has thus been determined.

To determine the type of equilibrium we evaluate the second derivative. We get
$$\frac{d^2V}{d\theta^2} = -\frac{3}{2} RMg \cos \theta$$

and at $\theta = 0$
$$\frac{d^2V}{d\theta^2} < 0$$

The equilibrium is therefore unstable.

Example (B)   Let us continue with a similarly simple example of a sphere of diameter R resting at the bottom of a fixed spherical bowl of radius R

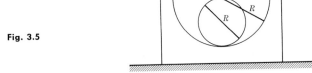

Fig. 3.5

(Fig. 3.5).   In this case the potential energy of the sphere in the displaced position is positive with respect to that in the original position.   Thus
$$V(\theta) = (\tfrac{1}{2}R + \tfrac{1}{2}R \cos \theta)Mg$$

or
$$V(\theta) = \tfrac{1}{2}R(1 - \cos \theta)Mg$$

Now
$$\frac{dV}{d\theta} = \frac{1}{2} RMg \sin \theta$$

and
$$\left[\frac{dV}{d\theta}\right]_{\theta=0} = 0$$

Further
$$\frac{d^2V}{d\theta^2} = \frac{1}{2} RMg \cos \theta$$

and we see that the equilibrium is stable because
$$\left[\frac{d^2V}{d\theta^2}\right]_{\theta=0} > 0$$

3–4   *The General Theory of Stability of Equilibrium for Conservative Systems*

We will consider systems describable by a potential energy which is a function of position only.   Such systems are called conservative.   We will limit ourselves to the case when
$$V = V(q)$$

i.e., to the case when the potential energy is a function of one coordinate only. Suppose that the position of equilibrium is at

$$q = q_0$$

and let us shift the coordinate axes so that

$$q_0 = 0$$

Now, the value of the function in the vicinity of $q_0 = 0$ is given by Taylor's expansion:

$$V(q) = V(0) + q\left(\frac{dV}{dq}\right)_{q=0} + \frac{1}{2}q^2\left(\frac{d^2V}{dq^2}\right)_{q=0} + \frac{q^3}{3!}\left(\frac{d^3V}{dq^3}\right)_{q=0}$$
$$+ \frac{q^4}{4!}\left(\frac{d^4V}{dq^4}\right)_{q=0} + \cdots \tag{3.14}$$

We investigated the stability of equilibrium by examining the behavior of the system when it was slightly displaced from the position of equilibrium. In examining this behavior it is sufficient to retain the first three terms because we are looking for the values of $V(q)$ for very small q's. Now, we may set arbitrarily

$$V(0) = 0$$

Further

$$\left(\frac{dV}{dq}\right)_{q=0} = 0 \tag{3.15}$$

because this is the necessary condition for equilibrium. Thus we are left with

$$V(q) = \frac{1}{2}q^2\left(\frac{d^2V}{dq^2}\right)_{q=0} \tag{3.16}$$

When

$$\left(\frac{d^2V}{dq^2}\right)_{q=0} > 0 \tag{3.17}$$

then

$$V(q) > 0$$

and when

$$\left(\frac{d^2V}{dq^2}\right)_{q=0} < 0 \tag{3.18}$$

then

$$V(q) < 0$$

In the first of the two cases $\left(\frac{d^2V}{dq^2} > 0\right)$, $V(q)$ has a minimum at $q = 0$, and the equilibrium is stable. In the second case $\left(\frac{d^2V}{dq^2} < 0\right)$, $V(q)$ has a maximum at $q = 0$, and the system is in unstable equilibrium.

In most cases the procedure outlined above is sufficient to establish the type of equilibrium. However, there are systems, described by the potential energy $V = V(q)$, for which

$$\left(\frac{d^2V}{dq^2}\right)_{q=0} = 0 \tag{3.19}$$

In this case
$$V(q) = (q^3/3!)\left(\frac{d^3V}{dq^3}\right)_{q=0} \tag{3.20}$$

We notice that $V(q)$ is positive on one side of $q = 0$ and negative on the other. When

$$\left(\frac{d^3V}{dq^3}\right)_{q=0} > 0$$

then $V(q) > 0$ for $q > 0$ and for $q < 0$, $V(q) < 0$.

Considerations on the behavior of the system placed in such a potential energy field, and slightly displaced from the position of equilibrium, lead to the conclusion that the equilibrium is unstable.

When

$$\left(\frac{d^3V}{dq^3}\right)_{q=0} = 0 \tag{3.21}$$

then
$$V(q) = (q^4/4!)\left(\frac{d^4V}{dq^4}\right)_{q=0} \tag{3.22}$$

here a similar procedure is used, and similar results obtained as in the case when the second derivative did not vanish.

When the potential energy function depends on more than one coordinate the multiple Taylor expansion has to be used,* and the behavior of the system examined in a similar way as above.

3–5   The Principle of Virtual Work

The principle of virtual work can be taken as the definition of equilibrium and the starting point of statics.

Consider a single particle under the action of a set of forces

$$\mathbf{F}_1, \mathbf{F}_2, \ldots, \mathbf{F}_n$$

Imagine that the particle be displaced from its given position by an amount $\delta\mathbf{r}$. During this displacement all the forces acting on the particle will do work. The work performed by the force $\mathbf{F}_i$ is defined as the scalar product $\mathbf{F}_i \cdot \delta\mathbf{r}$ and the total work is given by

$$\delta W = \mathbf{F}_1 \cdot \delta\mathbf{r} + \mathbf{F}_2 \cdot \delta\mathbf{r} + \cdots + \mathbf{F}_n \cdot \delta\mathbf{r} \tag{3.23}$$

If during this imagined displacement

$$\delta W = 0 \tag{3.24}$$

then the particle is in equilibrium. This is the principle of virtual work applied to a single particle.

---

* The expression for Taylor's expansion of $V = V(q_1, q_2, \ldots, q_n)$ is written out in Chapter 16, Small Oscillations.

We notice that if the principle of virtual work is taken as a statement defining the equilibrium of the particle then the definition of equilibrium given in Section 3–2 follows, for Eq. (3.23) can also be written as

$$\delta W = (\mathbf{F}_1 + \mathbf{F}_2 + \cdots + \mathbf{F}_n) \cdot \delta \mathbf{r} \tag{3.25}$$

or
$$\delta W = \mathbf{R} \cdot \delta \mathbf{r} \tag{3.26}$$

where
$$\mathbf{R} = \mathbf{F}_1 + \mathbf{F}_2 + \cdots + \mathbf{F}_n$$

is the resultant force acting on the particle. If $\delta W = 0$ for arbitrary $\delta \mathbf{r}$ then $\mathbf{R} = 0$.

The displacement $\delta \mathbf{r}$ is called the *virtual displacement* of the particle. In order to understand the concept of the virtual displacement consider a point P moving on a certain surface S. Suppose that the point is displaced by an amount PP'. If PP' lies in the surface, we will call PP' a possible displacement, otherwise the displacement will be called impossible. Suppose now that the point P is given a velocity $\mathbf{v}$. If this velocity is such that the point moves on the surface then we will call it a possible velocity; otherwise it will be referred to as an impossible velocity. Possible velocities are all the velocity vectors which are tangent to the surface. An important type of *displacement* is that which is *proportional to the possible velocity*; such a displacement is called a virtual displacement. We notice that, in the sense defined here, *a virtual displacement, in general, is not a possible displacement*.

Let the surface S be specified by the equation

$$f(x, y, z) = 0 \tag{3.27}$$

If the point P is on this surface then at all times its coordinates satisfy the equation of the surface. Assume that P moves on S in any manner. Differentiating the equation of the surface with respect to time we obtain

$$\frac{\partial f}{\partial x}\, \dot{x} + \frac{\partial f}{\partial y}\, \dot{y} + \frac{\partial f}{\partial z}\, \dot{z} = 0 \tag{3.28}$$

which can also be written as

$$\frac{\partial f}{\partial x}\, v_x + \frac{\partial f}{\partial y}\, v_y + \frac{\partial f}{\partial z}\, v_z = 0$$

or, in vector form,

$$\nabla f \cdot \mathbf{v} = 0 \tag{3.29}$$

where
$$\nabla f = \mathbf{grad}\, f = \frac{\partial f}{\partial x}\, \mathbf{i} + \frac{\partial f}{\partial y}\, \mathbf{j} + \frac{\partial f}{\partial z}\, \mathbf{k}$$

Since $\mathbf{grad}\, f$ is a vector normal to the surface, $\mathbf{v}$ is in the plane tangent to the surface.

Let $\delta \mathbf{s} = \delta x \mathbf{i} + \delta y \mathbf{j} + \delta z \mathbf{k}$ denote an arbitrary displacement of the point P. According to our definition, a displacement $\delta \mathbf{s}$ proportional to $\mathbf{v}$ will be a virtual displacement and, in particular, a displacement $\delta \mathbf{s} = k \mathbf{v}$ will also be a virtual displacement. Thus the components of a virtual displacement will satisfy the equation

$$\frac{\partial f}{\partial x}\, \delta x + \frac{\partial f}{\partial y}\, \delta y + \frac{\partial f}{\partial z}\, \delta z = 0 \qquad (3.30)$$

We can therefore say that *a virtual displacement is a vector $\delta\mathbf{s}$, the components of which satisfy the above Eq. (3.30)*.

Consider now a system of n particles. Let the resultant forces acting on the particles $1, 2, \ldots, n$ be denoted by

$$\mathbf{R}_1, \mathbf{R}_2, \ldots, \mathbf{R}_n$$

respectively. *All the virtual displacements have to be consistent with the constraints of the system and satisfy the requirements of the geometrical configurations imposed on the system;* in addition they all have to form an independent set; otherwise they are arbitrary. (This statement will become clear when we solve an example.) The total virtual work performed by all the forces will then be

$$\delta W = \mathbf{R}_1 \cdot \delta\mathbf{r}_1 + \mathbf{R}_2 \cdot \delta\mathbf{r}_2 + \cdots + \mathbf{R}_n \cdot \delta\mathbf{r}_n \qquad (3.31)$$

Again, the system will be in equilibrium if

$$\delta W = 0$$

This is the principle of virtual work applied to a system of particles.

The principle can be applied to rigid bodies or systems of rigid bodies. Given a rigid body on which a set of forces

$$\mathbf{F}_1, \mathbf{F}_2, \ldots, \mathbf{F}_n$$

is acting, we subject it to a virtual displacement and calculate the total virtual work δW performed by all the forces of the above set. If

$$\delta W = 0$$

then the rigid body is at equilibrium. In calculating δW we have to calculate the virtual displacements of the points of application of the forces $\mathbf{F}_1, \mathbf{F}_2, \ldots,$ $\mathbf{F}_n$. Again, all the geometrical relationships between the various displacements have to be considered.

In order to demonstate the meaning and the usefulness of the principle of virtual work we will solve an example.

Example: The structure shown in Figure 3.6 consists of three light rods connected by smooth pins. Determine all the reactions.

In problems of this nature the procedure is to produce a virtual displacement of the point where the reaction is to be determined, and—if possible—keep those points at which some other unknown reactions act, stationary. The resulting virtual motion must be consistent with the configurations of the system. In order to determine a reaction at some other point, a new virtual displacement, independent of the previous one, must be introduced.

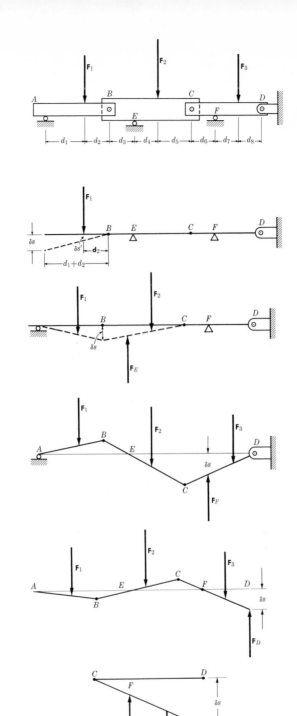

Fig. 3.6

Fig. 3.7a

Fig. 3.7b

Fig. 3.7c

Fig. 3.7d

Fig. 3.7e

3–5 The principle of virtual work

49

Reaction at A. Remove the roller at A, replace its action by a force F_A and produce a virtual displacement δs downwards (Fig. 3.7(a)). During this displacement only the rod AB will move and the rest of the system will remain stationary. The only other force acting here is the force F_1. The displacement $\delta s'$ of the point of application of this force is not independent but geometrically related to δs. In fact we see that

$$\frac{\delta s}{d_1 + d_2} = \frac{\delta s'}{d_2}$$

therefore

$$\delta W = F_A\, \delta s + F_1 \frac{d_2}{d_1 + d_2}\, \delta s$$

$$= \left(F_A + F_1 \frac{d_2}{d_1 + d_2} \right) \delta s$$

During this displacement

$$\delta W = 0$$

Thus F_A can be obtained from

$$F_A + F_1 \frac{d_2}{d_1 + d_2} = 0$$

Reaction at E. Remove the fulcrum at E and replace its action by a force F_E. When this is done, there is no longer any fulcrum at E, therefore no lever action. Drop B by a virtual displacement δs (Fig. 3.7(b)). Calculate the three resulting virtual displacements at the points of application of the forces F_1, F_E and F_2; all the displacements can be expressed in terms of δs. Application of the principle of virtual work then yields F_E.

Reaction at F. Displace the whole system as shown in Figure 3.7(c); since there is a roller at A, no constraints are violated.

Reaction at D. Remove the pin at D and replace its action by the force F_D. Retain all other supports. Drop D by a virtual displacement δs. The whole system then takes the shape shown in Figure 3.7(d).

As a further clarification of the method of virtual work, we can recalculate the reaction at D by introducing different virtual displacements. Let us assume that we know the reaction at F. Remove the fulcrum at F and replace it by the force F_F evaluated previously. In addition, remove the pin at D and replace it by the force F_D. Drop D by a virtual displacement δs as shown in Figure 3.7(e). Since there is no fulcrum at F, there will be no lever action there. Point F will drop proportionally and the rest of the system to the left of C will remain stationary in the horizontal position. Application of the principle of virtual work to this latter case will check the previous result.

3–5   The principle of virtual work

PROBLEMS

3.1 Show that the following system of forces is reducible to a single force:

(a) Force $5\sqrt{2}$ acting through the point $(0, 0, 1/5)$ in the direction of $3:4:-5$,

(b) Force $3\sqrt{11}$ through the point $(1/3, 0, 0)$ in the direction $5:5:-7$,

(c) Force $\sqrt{11}$ through the point $(0, 1/4, 0)$ in the direction $-3:1:1$.

3.2 A force of magnitude P acts parallel to Ox through the point $(0, 0, 1)$. A second force of magnitude $3P$ acts along a line through the point $(1, 0, 0)$; the directions cosines of this line are $(0, 3/5, 4/5)$. Find the resultant system.

3.3 A, B, C, D is a square. A force P acts along AB, and another force P along CD. A force $P\sqrt{2}$ acts along the diagonal BD and a force $2\sqrt{2}\,P$ along CA. Find the magnitude and the line of action of a single equivalent force.

3.4 Consider the system of three rods, each having the same mass and length 2ℓ. The lowest rod is connected to a massless piston fitted in a cylinder (Fig. 3.8). The gas between the piston and the bottom of the cylinder exerts an upward force $F = A[(\ell/x) - 1]$ on the piston. If it were possible to make all rods vertical, the piston would be at the bottom of the cylinder. By the method of virtual work determine the equilibrium value of ϕ.

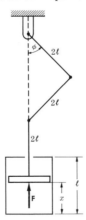

Fig. 3.8

3.5 A system has the potential function given by

$$\phi(x) = ax^3 - bx$$

where $a > 0, b > 0, b > a$. Determine all the values of x for which the system is at equilibrium, and determine whether the equilibrium is stable or unstable.

3.6 A framework $ABCD$, which lies in a vertical plane, consists of four rods each of weight W and length $2a$ which are smoothly pivoted at their ends.

AB is fixed in a horizontal position, and A and C are joined by a light string of length $2a$. The framework is at equilibrium. Using the method of virtual work find the tension in the string.

3.7 Two point masses A and B move on a smooth circular track in a vertical plane. The point masses A and B are connected by a rod whose length is equal to the radius of the path and whose weight can be neglected. The weight of A is twice that of B. For each equilibrium position determine the type of equilibrium.

3.8 An endless elastic string of natural length πa, weight A and modulus $2W$ rests in equilibrium on the smooth surface of a sphere of radius a in the form of a horizontal circle of the radius $a \sin \theta$. Prove that $\tan \theta = 4\pi(2 \sin \theta - 1)$.

3.9 A solid hemisphere of radius r has its base fixed to the base of a solid cone of base radius r and height h, both solids being uniform and of the same density. Obtain the potential energy of the body in any position and show that there is a stable position of equilibrium with the axis vertical provided $h < \sqrt{3}\, r$.

3.10 A uniform elastic string is in the form of a closed curve. It is of weight W and natural length ℓ_o and modulus λ. It rests in a horizontal position on a smooth circular cone whose axis is vertical and whose semivertical angle is α. Find the depth of the string below the vertex of the cone.

3.11 Two rods of weight W each are hinged at C (Fig. 3.9) and are placed in a vertical plane. Their middle points are joined by a string. Find the condition of equilibrium if (a) the string EF is weightless and (b) if the weight of the string is W'.

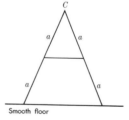

Fig. 3.9

3.12 (a) Consider a moving frame of reference. When a point mass is at rest in the moving frame then—using the notation of Section 2.10—$\mathbf{a}_r = \mathbf{0}$ and $\mathbf{v}_r = \mathbf{0}$. This is a case of relative equilibrium, i.e., an equilibrium with respect to a moving frame. Show that in this case the absolute force $\mathbf{F}_s$ balances the lifting force $\mathbf{F}_e$.

(b) A point mass m hangs from an inextensible string in an elevator moving with acceleration a. Obtain expressions for the tension T in the string when the elevator moves up and when it moves down with the same acceleration.

4

HARMONIC VIBRATIONS

The atoms or molecules constituting all matter are in a state of continuous motion. In gases and liquids this motion is mostly translational. In solids the molecules are at given sites and are continuously oscillating about their positions of equilibrium. It is quite natural that we seek models for such oscillations. Of the possible models, the one by far most frequently used is the harmonic oscillator. We propose to study the mathematical problems connected with this oscillator. We will first discuss free oscillators, linear and angular, then damped oscillatory motion and finally forced harmonic oscillations.

4–1   *The Simple Linear Harmonic Oscillator*

The simple linear harmonic oscillator consists of a point mass vibrating about a position of equilibrium under the action of a force which is

(1) *always proportional to the displacement from the position of equilibrium, and*

(2) *always directed towards the position of equilibrium.*

Let the motion take place along the x-axis and let O be the position of equilibrium from which the displacement x will be measured. If F is the force acting on the point mass m then, according to the first part of the definition,

$$F \propto x \qquad (4.1)$$

In order to obtain an equation out of this proportionality relation, and to conform to the second part of the definition we write

$$F = -kx \qquad (4.2)$$

The proportionality constant k is called the *force constant.** The negative sign in Eq. (4.2) follows from part (2) of the definition given above.

At the same time Newton's second law is obeyed for m; thus

$$F = m\ddot{x} \qquad (4.3)$$

---

* In the case when the particle is attached to a spring which is responsible for the harmonic oscillations, the constant k is called the spring constant.

From (4.2) and (4.3) we obtain

$$m\ddot{x} = -kx$$

or
$$\ddot{x} + (k/m)x = 0 \tag{4.4}$$

This is one form of the differential equation of the simple harmonic oscillator. In this form, as we see, the differential equation contains the physical quantities k and m.

This equation is of a very common occurrence in mathematics and its solution is of the form

$$x = A \cos \sqrt{\frac{k}{m}}\, t + B \sin \sqrt{\frac{k}{m}}\, t \tag{4.5}$$

or
$$x = a \cos \left(\sqrt{\frac{k}{m}}\, t + \delta \right) \tag{4.6}$$

Of course, one form of the solution is as good as the other because both satisfy the differential equation and both contain two constants: A and B in Eq. (4.5) and a and δ in Eq. (4.6). Besides, as is shown in Problem 4–1, one follows from the other.

The behavior of the simple harmonic oscillator is seen quite clearly from Eq. (4.6). The most important characteristic is that the time behavior of the particle executing simple harmonic motion is sinusoidal.

We can write Eq. (4.6) in the form

$$x = a \cos \phi \tag{4.7}$$

where
$$\phi = \sqrt{(k/m)}\, t + \delta \tag{4.8}$$

is called the *phase of the motion*. δ is the value of the phase at $t = 0$, i.e., the initial phase; we will call it the *epoch angle*. We notice that the displacement x is maximum when

$$x = a$$

a is called the *amplitude of the motion*.

The properties of the simple harmonic oscillator can also be examined with the help of a useful device called the reference circle. Let a particle m' move with uniform speed on the perimeter of a circle of radius a (Fig. 4.1).

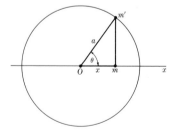

Fig. 4.1
The reference circle.

Its projection m on any diameter executes simple harmonic motion. Indeed, the displacement of the projection is

$$x = a \cos \phi \qquad (4.9)$$

But
$$\phi = \omega t \qquad (4.10)$$

where ω is the angular velocity of the particle m'. Thus

$$x = a \cos \omega t \qquad (4.11)$$

Here we are starting the motion at the zero epoch angle. If this were not

so then
$$x = a \cos (\omega t + \delta) \qquad (4.12)$$

This is an equation of exactly the same form as (4.6) provided we put

$$\omega^2 = \frac{k}{m} \qquad (4.13)$$

Eq. (4.12) contains a new physical characteristic of the simple harmonic oscillator, namely its *angular frequency* ω. Eq. (4.13) relates ω with the force constant and the mass. In terms of the ordinary *frequency* ν, which signifies the number of complete vibrations per second,

$$\omega = 2\pi\nu \qquad (4.14)$$

Another important physical characteristic of the oscillator is its *period* τ which denotes the time of one complete vibration. The relation between the frequency and the period can be obtained with the help of Fig. 4.2. The

Fig. 4.2
Relation between the
frequency and the period.

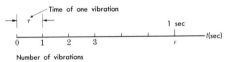

horizontal line is the time axis of which 1 second is shown. There are ν vibrations in 1 second each lasting for a time τ. Thus

$$\tau\nu = 1 \qquad (4.15)$$

or
$$\tau = \frac{1}{\nu} \qquad (4.16)$$

Therefore, the period is the inverse of the frequency.

Differentiating Eq. (4.12) twice with respect to time we obtain

$$\ddot{x} + \omega^2 x = 0 \qquad (4.17)$$

which is the differential equation of the simple harmonic oscillator including the angular frequency.

Other quantities of interest are the kinetic, potential, total and average energies of the oscillator. Let us evaluate the potential energy first. When m is at the distance x from the position of equilibrium the force acting on it is $F = -kx$. In order to displace m an additional distance dx, we have to perform an amount of work given by

$$dW = F\,dx$$

or
$$dW = -kx\,dx \tag{4.18}$$

The total work done in bringing the particle from O to some point x_0 is

$$W = -\int_0^{x_0} kx\,dx \tag{4.19}$$

or
$$W = -\tfrac{1}{2}kx_0{}^2 \tag{4.20}$$

Therefore the potential energy at any point x is

$$V = -\tfrac{1}{2}kx^2 \tag{4.21}$$

The kinetic energy is
$$T = \tfrac{1}{2}m\dot{x}^2 \tag{4.22}$$

where $\dot{x}$ can be obtained from Eq. (4.12). We see that

$$\dot{x} = -a\omega \sin(\omega t + \delta) \tag{4.23}$$

or
$$\dot{x} = -a\omega \sin \phi \tag{4.24}$$

Noting that $\sin \phi = \sqrt{1 - \cos^2 \phi}$ we can write

$$\dot{x} = -\omega\sqrt{a^2 - x^2} \tag{4.25}$$

Therefore
$$T = \tfrac{1}{2}m\omega^2(a^2 - x^2) \tag{4.26}$$

The maximum of the kinetic energy is

$$T_{\max} = \tfrac{1}{2}m\omega^2 a^2 \tag{4.27}$$

Now, the maximum of the potential energy is

$$V_{\max} = \tfrac{1}{2}ka^2 \tag{4.28}$$

But $k = m\omega^2$, therefore
$$V_{\max} = \tfrac{1}{2}m\omega^2 a^2 \tag{4.29}$$

and we see that
$$V_{\max} = T_{\max} \tag{4.30}$$

This is quite understandable from physical considerations because when $V = V_{\max}$ then $T = 0$, as at this instant the particle stops momentarily. Also when $T = T_{\max}$ then $V = 0$. Since the total energy E is given by

$$E = T + V$$

and it is constant, therefore—in view of the previous results—

$$E = T_{\max} = V_{\max} \tag{4.31}$$

therefore

$$E = \tfrac{1}{2}m\omega^2 a^2 \tag{4.32}$$

We should be able to obtain this result in another way. Thus

$$
\begin{aligned}
E &= T + V \\
&= \tfrac{1}{2}m\omega^2(a^2 - x^2) + \tfrac{1}{2}kx^2 \\
&= \tfrac{1}{2}m\omega^2 a^2 - \tfrac{1}{2}m\omega^2 x^2 + \tfrac{1}{2}m\omega^2 x^2
\end{aligned}
$$

or, indeed

$$E = \tfrac{1}{2}m\omega^2 a^2$$

We notice the significant fact that the *total energy is proportional to the square of the amplitude of the oscillator*.

It is of interest to compute the average kinetic and potential energies. For the potential energy we have

$$
\begin{aligned}
\langle V \rangle &= \frac{1}{\tau} \int_0^\tau V \, dt \\
&= \frac{1}{\tau} \int_0^\tau \frac{1}{2} ka^2 \cos^2 \omega t \, dt \tag{4.33} \\
&= \tfrac{1}{4}ka^2
\end{aligned}
$$

In a similar fashion we find that also

$$\langle T \rangle = \tfrac{1}{4}ka^2 \tag{4.34}$$

We have thus obtained another interesting result that

$$\langle V \rangle = \langle T \rangle = \tfrac{1}{2}E \tag{4.35}$$

i.e., *the average potential energy of the oscillator is equal to the average of its kinetic energy and both are equal to one half of the total energy.*

The plot of the potential energy is shown in Figure 4.3. It is a parabola with its minimum at the origin.

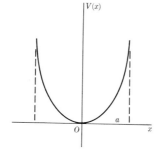

Fig. 4.3
The potential energy
function of the simple
harmonic oscillator.

The definition of the angular simple harmonic oscillator will be quite parallel to that of the linear oscillator, except that the angular quantities will replace the linear quantities. Physically, the angular simple harmonic oscillator will consist of a rigid body executing oscillations about some position of equilibrium under the action of a torque G which

(1) will always be proportional to the angular displacement from the equilibrium position, and

(2) will force the rigid body towards the position of equilibrium.

Both statements are contained in the expression

$$G = -\gamma\theta \qquad\qquad (4.36)$$

where γ is the torque constant of the oscillator and θ is the angular displacement from the position of equilibrium. Now, for any rotation about a fixed axis we have

$$G = I\ddot{\theta} \qquad\qquad (4.37)$$

where I is the moment of inertia about this axis. Therefore

$$I\ddot{\theta} = -\gamma\theta \qquad\qquad (4.38)$$

or $\qquad\qquad\qquad \ddot{\theta} + (\gamma/I)\theta = 0$

This is the differential equation of the angular simple harmonic oscillator. We see that—apart from the different physical constants—it is exactly the same form as that of the linear oscillator. The whole mathematical treatment of the angular oscillator is therefore the same as that of the linear oscillator.

4–3   *Damped Harmonic Oscillator*

Macroscopic oscillators occurring in nature or those constructed in the laboratory are never simple in the sense discussed above and described by the differential Eq. (4.4). Such a simple oscillator when left alone would oscillate for ever with exactly the same amplitude. The motion of an actual macroscopic oscillator is always damped, i.e., its amplitude decreases with time. We realize immediately that the degree of damping may be different. In some cases only slight damping will be present. In such a case the damped oscillator will behave almost as the simple oscillator, except its amplitude will diminish at a very slow rate, and its frequency will be slightly different. The other extreme case is that of an excessive damping, so heavy in fact that no oscillations are possible. In this latter case, when displaced, the particle will return to its equilibrium after a very long time. Such an oscillator is called an overdamped oscillator, and that with a slight damping, an underdamped oscillator.

The physical reason for damping will be some sort of frictional force F_r. The differential equation of such an oscillator will therefore be of the form

$$m\ddot{x} = -kx - F_r \qquad (4.39)$$

The reason for the negative sign of F_r is that it will always oppose the motion of the oscillating particle. In order to proceed further we must make specific assumptions about the functional form of F_r. The assumption most often made is that F_r is proportional to the velocity of the oscillating particle, i.e.

$$F_r = \beta\dot{x} \qquad (4.40)$$

This assumption has been verified experimentally for a large range of velocities. Thus the differential equation of the damped oscillator which we have to solve is of the form

$$m\ddot{x} + \beta\dot{x} + kx = 0 \qquad (4.41)$$

In examining the problem of damped oscillations above, we stated that in some cases the oscillations will persist and in others the particle will not oscillate at all but will come back to its equilibrium position after a very long time. In both cases we may expect that the solution will be exponential in form. We thus assume that

$$x = Ae^{\lambda t} \qquad (4.42)$$

where λ may be complex. Substitution in (4.41) yields

$$m\lambda^2 + \beta\lambda + k = 0 \qquad (4.43)$$

If (4.42) is to be the solution of our differential equation then the latter equation must be satisfied. This equation yields

$$\lambda_{1,2} = \frac{-\beta \pm \sqrt{\beta^2 - 4mk}}{2m} \qquad (4.44)$$

These two values of λ have to be used. Thus the general solution of our differential equation is of the form

$$x = Ae^{\lambda_1 t} + Be^{\lambda_2 t} \qquad (4.45)$$

We notice that the mathematical treatment of the problem yields two cases depending on the sign of the expression under the square root of Eq. (4.44). We will see that the two cases actually correspond to the two types of damping mentioned above. We will now consider the two cases in turn.

Case 1. Let $\beta^2 > 4km$. In this case the general solution is

$$x = e^{-\beta/(2m)t}[Ae^{1/(2m)\sqrt{\beta^2-4km}\,t} + Be^{-1/(2m)\sqrt{\beta^2-4km}\,t}] \qquad (4.46)$$

The exponents are real. This corresponds to the overdamped case: x becomes zero after a very long time (mathematically, at $t = \infty$).

Case 2. Let us now suppose that $\beta^2 < 4km$. The exponents are then imaginary and we can write the solution in the form

$$x = e^{-\beta/(2m)t}[Ae^{i/(2m)\sqrt{4km-\beta^2}\,t} + Be^{-i/(2m)\sqrt{4km-\beta^2}\,t}] \qquad (4.47)$$

This expression represents oscillatory behavior of x. We can see that this is so by using Euler's identity $e^{i\phi} = \cos\phi + i\sin\phi$ and thus transforming the last expression to

$$x = ae^{-\beta/(2m)t}\cos[1/(2m)\sqrt{4km - \beta^2}\,t - \delta] \qquad (4.48)$$

which is almost of the same form as (4.12), except it has a different frequency, namely

$$\nu = 1/(4\pi m)\sqrt{4km - \beta^2} \qquad (4.49)$$

as compared with the frequency of

$$\nu = 1/(2\pi)\sqrt{k/m} \qquad (4.50)$$

of a simple harmonic oscillator; in addition the amplitude in the present case is

$$a' = ae^{-\beta/(2m)t} \qquad (4.51)$$

which means that the amplitude decreases exponentially with time.

Examination of the solution reveals another special case, viz., that when

$$\beta^2 = 4km$$

It would appear that the solution in this case is

$$x = Ae^{-\beta/(2m)t}$$

However, we cannot be satisfied with this solution because our differential equation is of the second order and its general solution should have two constants. In this case we try another function, viz.

$$x = te^{-\beta/(2m)t}$$

Substitution of this in Eq. (4.41) shows that the differential equation is satisfied by it. Since

$$x = e^{-\beta/(2m)t}$$

also satisfies our differential equation, therefore the general solution of the equation in this special case is

$$x = Ae^{-\beta/(2m)t} + Bte^{-\beta/(2m)t}$$

or

$$x = (A + Bt)e^{-\beta/(2m)t} \qquad (4.52)$$

This case ($\beta^2 = 4km$) is referred to as the case of critical damping.

The above cases of the simple and damped oscillator deal with instances when the oscillator is set into vibration and then left alone. Internal elastic forces are responsible for the oscillations and (in the damped case) the medium exerts a resistive force. It may so happen that additional forces are acting. A really interesting case arises when a periodic force is applied to the oscillator. Let this applied force be of the form

$$F_a = F_0 \cos \omega t \qquad (4.53)$$

where ω is the angular frequency with which the force is applied. In the case when the damping is operative and the applied force is acting, the oscillating particle m will be under the action of three forces, and so Newton's second law will be of the form

$$m\ddot{x} = -kx - \beta\dot{x} + F_a \qquad (4.54)$$

and the differential equation to be solved is of the form

$$m\ddot{x} + \beta\dot{x} + kx = F_0 \cos \omega t \qquad (4.55)$$

This is a non-homogeneous differential equation of the second order. This type of an equation is solved by seeking the general solution $f(t)$ of the corresponding homogeneous differential equation, and a particular solution $g(t)$ of the whole differential equation. The general solution is then given by

$$x = f(t) + g(t)$$

In our case the homogeneous equation has been solved already in the previous section and its general solution is given by Eqs. (4.46), (4.47), or (4.48).

As to the particular solution, it is sufficient to find a function which will satisfy the given differential equation. This function $g(t)$ should represent forced vibration and therefore should be of an oscillatory nature. A sine function alone or a cosine function alone will not satisfy our differential equation. We therefore try the solution of the form

$$x = p \cos \omega t + q \sin \omega t \qquad (4.56)$$

In order to determine the values of p and q we substitute Eq. (4.56) in the differential Eq. (4.55) and separately equate the coefficients of $\cos \omega t$ and of $\sin \omega t$ to zero. We first write Eq. (4.55) in the form

$$\ddot{x} + (\beta/m)\dot{x} + \omega_0^2 x = (F_0/m) \cos \omega t$$

where
$$\omega_0 = \sqrt{k/m}$$

is the natural frequency of the undamped motion. Proceeding as outlined above we get

$$p(\omega_0^2 - \omega^2) + q(\beta\omega/m) = F_0/m$$

and $$(\beta\omega/m)p - q(\omega_0{}^2 - \omega^2) = 0$$

from which p and q can be determined. Now, the particular solution can also be written as

$$x = \sqrt{p^2 + q^2}\,\cos\,(\omega t - \chi) \tag{4.57}$$

where $$\tan \chi = q/p \tag{4.58}$$

We find that

$$\sqrt{p^2 + q^2} = \frac{F_0}{\sqrt{m^2(\omega_0{}^2 - \omega^2) + \beta^2\omega^2}} \tag{4.59}$$

and $$\tan \chi = \frac{\beta\omega}{m(\omega_0{}^2 - \omega^2)} \tag{4.60}$$

The general solution of the forced vibrations therefore becomes

$$\begin{aligned}
x = {} & ae^{-\beta/(2m)t}\,\cos\,[1/(2m)\sqrt{4km - \beta^2}\,t - \delta] \\
& + \frac{F_0}{\sqrt{m^2(\omega_0{}^2 - \omega^2) + \beta^2\omega^2}}\,\cos\,(\omega t - \chi)
\end{aligned} \tag{4.61}$$

4–5 Complex Representation of Vibrations

All problems connected with vibrations can most effectively be represented by complex functions. The whole problem of employing complex numbers in describing physical phenomena should not be approached timidly because it is rather simple and very convenient. Neither are there any logical difficulties involved which might stem from the fact that we are representing real physical phenomena by complex numbers, if we will remember that complex functions are just used for mathematical manipulations. If the final result is represented as a complex number then the physical counterpart corresponds to the real part of the complex number.

Let us return to the reference circle which we found helpful in representing the simple harmonic motion. We are showing it once more in Figure 4.4.

Fig. 4.4

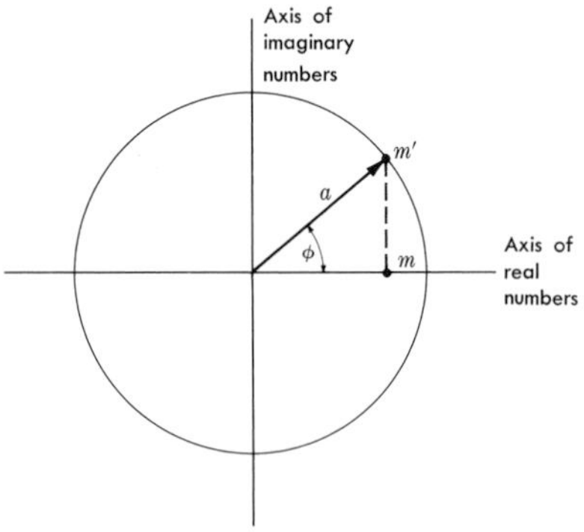

Axis of imaginary numbers

Axis of real numbers

m'

a

ϕ

m

The simple harmonic motion is the projection of m' on the horizontal diameter. Thus

$$x = a \cos \phi$$

where

$$\phi = \omega t - \delta$$

We may also write

$$x = ae^{i\phi} \tag{4.62}$$

or, since $\phi = \omega t - \delta$,

$$x = ae^{i(\omega t - \delta)} \tag{4.63}$$

This is the complex representation of the simple harmonic vibration with the understanding that it is the real part of it (i.e., $a \cos \phi$) which actually corresponds to the oscillation.

In order to illustrate the convenience afforded by the use of complex functions, consider again the case of the forced vibrations. Here we will represent the external periodic force as

$$F_a = F_0 e^{i\omega t} \tag{4.64}$$

The differential equation will therefore be written as

$$\ddot{x} + (\beta/m)\dot{x} + \omega_0{}^2 x = (F_0/m)e^{i\omega t} \tag{4.65}$$

We assume the solution to be of the form

$$x = ae^{i(\omega t - \chi)} \tag{4.66}$$

Substitution of this in Eq. (4.65) yields

$$a(\omega_0{}^2 - \omega^2 + i\beta\omega/m) = (F_0/m)e^{i\chi} \tag{4.67}$$

Both sides are complex numbers, and two complex numbers are equal if separately their real and imaginary parts are equal. As shown in Figure 4.5

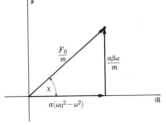

Fig. 4.5

we can represent the right-hand side on an Argand diagram by the tip of the vector of length F_0/m inclined at an angle χ to the real axis. Now, the left-hand side affords the components of this vector, i.e., the real and imaginary parts of the complex number $(F_0/m)e^{i\chi}$. It is obvious then that

$$(F_0/m)^2 = a^2[(\omega_0{}^2 - \omega^2)^2 + \beta^2\omega^2/m^2] \tag{4.68}$$

from which

$$a = \frac{F_0}{\sqrt{m^2(\omega_0{}^2 - \omega^2)^2 + \beta^2\omega^2}} \tag{4.69}$$

Also
$$\tan \chi = \frac{1}{m(\omega_0{}^2 - \omega^2)} \tag{4.70}$$

The simplicity and neatness of this latter procedure should be appreciated.

4–6 Resonance

The general expression for the forced vibrations is given by Eq. (4.61). This expression consists of two parts: the first term represents the natural (damped) vibrations and the second, the forced vibrations. The natural vibrations will die down, in many cases rather quickly, and only the forced part will be left. The amplitude of the forced vibrations is

$$a = \frac{F_0}{\sqrt{m^2(\omega_0{}^2 - \omega^2)^2 + \omega^2\beta^2}}$$

It contains the natural frequency ω_0 and the frequency ω of the applied periodic force. We notice that

$$a = a_{\max}$$

when $\omega = \omega_0$. In this case the forced vibrations have most pronounced amplitudes. This condition is called *resonance*.

PROBLEMS

4.1 One of the forms of the solutions of the differential equation $\ddot{x} + \omega^2 x = 0$, is $x = A \cos \omega t + B \sin \omega t$. Transform this solution into one of the form $x = a \cos (\omega t + \delta)$, i.e., express the two new constants of integration a and δ in terms of A and B.

4.2 Prove that the bob of a simple pendulum executes simple harmonic oscillations. The proof will consist of determining the differential equation of the bob of the pendulum; the equation should be of the form of that of the simple harmonic oscillator. What is the frequency of the oscillations of the pendulum in terms of the physical constants of the pendulum?

4.3 Prove that a physical pendulum executing small oscillations about a fixed axis not passing through the center of mass constitutes an angular simple harmonic oscillator.

4.4 A smooth tunnel is bored through the earth in the manner shown in Figure 4.6. A particle m is dropped into the tunnel at A. Prove that the particle will move to and fro along the whole length of the tunnel with simple harmonic motion.

64

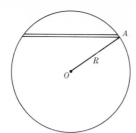

Fig. 4.6

4.5 A particle M attached to an elastic string suspended in the manner shown in Figure 4.7 will execute simple harmonic oscillations if displaced a small distance downwards and released. The displacement must be such that Hooke's law will be obeyed. If the mass of the elastic string is m, prove that the particle will execute simple harmonic oscillations but its effective mass will be $(M + \frac{1}{3}m)$.

Fig. 4.7

4.6 A particle m is attached to an elastic string the ends of which are attached to the walls as shown in Figure 4.8. The particle is slightly displaced in the vertical direction and released. Assume that the tension in the string is constant at all times. Discuss the resulting motion.

Fig. 4.8

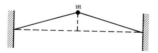

4.7 Consider the pendulum represented in Figure 4.9.

Fig. 4.9

(a) Show that $\ddot{\phi} + (g/\ell) \sin \phi = 0$

(b) Obtain the differential equation for small oscillations and write down the period of the motion.

(c) Drop the assumption that ϕ_0, the angle at $t = 0$, is small. (At this angle the pendulum starts to move from rest.) Show that

$$\dot{\phi} = \pm \sqrt{(2g/\ell)} \sqrt{\cos \phi - \cos \phi_0}$$

Obtain an expression for the period in the form of an integral. (Half of the period corresponds to the angular displacement between ϕ_0 and $-\phi_0$.)

4.8 (a) Consider a simple harmonic oscillator of period τ for which $x_{t=0} = 0$, and $\dot{x}_{t=0} = u > 0$. Find its amplitude.

(b) When $t = (1/3)\tau$ the velocity is suddenly doubled. Find the new amplitude.

4.9 The period of a simple harmonic vibration is 3 sec, and its greatest speed is 6 ft/sec. Prove that the amplitude is about 2.9 ft and the maximum acceleration is approximately 12.6 ft/sec^2.

4.10 The hydrogen atom of an H_2O molecule in ice has several modes of vibration. Consider two such modes, viz: the "stretching" and the "librational" modes shown in Figures 4.10 (a) and (b) respectively. These can be

Fig. 4.10
Longitudinal
and librational
vibrations of
the H-atom in the
H_2O molecule.

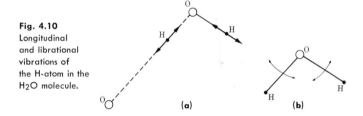

(a)   (b)

treated as simple harmonic oscillations (linear and angular respectively). At very low temperatures the total energy of such an oscillator is given by $E_0 = \frac{1}{2}h\nu$, where h is Planck's constant and ν is the linear frequency of the oscillator. Express the amplitude in terms of the frequency ν and the mass of the hydrogen atom in the linear case, and the angular amplitude in terms of the frequency and the moment of inertia of the hydrogen atom in the case of the angular simple harmonic motion.

4.11 The equal uniform rods PQ, QR, RS (Fig. 4.11) each of length $2a$ are

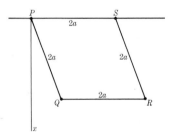

Fig. 4.11

smoothly jointed at Q and R and suspended from points P and S in the same horizontal line at distance $2a$ apart. Show that when the rods are slightly displaced in the vertical plane, they oscillate with the period of a simple pendulum the length of which is $5a/3$.

4.12 A uniform disc of radius a is suspended by three uniform inextensible strings of length ℓ (Fig. 4.12). Find the period of small oscillations of the system.

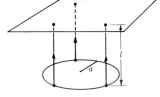

Fig. 4.12

4.13 Consider a pendulum whose point of suspension is moved horizontally to and fro in a given manner. It is assumed that the conditions are such that the inclination of the string to the vertical is always small. Write down the differential equation for the motion of the bob.

Let the imposed motion be simple harmonic and given by $\xi = a \cos \omega t$, where ξ is the coordinate shown in Figure 4.13. Find the explicit solution

Fig. 4.13
An example of a scleronomic system.

for x. Express the solution in terms of the quantity ℓ' defined by $\omega^2 = g/\ell'$ and interpret the meaning of your results.

(This is an example of a system which moves under constraints which depend on time. Such constraints are called scleronomic. Cf. Chapter 9.)

4.14 A pendulum consists of a bead of mass m at the end of a massless rod of length T. The bead travels along a smooth semicircular track of radius R and is fastened to one end of a spring of length $(\frac{1}{3})R$. The other end of the spring is secured to the ceiling and the spring moves along the semicircular track. The spring constant is k (Fig. 4.14).

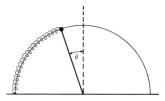

Fig. 4.14

(a) If the system is at equilibrium, find θ_{eq}.

(b) The bead is displaced from its equilibrium position by an angle θ and then released. Determine the frequency of oscillation of the system.

(c) Determine the position, velocity and the acceleration of the bead at any time t after it has been released.

4.15 A small sphere of negligible dimensions and of mass m has a smooth hole drilled through it and can slide on a horizontal wire AB. The sphere is attached to an elastic string the other end of which is affixed to the point C, as shown in Figure 4.15. There is a constant tension F in the string. Find the angular frequency of small oscillations of m about O. ($x \ll \ell$).

Fig. 4.15

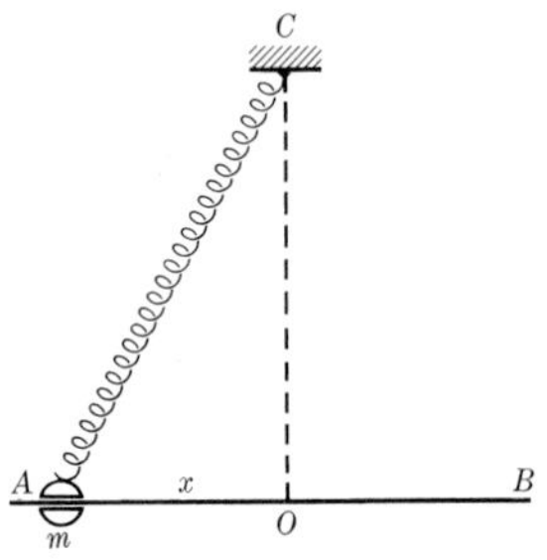

4.16 The differential equation of motion of a system executing simple harmonic motion is a linear equation with constant coefficients. For such an equation the principle of superposition holds. This means that if two particular solutions of the equation of motion are found, their sum also is a solution of the equation.

Consider now the linear differential equation with variable coefficients

$$\ddot{x} + g(t)\dot{x} + f(t)x = 0$$

If $x_1 = \phi_1(t)$ and $x_2 = \phi_2(t)$ are each a particular solution of the equation, show that

$$x = c_1\phi_1(t) + c_2\phi_2(t)$$

where c_1 and c_2 are constants, is also a solution of the differential equation. (This shows that the superposition principle holds for a linear differential equation, whether or not the coefficients are constant.)

Show that the superposition principle does not hold for a nonlinear differential equation such as

$$\ddot{x} + cx^2 = 0$$

4.17 One and the same particle is set into two simple harmonic motions at right angles to each other. The two equations of motion are

$$x = a_1 \sin(\omega t + \delta_1)$$

and
$$y = a_2 \sin(\omega t + \delta_2)$$

Thus both motions are of equal frequencies but of different amplitudes and of different epoch angles. Determine the equation of the path of the particle. (The path of the particle is obtained by eliminating the time from the equations.)

Denote the difference in phase $\delta_1 - \delta_2$ of the two vibrations by δ. Plot the resultant path for $\delta = 0,\ \pi/4,\ 2(\pi/4),\ 3(\pi/4),\ \ldots,\ 2\pi$. When will the resultant path be a circle?

This problem has wide applications in various branches of physics, for instance in the case of the superposition of two plane polarized beams of light.

4.18 A light spring of force constant 100 gm/cm and of natural length ℓ_0 has a mass $m = 50$ gm attached to its end (Fig. 4.16).

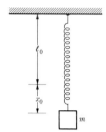

Fig. 4.16

(a) Find the equilibrium position of m.

(b) Find the frequency ν_0 of small oscillations in a non-resistive medium.

The mass m is now placed in a resistive medium such that the resistive force is given by $-\beta \dot{x}$.

(c) Determine the value of β for which the mass, when displaced from the equilibrium position, will just return to it.

(d) Find the value of β for which the frequency of the resulting damped motion will be $\frac{1}{2}\nu_0$.

4.19 The mathematical treatment of oscillatory electric circuits is exactly of the same form as that of harmonic oscillations. In the most general case the circuit consists of the elements shown in Figure 4.17. R, L, and C denote

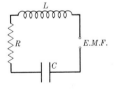

Fig. 4.17

the resistance, the inductance, and the capacitance of the circuit. At A and B the varying electromotive force is applied. In the electrical problem, L corresponds to the mass m of the harmonic oscillator, R to k and $1/C$ to β. The applied electromotive force is given by $E = E_0 \sin \omega t$. The quantity corresponding to the displacement x is the charge q.

Discuss the main results of the theory presented in this chapter as it applies to the case of electric oscillations. Thus you will form a differential equation of exactly the same form as Eq. (4.55) but with the replacements indicated above. Then proceed to write down the various solutions. The results may be stated in terms of the charge q and also in terms of the electric current which is defined as $i = dq/dt$. In particular consider

(a) an L, C circuit with no applied E.M.F. Write down the differential equation and obtain an expression for the "purely oscillatory electric discharge." Next obtain solution when the E.M.F. is applied (Fig. 4.18(a)).

(b) the case of R, L and R, C circuits with the applied E.M.F. [Figs. 4.18 (b), (c)].

(c) the general case.

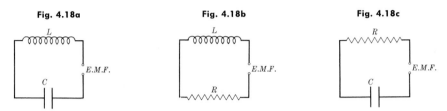

Fig. 4.18a **Fig. 4.18b** **Fig. 4.18c**

4.20 The classical electromagnetic theory of dispersion of light is based on the theory of forced harmonic oscillations. Let us assume that the medium on which a beam of light is incident consists of neutral atoms. In such atoms the center of the positive charge coincides with the center of negative charge. The electric intensity vector of the incident lightwave executes vibrations, and at a particular atom these vibrations will be represented by $\mathbf{E} = e\mathbf{E}_0\epsilon^{i\omega t}$, where e is the charge of the nucleus. The electric intensity vector will create an induced electric dipole by simply displacing the center of the negative charge from the center of the positive charge (Fig. 4.19). This dipole will oscillate. Let the oscillating mass be M and force constant f_1.

Fig. 4.19
A polarized atom.

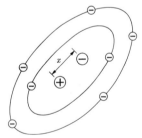

(a) Neglect damping and obtain the steady state solution $x = x(t)$ for the dipole oscillations. Hence obtain the dipole moment $p = -ex$.

(b) Assume the damping force $-\beta\dot{x}$ and obtain the dipole moment for this case.

(c) The polarizability α of the medium is defined by the relation $\mathbf{p} = \alpha\mathbf{E}$. Obtain the polarizability for the cases discussed in (a) and (b). (This will be the coefficient of $\mathbf{E}$ in your expressions for $\mathbf{p}$.)

(d) Assume a resistive force proportional to x and solve the resultant equation for x as a function of time.

70

5

CENTRAL FORCES

There is a class of force fields which is important in applications, and in many instances can be handled analytically in a relatively straightforward manner. These are the central force fields. *A central force field is one in which the force acting on a particle placed in it is always directed towards one point; this point is the source of the field.* We will describe some basic properties of such a field, then set out some general procedures for analytic handling of the motion of a particle in this field and finally discuss some applications.

5–1 General Properties of Central Force Fields

Let a particle of mass m move in a central force field as illustrated in Figure 5.1. If the position vector of the particle, measured from the center of

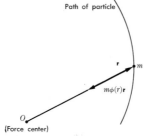

Fig. 5.1
Motion of a particle in a central force field.

force, is r then its acceleration can always be written as

$$\ddot{\mathbf{r}} = \phi(r)\mathbf{r} \tag{5.1}$$

where $\phi(r)$ is a scalar function of position. The force acting on the particle then will be

$$\mathbf{F} = m\phi(r)\mathbf{r} \tag{5.2}$$

Consider the vector product $\mathbf{r} \times \dot{\mathbf{r}}$ of the position vector $\mathbf{r}$ and the velocity vector $\dot{\mathbf{r}}$ of the particle. Time differentiation of this product yields

$$\frac{d}{dt}(\mathbf{r} \times \dot{\mathbf{r}}) = \dot{\mathbf{r}} \times \dot{\mathbf{r}} + \mathbf{r} \times \ddot{\mathbf{r}}$$

$$= \mathbf{0} + \mathbf{r} \times \phi(r)\mathbf{r}$$

$$= \phi(r)\mathbf{r} \times \mathbf{r}$$

or

$$\frac{d}{dt} (\mathbf{r} \times \dot{\mathbf{r}}) = \mathbf{0}$$

and so

$$\mathbf{r} \times \dot{\mathbf{r}} = \mathbf{c} \tag{5.3}$$

where $\mathbf{c}$ is a constant vector. This result states that the position vector and the velocity vector of m are always perpendicular to one direction (that of $\mathbf{c}$). In other words, the motion of the particle is coplanar.

The motion of a particle in a central force field can best be described in terms of radial and transverse components.* The advantage of their use stems from the fact that the particle has no transverse acceleration. This immediately furnishes one constant of motion because the transverse acceleration can be written in the form

$$a_t = \frac{1}{r} \frac{d}{dt} (r^2 \dot{\theta})$$

If $a_t = 0$ then

$$r^2 \dot{\theta} = h \tag{5.4}$$

where h is a constant. This constant is related to angular momentum. Actually it is the angular momentum per unit mass. The angular momentum is the moment of momentum, and in our case it is $r \times mr\dot{\theta}$ or $mr^2\dot{\theta}$. Thus the angular momentum is mh and is constant.

We can arrive at the same result through the use of dynamical considerations. In Chapters 2 and 6 we show that the time rate of change of the angular momentum is equal to the torque applied. By definition, the torque is $\mathbf{r} \times \mathbf{F}$, where $\mathbf{F}$ is the force acting on the particle. In our case the torque is zero because $\mathbf{F}$ lies along $\mathbf{r}$. Thus the angular momentum does not vary with time.

In the section on radial and transverse components (Sec. 2–4) we introduced the areal velocity. We have seen that this areal velocity $\dot{A}$ is equal to $\frac{1}{2}r^2\dot{\theta}$, i.e., for our particle moving in the central force field

$$\dot{A} = \tfrac{1}{2}h \tag{5.5}$$

and again it is constant.

Another important characteristic of the central force field is that it is conservative. This can be seen from the fact that the potential energy difference

$$V(\mathbf{r}_2) - V(\mathbf{r}_1) = -\int_{\mathbf{r}_1}^{\mathbf{r}_2} \phi(r)\mathbf{r} \cdot d\mathbf{s} \tag{5.6}$$

is a function of the limits of integration only, i.e., the line integral on the right of Eq. (5.6) depends on the end points only. Since the central force field is conservative, therefore the total energy of a particle moving in it must be conserved.

Summarizing the basic characteristics of the motion of a point mass *in a*

* See Section 2–4.

central force field we can say that

    (1) *the particle moves in one plane,*
    (2) *its angular momentum is constant,*
    (3) *its areal velocity is constant,* and
    (4) *its total energy is conserved.*

5–2 The Motion and the Orbit under a Central Force

We start with the two equations $\;$ for $\;$ acceleration

$$\ddot{r} - r\dot{\theta}^2 = f(r) \qquad \text{radical component (5.7)}$$

and

$$\frac{d}{dt}(r^2\dot{\theta}) = 0 \qquad \text{Tranverse} \quad \text{''} \qquad (5.8)$$

The first one states that the radial acceleration is a given function of position and the second that the transverse acceleration is zero. As before, the second equation yields

$$r^2\dot{\theta} = h \qquad (5.9)$$

where h is a constant of motion which will be given. Elimination of $\dot{\theta}$ between Eqs. (5.7) and (5.9) yields

$$\ddot{r} = \frac{h^2}{r^3} + f(r)$$

where the right-hand side is just a function of position. Now

$$\ddot{r} = \dot{r}\frac{d\dot{r}}{dr}$$

[Compare Eq. (2.10)]. Therefore

$$\frac{\dot{r}\,d\dot{r}}{dr} = \frac{h^2}{r^3} + f(r)$$

or

$$\dot{r}\,d\dot{r} = \left[\frac{h^2}{r^3} + f(r)\right]dr$$

and

$$\int \dot{r}\,d\dot{r} = \int \left[\frac{h^2}{r^3} + f(r)\right]dr$$

hence

$$\frac{1}{2}\dot{r}^2 = -\frac{h^2}{2r^2} + \int f(r)\,dr$$

or

$$\dot{r}^2 + \frac{h^2}{r^2} = 2\int f(r)\,dr$$

Now

$$(r\dot{\theta})^2 = \frac{h^2}{r^2}$$

therefore

$$\dot{r}^2 + (r\dot{\theta})^2 = 2\int f(r)\,dr \qquad (5.10)$$

But the left-hand side represents the square of the speed of the particle. Thus

$$v^2 = 2 \int f(r)\, dr \tag{5.11}$$

The kinetic energy of the particle therefore is

$$T = m \int f(r)\, dr \tag{5.12}$$

In order to find the equation of the orbit of the particle we write

$$\frac{dr}{d\theta} = \frac{\dot{r}}{\dot{\theta}} \tag{5.13}$$

and

$$\left(\frac{dr}{d\theta}\right)^2 = \frac{\dot{r}^2}{\dot{\theta}^2}$$

From Eq. (5.10)

$$\frac{\dot{r}^2}{\dot{\theta}^2} + r^2 = \frac{2}{\dot{\theta}^2} \int f(r)\, dr$$

Combination of Eqs. (5.13), (5.9), and the last equation gives

$$\left(\frac{dr}{d\theta}\right)^2 = 2\, \frac{r^4}{h^2} \int f(r)\, dr - r^2 \tag{5.14}$$

Thus

$$\frac{dr}{d\theta} = F(r) \tag{5.15}$$

where

$$F(r) = \sqrt{2\, \frac{r^4}{h^2} \int f(r)\, dr - r^2} \tag{5.16}$$

Therefore

$$\frac{dr}{F(r)} = d\theta \tag{5.17}$$

which, upon integration, yields the equation of the path.

5-3   Inverse Square Attractive Force

We will illustrate the motion of a particle in an inverse square field in the case of the gravitational forces but the results apply equally well to any inverse square fields, such as those originating from electrostatic forces.

According to Newton's law of universal attraction two point masses attract each other with a force which lies along the line joining the two masses and whose magnitude is given by

$$F = G\, \frac{Mm}{r^2} \tag{5.18}$$

where r is the distance between the two point masses M and m and G is a universal constant. Let us treat M as a stationary source of a force field; in that

74

field the point mass m is projected. The particle will then describe some path as shown in Figure 5.2. If M is the center of force and $\mathbf{r}$ is the vector position

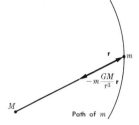

Fig. 5.2
Motion of particle in
a gravitational field.

Path of m

of m with respect to M, then the force exerted on m can be written as

$$\mathbf{F} = -mG\,\frac{M}{r^3}\,\mathbf{r} \tag{5.19}$$

From this we can see that the magnitude of the central acceleration is given by

$$f(r) = -G\,\frac{M}{r^2} \tag{5.20}$$

Integration of Eq. (5.14) yields the orbit of the particle, and it will be an ellipse, a parabola or a hyperbola depending on the velocity of the particle at distance r from M.*

5–4 Bohr's Theory of the Atom

One of the great advances in modern physics has been made by Bohr with the introduction of his theory of the hydrogen atom.† Bohr assumed the validity of Rutherford's model of the atom which consists of a massive positive nucleus and light negative electrons circulating around the nucleus, much like the planets circulate in the solar system. In the hydrogen atom, only one electron is present. The force exerted by the nucleus on the electron is the Coulomb force, i.e., an inverse square attractive force. The electron therefore moves in a central force field. In general the orbit is elliptic, but Bohr assumed a circular orbit.

Classically the electron can move in a circular orbit of any radius. Bohr assumed that only certain discrete orbits are permissible. His postulate, alien to classical mechanics, is called quantization of angular momentum and it states that the angular momentum h_a of the electron cannot have any arbitrary value but can only take the values given by

$$h_a = nh/2\pi \qquad n = 1, 2, \ldots$$

where h is a universal constant (the Planck constant).

* See Problem 5.5.
† N. Bohr, *Phil. Mag.* **26,** 476 (1913).

If we accept the above stipulation, then the rest of the theory of the Bohr atom is extremely simple. The validity of classical mechanics is assumed. Consider an atom with a nucleus of charge $+Ze$ and one electron of charge $-e$. The force exerted by the nucleus on the electron is

$$F = -\frac{Ze^2}{r^2} \tag{5.21}$$

The electrostatic potential energy is

$$V = -\frac{Ze^2}{r} \tag{5.22}$$

and the kinetic energy is

$$T = \tfrac{1}{2}mv^2$$

or if ω denotes the angular velocity of the electron then

$$T = \tfrac{1}{2}mr^2\omega^2 \tag{5.23}$$

The total energy therefore becomes

$$E = \frac{1}{2}mr^2\omega^2 - \frac{Ze^2}{r} \tag{5.24}$$

The Coulomb force balances the centrifugal force, therefore

$$\frac{Ze^2}{r^2} = m\omega^2 r$$

from which

$$\frac{Ze^2}{r} = m\omega^2 r^2 \tag{5.25}$$

The kinetic energy therefore becomes

$$T = \tfrac{1}{2}m\omega^2 r^2$$

$$= \frac{1}{2}\frac{Ze^2}{r}$$

Thus the total energy is

$$E = -\frac{1}{2}\frac{Ze^2}{r} \tag{5.26}$$

which is also equal to the negative of the kinetic energy.

The angular momentum of the electron is

$$h_a = mr^2\omega \tag{5.27}$$

and from the quantization of the angular momentum we have

$$mr^2\omega = nh/2\pi \tag{5.28}$$

We square this equation, eliminate ω^2 between this relation and Eq. (5.25) and solve for the radius, which is then given by

$$r = \frac{h^2}{4\pi^2 Zme^2} n^2 \qquad (5.29)$$

The total energy of the electron becomes

$$E = -\frac{2\pi^2 mZ^2 e^4}{h^2} \frac{1}{n^2} \qquad n = 1, 2, \ldots \qquad (5.30)$$

The last two equations contain the significant results of Bohr's theory, namely the radii of possible orbits and the energies in the individual orbits (designated by n).*

5–5 Inverse Square Repulsive Field. Rutherford's Scattering Experiment

We shall now consider the inverse square repulsive field. We will illustrate this field by discussing the theory of Rutherford's famous scattering experiment** the result of which was the modern model of the atom.*** From the theoretical point of view, the basic problem that Rutherford considered was of the following nature: A fixed charge $+Ze$ forms the source of an inverse square field; into this field a positive charge E and of mass m is projected with a velocity v. In an actual experiment there was a beam of α particles each of charge E projected onto a thin foil. The fixed charges Ze, considered as scattering centers, were the nuclei of the atoms constituting the foil. Rutherford was interested in the number of α particles scattered in a given direction φ, per unit solid angle.

To obtain the orbit of the α particle we should again use the radial and transverse components for the position, velocity and acceleration of the α particle. The force exerted on it is

$$\mathbf{F} = \frac{ZeE}{r^3} \mathbf{r} \qquad (5.31)$$

from which the radial acceleration can be obtained.

Integration of the equations

$$\ddot{r} - r\dot{\theta}^2 = f(r)$$

and

$$r^2 \dot{\theta} = h$$

where h is a constant and

$$f(r) = \frac{ZeE}{r^2}$$

* Actually, the most significant result of Bohr's theory is his prediction that the atom will radiate energy only in the case when the energy of the electron changes from one value predicted by Eq. (5.30) to another, the direction being from higher to lower values of n.
** E. Rutherford, *Phil. Mag.* **21,** 669 (1911).
*** As indicated in Sec. 5–4, this model was taken over by Bohr in his theory of the hydrogen atom.

5–5 Inverse square repulsive field. Rutherford's scattering experiment

77

yields the orbit of the α particle and it is a branch of a hyperbola further away from the scattering center (Fig. 5.3).*

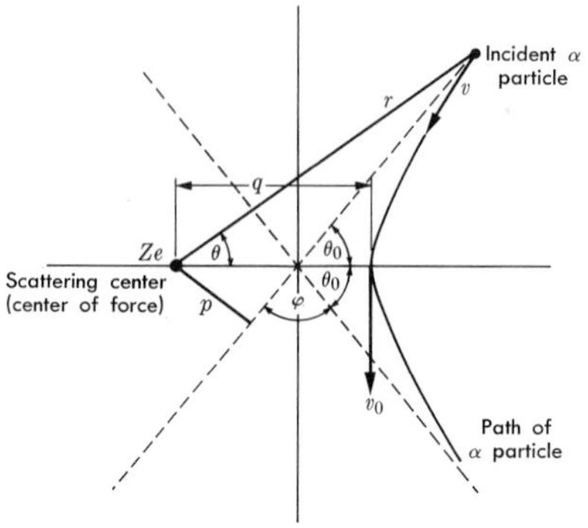

Fig. 5.3
Scattering of
an α-particle.

5–6 Satellite Mechanics

The basic principles of the mechanics of artificial satellites is rather simple. A particle (in the form of a capsule) will travel in an orbit about the earth if it is carried to high altitudes, outside of the atmosphere, and then given a tangential velocity. The escape from the earth is accomplished by means of a rocket. When left alone, the particle will constantly be attracted by the earth, and it will therefore move in a central force field. Its orbit will be elliptical (provided the tangential velocity is not too great), but under special conditions it will be circular.

Let m be the mass of the particle and M that of the earth. The force of attraction between the earth and the particle, when the particle is at a distance r from the center of the earth, is given by Newton's law of universal gravitation, Eq. (5.18). By Newton's second law the same force is

$$\mathbf{F} = m\ddot{\mathbf{r}}$$

Therefore
$$\ddot{\mathbf{r}} = -\frac{GM}{r^3}\,\mathbf{r} \tag{5.32}$$

$\ddot{\mathbf{r}}$ is the acceleration due to gravity and is usually denoted by g.

In the vicinity of the earth $\ddot{\mathbf{r}}$ does not vary much with height because the variations of height are usually small in comparison with the radius of the earth (4,000 miles). However, when the particle is moved to distances which are large in comparison with the radius of the earth, the changes of $\ddot{\mathbf{r}}$ are considerable. Consider this latter case. As we know

$$\ddot{r} = \frac{\dot{r}\,d\dot{r}}{dr} \tag{5.33}$$

Rewriting Eq. (5.32) in scalar form and substituting (5.33) in it, we get

$$\dot{r}\,d\dot{r} = -\frac{GM}{r^2}\,dr \tag{5.34}$$

* See Problem 5.6.

and

$$\int_{v_0}^{v} \dot{r} \, d\dot{r} = -GM \int_{r_0}^{r} \frac{dr}{r^2} \qquad (5.35)$$

Let R be the radius of the earth and let us drop the particle from rest at a height h above the earth's surface. Let v be the velocity of the particle when it strikes the earth. Then integrating Eq. (5.35) and inserting the appropriate limits, we obtain

$$\frac{1}{2} \left[r^2 \right]_0^v = GM \left[\frac{1}{r} \right]_{R+h}^{R}$$

from which

$$v^2 = 2GM \left[\frac{1}{R} - \frac{1}{R+h} \right] \qquad (5.36)$$

or

$$v^2 = \frac{2GMh}{Rh + R^2} \qquad (5.37)$$

When $h \gg R$ then

$$v_\infty = \sqrt{\frac{2GM}{R}} \qquad (5.38)$$

If, on the other hand, we project the particle from the earth with the velocity given by the last relation then the particle will escape to infinity. For this reason v_∞ is given the name "escape velocity."

Suppose that the rocket will attain the escape velocity and will project the particle to a considerable height where it will leave it alone. A booster rocket will then give it a tangential velocity V. Then, as before

$$F = G \frac{Mm}{r^2}$$

Also, if the orbit is circular, the same force is given by

$$F = \frac{mV^2}{r}$$

Therefore

$$\frac{GMm}{r^2} = \frac{mV^2}{r}$$

from which

$$V = \sqrt{\frac{GM}{r}} \qquad (5.39)$$

or, since

$$g = \frac{GM}{r^2}$$

$$V = \sqrt{gr} \qquad (5.40)$$

In the last relation g is the acceleration due to gravity at the height of the satellite. Both Eqs. (5.39) and (5.40) are relations between the velocity of the space capsule and its distance from the center of the earth.

5–6 Satellite mechanics

PROBLEMS

5.1 A particle of mass m, moving on a smooth table, is attached to a string which passes through a small hole in the table and carries a mass M hanging vertically. Show that the force acting on the particle m is given by

$$P = \frac{Mm}{M+m}\left[g + \frac{h^2}{r^3}\right]$$

where $h = r^2\dot{\theta}$.

5.2 Consider a repulsive central field of force which is given by μr. When $r = a$ the magnitude of the velocity is $1/a$ and its direction is $30°$ to r and away from the center of force. Obtain the differential equation in terms of r and t and solve it to obtain the speed of the particle at any distance r.

5.3 Solve the problem of the inverse cube repulsive field. Let the acceleration acting away from the center of force, be a/r^3. When $\mathbf{r} = \mathbf{c}$, the magnitude and the direction of the velocity are as shown in Figure 5.4. (When seeking the solutions, the substitution $u = 1/r$ might be helpful.)

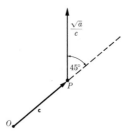

Fig. 5.4

5.4 The orbit of a particle is of the form

$$r = ae^{b\theta}$$

where a and b are constants.
    (a) What is the magnitude of the velocity, expressed as a function of r and in terms of the angular momentum h?
    (b) Write an expression for the law of force in terms of h.

5.5 Consider a particle of mass m projected in the gravitational field created by a stationary point mass M (Sec. 5–2). Show that the orbit of the point m is a conic section the equation of which is

$$\ell = r[1 - e \cos (\theta - \theta_0)]$$

where ℓ is the semi-latus rectum and e is the eccentricity of the conic section (Fig. 5.5).
    Show that there is a critical velocity $v_c = \sqrt{2GM/r}$ for which the orbit is a parabola; when $v > v_c$, the particle will describe a hyperbolic path and for $v < v_c$ the orbit will be an ellipse.

80

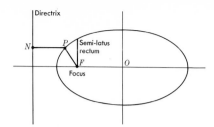

Fig. 5.5

5.6 Show that the orbit of the α particle in Rutherford's scattering experiment (Sec. 5.5) is a branch of a hyperbola further away from the scattering center shown in Figure 5.3.

6

SYSTEM OF PARTICLES

The study of the mechanical properties and the motion of a system of particles is important in that it forms the basis for a natural transition to the investigation of rigid body motion. All of the important definitions which will be used later are introduced here along with the derivation of basic laws. These basic laws apply to rigid bodies because a rigid body is a particularly simple system of particles, namely, one for which the distance between any two particles is constant.

The detailed study of the motion of all the particles in a system, in which the behavior of every particle can be predicted, is extremely difficult. However, a great deal of information can be gained if one studies the motion of the center of mass of the system. For this reason we will now concentrate on the behavior of the center of mass.

6-1 The Center of Mass and the Moment of Inertia

We will assume a three-dimensional distribution of particles as shown in Figure 6.1. The masses

$$m_1, m_2, \ldots, m_i, \ldots, m_n$$

are situated respectively at the tips of the position vectors

$$\mathbf{r}_1, \mathbf{r}_2, \ldots, \mathbf{r}_i, \ldots, \mathbf{r}_n$$

Fig. 6.1

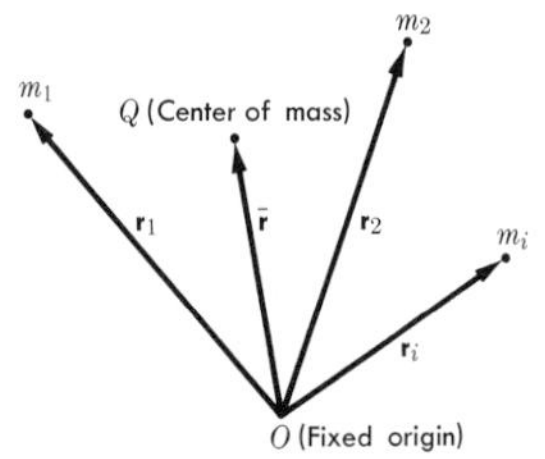

The *center of mass* $\mathbf{r}$ of a system of particles is defined by

$$M\bar{\mathbf{r}} = \sum_{i=1}^{n} m_i \mathbf{r}_i \tag{6.1}$$

where

$$M = \sum_{i=1}^{n} m_i$$

The *polar moment of inertia about the point* O of the system of particles is defined by the relation

$$J_O = \sum_{i=1}^{n} m_i r_i^{\,2} \tag{6.2}$$

In both Eqs. (6.1) and (6.2) the $\mathbf{r}_i$'s are the position vectors measured from the common origin O (Fig. 6.1).

The *moment of inertia*, which is used much more often than the polar moment of inertia, is defined in relation to an axis. Referring to Figure 6.2 we define the moment of inertia of a system of particles with respect to a given axis as

$$I = \sum_{i} m_i r_i^{\,2} \tag{6.3}$$

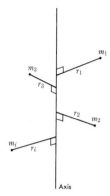

Fig. 6.2

Here r_i is the distance of the particle m_i from the axis.

If we refer the moments of inertia to the three rectangular Cartesian axes then

$$I_{xx} = \sum_{i} m_i (y_i^{\,2} + z_i^{\,2})$$

$$I_{yy} = \sum_{i} m_i (z_i^{\,2} + x_i^{\,2}) \tag{6.4}$$

$$I_{zz} = \sum_{i} m_i (x_i^{\,2} + y_i^{\,2})$$

Summing these three moments of inertia gives

$$I_{xx} + I_{yy} + I_{zz} = 2 \sum_{i} m_i (x_i^{\,2} + y_i^{\,2} + z_i^{\,2})$$

$$= 2 \sum_{i} m_i r_i^{\,2}$$

where again r_i is the distance from the origin. Thus

$$J_O = \tfrac{1}{2}(I_{xx} + I_{yy} + I_{zz}) \tag{6.5}$$

This gives a relation between the polar moment of inertia and the moments of inertia referred to the three coordinate axes.

The *linear momentum* of the system of particles is the vector sum of the linear momenta of the individual particles. Thus

$$\mathbf{p} = \sum_i m_i \dot{\mathbf{r}}_i \tag{6.6}$$

Now, differentiating (6.1) with respect to time, we obtain

$$M\dot{\mathbf{r}} = \sum_i m_i \dot{\mathbf{r}}_i$$

Therefore the resultant linear momentum of the system of all the particles is given by

$$\mathbf{p} = M\dot{\mathbf{r}} \tag{6.7}$$

It is thus sufficient to know the velocity of the center of mass of the system and the mass of all the particles to be able to obtain the resultant linear momentum of the system of particles.

6–3   Motion of the Center of Mass

Differentiating Eq. (6.1) twice with respect to time we obtain

$$M\ddot{\mathbf{r}} = \sum_i m_i \ddot{\mathbf{r}}_i$$

On the right-hand side of this equation, $m_i \ddot{\mathbf{r}}_i$ is the product of the mass of the i-th particle and its acceleration. By Newton's second law, this product is equal to the force $\mathbf{F}_i$ acting on the particle. Thus

$$M\ddot{\mathbf{r}} = \sum_i \mathbf{F}_i$$

Now, $\sum_i \mathbf{F}_i$ is the resultant force $\mathbf{F}$ acting on the whole system; thus

$$\mathbf{F} = M\ddot{\mathbf{r}} \tag{6.8}$$

This is a rather important result in that it states that *the center of mass of the system of particles moves as if all the mass of the system were concentrated there and as if the resultant of all the forces acting on the system acted there.*

Since $p = M\dot{\mathbf{r}}$, we can therefore write

$$\mathbf{F} = \dot{\mathbf{p}} \tag{6.9}$$

6–4   The Angular Momentum

The moment of any vector $\mathbf{a}$ (Fig. 6.3) about an axis O perpendicular to the

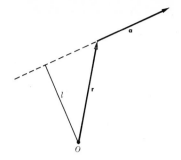

Fig. 6.3

plane of the paper is defined by

$$\mathbf{h} = \mathbf{r} \times \mathbf{a} \tag{6.10}$$

where $\mathbf{r}$ is the position vector of the point of application of $\mathbf{a}$. We can readily verify that this definition complies with the elementary definition of a moment as the product of the vector and the perpendicular distance ℓ from O to the line of action of $\mathbf{a}$. Our definition given by Eq. (6.10) includes also the vector nature of the moment.

The angular momentum is defined as the moment of momentum. The angular momentum of the i-th particle of the system is then given by

$$\mathbf{h}_i = \mathbf{r}_i \times m_i \dot{\mathbf{r}}_i \tag{6.11}$$

and the resultant angular momentum of the whole system is

$$\mathbf{h} = \sum_i \mathbf{r}_i \times m_i \dot{\mathbf{r}}_i \tag{6.12}$$

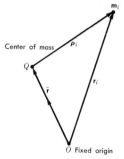

Fig. 6.4

We will now refer the angular momentum to the center of mass. From Figure 6.4 we have

$$\mathbf{r}_i = \bar{\mathbf{r}} + \boldsymbol{\rho}_i \tag{6.13}$$

therefore $\quad \mathbf{h} = \sum_i (\bar{\mathbf{r}} + \boldsymbol{\rho}_i) \times m_i(\dot{\bar{\mathbf{r}}} + \dot{\boldsymbol{\rho}}_i)$

$$= \sum_i (\bar{\mathbf{r}} \times m_i \dot{\bar{\mathbf{r}}} + \boldsymbol{\rho}_i \times m_i \dot{\boldsymbol{\rho}}_i + \boldsymbol{\rho}_i \times m_i \dot{\bar{\mathbf{r}}} + \bar{\mathbf{r}} \times m_i \dot{\boldsymbol{\rho}}_i)$$

$$= \bar{\mathbf{r}} \times M\dot{\bar{\mathbf{r}}} + \sum_i \boldsymbol{\rho}_i \times m_i \dot{\boldsymbol{\rho}}_i - \dot{\bar{\mathbf{r}}} \times \sum_i m_i \boldsymbol{\rho}_i + \bar{\mathbf{r}} \times \sum_i m_i \dot{\boldsymbol{\rho}}_i$$

Now, consider the definition of the center of mass given by Eq. (6.1). Applying this to the system referred to Q we get

$$M\bar{\boldsymbol{\rho}} = \sum_i m_i \boldsymbol{\rho}_i$$

But the center of mass is at Q, and so $\bar{\boldsymbol{\rho}} = \mathbf{0}$; therefore

$$\sum_i m_i \boldsymbol{\rho}_i = \mathbf{0} \tag{6.14}$$

Similarly

$$M\dot{\boldsymbol{\rho}} = \sum_i m_i \dot{\boldsymbol{\rho}}_i$$

and since $\dot{\boldsymbol{\rho}} = \mathbf{0}$

$$\sum_i m_i \dot{\boldsymbol{\rho}}_i = \mathbf{0} \tag{6.15}$$

Thus the last two terms in the expression for $\mathbf{h}$ vanish, and we get

$$\mathbf{h}_O = \bar{\mathbf{r}} \times M\dot{\bar{\mathbf{r}}} + \mathbf{h}_Q \tag{6.16}$$

where

$$\mathbf{h}_Q = \sum_i \boldsymbol{\rho}_i \times m_i \dot{\boldsymbol{\rho}}_i \tag{6.17}$$

is the angular momentum of the system with respect to the center of mass. Relation (6.16) states that *the angular momentum of a system of particles with respect to a fixed origin O is equal to the angular momentum with respect to O of a particle M placed at and moving with the center of mass, plus the angular momentum of the system of particles referred to the center of mass.*

6–5   The Kinetic Energy

The kinetic energy of the system of particles is given by

$$T = \tfrac{1}{2} \sum_i m_i \dot{\mathbf{r}}_i \cdot \dot{\mathbf{r}}_i \tag{6.18}$$

Again, using $\mathbf{r}_i = \bar{\mathbf{r}} + \boldsymbol{\rho}_i$, we get

$$T = \tfrac{1}{2} \sum_i m_i (\dot{\bar{\mathbf{r}}} + \dot{\boldsymbol{\rho}}_i) \cdot (\dot{\bar{\mathbf{r}}} + \dot{\boldsymbol{\rho}}_i)$$

$$= \tfrac{1}{2} M\dot{\bar{\mathbf{r}}} \cdot \dot{\bar{\mathbf{r}}} + \tfrac{1}{2} \sum_i m_i \dot{\boldsymbol{\rho}}_i \cdot \dot{\boldsymbol{\rho}}_i + \dot{\bar{\mathbf{r}}} \cdot \sum_i m_i \dot{\boldsymbol{\rho}}_i$$

The last term vanishes and we obtain

$$T = \tfrac{1}{2} M\dot{\bar{\mathbf{r}}}^2 + \tfrac{1}{2} \sum_i m_i \dot{\boldsymbol{\rho}}_i^2 \tag{6.19}$$

which states that *the kinetic energy of a system of particles is equal to the kinetic energy of a single particle of mass M moving with the center of mass, together with the kinetic energy of the system of particles relative to the center of mass.* This theorem often finds practical applications.

6-6 The Moment Equation

The motion of the i-th particle of our system is governed by Newton's second law

$$m_i \ddot{\mathbf{r}}_i = \mathbf{F}_i + \sum_j \mathbf{F}_{ij} \qquad (6.20)$$

here $\mathbf{F}_i$ is the external force acting on the i-th particle and $\mathbf{F}_{ij}$ is the force with which the j-th particle acts on the i-th particles; thus $\sum_j \mathbf{F}_{ij}$ is the sum of all the internal forces acting on the particle. Vector-premultiplying both sides of the last equation by $\mathbf{r}_i$ and summing over all particles we get

$$\sum_i \mathbf{r}_i \times m_i \ddot{\mathbf{r}}_i = \sum_i \mathbf{r}_i \times \mathbf{F}_i + \sum_{i,j} \mathbf{r}_i \times \mathbf{F}_{ij} \qquad (6.21)$$

Out of the double sum of the last expression consider the two terms $\mathbf{r}_i \times \mathbf{F}_{ij} + \mathbf{r}_j \times \mathbf{F}_{ji}$. Invoking Newton's third law we can write

$$\begin{aligned} \mathbf{r}_i \times \mathbf{F}_{ij} + \mathbf{r}_j \times \mathbf{F}_{ji} &= \mathbf{r}_i \times \mathbf{F}_{ij} - \mathbf{r}_j \times \mathbf{F}_{ij} \\ &= (\mathbf{r}_i - \mathbf{r}_j) \times \mathbf{F}_{ij} \qquad (6.22) \\ &= \mathbf{0} \end{aligned}$$

The latter result follows from the fact that the vector difference $(\mathbf{r}_i - \mathbf{r}_j)$ lies along the same line as $\mathbf{F}_{ij}$ (Fig. 6.5), and therefore their vector product van-

Fig. 6.5

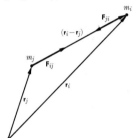

ishes. This is valid for any pair of points and so the whole double sum in Eq. (6.21) is zero and this equation reduces to

$$\sum_i \mathbf{r}_i \times m_i \ddot{\mathbf{r}}_i = \sum_i \mathbf{r}_i \times \mathbf{F}_i \qquad (6.23)$$

We notice that the right hand side is the resultant moment $\mathbf{G}_O$ about the fixed origin O of all the external forces, or

$$\mathbf{G}_O = \sum_i \mathbf{r}_i \times \mathbf{F}_i \qquad (6.24)$$

Furthermore $\qquad \mathbf{h}_O = \sum_i \mathbf{r}_i \times m_i \dot{\mathbf{r}}_i$

and $\qquad \dot{\mathbf{h}}_O = \sum_i \dot{\mathbf{r}}_i \times m_i \dot{\mathbf{r}}_i + \sum_i \mathbf{r}_i \times m_i \ddot{\mathbf{r}}_i$

or
$$\dot{\mathbf{h}}_O = \sum_i \mathbf{r}_i \times m_i \ddot{\mathbf{r}}_i \qquad (6.25)$$

Substitution of this and of (6.24) in (6.23) yields

$$\mathbf{G}_O = \dot{\mathbf{h}}_O \qquad (6.26)$$

This is the all important *moment equation*. It states that the *resultant moment of all the external forces about a fixed point is equal to the time rate of change of the resultant angular momentum about the same point.*

6-7 The Moment Equation about a Moving Origin

We will now investigate the form of the moment equation when the moment of the external forces and the angular momentum are referred to a moving origin. Of particular interest will be the case when the moving origin is at the center of mass.

Let P be a moving point which will serve as a new origin. Its position vector with respect to the fixed origin O is $\mathbf{c}$ as shown in Figure 6.6. To start, it will

Fig. 6.6

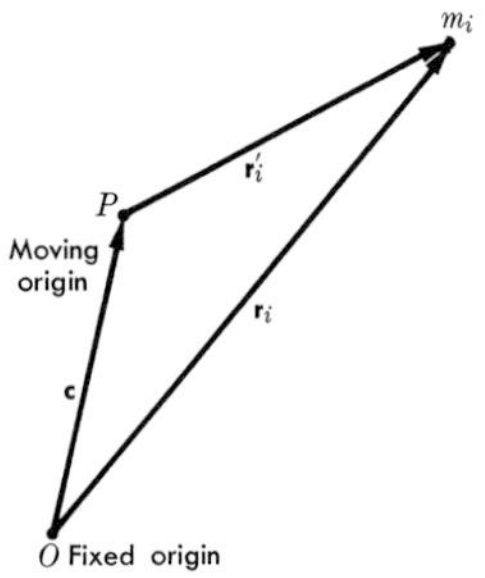

be necessary to define what we mean by the angular momentum with respect to a moving origin. The angular momentum is the moment of momentum. Now, *we have a choice of defining the angular momentum as the moment about P of momentum relative to O, or as the moment about P of momentum relative to P.* We will use both these definitions. We will show later that in the important case when P is the center of mass, both definitions are equivalent.* The torque about P is

$$\mathbf{G}_P = \sum_i \mathbf{r}_i' \times \mathbf{F}_i \qquad (6.27)$$

But
$$\mathbf{F}_i = \frac{d}{dt} m_i \dot{\mathbf{r}}_i \qquad (6.28)$$

---

* It might appear to be unnecessary to consider two definitions of angular momentum. Just two lines below the asterisk we introduce the moment of the external forces about the moving origin P, by the equation

$$\mathbf{G}_P = \sum_i \mathbf{r}_i' \times \mathbf{F}_i$$

In it we replace the external force $\mathbf{F}_i$ by the time rate of change of momentum about O. Here we have no choice because $\mathbf{F}_i = (d/dt)(m_i\dot{\mathbf{r}}_i)$ is Newton's second law, and it is valid for a fixed frame of reference.

88

therefore
$$\mathbf{G}_P = \sum_i \mathbf{r}_i' \times (d/dt)(m_i\dot{\mathbf{r}}_i) \qquad (6.29)$$

Now, $\dot{\mathbf{r}}_i = \dot{\mathbf{c}} + \dot{\mathbf{r}}_i'$, and so

$$\mathbf{G}_P = \sum_i \mathbf{r}_i' \times \frac{d}{dt} m_i(\dot{\mathbf{c}} + \dot{\mathbf{r}}_i')$$

$$= \sum_i \mathbf{r}_i' \times m_i\ddot{\mathbf{c}} + \sum_i \mathbf{r}_i' \frac{d}{dt} m_i\dot{\mathbf{r}}_i'$$

$$= -\ddot{\mathbf{c}} \times \sum_i m_i\mathbf{r}_i' + \sum_i \mathbf{r}_i' \times m_i\ddot{\mathbf{r}}_i'$$

Now

$$\frac{d}{dt}(\mathbf{r}_i' \times m_i\dot{\mathbf{r}}_i') = \mathbf{r}_i' \times m_i\ddot{\mathbf{r}}_i'$$

thus

$$\mathbf{G}_P = -\ddot{\mathbf{c}} \times \sum_i m_i\mathbf{r}_i' + (d/dt) \sum_i \mathbf{r}_i' \times m_i\dot{\mathbf{r}}_i' \qquad (6.30)$$

If we call the angular momentum the moment about P of momentum relative to P then the second term in the last equation is the time rate of change of the angular momentum about P. Therefore

$$\mathbf{G}_P = -\ddot{\mathbf{c}} \times \sum_i m_i\mathbf{r}_i' + \dot{\mathbf{h}}_P \qquad (6.31)$$

When P becomes the center of mass Q then

$$\sum_i m_i\mathbf{r}_i' = \mathbf{0}$$

and
$$\mathbf{G}_Q = \dot{\mathbf{h}}_Q \qquad (6.32)$$

However, there are also other cases when we can write

$$\mathbf{G}_P = \dot{\mathbf{h}}_P \qquad (6.33)$$

One is obviously the case when P is fixed or moves with uniform motion and the other occurs when the acceleration of P is directed through the center of mass. To verify that the latter is true we recall the definition of the center of mass given by Eq. (6.1). When P is the origin then the center of mass is defined by

$$M\bar{\mathbf{r}}' = \sum_i m_i\mathbf{r}_i'$$

Thus $\sum_i m_i\mathbf{r}_i'$ is a vector starting at P and going through the center of mass. If the acceleration $\ddot{\mathbf{c}}$ of P also goes through the center of mass then

$$\ddot{\mathbf{c}} \times \sum_i m_i\mathbf{r}_i' = \mathbf{0}$$

We will now approach the same problem in a slightly different way. If we define the angular momentum about P as the moment about P of momentum relative to O then

$$\mathbf{h}_P = \sum_i \mathbf{r}_i' \times m_i \dot{\mathbf{r}}_i$$

From Figure 6.6

$$\mathbf{r}_i' = \mathbf{r}_i - \mathbf{c}$$

Therefore

$$\mathbf{h}_P = \sum_i (\mathbf{r}_i - \mathbf{c}) \times m_i \dot{\mathbf{r}}_i$$

$$= \sum_i \mathbf{r}_i \times m_i \dot{\mathbf{r}}_i - \mathbf{c} \times \sum_i m_i \dot{\mathbf{r}}_i$$

or

$$\mathbf{h}_P = \sum_i \mathbf{r}_i \times m_i \dot{\mathbf{r}}_i - \mathbf{c} \times \mathbf{p} \tag{6.34}$$

where $\mathbf{p}$ is the resultant linear momentum of the system. Differentiating the last relation with respect to t yields

$$\dot{\mathbf{h}}_P = \sum_i \dot{\mathbf{r}}_i \times m_i \dot{\mathbf{r}}_i + \sum_i \mathbf{r}_i \times m_i \ddot{\mathbf{r}}_i - \dot{\mathbf{c}} \times \mathbf{p} - \mathbf{c} \times \dot{\mathbf{p}}$$

or

$$\dot{\mathbf{h}}_P = \sum_i \mathbf{r}_i \times \mathbf{F}_i - \dot{\mathbf{c}} \times \mathbf{p} - \mathbf{c} \times \mathbf{F} \tag{6.35}$$

where we have put $\mathbf{F} = \dot{\mathbf{p}}$. Further

$$\mathbf{G}_P = \sum_i \mathbf{r}_i' \times \mathbf{F}_i$$

or

$$\mathbf{G}_P = \sum_i \mathbf{r}_i \times \mathbf{F}_i - \mathbf{c} \times \mathbf{F} \tag{6.36}$$

Comparison of (6.35) and (6.36) yields

$$\mathbf{G}_P = \dot{\mathbf{h}}_P + \dot{\mathbf{c}} \times \mathbf{p} \tag{6.37}$$

Notice that

$$\mathbf{G}_P = \dot{\mathbf{h}}_P$$

when $\dot{\mathbf{c}} = \mathbf{0}$, or when $\mathbf{c}$ is parallel to $\mathbf{p}$, or when the point P becomes the center of mass.

We will now show that, when the point P is the center of mass, the moment about Q of momentum relative to O is also the moment about Q of momentum relative to Q. Referring to Figure 6.4 we get

$$\mathbf{h}_Q = \sum_i \boldsymbol{\rho}_i \times m_i \dot{\mathbf{r}}_i$$

$$= \sum_i \boldsymbol{\rho}_i \times m_i (\dot{\bar{\mathbf{r}}} + \dot{\boldsymbol{\rho}}_i)$$

$$= -\dot{\bar{\mathbf{r}}} \times \sum_i m_i \boldsymbol{\rho}_i + \sum_i \boldsymbol{\rho}_i \times m_i \dot{\boldsymbol{\rho}}_i$$

Now

$$\sum_i m_i \boldsymbol{\rho}_i = \mathbf{0}$$

therefore
$$\mathbf{h}_Q = \sum_i \boldsymbol{\rho}_i \times m_i \dot{\boldsymbol{\rho}}_i$$

The most important results which we have obtained for the system of particles are contained in the two vector equations

$$\mathbf{F} = \dot{\mathbf{p}}$$

and
$$\mathbf{G}_O = \dot{\mathbf{h}}_O$$

The latter equation can always be replaced by

$$\mathbf{G}_Q = \dot{\mathbf{h}}_Q$$

We notice in passing that the theorems of conservation of linear momentum and angular momentum suggest themselves readily. When $\mathbf{F} = \mathbf{0}$, then $\mathbf{p}$ is a constant, and when $\mathbf{G}_O = \mathbf{0}$, $\mathbf{h}_O$ is a constant.

PROBLEMS

6.1 Consider a system of three particles of masses 2, 1, 3, position coordinates $(2, -4)$, $(0, 6)$, $(-2, -2)$, and velocity components $(2, 0)$, $(2, -4)$, $(0, -2)$ respectively. Determine
  (a) The position of the center of mass.
  (b) The velocity of the center of mass.
  (c) The momentum of the center of mass, (if all the mass were concentrated there).
  (d) The angular momentum of the system about the origin.
  (e) The total kinetic energy.

6.2 Prove that the location of the center of mass of a system of particles does not depend on the choice of the coordinate system.

6.3 Prove that the center of mass of a system of particles will not change if some of the particles are replaced by their total mass placed at the center of mass of the particles which were removed.

6.4 Prove that if a system of points, all of the same mass, has a center of symmetry then this center of symmetry is the center of mass.

6.5 Two point masses m_1 and m_2 move along the x-axis and attract each other according to Newton's law of universal attraction with a force $F = Gm_1m_2/r^2$ (Fig. 6.7). At $t = 0$, let $x_1 = x_1{}^0$, $x_2 = x_2{}^0$, $\dot{x}_1 = \dot{x}_2 = 0$.

Fig. 6.7

Show that
$$m_1 \dot{x}_1 + m_2 \dot{x}_2 = 0$$
and
$$m_1 x_1 + m_2 x_2 = m_m x_1{}^0 + m_2 x_2{}^0$$

Let $x_2 - x_1 = r$ and $G(m_1 + m_2) = q$. Deduce that
$$r = -\sqrt{2q[(1/r) - (1/r_0)]}$$

hence, obtain the time t in terms of r, r_0 and q.

6.6 A uniform heavy rod of length ℓ moves in a vertical plane in such a way that its lower end is in contact with a smooth horizontal plane. Determine the equation of the curve described by the other end of the rod.

6.7 Let there be a system of N material points originally at rest with no external forces acting. Suppose that under the action of the internal forces a part, n_1, of the particles starts rotating about an axis ℓ. Let I_1 and ω_1 be the moment of inertia and the angular velocity of this part with respect to ℓ. If the rest of the system has the moment of inertia I_2 and rotates with the angular velocity ω_2 about the same axis, show that $\omega_1/\omega_2 = -I_2/I_1$.

6.8 The point masses A_1 and A_2 are connected by an inextensible string which passes over a smooth peg at O (Fig. 6.8). Show that the net work performed by the tensions in the string on the two points is zero.

Fig. 6.8

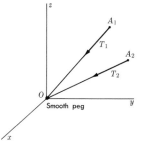

6.9 If two points M and m attract each other according to Newton's law of universal attraction, show that the motion of m relative to M is the same as if M were at rest and its mass were increased by m.

6.10 Let m_e denote the mass of the earth, m_m that of the moon and m_s the mass of the sun. It is known that $m_s = (1/3)10^6 m_e$ and $m_m = (1/80)m_e$. The distance between the earth and the sun is about 400 times that between the earth and the moon. Show that, to a first approximation, the motion of the moon relative to earth can be obtained by neglecting the influence of the sun.

7

GENERALIZED COORDINATES

7-1 *The concept of Generalized Coordinates*

We now enter into a study of more advanced topics, the starting point of which is the introduction of generalized coordinates. In the past, most of our treatment of mechanics has been in terms of space coordinates; of these, rectangular coordinates x, y, z have been used most of the time.

We now wish to generalize our procedure in the sense that we will use any set of parameters

$$q_1, q_2, \ldots, q_n \qquad (7.1)$$

which is best suited to describe the system under consideration. The number n of the parameters q depends on the type of system with which we are dealing. We always attempt to use a set q such that its members are independent. *If n independent parameters are needed to describe a system, we say that the system has n degrees of freedom and the n parameters are called generalized coordinates of the system.*

It often occurs in practice that the first set of generalized coordinates are chosen in such a way that they are not all independent, but are of such a nature that there are m equations which can be written to express m relationships between the q's. These equations are called the *equations of constraint* (or the *equations of condition*) and in this case the number of degrees of freedom is given by

$$n = N - m$$

where N is the original number of generalized coordinates.

As an example we may consider a particle moving on the surface of a sphere. This is a case of three-dimensional motion and at first it may appear that we need three generalized coordinates for which we can choose the rectangular coordinates x, y, z or, better, the spherical polar coordinates r, θ, φ. However, we immediately see that there is one equation of condition, which, in the first case is of the form $x^2 + y^2 + z^2 = $ const., and in the second, simply $r = $ const. Thus two generalized coordinates are needed for a complete description of our system.

It should be mentioned that basically nothing new is introduced with generalized coordinates. The Cartesian coordinates which so far were used most of the time, actually constituted one type of generalized coordinates. We now wish to use other parameters. These new parameters can be of a most varied nature (angles, areas and many others). By using Cartesian coordinates we placed our system in three-dimensional space and could picture the changes of the system when changes of its rectangular coordinates were given. In many cases the introduction of non-rectangular coordinates results in many advantages which far surpass the advantages of possible visualizations resulting from the use of Cartesian coordinates. Let us consider a particular example. If we study the general motion of three particles, say, then we would ascribe to them their respective Cartesian coordinates

$$x_1, y_1, z_1$$
$$x_2, y_2, z_2$$
$$x_3, y_3, z_3$$

The motion of the particles can be visualized by following the changes of these Cartesian coordinates. Let us now introduce the generalized coordinates

$$q_1, q_2, \ldots, q_9$$

We can introduce a nine-dimensional space and replace the complete spatial description of our system by stating the nine coordinates of a single point. The changes of the system in space will then be given if the motion of this single point can be predicted.

Such procedures are of particular value in studies of large aggregates of particles. Statistical mechanics deals with such problems.

As we have already stated above, the nature of generalized coordinates need not, and in general will not, refer to space. Nevertheless, for n generalized coordinates we form an n-dimensional space. We introduce the concept of a point in this space, as we have done in the above example. This is extended to paths, surfaces and volumes in these n-dimensional spaces. What is more, kinematical and dynamical concepts such as velocity, acceleration and force are extended to these spaces and are then termed generalized velocity, generalized acceleration and generalized force respectively. We will first study some purely algebraic aspects of this procedure, and then apply it to physical situations.

7–2 Length, Surface and Volume Elements*

It is quite important to acquire the rudiments of the transformation theory between space and generalized coordinates. For space coordinates we will take the Cartesian coordinates x, y, z. As a starting point we will take various mathematical forms expressed in space coordinates and transform them into corresponding forms expressed in terms of generalized coordinates.

* The transformation theory between space and generalized coordinates follows rather closely D. E. Rutherford's treatment in Vector Methods, *Op. cit.*

For simplicity let us consider three generalized coordinates q_1, q_2, q_3. In every case we must be given, or we must find, the functional relationship which exists between the space and generalized coordinates. Let the transformation equations be of the form

$$x = x(q_1, q_2, q_3)$$
$$y = y(q_1, q_2, q_3) \tag{7.2}$$
$$z = z(q_1, q_2, q_3)$$

The total differentials of these functions are

$$dx = \frac{\partial x}{\partial q_1} dq_1 + \frac{\partial x}{\partial q_2} dq_2 + \frac{\partial x}{\partial q_3} dq_3$$

$$dy = \frac{\partial y}{\partial q_1} dq_1 + \frac{\partial y}{\partial q_2} dq_2 + \frac{\partial y}{\partial q_3} dq_3 \tag{7.3}$$

$$dz = \frac{\partial z}{\partial q_1} dq_1 + \frac{\partial z}{\partial q_2} dq_2 + \frac{\partial z}{\partial q_3} dq_3$$

The element of length in Cartesian form is

$$d\ell^2 = dx^2 + dy^2 + dz^2 \tag{7.4}$$

After substitution of (7.3) into the last expression, the resulting relation will contain terms of the form

$$g_{ij} = \frac{\partial x}{\partial q_i} \frac{\partial x}{\partial q_j} + \frac{\partial y}{\partial q_i} \frac{\partial y}{\partial q_j} + \frac{\partial z}{\partial q_i} \frac{\partial z}{\partial q_j} \tag{7.5}$$

These terms are symmetrical, i.e.

$$g_{ij} = g_{ji}$$

The square of the element of length expressed in terms of generalized coordinates then becomes

$$d\ell^2 = g_{11} dq_1{}^2 + g_{22} dq_2{}^2 + g_{33} dq_3{}^2 + 2g_{23} dq_2 dq_3$$
$$+ 2g_{31} dq_3 dq_1 + 2g_{12} dq_1 dq_2 \tag{7.6}$$

This is the general form of the element of length. The element of length along the line for which $q_2 = $ const., $q_3 = $ const. is

$$d\ell_1 = \sqrt{g_{11}} \, dq_1 \tag{7.7}$$

Similarly for the line $q_3 = $ const. and $q_1 = $ const.

$$d\ell_2 = \sqrt{g_{22}} \, dq_2 \tag{7.8}$$

and for the line $q_1 = $ const. and $q_2 = $ const.

$$d\ell_3 = \sqrt{g_{33}} \, dq_3 \tag{7.9}$$

For convenience we may write

$$h_1 = \sqrt{g_{11}} \qquad h_2 = \sqrt{g_{22}} \qquad h_3 = \sqrt{g_{33}} \qquad (7.10)$$

Suppose that q_1, q_2, q_3 form an orthogonal system so that the element of length becomes

$$d\ell^2 = h_1^2 \, dq_1^2 + h_2^2 \, dq_2^2 + h_3^2 \, dq_3^2 \qquad (7.11)$$

An element of volume in such an orthogonal system is

$$dV = h_1 h_2 h_3 \, dq_1 \, dq_2 \, dq_3 \qquad (7.12)$$

and an element of area on the surface $q_1 = $ const. is

$$dS = h_2 h_3 \, dq_2 \, dq_3 \qquad (7.13)$$

Example: The elements of length, surface and volume for spherical polar coordinates.

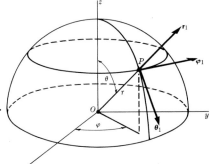

Fig. 7.1
Spherical polar coordinates.

The spherical polar coordinates can be treated as generalized coordinates which are defined as shown in Figure 7.1. The functional relationships [Eq. (7.2)] obtained from Figure 7.1 are

$$x = r \sin \theta \cos \varphi$$
$$y = r \sin \theta \sin \varphi \qquad (7.14)$$
$$z = r \cos \theta$$

The coordinates r, θ, φ form an orthogonal system with unit vectors $\mathbf{r}_1$, $\boldsymbol{\theta}_1$, $\boldsymbol{\varphi}_1$, as shown in Figure 7.1. These unit vectors indicate the directions in which the respective coordinates are assumed to increase. The element of length $d\ell$ can be obtained geometrically as indicated in Figure 7.2 and is given by

$$d\ell = dr\mathbf{r}_1 + r \, d\theta\boldsymbol{\theta}_1 + r \sin \theta \, d\varphi\boldsymbol{\varphi}_1 \qquad (7.15)$$

from which the square of the element of length becomes

$$d\ell^2 = dr^2 + r^2 \, d\theta^2 + r^2 \sin^2 \theta \, d\varphi^2 \qquad (7.16)$$

96

Fig. 7.2
An element of volume
in spherical polar
coordinates.

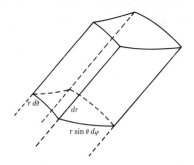

The element of surface for $r = $ const. is

$$dS = r^2 \sin \theta \, d\theta \, d\varphi \qquad (7.17)$$

and the element of volume is

$$dV = r^2 \sin \theta \, dr \, d\theta \, d\varphi \qquad (7.18)$$

These last two expressions can also be obtained from Figure 7.2.

We will now obtain the same expressions using the results of transformation theory as derived on the preceding pages. For the element of length we will use the expression (7.11). We need to evaluate g_{11}, g_{22}, g_{33}. For the first we write

$$g_{11} = \left(\frac{\partial x}{\partial r}\right)^2 + \left(\frac{\partial y}{\partial r}\right)^2 + \left(\frac{\partial z}{\partial r}\right)^2 \qquad (7.19)$$

$$= (\sin \theta \cos \varphi)^2 + (\sin \theta \sin \varphi)^2 + \cos^2 \theta$$

$$= \sin^2 \theta \, (\cos^2 \varphi + \sin^2 \varphi) + \cos^2 \theta$$

or $\qquad g_{11} = 1 \qquad (7.20)$

In a similar way we have

$$g_{22} = \left(\frac{\partial x}{\partial \theta}\right)^2 + \left(\frac{\partial y}{\partial \theta}\right)^2 + \left(\frac{\partial z}{\partial \theta}\right)^2 \qquad (7.21)$$

and $\qquad g_{33} = \left(\frac{\partial x}{\partial \varphi}\right)^2 + \left(\frac{\partial y}{\partial \varphi}\right)^2 + \left(\frac{\partial z}{\partial \varphi}\right)^2 \qquad (7.22)$

which becomes

$$g_{22} = r^2 \qquad (7.23)$$

and $\qquad g_{33} = r^2 \sin^2 \theta \qquad (7.24)$

Thus

$$h_1 = 1 \qquad h_2 = r \qquad h_3 = r \sin \theta \qquad (7.25)$$

and $\qquad d\ell^2 = dr^2 + r^2 \, d\theta^2 + r^2 \sin^2 \theta \, d\phi^2 \qquad (7.26)$

Having obtained the h_i's, the elements of surface and volume can be obtained immediately.

Consider again the fundamental relationships between the space and generalized coordinates. We now write them in a more general way as

$$
\begin{aligned}
x_i &= x_i(q_1, q_2, \ldots, q_n) \\
y_i &= y_i(q_1, q_2, \ldots, q_n) \\
z_i &= z_i(q_1, q_2, \ldots, q_n)
\end{aligned}
\tag{7.27}
$$

When the system described by the generalized coordinates $q_1, q_2, \ldots, q_n$ is set into arbitrary motion consistent with the imposed constraints, then the generalized coordinates are functions of time. Thus, differentiating (7.27) yields

$$
\begin{aligned}
\dot{x}_i &= \frac{\partial x_i}{\partial q_1}\,\dot{q}_1 + \frac{\partial x_i}{\partial q_2}\,\dot{q}_2 + \cdots + \frac{\partial x_i}{\partial q_n}\,\dot{q}_n \\
\dot{y}_i &= \frac{\partial y_i}{\partial q_1}\,\dot{q}_1 + \frac{\partial y_i}{\partial q_2}\,\dot{q}_2 + \cdots + \frac{\partial y_i}{\partial q_n}\,\dot{q}_n \\
\dot{z}_i &= \frac{\partial z_i}{\partial q_1}\,\dot{q}_1 + \frac{\partial z_i}{\partial q_2}\,\dot{q}_2 + \cdots + \frac{\partial z_i}{\partial q_n}\,\dot{q}_n
\end{aligned}
\tag{7.28}
$$

Conversely, if we assume that $q_1, q_2, \ldots, q_n$ are arbitrary functions of time, then Eqs. (7.27) describe the motion of the system and Eqs. (7.28) determine the velocities of the system in that motion. It follows that if the system is in a certain position specified by the generalized coordinates $q_1, q_2, \ldots, q_n$, then all the sets of possible velocities of the system in that position are obtained if in Eqs. (7.28) we substitute *arbitrary* values for $\dot{q}_1, \dot{q}_2, \ldots, \dot{q}_n$. *The quantities* $\dot{q}_1, \dot{q}_2, \ldots, \dot{q}_n$ *form a set of generalized velocities.*

We have introduced the above transformations because they will be useful when we wish to write the equations of dynamics in terms of generalized coordinates. We repeat, the above set $(\dot{q})$ by definition constitutes the generalized velocities. For reasons given above, *this new set* $(\dot{q})$ *of variables can be treated as an independent set.*

As stated above, the actual velocities of material particles are given by Eqs. (7.28). To derive more useful expressions for the velocities in terms of generalized coordinates, we notice that the velocity vectors are in the same directions as the displacements. Thus if $d\boldsymbol{\ell}_i$ is a vector element of displacement then the velocity in this direction is

$$
\mathbf{v}_i = \frac{d\boldsymbol{\ell}_i}{dt}
\tag{7.29}
$$

Now, consider an orthogonal system of generalized coordinates and let $d\boldsymbol{\ell}_i$ go along one of the coordinates. Then, as we have seen,

$$
d\boldsymbol{\ell}_i = h_i\, d\mathbf{q}_i
$$

Thus

$$
\mathbf{v}_i = h_i\dot{\mathbf{q}}_i
\tag{7.30}
$$

Example: The velocity in spherical polar coordinates.

The vector element of displacement is given by

$$d\boldsymbol{\ell} = dr\,\mathbf{r}_1 + r\,d\theta\,\boldsymbol{\theta}_1 + r\sin\theta\,d\varphi\,\boldsymbol{\varphi}_1$$

From this we immediately obtain the velocity as

$$\frac{d\boldsymbol{\ell}}{dt} = \frac{dr}{dt}\,\mathbf{r}_1 + r\,\frac{d\theta}{dt}\,\boldsymbol{\theta}_1 + r\sin\theta\,\frac{d\varphi}{dt}\,\boldsymbol{\varphi}_1$$

or

$$\dot{\boldsymbol{\ell}} = \dot{r}\,\mathbf{r}_1 + r\dot{\theta}\,\boldsymbol{\theta}_1 + r\sin\theta\,\dot{\varphi}\,\boldsymbol{\varphi}_1 \tag{7.31}$$

from which we see that

$$v_r = \dot{r}, \qquad v_\theta = r\dot{\theta}, \qquad v_\varphi = r\sin\theta\,\dot{\varphi} \tag{7.32}$$

The square of the velocity, which is important in the determination of kinetic energy, is given by

$$v^2 = \dot{r}^2 + r^2\dot{\theta}^2 + r^2\sin^2\theta\,\dot{\varphi}^2 \tag{7.33}$$

We can also determine the velocity components from (7.30) which in our case become

$$v_r = h_1\dot{r}, \qquad v_\theta = h_2\dot{\theta}, \qquad v = h_3\dot{\varphi} \tag{7.34}$$

We have seen that in the case of spherical polar coordinates

$$h_1 = 1, \qquad h_2 = r, \qquad h_3 = r\sin\theta$$

therefore again

$$v_r = \dot{r}, \qquad v_\theta = r\dot{\theta}, \qquad v = r\sin\theta\,\dot{\varphi} \tag{7.35}$$

7-4 Acceleration

The x component of the velocity of the i-th particle was given by

$$\dot{x}_i = \sum_{j=1}^{n} \frac{\partial x_i}{\partial q_j}\,\dot{q}_j$$

The time derivative of this expression is

$$\ddot{x}_i = \sum_{j}\left\{\frac{\partial x_i}{\partial q_j}\,\ddot{q}_j + \sum_{k}\dot{q}_j\dot{q}_k\,\frac{\partial^2 x_i}{\partial q_k\,\partial q_j}\right\} \tag{7.36}$$

This is the Cartesian x-component of the acceleration expressed in terms of generalized coordinates.

The components of the acceleration in generalized coordinates are in general hard to find because the time derivatives of the unit vectors for generalized coordinates are not zero. Again, the magnitude of the i-th component of the velocity is

$$v_i = h_i\dot{q}_i \tag{7.37}$$

To get the vector form of this component, we will introduce a unit vector $\mathbf{q}_i$; it indicates the direction of increase of the q_i-th generalized coordinate. Thus the vector component of the velocity is

$$\mathbf{v}_i = h_i \dot{q}_i \mathbf{q}_i \tag{7.38}$$

We now differentiate this expression with respect to time, i.e., we evaluate

$$\frac{d\mathbf{v}_i}{dt} = \frac{d}{dt}(h_i \dot{q}_i \mathbf{q}_i) \tag{7.39}$$

Here the time derivative of the unit vector $\mathbf{q}_i$ has to be considered also.

Such time differentiation has to be performed for every component of the velocity. After that, the various terms are grouped according to the unit vectors. We will not carry out this procedure in the general case but illustrate it by an example.*

Example: Acceleration in spherical polar coordinates.

We start with the velocity vector

$$\mathbf{v} = \dot{r}\mathbf{r}_1 + r\dot{\theta}\boldsymbol{\theta}_1 + r\sin\theta\,\dot{\varphi}\boldsymbol{\varphi}_1$$

from which we read off that

$$\mathbf{v}_r = \dot{r}\mathbf{r}_1 \qquad \mathbf{v}_\theta = r\dot{\theta}\boldsymbol{\theta}_1 \qquad \mathbf{v} = r\sin\theta\,\dot{\varphi}\boldsymbol{\varphi}_1$$

Let us start with $\mathbf{v}_r = \dot{r}\mathbf{r}_1$ for which

$$\frac{d\mathbf{v}_r}{dt} = \ddot{r}\mathbf{r}_1 + \dot{r}\frac{d\mathbf{r}_1}{dt}$$

$$= r\mathbf{r}_1 + r\left(\frac{\partial\mathbf{r}_1}{\partial r}\dot{r} + \frac{\partial\mathbf{r}_1}{\partial\theta}\dot{\theta} + \frac{\partial\mathbf{r}_1}{\partial\varphi}\dot{\varphi}\right)$$

In the brackets we have various partial derivatives. The first one, $\dfrac{\partial\mathbf{r}_1}{\partial r}$, indicates the change of $\mathbf{r}_1$ when r alone changes; no change occurs in this case; thus

$$\frac{\partial\mathbf{r}_1}{\partial r} = \mathbf{0}$$

From Figure 7.3(a) we see that

$$d\theta\boldsymbol{\theta}_1 = d\mathbf{r}_1$$

and so, when θ alone changes

$$\frac{\partial\mathbf{r}_1}{\partial\theta} = \boldsymbol{\theta}_1$$

* Another way of obtaining the components of acceleration is discussed in Section 8.1.

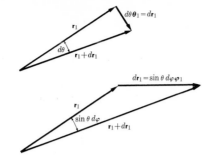

Fig. 7.3a

Fig. 7.3b

From Figure 7.3(b), when φ alone changes we get

$$d\mathbf{r}_1 = \sin \theta \, d\varphi \boldsymbol{\varphi}_1$$

therefore

$$\frac{\partial \mathbf{r}_1}{\partial \varphi} = \sin \theta \boldsymbol{\varphi}_1$$

Substitution of the various expressions in $\dot{\mathbf{v}}_r = \dfrac{d}{dt}(\dot{r}\mathbf{r}_1)$ results in

$$\dot{\mathbf{v}}_r = \ddot{r}\mathbf{r}_1 + \dot{r}\dot{\theta}\boldsymbol{\theta}_1 + \sin \theta \dot{\varphi}\boldsymbol{\varphi}_1 \tag{7.40}$$

Next consider

$$\mathbf{v}_\theta = r\dot{\theta}\boldsymbol{\theta}_1$$

Time-differentiating yields

$$\dot{\mathbf{v}}_\theta = \frac{d}{dt}(r\dot{\theta}\boldsymbol{\theta}_1)$$

$$= \boldsymbol{\theta}_1(\dot{r}\dot{\theta} + r\ddot{\theta}) + r\dot{\theta}\dot{\boldsymbol{\theta}}_1$$

$$= \boldsymbol{\theta}_1(\dot{r}\dot{\theta} + r\ddot{\theta}) + r\dot{\theta}\left(\frac{\partial \boldsymbol{\theta}_1}{\partial r}\dot{r} + \frac{\partial \boldsymbol{\theta}_1}{\partial \theta}\dot{\theta} + \frac{\partial \boldsymbol{\theta}_1}{\partial \varphi}\dot{\varphi}\right)$$

When r alone changes

$$\frac{\partial \boldsymbol{\theta}_1}{\partial r} = \mathbf{0}$$

From Figures 7.4(a), (b)

$$d\boldsymbol{\theta}_1 = -\mathbf{r}_1 \, d\theta$$

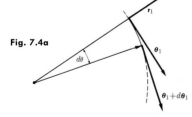

Fig. 7.4a

Fig. 7.4b

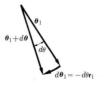

therefore
$$\frac{\partial \boldsymbol{\theta}_1}{\partial \theta} = -\mathbf{r}_1$$

For the partial derivative $\dfrac{\partial \boldsymbol{\theta}_1}{\partial \varphi}$ examine Figure 7.5. We notice that as φ alone changes there is no change of the component of $\boldsymbol{\theta}_1$ along the z axis. Let us therefore project $\boldsymbol{\theta}_1$ and $\boldsymbol{\theta}_1 + d\boldsymbol{\theta}_1$ on the (xy)-plane. This projection is drawn in Figure 7.5 (b), and from it we see that

$$d\boldsymbol{\theta}_1 = \cos \theta \, d\varphi \boldsymbol{\varphi}_1$$

Fig. 7.5a

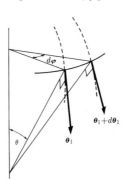

Fig. 7.5b

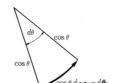

Thus
$$\frac{\partial \boldsymbol{\theta}_1}{\partial \varphi} = \cos \theta \boldsymbol{\varphi}_1$$

Combining all the results for the $\mathbf{v}_\theta$ component we get

$$\dot{\mathbf{v}}_\theta = -r\dot{\theta}\mathbf{r}_1 + (r\ddot{\theta} + \dot{r}\dot{\theta})\boldsymbol{\theta}_1 + r\dot{\theta}\dot{\varphi} \cos \theta \boldsymbol{\varphi}_1 \qquad (7.41)$$

We now investigate the last remaining component of the velocity, the φ-component. We have

$$\dot{\mathbf{v}}_\varphi = \frac{d}{dt} (r \sin \theta \dot{\varphi} \boldsymbol{\varphi}_1)$$

$$= \boldsymbol{\varphi}_1(r \sin \theta \ddot{\varphi} + \dot{r}\dot{\varphi} \sin \theta + r\dot{\theta}\dot{\varphi} \cos \theta)$$

$$+ r \sin \theta \dot{\varphi} \left(\frac{\partial \boldsymbol{\varphi}_1}{\partial r} \dot{r} + \frac{\partial \boldsymbol{\varphi}_1}{\partial \theta} \dot{\theta} + \frac{\partial \boldsymbol{\varphi}_1}{\partial \varphi} \dot{\varphi} \right)$$

We first notice that when r and θ change alone then

$$\frac{\partial \boldsymbol{\varphi}_1}{\partial r} = \frac{\partial \boldsymbol{\varphi}_1}{\partial \theta} = \mathbf{0}$$

Fig. 7.6

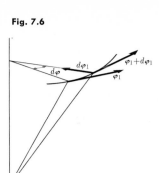

Fig. 7.7a

Fig. 7.7b

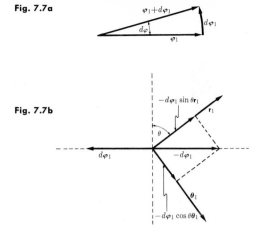

The change of $\boldsymbol{\varphi}_1$ with φ is illustrated in Figures 7.6 and 7.7. In Figure 7.7(b), $-d\boldsymbol{\varphi}_1$ has been resolved along $\mathbf{r}_1$ and $\boldsymbol{\theta}_1$; we therefore have

$$d\boldsymbol{\varphi}_1 = -\boldsymbol{\theta}_1 \cos \theta \, d\varphi - \mathbf{r}_1 \sin \theta \, d\varphi$$

where we made use of the fact that the magnitude of $d\boldsymbol{\varphi}_1$ is $d\varphi$ (Fig. 7.7(a)). From the last equation we obtain

$$\frac{\partial \boldsymbol{\varphi}_1}{\partial \varphi} = -\boldsymbol{\theta}_1 \cos \theta - \mathbf{r}_1 \sin \theta$$

Combining all the terms for $\dot{\mathbf{v}}_\varphi$ we get

$$\begin{aligned} \dot{\mathbf{v}}_\varphi = \boldsymbol{\varphi}_1(r \sin \theta \ddot{\varphi} + \dot{r}\dot{\varphi} \sin \theta + r\dot{\varphi}\dot{\theta} \cos \theta) \\ - \mathbf{r}_1 r\dot{\varphi}^2 \sin^2 \theta - \boldsymbol{\theta}_1 r\dot{\varphi}^2 \sin \theta \cos \theta \end{aligned} \tag{7.42}$$

The resultant acceleration is given by summing $\dot{\mathbf{v}}_r$, $\dot{\mathbf{v}}_\theta$ and $\dot{\mathbf{v}}_\phi$ which are given by Eqs. (7.40), (7.41) and (7.42) respectively. We now combine terms containing the same unit vectors and obtain

$$\mathbf{a} = \mathbf{a}_r + \mathbf{a}_\theta + \mathbf{a}_\varphi$$
$$\mathbf{a}_r = \mathbf{r}_1(\ddot{r} - r\dot{\theta}^2 - r\dot{\varphi}^2 \sin^2 \theta)$$
where $\qquad \mathbf{a}_\theta = \boldsymbol{\theta}_1(r\ddot{\theta} + 2\dot{r}\dot{\theta} - r\dot{\varphi}^2 \sin \theta \cos \theta) \tag{7.43}$
and $\qquad \mathbf{a}_\varphi = \boldsymbol{\varphi}_1(r \sin \theta \ddot{\varphi} + 2\dot{r}\dot{\varphi} \sin \theta + 2r\dot{\theta}\dot{\varphi} \cos \theta)$

In Section 2–4 we derived the components of acceleration in polar coordinates for two dimensions. We notice that the above components reduce to the two-dimensional case when there is no change in φ.

We should perhaps state that the above example is not intended to illustrate the transformation theory from space to generalized coordinates. We have seen that geometrical intuition was used most of the time. Nevertheless, the exercise should serve the useful purpose of showing how the acceleration vector is obtained from the velocity vector when curvilinear coordinates are used.

THE LAGRANGIAN FORMALISM. DYNAMICS OF A
POINT MOVING UNDER NO CONSTRAINTS

At this point we will proceed to develop the appropriate analytic apparatus necessary to understand mechanics in its more advanced forms. We will begin with a development of Lagrange's procedure, first for a single particle and then for a system of particles moving with and without constraints.

8-1 Velocity and Acceleration in Generalized Coordinates

We will first consider certain aspects of the kinematics of a single particle whose motion is not constrained. In Cartesian coordinates such a motion may be described by a system of equations of the form

$$x = x(t) \qquad y = y(t) \qquad z = z(t) \tag{8.1}$$

Let us introduce three generalized coordinates q_1, q_2, q_3 describing the motion of the same point. We are assuming that the functional relationships between the Cartesian and generalized coordinates are given, i.e., we know the relations

$$x = x(q_1, q_2, q_3)$$
$$y = y(q_1, q_2, q_3) \tag{8.2}$$
$$z = z(q_1, q_2, q_3)$$

In terms of the generalized coordinates, the motion of our particle may be described by the equations

$$q_1 = q_1(t) \qquad q_2 = q_2(t) \qquad q_3 = q_3(t) \tag{8.3}$$

This is so because substitution of (8.3) in (8.2) yields the original equations of motion (8.1). Differentiation of the set (8.2) with respect to time yields

$$\dot{x} = \sum_{i=1}^{3} \frac{\partial x}{\partial q_i} \dot{q}_i \qquad \dot{y} = \sum_{i=1}^{3} \frac{\partial y}{\partial q_i} \dot{q}_i \qquad \dot{z} = \sum_{i=1}^{3} \frac{\partial z}{\partial q_i} \dot{q}_i \tag{8.4}$$

We notice that the time derivatives $\dot{x}$, $\dot{y}$, $\dot{z}$ are linear functions of the generalized velocities $\dot{q}_1$, $\dot{q}_2$, $\dot{q}_3$. Actually equations (8.4) are of the form

$$\dot{x} = \dot{x}(q_1, q_2, q_3, \dot{q}_1, \dot{q}_2, \dot{q}_3)$$
$$\dot{y} = \dot{y}(q_1, q_2, q_3, \dot{q}_1, \dot{q}_2, \dot{q}_3) \qquad (8.5)$$
$$\dot{z} = \dot{z}(q_1, q_2, q_3, \dot{q}_1, \dot{q}_2, \dot{q}_3)$$

Taking the partial derivatives of (8.4) with respect to $\dot{q}_i (i = 1, 2, 3)$ we obtain

$$\frac{\partial \dot{x}}{\partial \dot{q}_i} = \frac{\partial x}{\partial q_i} \qquad \frac{\partial \dot{y}}{\partial \dot{q}_i} = \frac{\partial y}{\partial q_i} \qquad \frac{\partial \dot{z}}{\partial \dot{q}_i} = \frac{\partial z}{\partial q_i} \qquad (8.6)$$

We shall have occasion to use these results frequently. As we can see, the following mnemonic rule encompasses these relations: In the symbols

$$\frac{\partial x}{\partial q_i} \qquad \frac{\partial y}{\partial q_i} \qquad \frac{\partial z}{\partial q_i}$$

it is permissible in the numerator and the denominator to *add dots* simultaneously, and in the relations

$$\frac{\partial \dot{x}}{\partial \dot{q}_i} \qquad \frac{\partial \dot{y}}{\partial \dot{q}_i} \qquad \frac{\partial \dot{z}}{\partial \dot{q}_i}$$

it is permissible to *cancel the dots*.

We now derive another set of useful results. Consider the functions

$$\frac{\partial x}{\partial q_i} \qquad \frac{\partial y}{\partial q_i} \qquad \frac{\partial z}{\partial q_i}$$

Taking the time derivative of the first one we obtain

$$\frac{d}{dt}\left(\frac{\partial x}{\partial q_i}\right) = \frac{\partial^2 x}{\partial q_1 \, \partial q_i} \dot{q}_1 + \frac{\partial^2 x}{\partial q_2 \, \partial q_i} \dot{q}_2 + \frac{\partial^2 x}{\partial q_3 \, \partial q_i} \dot{q}_3 \qquad (8.7)$$

On the other hand, partially differentiating $\dot{x}$ from (8.4) with respect to q_i we see that

$$\frac{\partial \dot{x}}{\partial q_i} = \frac{\partial^2 x}{\partial q_i \, \partial q_1} \dot{q}_1 + \frac{\partial^2 x}{\partial q_i \, \partial q_2} \dot{q}_2 + \frac{\partial^2 x}{\partial q_i \, \partial q_3} \dot{q}_3 \qquad (8.8)$$

The second partial derivatives are continuous; therefore

$$\frac{\partial^2 x}{\partial q_i \, \partial q_k} = \frac{\partial^2 x}{\partial q_k \, \partial q_i}$$

Thus the right-hand sides of (8.7) and (8.8) are equal, and hence

$$\frac{d}{dt}\left(\frac{\partial x}{\partial q_i}\right) = \frac{\partial \dot{x}}{\partial q_i} \qquad (8.9)$$

In order to understand the full significance of this relation we write it in the form

$$\frac{d}{dt} \frac{\partial}{\partial q_i} x = \frac{\partial}{\partial q_i} \frac{d}{dt} x$$

Similar results obtain for functions y and z. We thus have

$$\frac{d}{dt}\left(\frac{\partial x}{\partial q_i}\right) = \frac{\partial \dot{x}}{\partial q_i} \qquad \frac{d}{dt}\left(\frac{\partial y}{\partial q_i}\right) = \frac{\partial \dot{y}}{\partial q_i} \qquad \frac{d}{dt}\left(\frac{\partial z}{\partial q_i}\right) = \frac{\partial \dot{z}}{\partial q_i} \qquad (8.10)$$

These relations express the fact that the *operator d/dt signifying the total time differentiation and the operator $\partial/\partial q_i$ signifying partial differentiation with respect to q_i are commutative.*

Let ℓ be the arc of the path that our point describes. In the chapter on generalized coordinates we have shown that the element of length of this arc is given by

$$d\ell^2 = \sum_{i=1}^{3} \sum_{j=1}^{3} g_{ij}\, dq_i\, dq_j \qquad (8.11)$$

where $g_{ij} = g_{ji}$ are functions of q_1, q_2, q_3. We have also seen that when two of the generalized coordinates q_1, q_2, q_3 are constant then—in the three respective cases—

$$d\ell_1 = h_1\, dq_1 \qquad d\ell_2 = h_2\, dq_2 \qquad d\ell_3 = h_3\, dq_3 \qquad (8.12)$$

where $h_i = \sqrt{g_{ii}}$. These are elements of lengths along what we may call coordinate curves; a term which is analogous to the coordinate axes in the Cartesian case. Consider now the curve q_i lying at the intersection of two surfaces (e.g., the curve q_1 lying at the intersection of $q_2 = $ const. and $q_3 = $ const.). Let $\alpha_i, \beta_i, \gamma_i$ be the angles that the tangent to this curve makes with the Cartesian coordinate axes. The direction cosines are then given by

$$\cos \alpha_i = \frac{dx}{d\ell_i} \qquad \cos \beta_i = \frac{dy}{d\ell_i} \qquad \cos \gamma_i = \frac{dz}{d\ell_i} \qquad (8.13)$$

Making use of (8.12) we obtain

$$\cos \alpha_i = \frac{1}{h_i}\frac{\partial x}{\partial q_i} \qquad \cos \beta_i = \frac{\partial y}{\partial q_i} \qquad \cos \gamma_i = \frac{1}{h_i}\frac{\partial z}{\partial q_i} \qquad (8.14)$$

In these expressions we have to substitute into

$$\frac{\partial x}{\partial q_i} \qquad \frac{\partial y}{\partial q_i} \qquad \frac{\partial z}{\partial q_i}$$

the coordinates q_1, q_2, q_3 of the point at which the tangent is drawn.

Consider the point A of the trajectory at which our point arrived at time t. Through this point there will pass three coordinate curves. Let AM_i (Fig. 8.1) be the tangent to the coordinate curve q_i. We will find the orthogonal component of the velocity of our point along this tangent. If the velocity is $\mathbf{v}(t)$ and $\mathbf{u}_i(t)$ is the unit vector along AM_i then we are seeking the quantity $\mathbf{v}(t) \cdot \mathbf{u}_i(t)$. Now

$$\mathbf{v}(t) = \dot{x}(t)\mathbf{i} + \dot{y}(t)\mathbf{j} + \dot{z}(t)\mathbf{k} \qquad (8.15)$$

and

$$\mathbf{u}_i(t) = \cos \alpha_i \mathbf{i} + \cos \beta_i \mathbf{j} + \cos \gamma_i \mathbf{k} \qquad (8.16)$$

8–1 Velocity and acceleration in generalized coordinates

Fig. 8.1

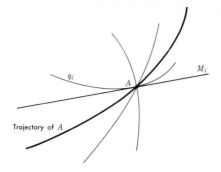

Therefore $\quad \mathbf{v}(t) \cdot \mathbf{u}_i(t) = \dot{x}(t)\cos\alpha_i + \dot{y}(t)\cos\beta_i + \dot{z}(t)\cos\gamma_i$

$$= (1/h_i)\left(\dot{x}\frac{\partial x}{\partial q_i} + \dot{y}\frac{\partial y}{\partial q_i} + \dot{z}\frac{\partial z}{\partial q_i}\right)$$

$$= (1/h_i)\left(\dot{x}\frac{\partial \dot{x}}{\partial \dot{q}_i} + \dot{y}\frac{\partial \dot{y}}{\partial \dot{q}_i} + \dot{z}\frac{\partial \dot{z}}{\partial \dot{q}_i}\right)$$

$$= (1/h_i)\frac{\partial}{\partial \dot{q}_i}\left[\frac{1}{2}(\dot{x}^2 + \dot{y}^2 + \dot{z}^2)\right]$$

$$= \frac{1}{h_i}\frac{\partial}{\partial \dot{q}_i}\left[\frac{1}{2}\left(\frac{d\ell}{dt}\right)^2\right] \tag{8.17}$$

Let

$$T_1 = \frac{1}{2}\left(\frac{d\ell}{dt}\right)^2 \tag{8.18}$$

and denote by $v_i(t)$ the required component of $\mathbf{v}(t)$ along the coordinate curve q_i. Then

$$v_i(t) = \frac{1}{h_i}\frac{\partial T_1}{\partial \dot{q}_i} \tag{8.19}$$

where

$$T_1 = \frac{1}{2}\sum_{i=1}^{3}\sum_{j=1}^{3} g_{ij}\dot{q}_i\dot{q}_j \tag{8.20}$$

This latter relation is obtained by dividing both sides of (8.11) by dt^2.

Example: We will apply the results to the case of spherical polar coordinates. For spherical polar coordinates we have

$$x = r\cos\varphi\sin\theta$$
$$y = r\sin\varphi\sin\theta \tag{8.21}$$
$$z = r\cos\theta$$

and

$$\dot{x} = \dot{r}\cos\varphi\sin\theta - r\sin\varphi\sin\theta\,\dot{\varphi} + r\cos\varphi\cos\theta\dot{\theta}$$
$$\dot{y} = \dot{r}\sin\varphi\sin\theta + r\cos\varphi\sin\theta\,\dot{\varphi} + r\sin\varphi\cos\theta\dot{\theta} \tag{8.22}$$
$$\dot{z} = \dot{r}\cos\theta \qquad\qquad\qquad\qquad - r\sin\theta\dot{\theta}$$

From these we may write

$$T_1 = \tfrac{1}{2}(\dot{x}^2 + \dot{y}^2 + \dot{z}^2)$$
$$= \tfrac{1}{2}(\dot{r}^2 + r^2\dot{\theta}^2 + r^2 \sin^2 \theta \dot{\varphi}^2) \tag{8.23}$$

Let v_r, v_θ, v_φ denote the components of the velocity along the coordinates r, θ, φ. Then

$$v_r = \frac{\partial T_1}{\partial \dot{r}} \qquad v_\theta = \frac{1}{r}\frac{\partial T_1}{\partial \dot{\theta}} \qquad v_\varphi = \frac{1}{r \sin \theta}\frac{\partial T_1}{\partial \dot{\varphi}}$$

or $\qquad\qquad v_r = \dot{r} \qquad\quad v_\theta = r\dot{\theta} \qquad\quad v_\varphi = r \sin \theta\dot{\varphi} \tag{8.24}$

The case of cylindrical polar coordinates can be dealt with in a similar manner.

We will now determine the components of the acceleration along the coordinate curves. Here we are looking for the scalar product $\mathbf{a} \cdot \mathbf{u}_i$. This will be denoted by a_i. Since $a = (\ddot{x}, \ddot{y}, \ddot{z})$ we have

$$a_i = \ddot{x} \cos \alpha_i + \ddot{y} \cos \beta_i + \ddot{z} \cos \gamma_i$$
$$= \frac{1}{h_i}\left[\ddot{x}\frac{\partial x}{\partial q_i} + \ddot{y}\frac{\partial y}{\partial q_i} + \ddot{z}\frac{\partial z}{\partial q_i}\right] \tag{8.25}$$

Now $\qquad\qquad \ddot{x}\frac{\partial x}{\partial q_i} = \frac{d}{dt}\left(\dot{x}\frac{\partial x}{\partial q_i}\right) - \dot{x}\frac{d}{dt}\left(\frac{\partial x}{\partial q_i}\right) \tag{8.26}$

and by (8.6) and (8.9) $\quad \ddot{x}\frac{\partial x}{\partial q_i} = \frac{d}{dt}\left(\dot{x}\frac{\partial \dot{x}}{\partial \dot{q}_i}\right) - \dot{x}\frac{\partial \dot{x}}{\partial q_i} \tag{8.27}$

Similar expressions exist for y and z. Substitution of these into (8.25) yields

$$a_i = \frac{1}{h_i}\left[\frac{d}{dt}\left(\dot{x}\frac{\partial \dot{x}}{\partial \dot{q}_i} + \dot{y}\frac{\partial \dot{y}}{\partial \dot{q}_i} + \dot{z}\frac{\partial \dot{z}}{\partial \dot{q}_i}\right) - \left(\dot{x}\frac{\partial \dot{x}}{\partial q_i} + \dot{y}\frac{\partial \dot{y}}{\partial q_i} + \dot{z}\frac{\partial \dot{z}}{\partial q_i}\right)\right]$$

or $\qquad\qquad a_i = \frac{1}{h_i}\left[\frac{d}{dt}\left(\frac{\partial T_1}{\partial \dot{q}_i}\right) - \frac{\partial T_1}{\partial q_i}\right] \tag{8.28}$

We wish to stress the fact that this result has been obtained from purely kinematical considerations. We are stressing it here because in this form (8.28) bears strong resemblance to the dynamical equations we wish to derive [cf. Eqs. (8.33) and (8.34)].

Example: Components of acceleration in spherical polar coordinates. As we have seen above

$$T_1 = \tfrac{1}{2}(\dot{r}^2 + r^2\dot{\theta}^2 + r^2 \sin^2 \theta \dot{\varphi}^2)$$
$$a_r = \ddot{r} - r \sin^2 \theta \dot{\varphi}^2 - r\dot{\theta}^2$$

Therefore $\qquad a_\theta = (1/r)\left[\frac{d}{dt}(r^2\dot{\theta}) - r^2 \sin \theta \cos \theta \dot{\varphi}^2\right] \tag{8.29}$

$$a_\varphi = \frac{1}{r \sin \theta}\frac{d}{dt}(r^2 \sin^2 \theta \dot{\varphi})^*$$

* The comparative ease with which these components have been obtained should be contrasted with the derivation given in Section 7.4.

It has been shown above that the orthogonal component of acceleration in generalized coordinates along the tangent to the curve q_i is

$$a_i = \frac{1}{\sqrt{g_{ii}}} \left[\frac{d}{dt} \frac{\partial T_1}{\partial \dot{q}_i} - \frac{\partial T_1}{\partial q_i} \right] \qquad i = 1, 2, 3$$

Multiply both sides of this equation by the mass m of the particle and let

$$a_{jk} = m g_{jk} \tag{8.30}$$

Notice further that in the resulting expression we will have

$$m T_1 = \tfrac{1}{2} m v^2 \tag{8.31}$$

which is the kinetic energy T. In terms of the generalized coordinates the kinetic energy is

$$T = \tfrac{1}{2} \sum_j \sum_k a_{jk} \dot{q}_j \dot{q}_k \tag{8.32}$$

where
$$a_{jk} = a_{kj}$$

Thus the orthogonal projection of the vector $m\mathbf{a}$ on the tangent to the curve q_i becomes

$$m a_i = \frac{1}{\sqrt{g_{ii}}} \left[\frac{d}{dt} \frac{\partial T}{\partial \dot{q}_i} - \frac{\partial T}{\partial q_i} \right] \tag{8.33}$$

We will denote this orthogonal projection by $Q_i/\sqrt{g_{ii}}$; then we obtain

$$Q_i = \frac{d}{dt} \frac{\partial T}{\partial \dot{q}_i} - \frac{\partial T}{\partial q_i} \qquad i = 1, 2, 3 \tag{8.34}$$

These are *Lagrange's equations for a single particle. Q_i is called the component of the generalized force.*

Let us determine *the relationships between the components Q_i of the generalized force and the components X, Y, Z of the force $\mathbf{F}$ in Cartesian coordinates.* The cosines of the angles between the tangent to the curve q_i and the Cartesian coordinates x, y, z are (8.14)

$$\frac{1}{\sqrt{g_{ii}}} \frac{\partial x}{\partial q_i} \qquad \frac{1}{\sqrt{g_{ii}}} \frac{\partial y}{\partial q_i} \qquad \frac{1}{\sqrt{g_{ii}}} \frac{\partial z}{\partial q_i} \tag{8.35}$$

Thus the component of $\mathbf{F}$ along q_i, which we have denoted by $Q_i/\sqrt{g_{ii}}$, becomes

$$\frac{Q_i}{\sqrt{g_{ii}}} = \frac{1}{\sqrt{g_{ii}}} \left[X \frac{\partial x}{\partial q_i} + Y \frac{\partial y}{\partial q_i} + Z \frac{\partial z}{\partial q_i} \right] \tag{8.36}$$

or
$$Q_i = X \frac{\partial x}{\partial q_i} + Y \frac{\partial y}{\partial q_i} + Z \frac{\partial z}{\partial q_i} \tag{8.37}$$

The generalized force Q_i need not have the dimensions of the Newtonian force unless

$$\frac{\partial x}{\partial q_i} \qquad \frac{\partial y}{\partial q_i} \qquad \frac{\partial z}{\partial q_i}$$

are pure numbers which in turn makes it necessary that q_i be of the dimension of length.

We will now rewrite Lagrange's equations in a different form from which we will be able to draw certain conclusions. From (8.32) we get

$$\frac{\partial T}{\partial \dot{q}_i} = \sum_k a_{ik}\dot{q}_k \tag{8.38}$$

and

$$\frac{\partial T}{\partial q_i} = \frac{1}{2}\sum_j \sum_k \frac{\partial a_{jk}}{\partial q_i}\dot{q}_j\dot{q}_k \tag{8.39}$$

We next want to differentiate (8.38) with respect to time. Since the a_{ik}'s depend on time through q_1, q_2, q_3

$$\frac{da_{ik}}{dt} = \frac{\partial a_{ik}}{\partial q_1}\dot{q}_1 + \frac{\partial a_{ik}}{\partial q_2}\dot{q}_2 + \frac{\partial a_{ik}}{\partial q_3}\dot{q}_3 \tag{8.40}$$

and

$$\frac{d}{dt}\left(\frac{\partial T}{\partial \dot{q}_i}\right) = \sum_h a_{ih}\ddot{q}_h + \sum_k \sum_j \frac{\partial a_{ik}}{\partial q_j}\dot{q}_j\dot{q}_k \tag{8.41}$$

We will refer to $\ddot{q}_h$'s as *generalized accelerations*. Using the above results, and introducing the shorthand notation*

$$\begin{bmatrix} k & j \\ & i \end{bmatrix} = \frac{1}{2}\left(\frac{\partial a_{ik}}{\partial q_j} + \frac{\partial a_{ij}}{\partial q_k} - \frac{\partial a_{kj}}{\partial q_i}\right) \tag{8.42}$$

we can write Lagrange's equations in the form

$$\sum_h a_{ih}\ddot{q}_h + \sum_k \sum_j \begin{bmatrix} k & j \\ & i \end{bmatrix}\dot{q}_k\dot{q}_j = Q_i \qquad i = 1, 2, 3 \tag{8.43}$$

From these we see that *Lagrange's equations describing the motion of a point mass are differential equations of the second order in generalized coordinates.* We notice that *these equations are linear with respect to $\ddot{q}_h$.* The equations can always be solved. To see this we write (8.43) in the form

$$\begin{aligned}
a_{11}\ddot{q}_1 + a_{12}\ddot{q}_2 + a_{13}\ddot{q}_3 &= h_1 \\
a_{21}\ddot{q}_1 + a_{22}\ddot{q}_2 + a_{23}\ddot{q}_3 &= h_2 \\
a_{31}\ddot{q}_1 + a_{32}\ddot{q}_2 + a_{33}\ddot{q}_3 &= h_3
\end{aligned} \tag{8.44}$$

where

$$h_i = Q_i - \sum_k \sum_j \begin{bmatrix} k & j \\ & i \end{bmatrix}\dot{q}_k\dot{q}_j \tag{8.45}$$

* These are called Christoffel's symbols of the first kind.

These equations have solutions when the determinant

$$|A| = \begin{vmatrix} a_{11} & a_{12} & a_{13} \\ a_{21} & a_{22} & a_{23} \\ a_{31} & a_{32} & a_{33} \end{vmatrix} \qquad (8.46)$$

is different from zero. However, this determinant is also the determinant of of the quadratic form which represents the kinetic energy, viz.

$$T = \tfrac{1}{2} \sum_j \sum_k a_{jk}\dot{q}_j\dot{q}_k$$

This becomes zero only when all the generalized velocities are zero. Thus T is a definite form and for such a form $|A|$ is different from zero.

Let A_{ih} denote the cofactor of a_{ih} in the determinant $|A|$. Also, introduce another shorthand notation*

$$\begin{Bmatrix} h & j \\ & k \end{Bmatrix} = \sum_i \frac{A_{ih}}{|A|} \begin{bmatrix} k & j \\ & i \end{bmatrix} \qquad (8.47)$$

Then from (8.45) we get

$$\ddot{q}_h + \sum_k \sum_j \begin{Bmatrix} k & j \\ & h \end{Bmatrix} \dot{q}_k\dot{q}_j = \sum_i \frac{A_{ih}}{|A|} Q_i \qquad h = 1, 2, 3 \qquad (8.48)$$

When all the forces acting on the point balance out to zero, then $Q_i = 0$ and the last equation becomes:

$$\ddot{q}_h + \sum_k \sum_j \begin{Bmatrix} k & j \\ & h \end{Bmatrix} \dot{q}_k\dot{q}_j = 0 \qquad (8.49)$$

8-3 *Derivation from d'Alembert Principle*

Newton's equations can be replaced by two equivalent laws or principles. Choosing an arbitrary vector **r**, not necessarily the position vector of the point mass, the two principles can be expressed by the equations

$$\mathbf{r} \cdot (\mathbf{F} - m\mathbf{a}) = 0 \qquad (8.50)$$

and
$$\mathbf{r} \times (\mathbf{F} - m\mathbf{a}) = \mathbf{0} \qquad (8.51)$$

Of these, the first one is *d'Alembert's principle* in a modified form. If we set **r** = δ**r** where δ**r** is a virtual displacement, then we have

$$(\mathbf{F} - m\mathbf{a}) \cdot \delta\mathbf{r} = 0 \qquad (8.52)$$

Sometimes the equation
$$\mathbf{F} - m\mathbf{a} = \mathbf{0} \qquad (8.53)$$

is referred to as d'Alembert's principle, the equation being understood to read

* These are called Christoffel's symbols of the second kind.

$$\mathbf{F} + (-m\mathbf{a}) = \mathbf{0} \qquad (8.54)$$

which means that under the action of an applied force $\mathbf{F}$ and another applied force $-m\mathbf{a}$, the particle would be in equilibrium.

When $\mathbf{a} = \mathbf{0}$, then

$$\mathbf{F} \cdot \delta\mathbf{r} = 0 \qquad (8.55)$$

which expresses *the principle of virtual work*.

Referring the motion of the particle to rectangular Cartesian axes x, y, z in which the components of the applied force are X, Y, Z and those of $-m\mathbf{a}$ are $-m\ddot{x}$, $-m\ddot{y}$, $-m\ddot{z}$, d'Alembert's principle [Eq. (8.52)] becomes

$$(X - m\ddot{x})\,\delta x + (Y - m\ddot{y})\,\delta y + (Z - m\ddot{z})\,\delta z = 0 \qquad (8.56)$$

We will now derive Lagrange's equations from d'Alembert's principle. We start with the relations between Cartesian and generalized coordinates, viz.

$$x = x(q_1, q_2, q_3)$$
$$y = y(q_1, q_2, q_3)$$
$$z = z(q_1, q_2, q_3)$$

from which

$$\delta x = \sum_i \frac{\partial x}{\partial q_i}\,\delta q_i \qquad \delta y = \sum_i \frac{\partial y}{\partial q_i}\,\delta q_i \qquad \delta z = \sum_i \frac{\partial z}{\partial q_i}\,\delta q_i \qquad i = 1, 2, 3$$

This set of relations gives all the possible virtual displacements of our point. Substitution of these into (8.56) yields

$$\sum_i \left\{ (X - m\ddot{x})\frac{\partial x}{\partial q_i} + (Y - m\ddot{y})\frac{\partial y}{\partial q_i} + (Z - m\ddot{z})\frac{\partial z}{\partial q_i} \right\} \delta q_i = 0 \qquad (8.57)$$

Since the generalized displacements δq_i are arbitrary, the coefficients of each δq_i in Eq. (8.57) must each be equal to zero, i.e.

$$(X - m\ddot{x})\frac{\partial x}{\partial q_i} + (Y - m\ddot{y})\frac{\partial y}{\partial q_i} + (Z - m\ddot{z})\frac{\partial z}{\partial q_i} = 0 \qquad i = 1, 2, 3$$
$$(8.58)$$

Now, from the kinematical considerations, using relations developed in Sec. 8–1, we find that

$$\ddot{x}\frac{\partial x}{\partial q_i} + \ddot{y}\frac{\partial y}{\partial q_i} + \ddot{z}\frac{\partial z}{\partial q_i} = \frac{d}{dt}\frac{\partial T_1}{\partial \dot{q}_i} - \frac{\partial T_1}{\partial q_i} \qquad (8.59)$$

where

$$T_1 = \tfrac{1}{2}v^2$$

Introducing the kinetic energy

$$T = \tfrac{1}{2}mv^2$$

we can write

$$m\left(\ddot{x}\frac{\partial x}{\partial q_i} + \ddot{y}\frac{\partial y}{\partial q_i} + \ddot{z}\frac{\partial z}{\partial q_i} \right) = \frac{d}{dt}\frac{\partial T}{\partial \dot{q}_i} - \frac{\partial T}{\partial q_i} \qquad (8.60)$$

Using this result, Eq. (8.59) can be written as

$$\frac{d}{dt}\frac{\partial T}{\partial \dot{q}_i} - \frac{\partial T}{\partial q_i} = X\frac{\partial x}{\partial q_i} + Y\frac{\partial y}{\partial q_i} + Z\frac{\partial z}{\partial q_i} \tag{8.61}$$

or

$$\frac{d}{dt}\frac{\partial T}{\partial \dot{q}_i} - \frac{\partial T}{\partial q_i} = Q_i \qquad i = 1, 2, 3 \tag{8.62}$$

These are Lagrange's equations.

The work done during the virtual displacement by the resultant force on our point mass is

$$\delta W = X\,\delta x + Y\,\delta y + Z\,\delta z \tag{8.63}$$

or

$$\delta W = \sum_i \left(X\frac{\partial x}{\partial q_i} + Y\frac{\partial y}{\partial q_i} + Z\frac{\partial z}{\partial q_i} \right)\delta q_i \tag{8.64}$$

which can also be written as

$$\delta W = \sum_i Q_i\,\delta q_i \tag{8.65}$$

Notice that *in order to find the generalized force Q_i it is sufficient to calculate the work done by the resultant force acting on the point. Q_i will then be the coefficient of δq_i.*

8–4 The Law of Energy

Scalar-multiplying the equation

$$\mathbf{F} = m\mathbf{a}$$

by $\mathbf{v}$ we obtain

$$m\mathbf{a}\cdot\mathbf{v} = \mathbf{F}\cdot\mathbf{v}$$

or, as we can verify

$$\frac{dT}{dt} = \mathbf{F}\cdot\mathbf{v} \tag{8.66}$$

This states that *at any instant the time derivative of the kinetic energy is equal to the scalar product of the force and the velocity.*

We notice that this result could also be derived from d'Alembert's principle as expressed by (8.50), by setting the arbitrary vector $\mathbf{r}$ equal to the velocity vector $\mathbf{v}$.

The same law could also be written as

$$dT = \mathbf{F}\cdot d\mathbf{r} \tag{8.67}$$

or

$$dT = X\,dx + Y\,dy + Z\,dz \tag{8.68}$$

Integrating the last expression we obtain

$$T - T_o = \int_{t_o}^{t} (X\,dx + Y\,dy + Z\,dz) \tag{8.69}$$

which expresses *the principle of work and kinetic energy.*

In a special, but important case

$$\frac{dT}{dt} = X\dot{x} + Y\dot{y} + Z\dot{z}$$
$$= -\frac{dU}{dt} \tag{8.70}$$

where the function U is the potential energy.

Now, let us return to the case where the space in which the motion occurs is described by the generalized coordinates q_1, q_2, q_3. The generalized forces are

$$Q_i = X\frac{\partial x}{\partial q_i} + Y\frac{\partial y}{\partial q_i} + Z\frac{\partial z}{\partial q_i} \qquad i = 1, 2, 3 \tag{8.71}$$

These are functions of t, q, $\dot{q}$, i.e.

$$Q = Q(t, q, \dot{q})$$

If the generalized forces can be written in the form

$$Q_i = -\frac{\partial V(t, q, \dot{q})}{\partial q_i} \tag{8.72}$$

then the function $V(t, q, \dot{q})$ satisfying this equation is called the *potential energy function*.

Consider the special case when the potential energy of the generalized forces is independent of the generalized velocities $\dot{q}_i$. Thus

$$Q_i = -\frac{\partial V(t, q_i, q_2, q_3)}{\partial q_i} \tag{8.73}$$

In this case Lagrange's equations become

$$\frac{d}{dt}\frac{\partial T}{\partial \dot{q}_i} - \frac{\partial T}{\partial q_i} = -\frac{\partial V}{\partial q_i} \tag{8.74}$$

or

$$\frac{d}{dt}\frac{\partial T}{\partial \dot{q}_i} - \frac{\partial}{\partial q_i}(T - V) = 0$$

We define the *Lagrangian function* (also called the kinetic potential) as

$$L = T - V \tag{8.75}$$

In terms of L, Lagrange's equations are

$$\frac{d}{dt}\frac{\partial L}{\partial \dot{q}_i} - \frac{\partial L}{\partial q_i} = 0 \qquad i = 1, 2, 3 \tag{8.76}$$

The question which presents itself immediately is what are the methods of solving Lagrange's equations. One of the methods is suggested by the following considerations. Let us suppose that the Lagrangian L does not depend on q_k. Such a coordinate is called cyclic (or ignorable). In this case

$$\frac{\partial L}{\partial q_k} = 0 \tag{8.77}$$

which means also that

$$\frac{d}{dt}\frac{\partial L}{\partial \dot{q}_k} = 0 \tag{8.78}$$

or

$$\frac{\partial L}{\partial \dot{q}_k} = C \tag{8.79}$$

where C is a constant. Equation (8.79) gives the first integral of one of Lagrange's equations. We can deduce, therefore, that *if we were able to find a system of generalized coordinates which are all cyclic in the Lagrangian, then we have essentially found the first integrals of the equations of motion.*

PROBLEM

Consider the spherical polar coordinates r, θ, φ to be generalized coordinates.

(a) Using geometrical considerations obtain the elementary displacements $d\ell_r$, $d\ell_\theta$, $d\ell_\varphi$.

(b) Obtain the components of the velocity vector

$$\mathbf{v} = (v_r, v_\theta, v_\varphi)$$

A particle of mass m, situated at r, θ, φ, is acted on by a force $\mathbf{F} = (F_r, F_\theta, F_\varphi)$, where F_r, F_θ, F_φ are the components of the Newtonian force.

(c) Find the components of the generalized force.

(d) Set up Lagrange's equations for the particle.

9 DYNAMICS OF A POINT MOVING UNDER HOLONOMIC CONSTRAINTS

9–1 Constraints

So far in our studies of the more advanced aspects of mechanics we have considered the motion of a point moving without constraints. Such a point could occupy any position in space and it could acquire any velocity or acceleration. We are about to start a study of a point mass which is subject to *constraints*. This means that *not every position in space is accessible to the point*, or that there could be *limitations to the direction or magnitude of the velocity or the acceleration*. It would be easy to cite several examples of such a type of motion. One such example is the particle which is restricted to remain on the surface of a sphere of radius R, the center of which is (x_0, y_0, z_0) where (x_0, y_0, z_0) may move with uniform velocity. The coordinates of the point must at all times satisfy the equation

$$(x - x_0)^2 + (y - y_0)^2 + (z - z_0)^2 - R^2 = 0 \tag{9.1}$$

where

$$x_0 = \alpha t - \alpha_1 \qquad y_0 = \beta t - \beta_1 \qquad z_0 = \gamma t - \gamma_1 \tag{9.2}$$

Another example is the motion of a point on a curve. If the curve is fixed then the constraints would be specified by

$$f_1(x, y, z) = 0 \qquad f_2(x, y, z) = 0 \tag{9.3}$$

If the curve changes with time then the two constraining equations must contain the time; thus they would be of the form

$$g_1(x, y, z, t) = 0 \qquad g_2(x, y, z, t) = 0 \tag{9.4}$$

In general the constraints to which the motion of the point will be subjected can be expressed in the form of equations or inequalities. These take the form

$$f = 0 \tag{9.5}$$

or

$$f \geq 0 \tag{9.6}$$

where, depending on the type of the constraints, f can be a function of all or some of the arguments $t, x, y, z, \dot{x}, \dot{y}, \dot{z}, \ddot{x}, \ddot{y}, \ddot{z}$. When the constraints are specified by relations (9.5) or (9.6), we refer to them as *analytic constraints*.

116

We will assume that a point moving under constraints can be acted on by all the forces which can act on a free point. Let us denote this set of forces by $(\mathbf{F}_n)$. The case of a free point under the action of any forces is covered by the Newtonian scheme. In the case of constrained motion, however, it will be seen immediately that the results of the action of the forces will in general be different than in the case of a free particle. For instance, if the particle is constrained to move in a plane and a force is acting on it in the direction inclined to the plane, then the resultant acceleration of the particle will never be in the direction of the force. Thus one of the basic laws of Newtonian mechanics is immediately violated. It is obvious therefore that the Newtonian scheme used so far should be enlarged. The main feature of this generalization is the fact that *the very existence of constraints is a source of new forces.*

Consider the case when the number of constraining equations is not greater than two. There will then be either one equation of the form

$$f = 0 \tag{9.7}$$

or two equations
$$f_1 = 0 \qquad f_2 = 0 \tag{9.8}$$

The statement of the problem to be solved is the following: Given the forces $(\mathbf{F}_n)$ acting on the point and the constraints specified either by (9.7) or (9.8), find the laws of motion of the particle.

If the constraints are specified by equations of the form

$$f \geq 0 \tag{9.9}$$

then the number of such conditions can actually be unlimited. Of course, all such conditions should form a consistent set. The constraining conditions of the form (9.9) encompass two conditions, viz., $f > 0$ and $f = 0$. It is sometimes said that in the first of these two cases the constraints are not active and in the second case they are active.

We will be able to say that the point moves under the given constraints if the functions $x(t)$, $y(t)$, $z(t)$, specifying the laws of motion of this point, satisfy at all times the equalities and inequalities described by the constraints.

If the constraining equations do not include any derivatives, then the constraints described by them are called *holonomic.* Constraints expressed by the relations of the type

$$\frac{df(x, y, z, t)}{dt} \geq 0 \tag{9.10}$$

or
$$\frac{d^2 F(x, y, z, t)}{dt^2} \geq 0 \tag{9.11}$$

are sometimes called *semiholonomic.* Constraints described by equations

$$\varphi(x, y, z, \dot{x}, \dot{y}, \dot{z}, t) \geq 0 \tag{9.12}$$

or
$$\psi(x, y, z, \dot{x}, \dot{y}, \dot{z}, \ddot{x}, \ddot{y}, \ddot{z}, t) \geq 0 \tag{9.13}$$

are referred to as being *nonholonomic.*

Another independent division of constraints is into *scleronomic* and *rheonomic*. In scleronomic systems the constraining equations do not include time, whereas for rheonomic constraints they do.

9-2 Reactions

Closer examination of holonomic and nonholonomic constraints reveals that *the existence of the constraints influences the acceleration of the material point on which the constraints are acting.* To see this, consider a constrained point P for which the laws of motion are given by the equations

$$x = x(t) \qquad y = y(t) \qquad z = z(t) \tag{9.14}$$

Let the constraints be specified by the equation

$$f(x, y, z, t) = 0 \tag{9.15}$$

Substituting the three equations (9.14) into the last relation we then get

$$F(t) = f[x(t), y(t), z(t), t] \tag{9.16}$$

This is identically equal to zero. Thus

$$\frac{dF(t)}{dt} = \frac{\partial f}{\partial x}\,\dot{x} + \frac{\partial f}{\partial y}\,\dot{y} + \frac{\partial f}{\partial z}\,\dot{z} + \frac{\partial f}{\partial t} = 0 \tag{9.17}$$

and

$$\frac{d^2F(t)}{dt^2} = \frac{\partial f}{\partial x}\,\ddot{x} + \frac{\partial f}{\partial y}\,\ddot{y} + \frac{\partial f}{\partial z}\,\ddot{z} + \omega = 0 \tag{9.18}$$

where

$$\omega = \dot{x}\,\frac{d}{dt}\frac{\partial f}{\partial x} + \dot{y}\,\frac{d}{dt}\frac{\partial f}{\partial y} + \dot{z}\,\frac{d}{dt}\frac{\partial f}{\partial z} + \frac{d}{dt}\frac{\partial f}{\partial t}$$

$$= \frac{\partial^2 f}{\partial x^2}\,\dot{x}^2 + \frac{\partial^2 f}{\partial y^2}\,\dot{y}^2 + \frac{\partial^2 f}{\partial z^2}\,\dot{z}^2 + 2\,\frac{\partial^2 f}{\partial x\,\partial y}\,\dot{x}\dot{y} + 2\,\frac{\partial^2 f}{\partial y\,\partial z}\,\dot{y}\dot{z} + 2\,\frac{\partial^2 f}{\partial z\,\partial x}\,\dot{z}\dot{x}$$

$$+ \frac{\partial^2 f}{\partial t\,\partial x}\,\dot{x} + \frac{\partial^2 f}{\partial t\,\partial y}\,\dot{y} + \frac{\partial^2 f}{\partial t\,\partial z}\,\dot{z} + \frac{\partial^2 f}{\partial t^2} \tag{9.19}$$

Eq. (9.17) is a relation which limits the velocity of our point and Eq. (9.18) states the limitations imposed on the acceleration of the point.*

If we wish to continue the application of Newtonian mechanics to the constrained motion of the particle, we must postulate that the *existence of constraints is equivalent to the existence of sources of some forces.* These forces are called *reactions.* The sources of reactions are independent of the sources of the applied forces ($\mathbf{F}_n$). The action of these new forces and the action of the applied

* Here we are excluding special points, e.g., if Eq. (9.15) represented the surface of a cone, such a special point would be the vertex of the cone.

118

forces ($\mathbf{F}_n$) is subject to the same laws as is the action of the applied forces in the case of a free point. The forces of reaction have the same effect on the mass as do the constraints and hence we may use them instead of the constraints.

Using Newton's laws and the above postulate of reactions we deduce that the equation of motion of our point moving under constraints is of the form

$$m\ddot{\mathbf{r}} = \mathbf{F} + \mathbf{R} \tag{9.20}$$

where $\mathbf{F}$ is the resultant of the given forces ($\mathbf{F}_n$) and $\mathbf{R}$ is the reaction of the constraints. *All the theorems and results applicable to the motion of the free point apply to the case of constrained motion when the resultant $\mathbf{F}$ of the given forces is supplemented by the force of reaction $\mathbf{R}$.* Thus given a fixed axis and the angular momentum of our particle about this axis, we have

$$\dot{\mathbf{h}} = \mathbf{r} \times \mathbf{F} + \mathbf{r} \times \mathbf{R} \tag{9.21}$$

where $\mathbf{h}$ is the angular momentum, and $\mathbf{r}$ is the vector from the axis to the particle. Further, the differential of the kinetic energy is given by

$$dT = X\,dx + Y\,dy + Z\,dz + R_x\,dx + R_y\,dy + R_z\,dz \tag{9.22}$$

where

$$(X, Y, Z) = \mathbf{F} \text{ and } (R_x, R_y, R_z) = \mathbf{R}$$

9-3   The Problem of Determining the Reaction

An inevitable question poses itself, viz., to what degree can the reaction be determined? As we have seen, the equation of motion of our constrained particle is

$$m\ddot{\mathbf{r}} = \mathbf{F} + \mathbf{R} \tag{9.23}$$

which is equivalent to three scalar equations

$$m\ddot{x} = X + R_x \qquad m\ddot{y} = Y + R_y \qquad m\ddot{z} = Z + R_z \tag{9.24}$$

In addition, there are one or two equations of constraints. Thus, at most five equations are available. Now the number of unknown quantities is six (x, y, z, R_x, R_y, R_z), so that it would appear that the problem of the constrained motion of a particle has no definite solution. We will, however, see that the solutions can be determined in cases where, in addition to the geometrical properties of the mechanisms realizing the constraints, we are given certain physical properties. This statement will become clearer presently.

Consider the holonomic constraints specified by the single equation

$$f(x, y, z, t) = 0 \tag{9.25}$$

As we have seen above, the consequences of this relation are the equations

$$\frac{\partial f}{\partial x}\,\dot{x} + \frac{\partial f}{\partial y}\,\dot{y} + \frac{\partial f}{\partial z}\,\dot{z} + \frac{\partial f}{\partial t} = 0 \tag{9.26}$$

and
$$\frac{\partial f}{\partial x}\,\ddot{x} + \frac{\partial f}{\partial y}\,\ddot{y} + \frac{\partial f}{\partial z}\,\ddot{z} + \omega = 0 \tag{9.27}$$

Realizing that

$$\mathbf{grad}\, f = \nabla f$$
$$= \frac{\partial f}{\partial x}\,\mathbf{i} + \frac{\partial f}{\partial y}\,\mathbf{j} + \frac{\partial f}{\partial z}\,\mathbf{k} \tag{9.28}$$

$$\mathbf{v} = \dot{x}\mathbf{i} + \dot{y}\mathbf{j} + \dot{z}\mathbf{k} \tag{9.29}$$

and
$$\mathbf{a} = \ddot{x}\mathbf{i} + \ddot{y}\mathbf{j} + \ddot{z}\mathbf{k} \tag{9.30}$$

we can write the relations (9.26) and (9.27) in the form

$$\mathbf{v} \cdot \nabla f = -\frac{\partial f}{\partial t} \tag{9.31}$$

and
$$\mathbf{a} \cdot \nabla f = -\omega \tag{9.32}$$

From these relations we see that *the magnitude of the components of the velocity and acceleration along the normal to the surface are given functions which are entirely determined by the analytic constraints.*

We have mentioned above that the problem of the constrained motion of a point is undetermined when in addition to Newton's laws only the analytic constraints are given. We will now examine what deductions can be made about the reactions.

The scalar equations of motion of the particle are

$$m\ddot{x} = X + R_x \qquad m\ddot{y} = Y + R_y \qquad m\ddot{z} = Z + R_z \tag{9.33}$$

The functions $x(t)$, $y(t)$, $z(t)$ defining the motion of the point should satisfy these equations of motion as well as the constraining equation (9.25) and all the equations resulting from it, in particular Eq. (9.27). Substituting in this equation the values of x, y, z from (9.33) we get

$$R_x \frac{\partial f}{\partial x} + R_y \frac{\partial f}{\partial y} + R_z \frac{\partial f}{\partial z} + X \frac{\partial f}{\partial x} + Y \frac{\partial f}{\partial y} + Z \frac{\partial f}{\partial z} + m\omega = 0 \tag{9.34}$$

This can also be written in the form

$$\mathbf{R} \cdot \nabla f = -(\mathbf{F} \cdot \nabla f + m\omega) \tag{9.35}$$

from which
$$R = -\frac{1}{|\nabla f|\cos(\mathbf{R}, \nabla f)}\,[\mathbf{F} \cdot \nabla f + m\omega] \tag{9.36}$$

where R denotes the magnitude of $\mathbf{R}$.

For the reaction $\mathbf{R}$ we can write

$$\mathbf{R} = \mathbf{R}_n + \mathbf{R}_t \tag{9.37}$$

$\mathbf{R}_n$ is called the normal reaction and $\mathbf{R}_t$ is the tangential reaction or the force of friction.

We have proved that *the given forces and the analytical constraints determine the normal reaction.**

There are cases when the resultant reaction is along the normal to the surface over which the particle is constrained to move. The corresponding constraints are termed *perfect* or *smooth*. If they are not, the constraints will be referred to as *imperfect*.

We see immediately that *in the case of smooth constraints, the problem of the constrained motion of our particle ceases to be indeterminate.* Indeed, in this case

$$\cos (\mathbf{R}, \nabla f) = \pm 1$$

and in this case we see that the total reaction lies along ∇f, i.e., along the normal to the surface f. Since the direction cosines of this normal are known,** R_x, R_y, R_z can be determined.

9–4 Lagrange's Equations of the First Kind of a Point Moving under Single Constraints

We will now examine the case of smooth constraints in greater detail. As we have seen, when this type of constraints is operative, the total reaction is directed along the normal to the surface. This total reaction R_n is given by

$$R_n = - \frac{1}{|\nabla f|} [\mathbf{F} \cdot \nabla f + m\omega]$$

The Cartesian components of this reaction are

$$R_x = \frac{R_n}{|\nabla f|} \frac{\partial f}{\partial x} \qquad R_y = \frac{R_n}{|\nabla f|} \frac{\partial f}{\partial y} \qquad R_z = \frac{R_n}{|\nabla f|} \frac{\partial f}{\partial z} \qquad (9.38)$$

or, if we introduce the notation

$$\lambda = \frac{R_n}{|\nabla f|} \qquad (9.39)$$

$$R_x = \lambda \frac{\partial f}{\partial x} \qquad R_y = \lambda \frac{\partial f}{\partial y} \qquad R_z = \lambda \frac{\partial f}{\partial z} \qquad (9.40)$$

The equations of motion of our point therefore take the form

$$m\ddot{x} = X + \lambda \frac{\partial f}{\partial x} \qquad m\ddot{y} = Y + \lambda \frac{\partial f}{\partial y} \qquad m\ddot{z} = Z + \lambda \frac{\partial f}{\partial z} \qquad (9.41)$$

* We again emphasize, as we have done above, that we are not including in our considerations special points of the surface over which our point is constrained to move.
** The direction cosines are given by $\dfrac{1}{|\nabla f|} \dfrac{\partial f}{\partial x}$ $\dfrac{1}{|\nabla f|} \dfrac{\partial f}{\partial y}$ $\dfrac{1}{|\nabla f|} \dfrac{\partial f}{\partial z}$

These equations were first derived independently by Lagrange and by Euler. They are called *Lagrange's equations of the first kind*, or Lagrange's equations with multiplier.

9-5 Lagrange's Equations of the Second Kind for a Point Moving under Single Constraints

Let the constraints, which limit the motion of the particle, be again given by

$$f(x, y, z, t) = 0 \qquad (9.42)$$

At every moment this equation represents a certain surface. In general the function f is of such a type that x, y, z can be expressed as functions of two generalized coordinates, i.e., we can write

$$x = x(q_1, q_2, t) \qquad y = y(q_1, q_2, t) \qquad z = z(q_1, q_2, t) \qquad (9.43)$$

As an example we can again cite the point on a sphere, the center of which moves with uniform rectilinear motion. The constraining equation is of the form

$$(x - \alpha t)^2 + (y - \beta t)^2 + (z - \gamma t)^2 - R^2 = 0 \qquad (9.44)$$

Here we can introduce the spherical polar coordinates θ and φ, which will serve as the two generalized coordinates, and we can write

$$x = \alpha t + R \sin \theta \cos \varphi \qquad y = \beta t + R \sin \theta \sin \varphi$$
$$z = \gamma t + R \cos \theta \qquad (9.45)$$

Now, if we substitute the values (9.45) into (9.44) we obtain a function $F(q_1, q_2, t)$ which is identically equal to zero. In view of this, we get

$$\frac{\partial F}{\partial q_i} = \frac{\partial f}{\partial x}\frac{\partial x}{\partial q_i} + \frac{\partial f}{\partial y}\frac{\partial y}{\partial q_i} + \frac{\partial f}{\partial z}\frac{\partial z}{\partial q_i} = 0 \qquad (i = 1, 2) \qquad (9.46)$$

and deduce that to obtain the laws of motion of our point we should obtain the functions

$$q_1 = q_1(t) \qquad q_2 = q_2(t) \qquad (9.47)$$

We will now derive the differential equations the solutions of which will be the above functions. From (9.43) we obtain

$$x = \sum_{i=1}^{3} \frac{\partial x}{\partial q_i} \dot{q}_i + \frac{\partial x}{\partial t}$$

$$y = \sum_{i=1}^{3} \frac{\partial y}{\partial q_i} \dot{q}_i + \frac{\partial y}{\partial t} \qquad (9.48)$$

$$z = \sum_{i=1}^{3} \frac{\partial z}{\partial q_i} \dot{q}_i + \frac{\partial z}{\partial t}$$

From these we find

$$\frac{\partial x}{\partial q_i} = \frac{\partial \dot{x}}{\partial \dot{q}_i} \qquad \frac{\partial y}{\partial q_i} = \frac{\partial \dot{y}}{\partial \dot{q}_i} \qquad \frac{\partial z}{\partial q_i} = \frac{\partial \dot{z}}{\partial \dot{q}_i} \tag{9.49}$$

In addition we find that

$$\frac{d}{dt}\frac{\partial x}{\partial q_i} = \frac{\partial \dot{x}}{\partial q_i} \qquad \frac{d}{dt}\frac{\partial y}{\partial q_i} = \frac{\partial \dot{y}}{\partial q_i} \qquad \frac{d}{dt}\frac{\partial z}{\partial q_i} = \frac{\partial \dot{z}}{\partial q_i} \tag{9.50}$$

Both of these results (9.49) and (9.50) have already been obtained in the previous chapter.

The kinetic energy of our point is

$$T = \tfrac{1}{2}m(\dot{x}^2 + \dot{y}^2 + \dot{z}^2) \tag{9.51}$$

or

$$T = \tfrac{1}{2}\left[\sum_{i=1}^{2}\sum_{j=1}^{2} A_{ij}\dot{q}_i\dot{q}_j + \sum_{i=1}^{2} \alpha_i\dot{q}_i + \beta \right] \tag{9.52}$$

where

$$A_{ij} = m\left(\frac{\partial x}{\partial q_i}\frac{\partial x}{\partial q_j} + \frac{\partial y}{\partial q_i}\frac{\partial y}{\partial q_j} + \frac{\partial z}{\partial q_i}\frac{\partial z}{\partial q_j} \right) \tag{9.53}$$

$$\alpha_i = m\left(\frac{\partial x}{\partial q_i}\frac{\partial x}{\partial t} + \frac{\partial y}{\partial q_i}\frac{\partial y}{\partial t} + \frac{\partial z}{\partial q_i}\frac{\partial z}{\partial t} \right) \tag{9.54}$$

and

$$\beta = m\left[\left(\frac{\partial x}{\partial t}\right)^2 + \left(\frac{\partial y}{\partial t}\right)^2 + \left(\frac{\partial z}{\partial t}\right)^2 \right] \tag{9.55}$$

If the constraints are time independent then the constraining equation does not contain time explicitly, and in this case

$$\alpha_i = 0, \text{ and } \beta = 0 \tag{9.56}$$

The kinetic energy then becomes

$$T = \tfrac{1}{2}\sum_{i=1}^{2}\sum_{j=1}^{2} A_{ij}\dot{q}_i\dot{q}_j \tag{9.57}$$

Let us assume that the physical constraints which realize (9.42) are perfect. In this case, as we know, the equations of motion are

$$m\ddot{x} = X + \lambda\frac{\partial f}{\partial x} \qquad m\ddot{y} = Y + \lambda\frac{\partial f}{\partial y} \qquad m\ddot{z} = Z + \lambda\frac{\partial f}{\partial z} \tag{9.58}$$

Let us multiply these three equations by $\dfrac{\partial x}{\partial q_i}$, $\dfrac{\partial y}{\partial q_i}$, $\dfrac{\partial z}{\partial q_i}$ respectively, and add. Then, taking into consideration (9.46) we obtain

$$m\left(\ddot{x}\frac{\partial x}{\partial q_i} + \ddot{y}\frac{\partial y}{\partial q_i} + \ddot{z}\frac{\partial z}{\partial q_i} \right) = X\frac{\partial x}{\partial q_i} + Y\frac{\partial y}{\partial q_i} + Z\frac{\partial z}{\partial q_i} \tag{9.59}$$

It is easy to show that

$$\ddot{x}\frac{\partial x}{\partial q_i} = \frac{d}{dt}\left(\dot{x}\frac{\partial x}{\partial q_i}\right) - \dot{x}\frac{d}{dt}\frac{\partial x}{\partial q_i} \tag{9.60}$$

with similar identities for y and z. Using these, as well as (9.49) and (9.50) we obtain

$$\frac{d}{dt}\,m\left(\dot{x}\frac{\partial\dot{x}}{\partial\dot{q}_i} + \dot{y}\frac{\partial\dot{y}}{\partial\dot{q}_i} + \dot{z}\frac{\partial\dot{z}}{\partial\dot{q}_i}\right) - m\left(\dot{x}\frac{\partial\dot{x}}{\partial q_i} + \dot{y}\frac{\partial\dot{y}}{\partial q_i} + \dot{z}\frac{\partial\dot{z}}{\partial q_i}\right)$$

$$= X\frac{\partial x}{\partial q_i} + Y\frac{\partial y}{\partial q_i} + Z\frac{\partial z}{\partial q_i} \tag{9.61}$$

Now, as we can check

$$m\left(\dot{x}\frac{\partial\dot{x}}{\partial\dot{q}_i} + \dot{y}\frac{\partial\dot{y}}{\partial\dot{q}_i} + \dot{z}\frac{\partial\dot{z}}{\partial\dot{q}_i}\right) = \frac{\partial T}{\partial\dot{q}_i} \tag{9.62}$$

and

$$m\left(\dot{x}\frac{\partial\dot{x}}{\partial q_i} + \dot{y}\frac{\partial\dot{y}}{\partial q_i} + \dot{z}\frac{\partial\dot{z}}{\partial q_i}\right) = \frac{\partial T}{\partial q_i} \tag{9.63}$$

Also let

$$X\frac{\partial x}{\partial q_i} + Y\frac{\partial y}{\partial q_i} + Z\frac{\partial z}{\partial q_i} = Q_i \tag{9.64}$$

where Q_i is the generalized force. Then Eq. (9.61) becomes

$$\frac{d}{dt}\frac{\partial T}{\partial\dot{q}_i} - \frac{\partial T}{\partial q_i} = Q_i \qquad (i = 1, 2) \tag{9.65}$$

These are *Lagrange's equations of the second kind*, or Lagrange's equations without multipliers.

The solutions of Lagrange's equations yield q_1 and q_2 as functions of time, and four constants of integration. These four constants will be determined from the initial conditions of the point, i.e., from the initial values of q_1, q_2 and $\dot{q}_1, \dot{q}_2$.

Once the motion of our point is determined, the reactions of the constraints can be evaluated from (9.58) where now x, y, z and X, Y, Z will be given functions of time.

9–6 Constrained Motion of a Point along a Curve

We will now consider the case when two independent equations of holonomic constraints are given, viz.

$$f(x, y, z, t) = 0$$
$$\varphi(x, y, z, t) = 0 \tag{9.66}$$

At every instant of time these equations determine a curve along which our point is constrained to move. As always, the motion of the point will be determined if its coordinates can be found as functions of time, i.e., if we obtain the set of functions

$$x = x(t) \qquad y = y(t) \qquad z = z(t) \tag{9.67}$$

Differentiating (9.66) with respect to time, we obtain

$$\frac{df}{dt} = \frac{\partial f}{\partial x} \dot{x} + \frac{\partial f}{\partial y} \dot{y} + \frac{\partial f}{\partial z} \dot{z} + \frac{\partial f}{\partial t} = 0$$

$$\frac{d\varphi}{dt} = \frac{\partial \varphi}{\partial x} \dot{x} + \frac{\partial \varphi}{\partial y} \dot{y} + \frac{\partial \varphi}{\partial z} \dot{z} + \frac{\partial \varphi}{\partial t} = 0 \tag{9.68}$$

A second differentiation yields

$$\frac{d^2 f}{dt^2} = \frac{\partial f}{\partial x} \ddot{x} + \frac{\partial f}{\partial y} \ddot{y} + \frac{\partial f}{\partial z} \ddot{z} + \omega = 0 \tag{9.69}$$

$$\frac{d^2 \varphi}{dt^2} = \frac{\partial \varphi}{\partial x} \ddot{x} + \frac{\partial \varphi}{\partial y} \ddot{y} + \frac{\partial \varphi}{\partial z} \ddot{z} + \omega_1 = 0 \tag{9.70}$$

where ω and ω_1 are definite functions of x, y, z, $\dot{x}$, $\dot{y}$, $\dot{z}$, t. Eqs. (9.68) limit the velocity of our point and (9.69–70) limit its acceleration.

Again we are led to postulate the existence of reactions. As a result of this postulate the equation of motion of our particle is

$$m\ddot{\mathbf{r}} = \mathbf{F} + \mathbf{R} \tag{9.71}$$

where **F** is the resultant of the given forces and **R** is the reaction of the constraints. This equation is equivalent to three scalar equations

$$m\ddot{x} = X + R_x \qquad m\ddot{y} = Y + R_y \qquad m\ddot{z} = Z + R_z \tag{9.72}$$

Now, we substitute $\ddot{x}$, $\ddot{y}$, $\ddot{z}$ from these equations in (9.69) and (9.70), and after some manipulation, obtain

$$\begin{aligned} R_x \frac{\partial f}{\partial x} + R_y \frac{\partial f}{\partial y} + R_z \frac{\partial f}{\partial z} &= \mathbf{R} \cdot \nabla f \\ &= R|\nabla f| \cos (\mathbf{R}, \nabla f) \\ &= -\left(X \frac{\partial f}{\partial x} + Y \frac{\partial f}{\partial y} + Z \frac{\partial f}{\partial z} + m\omega \right) \end{aligned} \tag{9.73}$$

and

$$\begin{aligned} R_x \frac{\partial \varphi}{\partial x} + R_y \frac{\partial \varphi}{\partial y} + R_z \frac{\partial \varphi}{\partial z} &= \mathbf{R} \cdot \nabla \varphi \\ &= R|\nabla \varphi| \cos (\mathbf{R}, \nabla \varphi) \\ &= -\left(X \frac{\partial \varphi}{\partial x} + Y \frac{\partial \varphi}{\partial y} + Z \frac{\partial \varphi}{\partial z} + m\omega_1 \right) \end{aligned} \tag{9.74}$$

From these equations we deduce that *the analytic constraints given by (9.66) determine only the magnitudes of the components of the reactions along the normals* to the surfaces $f = 0$ and $\varphi = 0$. Both components are perpendicular to the curve along which our point is constrained to move and their resultant is the component of the reaction normal to the curve. This normal reaction will be denoted by $\mathbf{R}_n$. This is one of the components into which the reaction $\mathbf{R}$ can be resolved. The other, denoted by $\mathbf{R}_t$, will be the tangential reaction or the force of friction.

The normal reaction can be written in the form

$$\mathbf{R}_n = \lambda\, \nabla f + \mu\, \nabla\varphi \tag{9.75}$$

where λ and μ are two scalars.

The Cartesian components of the normal reaction are

$$R_{nx} = \lambda \frac{\partial f}{\partial x} + \mu \frac{\partial \varphi}{\partial x}$$

$$R_{ny} = \lambda \frac{\partial f}{\partial y} + \mu \frac{\partial \varphi}{\partial y} \tag{9.76}$$

$$R_{nz} = \lambda \frac{\partial f}{\partial z} + \mu \frac{\partial \varphi}{\partial z}$$

Now, since $\mathbf{R}_t$ is perpendicular to ∇f and to $\nabla\varphi$

$$\begin{aligned} \mathbf{R} \cdot \nabla f &= (\mathbf{R}_n + \mathbf{R}_t) \cdot \nabla f \\ &= \mathbf{R}_n \cdot \nabla f \end{aligned} \tag{9.77}$$

and
$$\begin{aligned} \mathbf{R} \cdot \nabla\varphi &= (\mathbf{R}_n + \mathbf{R}_t) \cdot \nabla\varphi \\ &= \mathbf{R}_n \cdot \nabla\varphi \end{aligned} \tag{9.78}$$

We can now take R_{nx}, R_{ny}, R_{nz} from (9.76) and substitute them into (9.73) and (9.74) for R_x, R_y, R_z. After rearrangement we obtain

$$\lambda(\nabla f)^2 + \mu\, \nabla f \cdot \nabla\varphi = -\left(X \frac{\partial f}{\partial x} + Y \frac{\partial f}{\partial y} + Z \frac{\partial f}{\partial z} + m\omega \right) \tag{9.79}$$

and

$$\lambda\, \nabla f \cdot \nabla\varphi + \mu(\nabla\varphi)^2 = -\left(X \frac{\partial \varphi}{\partial x} + Y \frac{\partial \varphi}{\partial y} + Z \frac{\partial \varphi}{\partial z} + m\omega_1 \right)$$

From these two equations the coefficients λ and μ can be determined.

When the physical constraints, which correspond to equations (9.66), are such that the frictional force is zero, the equations of motion become

$$m\ddot{x} = X + \lambda \frac{\partial f}{\partial x} + \mu \frac{\partial \varphi}{\partial x}$$

$$m\ddot{y} = Y + \lambda \frac{\partial f}{\partial y} + \mu \frac{\partial \varphi}{\partial y} \tag{9.80}$$

$$m\ddot{z} = Z + \lambda \frac{\partial f}{\partial z} + \mu \frac{\partial \varphi}{\partial z}$$

Such constraints are again termed perfect or smooth. As in the case of the single constraining equation, the motion can be determined uniquely when the constraints are smooth.*

At this point we could construct differential equations, the solutions of which will determine the motion of our particle. As before, we could first obtain equations which contain multipliers, but the procedure here is somewhat tedious and we will do away with it. Instead, we will proceed immediately to Lagrange's formulation.

9-7 Lagrange's Equations in the Case of Double Constraints

Assume that we are given the two equations of constraint

$$f(x, y, z, t) = 0$$

and   (9.81)

$$\varphi(x, y, z, t) = 0$$

which analytically express the fact that our point mass is to move along a curve. The first step in Lagrange's procedure in this case is to express the coordinates of the point, which satisfy the two constraining equations, by a parameter q and time t. Having accomplished that, we obtain

$$x = x(q, t) \qquad y = y(q, t) \qquad z = z(q, t) \tag{9.82}$$

which we substitute into the constraining equations to obtain

$$\frac{\partial f}{\partial x}\frac{\partial x}{\partial q} + \frac{\partial f}{\partial y}\frac{\partial y}{\partial q} + \frac{\partial f}{\partial z}\frac{\partial z}{\partial q} = 0 \tag{9.83}$$

and

$$\frac{\partial \varphi}{\partial x}\frac{\partial x}{\partial q} + \frac{\partial \varphi}{\partial y}\frac{\partial y}{\partial q} + \frac{\partial \varphi}{\partial z}\frac{\partial z}{\partial q} = 0 \tag{9.84}$$

Differentiating (9.82) with respect to time we obtain

$$\dot{x} = \frac{\partial x}{\partial q}\dot{q} + \frac{\partial x}{\partial t} \qquad \dot{y} = \frac{\partial y}{\partial q}\dot{q} + \frac{\partial y}{\partial t} \qquad \dot{z} = \frac{\partial z}{\partial q}\dot{q} + \frac{\partial z}{\partial t} \tag{9.85}$$

The kinetic energy of our particle is

$$\begin{aligned} T &= \tfrac{1}{2}mv^2 \\ &= \tfrac{1}{2}m(\dot{x}^2 + \dot{y}^2 + \dot{z}^2) \\ &= \tfrac{1}{2}(A\dot{q}^2 + \alpha\dot{q} + \beta) \end{aligned} \tag{9.86}$$

* Again, we are referring to ordinary points of the path of the particle, and we are excluding all special points.

where

$$A = m\left[\left(\frac{\partial x}{\partial q}\right)^2 + \left(\frac{\partial y}{\partial q}\right)^2 + \left(\frac{\partial z}{\partial q}\right)^2\right] \tag{9.87}$$

$$\alpha = 2m\left[\frac{\partial x}{\partial q}\frac{\partial x}{\partial t} + \frac{\partial y}{\partial q}\frac{\partial y}{\partial t} + \frac{\partial z}{\partial q}\frac{\partial z}{\partial t}\right] \tag{9.88}$$

and

$$\beta = m\left[\left(\frac{\partial x}{\partial t}\right)^2 + \left(\frac{\partial y}{\partial t}\right)^2 + \left(\frac{\partial z}{\partial t}\right)^2\right] \tag{9.89}$$

When the constraining equations do not contain time, we can always choose q in such a way that the functions (9.81) will be independent of time, so that

$$\alpha = 0 \qquad \beta = 0 \tag{9.90}$$

In this case

$$T = \tfrac{1}{2}A\dot{q}^2 \tag{9.91}$$

We now multiply the three equations (9.80) by $\dfrac{\partial x}{\partial q}$, $\dfrac{\partial y}{\partial q}$, $\dfrac{\partial z}{\partial q}$ respectively and add. Employing the identities expressed by Eqs. (9.83) and (9.84) we obtain

$$m\left(\ddot{x}\frac{\partial x}{\partial q} + \ddot{y}\frac{\partial y}{\partial q} + \ddot{z}\frac{\partial z}{\partial q}\right) = X\frac{\partial x}{\partial q} + Y\frac{\partial y}{\partial q} + Z\frac{\partial z}{\partial q} \tag{9.92}$$

From (9.85) we obtain

$$\frac{\partial \dot{x}}{\partial \dot{q}} = \frac{\partial x}{\partial q} \qquad \frac{\partial \dot{y}}{\partial \dot{q}} = \frac{\partial y}{\partial q} \qquad \frac{\partial \dot{z}}{\partial \dot{q}} = \frac{\partial z}{\partial q} \tag{9.93}$$

We also verify that

$$\frac{d}{dt}\frac{\partial x}{\partial q} = \frac{\partial \dot{x}}{\partial q} \qquad \frac{d}{dt}\frac{\partial y}{\partial q} = \frac{\partial \dot{y}}{\partial q} \qquad \frac{d}{dt}\frac{\partial z}{\partial q} = \frac{\partial \dot{z}}{\partial q} \tag{9.94}$$

Using the last two sets of relations we obtain, in the same way as we have already obtained previously

$$\frac{d}{dt}\frac{\partial T}{\partial \dot{q}} - \frac{\partial T}{\partial q} = Q \tag{9.95}$$

where

$$Q = X\frac{\partial x}{\partial q} + Y\frac{\partial y}{\partial q} + Z\frac{\partial z}{\partial q} \tag{9.96}$$

is the generalized force.

We have thus derived Lagrange's equation for a particle subjected to double smooth constraints. Its solution yields $q = q(t)$. The general solution will contain two constants of integration which can be evaluated from the initial values of q and $\dot{q}$. The reactions are obtained from (9.72).

PROBLEMS

9.1 (a) Consider a coplanar motion of a particle constrained to move on a smooth curve. Using the normal and tangential components (Sec. 2–4) obtain the differential equations of motion in component form. (The external force is $\mathbf{F} = (F_n, F_t)$ and the reaction is $\mathbf{R} = (R_n, 0)$.)

(b) Let a point move in the gravitational field of earth on a curve $z = f(x)$ placed in the vertical zx-plane shown in Figure 9.1. Find the time it takes the particle to move from $A(x_0)$ to $D(\xi)$ shown in Figure 9.1.

Fig. 9.1

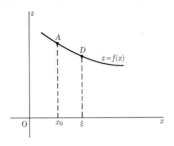

9.2 A plane, inclined at an angle α to the horizontal moves with uniform acceleration $\mathbf{a}$, where this acceleration lies in the plane vertical and perpendicular to the inclined plane (Fig. 9.2). A point mass m is placed on the plane. Find the acceleration of the point m with respect to the plane.

Fig. 9.2

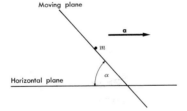

9.3 A particle is free to slide on a smooth horizontal rod which is constrained to rotate with constant angular velocity ω about a point which is fixed. Find the differential equation of motion and its solution.

9.4 A particle is free to slide on a smooth circular loop which is constrained to rotate in its plane with constant angular velocity ω about a point on its circumference. Find the differential equation of motion of the particle.

9.5 Consider the motion of a particle m on a spherical surface of radius a. Let R and S be the components of a force along the meridian and the parallel of latitude, tending to increase the spherical polar coordinates θ and ϕ respectively.

(a) Obtain Lagrange's equations.

(b) Apply to the case of a spherical pendulum which moves around the Oz-axis.

9.6 A massive particle slides smoothly on a curve in the horizontal xy-plane. The equations of the curve in parametric form are

$$x = a \cosh \eta$$
$$y = a \sinh \eta$$

Show analytically that (a) the energy of the particle is conserved, and (b) the angular momentum is not conserved.

9.7 A small sphere is placed in a cylindrical, semi-circular trough of radius R and length L at an angle θ_0 below the horizontal (Fig. 9.3(a)). It is given an

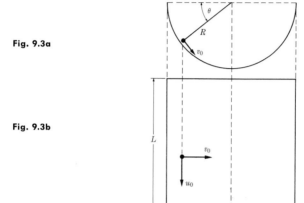

Fig. 9.3a

Fig. 9.3b

initial velocity tangent to the surface of the trough with components v_0 perpendicular to the axis, and u_0 parallel to the axis, as shown in Figure 9.3(b). Find the minimum value of v_0 such that the sphere will rise above the rim. Assume no friction between the sphere and the surface of the trough.

9.8 The vertical plane II shown in Figure 9.4 rotates about the z-axis with uniform angular velocity ω. A point P of mass m moves on this plane without friction. If the gravitational force is directed opposite to the z-axis, determine the motion of the point.

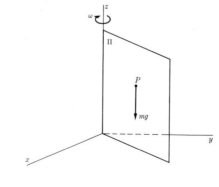

Fig. 9.4

10 LAGRANGE'S EQUATIONS OF A SYSTEM OF PARTICLES

We will now discuss the dynamics of a system of particles by proceeding roughly along the same lines as in the last two chapters. First, we will derive Lagrange's equations of particles moving under no constraints. This can be done in a straightforward manner. After that we will discuss the motion of a system of particles moving under both holonomic and nonholonomic constraints.

10–1 Lagrange's Equations for a System of Particles Moving Under no Constraints

Consider a system of N particles which move under no constraints and denote the Cartesian coordinates of the system by

$$x_1, x_2, \ldots, x_{3N} \tag{10.1}$$

The system can also be described by generalized coordinates. Since no constraints are present, the number of degrees of freedom will be $3N$, and the generalized coordinates will form the set

$$q_1, q_2, \ldots, q_{3N} \tag{10.2}$$

All the coordinates of the set (10.2) are independent.

We are assuming that we know the functional relationships between the Cartesian and the generalized coordinates which are of the form

$$x_i = x_i(q_1, q_2, \ldots, q_{3N}) \tag{10.3}$$

From these we obtain

$$\dot{x}_i = \sum_{j=1}^{3N} \frac{\partial x_i}{\partial q_j} \dot{q}_i \tag{10.4}$$

from which we notice that

$$\dot{x}_i = \dot{x}_i(q_1, q_2, \ldots, q_{3N}, \dot{q}_1, \dot{q}_2, \ldots, \dot{q}_{3N}) \tag{10.5}$$

i.e., $\dot{x}_i$ is a function of $6N$ variables, viz., $3N$ generalized coordinates and $3N$ generalized velocities. We can denote this fact more concisely by writing

$$\dot{x}_i = \dot{x}_i(q, \dot{q}) \tag{10.6}$$

where, of course,

$$q \equiv q_i, q_2, \ldots, q_{3N}$$

and

$$\dot{q} \equiv \dot{q}_1, \dot{q}_2, \ldots, \dot{q}_{3N}$$

Differentiating $\dot{x}_i$ from Eq. (10.4) partially with respect to $\dot{q}_k$ we obtain

$$\frac{\partial \dot{x}_i}{\partial \dot{q}_k} = \frac{\partial x_i}{\partial q_k} \tag{10.7}$$

Furthermore, partial differentiation of $\dot{x}_i$ with respect to q_k yields

$$\frac{\partial \dot{x}_i}{\partial q_k} = \sum_{j=1}^{3N} \frac{\partial^2 x_i}{\partial q_k \, \partial q_j} \dot{q}_j \tag{10.8}$$

But

$$\frac{d}{dt} \frac{\partial x_i}{\partial q_k} = \sum_{j=1}^{3N} \frac{\partial^2 x_i}{\partial q_j \, \partial q_k} \dot{q}_j \tag{10.9}$$

therefore

$$\frac{d}{dt} \frac{\partial x_i}{\partial q_k} = \frac{\partial \dot{x}_i}{\partial q_k} \tag{10.10}$$

Now, the kinetic energy of our system of particles is given by

$$T = \tfrac{1}{2} \sum_{i=1}^{3N} m_i \dot{x}_i{}^2 \tag{10.11}$$

and from (10.6) it follows that

$$T = T(q, \dot{q}) \tag{10.12}$$

Partial differentiation of T with respect to q_j yields

$$\frac{\partial T}{\partial q_j} = \sum_{i=1}^{3N} m_i \dot{x}_i \frac{\partial \dot{x}_i}{\partial q_j} \tag{10.13}$$

and with respect to $\dot{q}_j$

$$\frac{\partial T}{\partial \dot{q}_j} = \sum_{i=1}^{3N} m_i \dot{x}_i \frac{\partial \dot{x}_i}{\partial \dot{q}_j}$$

or by Eq. (10.7)

$$\frac{\partial T}{\partial \dot{q}_j} = \sum_{i=1}^{3N} m_i \dot{x}_i \frac{\partial x_i}{\partial q_j} \tag{10.14}$$

Differentiating the last expression with respect to time, we obtain

$$\frac{d}{dt}\left(\frac{\partial T}{\partial \dot{q}_j}\right) = \sum_{i=1}^{3N} \left[m_i \ddot{x}_i \frac{\partial x_i}{\partial q_j} + m_i \dot{x}_i \frac{\partial \dot{x}_i}{\partial q_j} \right] \tag{10.15}$$

where use was made of Eq. (10.10). Subtracting Eq. (10.13) from (10.15) we obtain

$$\frac{d}{dt} \frac{\partial T}{\partial \dot{q}_j} - \frac{\partial T}{\partial q_j} = \sum_{i=1}^{3N} m_i \ddot{x}_i \frac{\partial x_i}{\partial q_j} \tag{10.16}$$

But

$$m_i\ddot{x}_i = X_i \tag{10.17}$$

where X_i is the Cartesian component of the Newtonian force. Thus Eq. (10.16) becomes

$$\frac{d}{dt}\frac{\partial T}{\partial \dot{q}_j} - \frac{\partial T}{\partial q_j} = \sum_{i=1}^{3N} X_i \frac{\partial x_i}{\partial q_j} \tag{10.18}$$

From Eq. (10.3) we have

$$\delta x_i = \sum_{j=1}^{3N} \frac{\partial x_i}{\partial q_j} \delta q_j \tag{10.19}$$

The work done by the applied forces along the displacements δx_i is

$$\delta W = \sum_{i=1}^{3N} X_i \, \delta x_i$$

$$= \sum_{j=1}^{3N} \left[\sum_{i=1}^{3N} X_i \frac{\partial x_i}{\partial q_j} \right] \delta q_j \tag{10.20}$$

or

$$\delta W = \sum_{j=1}^{3N} Q_j \, \delta q_j \tag{10.21}$$

where

$$Q_j = \sum_{i=1}^{3N} X_i \frac{\partial x_i}{\partial q_j} \tag{10.22}$$

is the jth component of the generalized force. Thus Eq. (10.18) becomes

$$\frac{d}{dt}\frac{\partial T}{\partial \dot{q}_j} - \frac{\partial T}{\partial q_j} = Q_j \qquad j = 1, 2, \ldots, 3N \tag{10.23}$$

These are Lagrange's equations of our system of particles.

If the system is conservative, the forces can be derived from a potential $V(q_1, q_2, \ldots, q_{3N})$ and

$$\delta W = -\delta V \tag{10.24}$$

or

$$\delta W = -\sum_{j=1}^{3N} \frac{\partial V}{\partial q_j} \delta q_j \tag{10.25}$$

Comparing this with Eq. (10.21) we see that

$$Q_j = -\frac{\partial V}{\partial q_j}$$

Thus, in this special case, Eq. (10.23) becomes

$$\frac{d}{dt}\frac{\partial T}{\partial \dot{q}_j} - \frac{\partial T}{\partial q_j} = -\frac{\partial V}{\partial q_j}$$

Introducing the Lagrangian

$$L = T - V$$

we can write Lagrange's equations in the form

$$\frac{d}{dt} \frac{\partial L}{\partial \dot{q}_j} - \frac{\partial L}{\partial q_j} = 0 \qquad j = 1, 2, \ldots, 3N \qquad (10.26)$$

10–2 Constraints of a System of Particles

We have just considered a system of particles moving under no constraints. In such a case there are no limitations for the positions, velocities or accelerations of the particles. If this is not so, then constraints are present. The analytical expressions for the limitations for the positions, velocities and accelerations of the particles are given by some equations or inequalities.

Let us again consider a system of N particles having Cartesian coordinates.

$$x_1, x_2, \ldots, x_{3N}$$

The equations of constraints then take the form

$$f_i(t, x_j, \dot{x}_j, \ddot{x}_j) = 0 \qquad i = 1, 2, \ldots, r \qquad (10.27)$$

and

$$\varphi_k(t, x_j, \dot{x}_j, \ddot{x}_j) \geq 0 \qquad k = 1, 2, \ldots, s \qquad (10.28)$$

where $j = 1, 2, \ldots, 3N$. The two sets of equations should be consistent. Following our previous notations we can write Eqs. (10.27) and (10.28) in the form

$$f_i(t, x, \dot{x}, \ddot{x}) = 0 \qquad \varphi_k(t, x, \dot{x}, \ddot{x}) \geq 0$$

If the equations of constraints do not contain time explicitly, we will call the constraints scleronomic; if the opposite is true, the constraints will be termed rheonomic. If the equations of constraints do not contain the derivatives of the coordinates, then the constraints will be called holonomic. If such derivatives enter, and if the equations of constraints cannot be replaced by equivalent ones not containing the derivatives, then the corresponding constraints will be called nonholonomic. The divisions of constraints into scleronomic and rheonomic, and holonomic and nonholonomic are independent. Thus we can have *four categories of constraints:*

    (1) *scleronomic—holonomic*
    (2) *rheonomic—holonomic*
    (3) *scleronomic—nonholonomic*
    (4) *rheonomic—nonholonomic*

In what follows we will just consider constraints described by the equations (10.27). It is obvious that the number of constraining equations cannot be greater than $3N - 1$, for when $r = 3N$, the constraining equations alone would completely determine the condition of the system.

In general, the existence of constraints of the forms (10.27) will bring limitations for the accelerations of the particles of the system. In most cases this can be proved analytically.*

It is a basic principle of Newtonian mechanics that anything that in one way or another influences the accelerations of the points of the system is called a force, and the circumstances giving rise to such a force are referred to as the sources of the force. As a result of this we can formulate the following postulate: *The existence of the constraints of the type given by Eqs. (10.27), which limit the motion of our system, is, in general, the source of forces acting on that system. The forces are called the forces of reaction, or simply reactions.*

In order to formulate the dynamics of the constrained motion of a system, it is not sufficient to use Newton's laws in which given forces are used. It is necessary to introduce an additional postulate which can be formulated in the following way: *Every system P of particles on which the constraints specified by Eqs. (10.27) are acting can be treated as a system of nonconstrained particles if the set of given forces are supplemented by the forces of reaction. All of the forces, the applied forces and the reactions, are then used in Newton's laws as in the case of nonconstrained motion. The forces of reaction cause the motion to proceed in accordance with the impressed constraints.*

Newton's laws and the above postulates of reactions will serve as the basis for a mathematical scheme to describe the constrained motion of a system of particles. The validity of this scheme can only be determined by observation and experiment.

10–3 Lagrange's Equations of the First Kind

On the bases of the postulate of reactions the equations of motion of a system of N particles are

$$m\ddot{\mathbf{r}}_k = \mathbf{F}_k + \mathbf{R}_k \qquad k = 1, 2, \ldots, N \qquad (10.29)$$

where $\mathbf{F}_k$ is the resultant force acting on the kth particle and $\mathbf{R}_k$ is the resultant reaction acting on the same point. Equations (10.29) are equivalent to $3N$ scalar equations

$$m_j\ddot{x}_j = X_j + R_j \qquad j = 1, 2, \ldots, 3N \qquad (10.30)$$

where X_j and R_j are Cartesian components of the given forces and the forces of reaction respectively. The reactions $\mathbf{R}_k$, and also their components R_j, should be such that the accelerations $\ddot{x}_j$ obtained from Eqs. (10.30) will satisfy identically those equations which limit the accelerations and those which result from the constraint.** Let there be r equations of constraints

---

* In the case of a single point we have already obtained these analytical expressions, Eq. (9.18), which stated the limitations impressed on the acceleration of the point. Similar expressions can be obtained for a system of particles. There are cases, however, where such analytical expressions cannot be formulated.
** We emphasize again that we are referring here to equations of the type (9.18). We did not derive such equations for the system of particles.

$$f_1 = 0 \qquad f_2 = 0 \qquad \cdots \qquad f_r = 0 \qquad (10.31)$$

from which we can find that the accelerations of the points of our system are limited by some equations which we will denote by

$$\psi_1(\ddot{x}) = 0 \qquad \psi_2(\ddot{x}) = 0 \qquad \cdots \qquad \psi_r(\ddot{x}) = 0 \qquad (10.32)$$

These equations must be satisfied by the accelerations given by Eqs. (10.30). Thus we may write

$$\psi_1[(1/m)(X + R)] = 0 \qquad \psi_2[(1/m)(X + R)] = 0 \qquad \cdots$$
$$\psi_r[(1/m)(X + R)] = 0 \qquad (10.33)$$

where the subscripts of m_j, X_j, R_j have been omitted.

We notice that Eqs. (10.30) together with (10.31) form a system of $(3N + r)$ equations. But in order to determine the motion of our system we need to know $3N$ unknown functions R_j and $3N$ unknown functions $x_j(t)$, i.e., altogether $6N$ unknown functions. Since the number of equations specifying the constraints cannot be greater than $3N - 1$, the total number of available equations (10.30) and (10.31) can be $6N - 1$ at most. We see, therefore, that *the laws of motion and the postulate of reactions are not sufficient to determine the motion of a constrained system in a unique way.*

The missing conditions can be supplemented in the same way as in the case of a single particle (examined in Section 9–4), namely they are given when *the mechanisms which realize the constraints are known.*

Before we continue our discussion of the constrained motion of a system of particles let us return to the system of particles moving under no constraints. Any results obtained for such a system can be applied to the constrained motion when the forces of reactions will be added to the given forces. Consider a system of N particles moving under no constraints. The equations of motion will be

$$m_k \ddot{\mathbf{r}}_k = \mathbf{F}_k \qquad k = 1, 2, \ldots, N \qquad (10.34)$$

Let $\mathbf{A}_k (k = 1, 2, \ldots, N)$ denote a system of arbitrary vectors. Then from Eqs. (10.34) we can formulate the equation

$$\sum_{k=1}^{N} (\mathbf{F}_k - m_k \ddot{\mathbf{r}}_k) \cdot \mathbf{A}_k = 0 \qquad (10.35)$$

which at every instant is satisfied by all the functions $x_j(t)$ satisfying Eqs. (10.34). Equation (10.35) expresses d'Alembert's principle. It states that the unconstrained motion of a system of particles proceeds in such a way that at every instant Eq. (10.35) is valid.

Usually d'Alembert's principle is stated in a somewhat different way. For the set of arbitrary vectors $\mathbf{A}_k$ we choose a set of virtual displacements $\delta \mathbf{r}_k$ ($k = 1, 2, \ldots, N$). Equation (10.35) then takes the form

$$\sum_{k=1}^{N} (\mathbf{F}_k - m_k \ddot{\mathbf{r}}_k) \cdot \delta \mathbf{r}_k = 0 \qquad (10.36)$$

and this can be given a more concrete physical meaning. To see this new meaning of d'Alembert's principle we write the equations of motion of our system in the form

$$\mathbf{F}_k - m_k \ddot{\mathbf{r}}_k = \mathbf{0} \qquad k = 1, 2, \ldots, N \qquad (10.37)$$

This equation states that the sum of the given forces $\mathbf{F}_k$ and of another set, $-m_k \ddot{\mathbf{r}}_k$, of forces (sometimes called inertial forces) is zero.

Equation (10.36) can now be interpreted as expressing the fact that *the system of unconstrained particles moves in such a way that the work by all the given forces $\mathbf{F}_k$ and the inertial forces $-m_k \ddot{\mathbf{r}}_k$ along the virtual displacements of the system is zero.*

The form (10.36) of d'Alembert's principle can also be expressed in terms of rectangular components of the forces, the accelerations and the virtual displacements. Denoting these by X_j, $\ddot{x}_j$ and δx_j respectively, we can rewrite Eq. (10.26) in the form*

$$\sum_{j=1}^{3N} (X_j - m_j \ddot{x}_j)\, \delta x_j = 0 \qquad (10.38)$$

Turning to the constrained motion of the system we can write d'Alembert's principle for such a system in the two equivalent forms

$$\sum_{k=1}^{N} (\mathbf{F}_k + \mathbf{R}_k - m_k \ddot{\mathbf{r}}_k) \cdot \delta \mathbf{r}_k = 0 \qquad (10.39)$$

or

$$\sum_{j=1}^{3N} (X_j + R_j - m_j \ddot{x}_j)\, \delta x_j = 0 \qquad (10.40)$$

We have stated above that in order to obtain the equations of motion of a constrained system, we have to examine the physical situations which realize the particular constraints. This must be done in every particular case. Consider our system of N material particles P_k and let certain forces $\mathbf{R}_k$ act on them. Let $\delta \mathbf{r}_k$ denote the displacements of the points P_k which are specified in a certain way. We will say that the work done by the forces $\mathbf{R}_k$ along the displacements $\delta \mathbf{r}_k$ is given if at every moment the equation

$$\sum_{k=1}^{N} \mathbf{R}_k \cdot \delta \mathbf{r}_k = \sum_{k=1}^{N} \mathbf{B}_k \cdot \delta \mathbf{r}_k \qquad (10.41)$$

is specified where $\mathbf{B}_k$ are certain given vector functions depending on time and on the state of the system and the $\delta \mathbf{r}_k$'s are subject to certain conditions to be specified later. The functions $\mathbf{B}_k$ depend on the physical conditions which realize the constraints. We will show that the reactions of the constraints will be determined when the work done by these reactions along a certain specified set of displacements are given.

* In this notation the position of the kth particle is given by three rectangular components $x_{3k-2}, x_{3k-1}, x_{3k}$.

Let our system of N material points P_k be subjected to r constraints described by the equations

$$f_1 = 0 \qquad f_2 = 0 \qquad \cdots \qquad f_r = 0 \qquad (10.42)$$

Let us specify the displacements of the points P_k in such a way that they will satisfy the following set of independent equations

$$\sum_{k=1}^{N} \mathbf{A}_{ik} \cdot \delta \mathbf{r}_k = 0 \qquad i = 1, 2, \ldots, r \qquad (10.43)$$

where $\mathbf{A}_{ik}$ are given functions depending on time and on the state of the system. Further, let us assume that the work done by the reactions along the displacements $\delta \mathbf{r}_k$ satisfying Eqs. (10.43) is given. Then, under certain additional conditions which will be specified below, the reactions can be determined.

Equations (10.41) and (10.43) can be written as

$$\sum_{j=1}^{3N} R_j \, \delta x_j = \sum_{j=1}^{3N} B_j \, \delta x_j \qquad (10.44)$$

and

$$\sum_{j=1}^{3N} A_{ij} \, \delta x_j = 0 \qquad i = 1, 2, \ldots, r \qquad (10.45)$$

respectively. It then follows that the components R_j of the reactions which satisfy Eq. (10.44) for all the displacements δx_j satisfying Eqs. (10.45) will be given by

$$R_j = B_j + \sum_{i=1}^{n} \lambda_i A_{ij} \qquad (10.46)$$

where λ_i are arbitrary parameters which can be functions of time and of the state of the system.*

The differential equations of motion of our system are

$$m_j \ddot{x}_j = X_j + R_j \qquad j = 1, 2, \ldots, 3N \qquad (10.47)$$

Substituting R_j from Eqs. (10.46) into these equations we obtain

---

* The above statement follows from the following theorem: The necessary and sufficient condition that the equation

$$\sum_{k=1}^{p} R_k \alpha_k = 0$$

be valid for all α_k's which satisfy $r \, (<p)$ independent equations

$$\sum_{k=i}^{p} A_{ik} \alpha_k = 0 \; (i = 1, 2, \ldots, r)$$

is the existence of r numbers $\lambda_1, \lambda_2, \ldots, \lambda_r$ such that for every k the equation $R_k = \lambda_1 A_{1k} + \lambda_2 A_{2k} + \cdots + \lambda_r A_{rk}$ is satisfied.

$$m_j \ddot{x}_j = X_j + B_j + \sum_{i=1}^{n} \lambda_i A_{ij} \qquad j = 1, 2, \ldots, 3N \qquad (10.48)$$

We will call these equations the *generalized Lagrange's equations of the first kind*.

We still need to evaluate the functions λ_i. We have assumed that the accelerations $\ddot{x}_j$ at all times satisfy r equations

$$\psi_1 = 0 \qquad \psi_2 = 0 \qquad \cdots \qquad \psi_r = 0 \qquad (10.49)$$

which result from the equations of constraint. In those we substitute the expressions for $\ddot{x}_j$ obtained from Eqs. (10.48). We then obtain r equations which we may denote by

$$\omega_1(\lambda, t, x, \dot{x}) = 0$$
$$\omega_2(\lambda, t, x, \dot{x}) = 0 \qquad (10.50)$$
$$\vdots$$
$$\omega_r(\lambda, t, x, \dot{x}) = 0$$

From these equations the functions λ_i can be evaluated. The "certain additional conditions" mentioned above (in the paragraph after Eqs. (10.43)) require that Eqs. (10.50) should determine the λ_i's uniquely.

The displacements along which the work is done by the forces of reaction are specified by Eqs. (10.43) (in vector form) or by Eqs. (10.45). These can be replaced by the equations

$$\sum_{j=1}^{3N} \frac{\partial \psi_i}{\partial \ddot{x}_j} \, \delta x_j = 0 \qquad i = 1, 2, \ldots, r \qquad (10.51)$$

The displacements δx_j satisfying Eqs. (10.51) are virtual displacements. If at every moment the work done along these virtual displacements is given, then the equations of motion can be written in the form

$$m_j \ddot{x}_j = X_j + B_j + \sum_{i=1}^{n} \lambda_i \frac{\partial \psi_i}{\partial \ddot{x}_j} \qquad j = 1, 2, \ldots, 3N \qquad (10.52)$$

This is *another form of Lagrange's equations of the first kind* or Lagrange's equations with multipliers. The expressions

$$\lambda_i \frac{\partial \psi_i}{\partial \ddot{x}_j} \qquad j = 1, 2, \ldots, 3N$$

are components of the reactive forces; we will term them reactions of the constraints specified by equation $f_i = 0$.

If the work done by the reactions during virtual displacements is always zero, i.e., if at all times

$$B_j = 0 \qquad j = 1, 2, \ldots, 3N$$

then the constraints are called perfect; otherwise they are termed imperfect.

The equations of motion for a system of particles with perfect constraints are

$$m_j \ddot{x}_j = X_j + \sum_{i=1}^{n} \lambda_i \frac{\partial \psi_i}{\partial \ddot{x}_j} \qquad j = 1, 2, \ldots, 3N \qquad (10.53)$$

These equations follow from d'Alembert's principle written in the form (10.40). If we assume that

$$\sum_{j=1}^{3N} R_j \, \delta x_j = 0$$

for all virtual displacements, d'Alembert's principle then takes the form

$$\sum_{j=1}^{3N} (X_j - m_j \ddot{x}_j) \, \delta x_j = 0 \qquad (10.54)$$

or, when vectors are used,

$$\sum_{k=1}^{N} (\mathbf{F}_k - m_k \ddot{\mathbf{r}}_k) \cdot \delta \mathbf{r}_k = 0 \qquad (10.55)$$

We will now summarize our discussion leading to Lagrange's equations of the first kind. We are considering a system of N particles, the motion of which is limited by constraints which are specified by r independent of equations

$$f_1 = 0 \qquad f_2 = 0 \qquad \cdots \qquad f_r = 0 \qquad (10.56)$$

The constraints can be holonomic or nonholonomic. In general, as a result of Eqs. (10.56), certain conditions are imposed on accelerations $\ddot{x}_j$ and these are expressed by equations

$$\psi_j(\ddot{x}) = 0 \qquad \cdots \qquad \psi_r(\ddot{x}) = 0 \qquad (10.57)$$

We now subject the system to virtual displacements which satisfy the conditions given by the equations

$$\sum_j A_{ij} \, \delta x_j = 0 \qquad i = 1, 2, \ldots, r \qquad (10.58)$$

We are assuming that the work done along these virtual displacements is given, i.e.

$$\sum_{j=1}^{3N} R_j \, \delta x_j = \sum_{j=1}^{3N} B_j \, \delta x_j \qquad (10.59)$$

is known. The equations of motion of our system of particles then take the form

$$m_j \ddot{x}_j = X_j + B_j + \sum_{i=1}^{n} \lambda_i A_{ij} \qquad j = 1, 2, \ldots, 3N \qquad (10.60)$$

The equations given by (10.60) and by (10.57) form a set of $3N + r$ equations in $3N + r$ unknowns x_j and λ_i. These equations are of the second order with respect to x_j.

In the case when the work done by the reactions along the virtual displacements is given, and the virtual displacements satisfy the conditions

$$\sum_j \frac{\partial \psi_i}{\partial \ddot{x}_j} \delta x_j = 0 \tag{10.61}$$

Eqs. (10.60) take the form

$$m_j \ddot{x}_j = X_j + \sum_{i=1}^{n} \lambda_i \frac{\partial \psi_i}{\partial \ddot{x}_j} \tag{10.62}$$

and these are Lagrange's equations of the first kind.

The solution of the system of equations given by Eqs. (10.60) and (10.57) proceeds along the following lines: We substitute into Eqs. (10.57) the values of $\ddot{x}_j$ obtained from Eqs. (10.60). In this way we obtain r linear equations in λ_i. Solving these, we obtain

$$\lambda_i = \lambda_i(t, x, \dot{x})$$

which we then substitute into Eqs. (10.60). This will yield $3N$ equations of the second order in x_j. The integration of this system of equations will establish the motion of our system of particles. The constants of integration will be obtained from the initial conditions which, of course, should be consistent with the constraints.

10–4 Lagrange's Equations of the Second Kind

In the last section we discussed one possible procedure for solving the problem of constrained motion of a system of particles. This method presents considerable difficulties. First, it is necessary to determine the multipliers λ_i and then, in general, to integrate a system of $3N$ differential equations of the second order. We therefore wish to investigate the possibility of setting up a system of equations without the multipliers λ_i. We now wish to make use of the generalized coordinates. Historically this problem was solved, first for holonomic systems, independently by Lagrange and by Euler. The resulting equations are called Lagrange's equations of the second kind.

Consider a system of N particles subject to holonomic constraints which are specified by equations

$$f_1 = 0 \qquad f_2 = 0 \qquad \cdots \qquad f_r = 0$$

The constraints can be scleronomic or rheonomic. The number of degrees of freedom of our system is $n = 3N - r$. Thus n generalized coordinates will be needed to determine the state of the system at any time. We are assuming that the functional relations between the space coordinates x_j and the generalized coordinates are given, i.e., we know the functions

$$x_j = x_j(t, q_1, q_2, \ldots, q_n) \qquad j = 1, 2, \ldots, 3N \qquad (10.63)$$

From these relations we evaluate the time derivatives of the space coordinates and obtain

$$\dot{x}_j = \sum_{h=1}^{n} \frac{\partial x_j}{\partial q_h} \dot{q}_h + \frac{\partial x_j}{\partial t} \qquad (10.64)$$

the differentiation of which yields

$$\frac{\partial x_j}{\partial q_h} = \frac{\partial \dot{x}_j}{\partial \dot{q}_h} \qquad (10.65)$$

Partially differentiating relation (10.64) with respect to an arbitrary generalized coordinate q_k, and Eq. (10.65) with respect to time we find that

$$\frac{\partial \dot{x}_j}{\partial q_k} = \frac{d}{dt} \frac{\partial x_j}{\partial q_k} \qquad j = 1, 2, \ldots, 3N \qquad k = 1, 2, \ldots, n \qquad (10.66)$$

The possible displacements of the particles are given by

$$\delta x_j = \sum_{h=1}^{n} \frac{\partial x_j}{\partial q_h} \delta q_h \qquad (10.67)$$

where δq_h are arbitrary.

D'Alembert's principle for our system of particles is of the form

$$\sum_{j} (m_j \ddot{x}_j - X_j - B_j)\, \delta x_j = 0$$

where the B_j's are the functions introduced in Eq. (10.41).

Using this principle and the forms of the virtual displacements given by Eqs. (10.67) we obtain

$$\sum_{h} \delta q_h \sum_{j} (m_j \ddot{x}_j - X_j - B_j) \frac{\partial x_j}{\partial q_h} = 0 \qquad (10.68)$$

We will transform the second sum (over j) of Eq. (10.68) using the relations (10.65) and (10.66). We first note that

$$\ddot{x}_j \frac{\partial x_j}{\partial q_h} = \frac{d}{dt}\left(\dot{x}_j \frac{\partial x_j}{\partial q_h}\right) - \dot{x}_j \frac{d}{dt} \frac{\partial x_j}{\partial q_h}$$

which by Eqs. (10.65) and (10.66) becomes

$$\ddot{x}_j \frac{\partial x_j}{\partial q_h} = \frac{d}{dt}\left(\dot{x}_j \frac{\partial \dot{x}_j}{\partial \dot{q}_h}\right) - \dot{x}_j \frac{\partial \dot{x}_j}{\partial q_h}$$

so that

$$\sum_{j} m_j \ddot{x}_j \frac{\partial x_j}{\partial q_h} = \frac{d}{dt} \sum_{j} m_j \dot{x}_j \frac{\partial \dot{x}_j}{\partial q_h} - \sum_{j} m_j \dot{x}_j \frac{\partial \dot{x}_j}{\partial q_h} \qquad (10.69)$$

Now, the kinetic energy of our system is given by

$$T = \tfrac{1}{2} \sum_{j=1}^{3N} m_j \dot{x}_j{}^2 \tag{10.70}$$

In this expression we substitute our expression for $\dot{x}_j$ from Eq. (10.64). Partially differentiating T with respect to $\dot{q}_h$ and q_h we obtain

$$\frac{\partial T}{\partial \dot{q}_h} = \sum_j m_j \dot{x}_j \frac{\partial \dot{x}_j}{\partial \dot{q}_h}$$

and

$$\frac{\partial T}{\partial q_h} = \sum_j m_j \dot{x}_j \frac{\partial \dot{x}_j}{\partial q_h}$$

Examining Eq. (10.69) we see that

$$\sum_j m_j \ddot{x}_j \frac{\partial x_j}{\partial q_h} = \frac{d}{dt} \frac{\partial T}{\partial \dot{q}_h} - \frac{\partial T}{\partial q_h} \tag{10.71}$$

Let us introduce the functions Q_h and $\mathcal{R}_h$ defined by the relations

$$Q_h = \sum_j X_j \frac{\partial x_j}{\partial q_h} \qquad \mathcal{R}_h = \sum_j B_j \frac{\partial x_j}{\partial q_h} \tag{10.72}$$

Since δq_h are arbitrary we can replace Eqs. (10.71) and (10.72) by the equivalent equations

$$\sum_h \delta q_h \sum_j m_j \ddot{x}_j \frac{\partial x_j}{\partial q_h} = \sum_j m_j \ddot{x}_j \, \delta x_j$$

$$= \sum_h \left(\frac{d}{dt} \frac{\partial T}{\partial \dot{q}_h} - \frac{\partial T}{\partial q_h} \right) \delta q_h \tag{10.73}$$

and

$$\sum_h \delta q_h \sum_j X_j \frac{\partial x_j}{\partial q_h} = \sum_j X_j \, \delta x_j = \sum_h Q_h \, \delta q_h$$

$$\sum_h \delta q_h \sum_j B_j \frac{\partial x_j}{\partial q_h} = \sum_j B_j \, \delta x_j = \sum_h \mathcal{R}_h \, \delta q_h \tag{10.74}$$

Eq. (10.68) now takes the form

$$\sum_h \frac{d}{dt} \left(\frac{\partial T}{\partial \dot{q}_h} - \frac{\partial T}{\partial q_h} - Q_h - \mathcal{R}_h \right) \delta q_h = 0 \tag{10.75}$$

This equation, valid for arbitrary values of δq_h, is *one of the forms of d'Alembert's principle for holonomic systems.*

Since the quantities δq_h are arbitrary, we deduce from Eq. (10.75) that

$$\frac{d}{dt} \frac{\partial T}{\partial \dot{q}_h} - \frac{\partial T}{\partial q_h} - Q_h - \mathcal{R}_h = 0$$

10–4 Lagrange's equations of the second kind

or
$$\frac{d}{dt}\frac{\partial T}{\partial \dot{q}_h} - \frac{\partial T}{\partial q_h} = Q_h + \Re_h \qquad h = 1, 2, \ldots, n \qquad (10.76)$$

Q_h are generalized forces corresponding to the given forces and $\Re_h$ are generalized forces of reactions. *Eqs. (10.76) are Lagrange's equations of the second kind for a system of particles moving under holonomic constraints.*

In the case of perfect constraints Lagrange's equations become

$$\frac{d}{dt}\frac{\partial T}{\partial \dot{q}_h} - \frac{\partial T}{\partial q_h} = Q_h \qquad h = 1, 2, \ldots, n \qquad (10.77)$$

10–5 *Evaluation of Kinetic Energy and Generalized Forces*

In order to form Lagrange's equations (10.76) we have to express the kinetic energy of the system in terms of generalized coordinates and generalized velocities. As stated above, we will obtain the appropriate form of the kinetic energy if we substitute the values of $\dot{x}_j$ from Eq. (10.64) into Eq. (10.70) and obtain

$$T = \tfrac{1}{2}\sum_j m_j \left[\sum_h \frac{\partial x_j}{\partial q_h}\dot{q}_h + \frac{\partial x_j}{\partial t}\right]^2$$

$$= \tfrac{1}{2}\left[\sum_h \sum_k A_{hk}\dot{q}_h\dot{q}_k + \sum_h \alpha_h\dot{q}_h + \beta\right] \qquad (10.78)$$

where
$$A_{hk} = A_{kh} = \sum_j m_j \frac{\partial x_j}{\partial q_h}\frac{\partial x_j}{\partial q_k}$$

$$\alpha_i = 2\sum_j m_j \frac{\partial x_j}{\partial q_i}\frac{\partial x_j}{\partial t} \qquad (10.79)$$

$$\beta = \sum_j m_j \left(\frac{\partial x_j}{\partial t}\right)^2$$

The last three expressions are all functions of time and of the generalized coordinates. We see therefore that the kinetic energy of the system of particles is of the form

$$T = T_2 + T_1 + T_0$$
where
$$T_2 = \tfrac{1}{2}\sum_h \sum_k A_{hk}\dot{q}_h\dot{q}_k$$

$$T_1 = \tfrac{1}{2}\sum_h \alpha_h\dot{q}_h \qquad (10.80)$$

$$T_0 = \tfrac{1}{2}\beta$$

When the constraints are scleronomic then

$$\frac{\partial x_j}{\partial t} = 0$$

and therefore $\qquad \alpha_h = 0 \qquad \beta = 0$

Thus, *when a system moves under holonomic and scleronomic constraints, it is possible to choose the generalized coordinates in such a way that the kinetic energy will be a quadratic function of generalized velocities* of the form

$$T = \tfrac{1}{2} \sum_h \sum_k A_{hk} \dot{q}_h \dot{q}_k \tag{10.81}$$

where the coefficients A_{hk} are functions of the generalized coordinates.

In order to determine the generalized forces Q_h corresponding to the given forces (which we may call for brevity the given generalized forces) and the generalized forces of reactions $\Re_h$, we notice that from Eqs. (10.67) and (10.72) we have

$$\sum_j X_j \, \delta x_j = \sum_h Q_h \, \delta q_h$$

$$\sum_j B_j \, \delta x_j = \sum_h \Re_h \, \delta q_h \tag{10.82}$$

From these relations we see that $\sum Q_h \, \delta q_h$ and $\sum \Re_h \, \delta q_h$ are the amounts of virtual work performed by the forces Q_h and $\Re_h$. Thus in order to evaluate Q_h and $\Re_h$ we express X_j and B_j as functions of t, q, $\dot{q}$, and then into the expressions

$$\sum X_j \, \delta x_j \qquad \sum B_j \, \delta x_j$$

we substitute for δx_j the values given by Eq. (10.67). The coefficients of δq_h in the resulting expression will constitute the required generalized forces Q_h and $\Re_h$. It follows from the expressions (10.82) that $Q_h \, \delta q_h$ and $\Re_h \, \delta q_h$ represent the work performed by the given generalized forces and the forces of reaction in the case when only one generalized coordinate q_h is subjected to a possible variation. For this reason we can call δq_h a displacement and $Q_h \, \delta q_h$ and $\Re_h \, \delta q_h$ the amounts of work of the given generalized force Q_h and the force of reaction $\Re_h$ along the displacement δq_h.

10–6   The Potential in Lagrange's Equations

We will say that a set of generalized forces

$$G_1, G_2, \ldots, G_n$$

can be derivable from a potential if there is a function $V(t, q, \dot{q})$ such that for every h

$$G_h = - \frac{\partial V(t, q, \dot{q})}{\partial q_h} \tag{10.83}$$

As an example, consider a holonomic system of n degrees of freedom acted on by a system of Newtonian forces which have a potential (as defined in Newtonian mechanics) which is independent of velocity. Denoting the components of the Newtonian forces by X_j we have

$$X_j = -\frac{\partial U(t, x_1, \ldots, x_{3N})}{\partial x_j} \tag{10.84}$$

Let the generalized forces corresponding to the Newtonian forces be denoted by Q_h and denote by $V(t, q)$ the Newtonian potential $U(t, x)$ in which the x_j's have been expressed in terms of t, q from the relations

$$x_j = x_j(t, q)$$

Thus
$$V(t, q) = U[t, x(t, q)] \tag{10.85}$$

From this relation we obtain

$$\frac{\partial V}{\partial q_h} = \sum_j \frac{\partial U}{\partial x_j} \frac{\partial x_j}{\partial q_h}$$

which in view of Eq. (10.84) can be rewritten as

$$\frac{\partial V}{\partial q_h} = -\sum X_j \frac{\partial x_j}{\partial q_h} \tag{10.86}$$

The right-hand side of the latter expression denotes the generalized force Q_h, therefore

$$Q_h = -\frac{\partial V}{\partial q_h} \tag{10.87}$$

We have shown that *if the Newtonian forces have a potential independent of the velocities then also the corresponding generalized forces have a potential which is independent of the generalized velocities.*

Consider the set of Lagrange's equations (10.76) of a certain holonomic system. Let us assume that the generalized forces $Q_h + \Re_h$ have a potential which is independent of the generalized velocities. Thus we can write

$$Q_h + \Re_h = -\frac{\partial V(t, q)}{\partial q_h} \tag{10.88}$$

As in previous cases we introduce the Lagrange function

$$L = T - V$$

in terms of which Eqs. (10.76) take the form

$$\frac{d}{dt} \frac{\partial L}{\partial \dot{q}_h} - \frac{\partial L}{\partial q_h} = 0 \qquad h = 1, 2, \ldots, n$$

10-7 *The Law of Energy*

Quite often it is convenient to replace one of Lagrange's equations of the

146

form (10.76) by an equation which is referred to as the *equation of energy or the law of energy*. We will now obtain this equation.

Let

$$T_h(q) \equiv \frac{d}{dt} \frac{\partial T}{\partial \dot{q}_h} - \frac{\partial T}{\partial q_h} \tag{10.89}$$

and let us evaluate the sum $\sum \dot{q}_h T_h(q)$. We obtain

$$\begin{aligned}
\sum_h \dot{q}_h T_h(q) &= \sum \dot{q}_h \frac{d}{dt} \frac{\partial T}{\partial \dot{q}_h} - \sum \dot{q}_h \frac{\partial T}{\partial q_h} \\
&= \frac{d}{dt} \sum \frac{\partial T}{\partial \dot{q}_h} \dot{q}_h - \sum \left(\frac{\partial T}{\partial \dot{q}_h} \ddot{q}_h + \frac{\partial T}{\partial q_h} \dot{q}_h \right)
\end{aligned} \tag{10.90}$$

As we have seen in Section 10–5, the kinetic energy can be written as

$$T = T_2 + T_1 + T_0$$

where T_2 is a quadratic function of the generalized velocities $\dot{q}$, T_1 is a linear function of the generalized velocities and T_0 does not depend on $\dot{q}$. Using Euler's theorem on homogeneous functions we write

$$\sum_h \frac{\partial T}{\partial \dot{q}_h} \dot{q}_h = \sum_h \frac{\partial T_2}{\partial \dot{q}_h} \dot{q}_h + \sum_h \frac{\partial T_1}{\partial \dot{q}_h} \dot{q}_h = 2T_2 + T_1 \tag{10.91}$$

We also have

$$\begin{aligned}
\sum_h \left(\frac{\partial T}{\partial \dot{q}_h} \ddot{q}_h + \frac{\partial T}{\partial q_h} \dot{q}_h \right) &= \frac{dT}{dt} - \frac{\partial T}{\partial t} \\
&= \frac{dT_2}{dt} + \frac{dT_1}{dt} + \frac{dT_0}{dt} - \frac{\partial T}{\partial t}
\end{aligned} \tag{10.92}$$

Substituting expression (10.91) and (10.92) in (10.90) we obtain

$$\sum \dot{q}_h T_h(q) = \frac{dT_2}{dt} - \frac{dT_0}{dt} + \frac{\partial T}{\partial t} \tag{10.93}$$

From Lagrange's equations (10.76) and from (10.89) we see that

$$T_h(q) = Q_h + \mathcal{R}_h$$

Eq. (10.93) can therefore be written as

$$\frac{dT_2}{dt} - \frac{dT_0}{dt} + \frac{\partial T}{\partial t} = \sum (Q_h + \mathcal{R}_h)\dot{q}_h \tag{10.94}$$

This equation expresses *the law of energy for holonomic systems*. An equivalent representation of the same law is

$$dT_2 - dT_0 + \frac{\partial T}{\partial t} dt = \sum_h (Q_h + \mathcal{R}_h) dq_h \tag{10.95}$$

10–7 The law of energy

147

It is of particular interest to consider a holonomic system which is sclero-nomic. As we know, in this case the kinetic energy will be a quadratic function of the generalized velocities $\dot{q}$, and time will not enter explicitly. Thus

$$T = T_2 \qquad T_0 = 0 \qquad \frac{\partial T}{\partial t} = 0$$

and Eq. (10.95) takes the form

$$dT = \sum_h (Q_h + \mathfrak{R}_h)\, dq_h \tag{10.96}$$

Considering the results of Section 10–4 we can also write

$$\sum_h (Q_h + \mathfrak{R}_h)\, dq_h = \sum_j (X_j + B_j)\, dx_j \tag{10.97}$$

from which it follows that $\sum(Q_h + \mathfrak{R}_h)\, dq_h$ is the work done by the given forces and the forces of reaction when the system is subjected to infinitesimal displacements.

A holonomic system is conservative if it is scleronomic and in addition, if the generalized forces corresponding to the forces acting on the system depend on the position of the system only; in this case the generalized forces are functions of generalized coordinates only. We add another limitation to the generalized forces, namely, that they have a potential which depends on the generalized coordinates only; thus

$$Q_h = -\frac{\partial V(q_1, \ldots, q_n)}{\partial q_h} \tag{10.98}$$

The law of energy given by Eq. (10.96) now takes the form

$$dT = -dV \tag{10.99}$$

from which we obtain $\qquad\qquad T + V = d \tag{10.100}$

where d is a constant of integration which can be obtained from the initial conditions.

Equation (10.100), which is a differential equation of the first order, expresses the law of conservation of mechanical energy of the system. As stated above, the energy equation can always replace one of Lagrange's equations.

10–8   Nonholonomic Systems

We will now discuss certain aspects of nonholonomic systems. Consider such a system consisting of N particles. To begin with, we refer it to Cartesian coordinates x_j. Let there be u holonomic constraints specified by equations

$$f_1(t, x) = 0, \ldots, f_u(t, x) = 0 \tag{10.101}$$

v nonholonomic constraints of the type specified by equations

148

$$f_{u+1}(t, x, \dot{x}) = 0, \ldots, f_{u+v}(t, x, \dot{x}) = 0 \qquad (10.102)$$

and w nonholonomic constraints of the type specified by equations

$$f_{u+v+1}(t, x, \dot{x}, \ddot{x}) = 0, \ldots, f_{u+v+w}(t, x, \dot{x}, \ddot{x}) = 0 \qquad (10.103)$$

Eqs. (10.103) should be linear with respect to $\ddot{x}$. As we know, the total number of constraining conditions $r = u + v + w$ can not be greater than $3N - 1$.

If the appropriate conditions are present, equations (10.101), (10.102) and (10.103) can be used to obtain relations which will limit the accelerations of the system. These relations will be of the form

$$\psi_1(t, x, \dot{x}, \ddot{x}) = 0, \ldots, \psi_r(t, x, \dot{x}, \ddot{x}) = 0 \qquad (10.104)$$

Invoking the postulate of reactions we can again consider our system as a nonconstrained system if to all the given forces we will add the reactions of all the constraints.*

Let us suppose that we are able to determine the reactions of p holonomic constraints specified by the equations

$$f_1 = 0, \ldots, f_p = 0 \qquad (10.105)$$

where $0 \leq p \leq u$. Using these equations, we can express the Cartesian coordinates x_j in terms of $s = 3N - p$ generalized coordinates $q_1, \ldots, q_s$, i.e., we can obtain the functional relationships

$$x_j = x_j(t, q_1, \ldots, q_s) \qquad (10.106)$$

The generalized forces Q_h and $\Re_h$ corresponding to the given forces and to the forces of reactions of constraints given by Eqs. (10.105) can be expressed in terms of the generalized coordinates q.

We substitute in the remaining $z = u - p$ equations (10.101) and in the sets (10.102), (10.103) the values of x_j from (10.106), and the values of $\dot{x}_j$ and $\ddot{x}_j$ evaluated from (10.106). We then obtain $z = u - p$ finite equations

$$\varphi_1(t, q) = 0, \ldots, \varphi_z(t, q) = 0 \qquad (10.107)$$

v first order differential equations

$$\varphi_{z+1}(t, q, \dot{q}) = 0, \ldots, \varphi_{z+v}(t, q, \dot{q}) = 0 \qquad (10.108)$$

and w second order differential equations

$$\varphi_{z+v+1}(t, q, \dot{q}, \ddot{q}) = 0, \ldots, \varphi_{z+v+w}(t, q, \dot{q}, \ddot{q}) = 0 \qquad (10.109)$$

The number $\ell = z + v + w$ of equations (10.107), (10.108) and (10.109)

* We are assuming that we know the way in which the constraints are physically realized.

satisfies the inequality $\qquad \ell < 3N - p$

Furthermore, we take the corresponding $\ell = r - p$ equations (10.104), express in them the values of x_j, $\dot{x}_j$ and $\ddot{x}_j$ in terms of t, q, $\dot{q}$, $\ddot{q}$, and obtain the equations

$$\theta_1(t, q, \dot{q}, \ddot{q}) = 0, \ldots, \theta_\ell(t, q, \dot{q}, \ddot{q}) = 0 \qquad (10.110)$$

These, in general, will form a system of independent equations which will be linear in $\ddot{q}$.

Once again invoking the postulate of reactions, we can consider our system of particles as an unconstrained system of s degrees of freedom, if to the given generalized forces Q_h we add reactions $\Re_h$ of the constraints given by Eqs. (10.105) and also reactions $\mathcal{P}_h$ of the constraints specified by Eqs. (10.107), (10.108), and (10.109). The equations of motion of our system expressed as d'Alembert's principle then take the form

$$\sum_h \left[\frac{d}{dt} \frac{\partial T}{\partial \dot{q}_h} - \frac{\partial T}{\partial q_h} - Q_h - \Re_h - \mathcal{P}_h \right] \delta q_h = 0 \qquad (10.111)$$

where T is the kinetic energy of the system given by

$$T = \tfrac{1}{2} \sum m_j \dot{x}_j^2$$

or
$$T = \tfrac{1}{2} \left[\sum_{h,k} A_{hk} \dot{q}_h \dot{q}_k + \sum_h \alpha_h \dot{q}_h + \beta \right] \qquad (10.112)$$

Eq. (10.111) is equivalent to s equations

$$T_h(q) = Q_h + \Re_h + \mathcal{P}_h \qquad (10.113)$$

where $T_h(q)$ is defined by the relation (10.89).

We will now obtain another form of the equations of motion of our system. In what follows we will assume that the reactions of all the holonomic constraints (and not only p, as assumed above) have been determined. We can therefore suppose that our system moves under nonholonomic constraints only; there will be v constraints of the type specified by equations

$$\varphi_1(t, q, \dot{q}) = 0, \ldots, \varphi_v(t, q, \dot{q}) = 0 \qquad (10.114)$$

and w constraints specified by equations

$$\varphi_{v+1}(t, q, \dot{q}, \ddot{q}) = 0, \ldots, \varphi_{v+w}(t, q, \dot{q}, \ddot{q}) = 0 \qquad (10.115)$$

The reactions of the constraints described by Eqs. (10.114) and (10.115) will be denoted by $\mathcal{P}_h$. Suppose that we know the work performed by these reactions along certain displacements, i.e., we know

$$\sum_h \mathcal{P}_h \, \delta q_h = \sum_h D_h \, \delta q_h \qquad (10.116)$$

subject to the ℓ independent conditions

$$\sum_h A_{\mu h}\,\delta q_h = 0 \qquad 1, 2, \ldots, \ell \qquad\qquad (10.117)$$

where D_h and $A_{\mu h}$ are given functions of t, q, $\dot{q}$.

The principle of d'Alembert can now be written as

$$\sum_h [T_h(q) - Q_h - \mathcal{R}_h - \mathcal{P}_h]\,\delta q_h = 0 \qquad\qquad (10.118)$$

where the δq_h's satisfy the conditions specified by Eq. (10.117). We will supplement the conditions (10.117) by $m = s - \ell$ equations

$$\sum_h A_{(\ell+g)h}\,\delta q_h = \delta\sigma_g \qquad g = 1, \ldots, m \qquad\qquad (10.119)$$

where $A_{(\ell+g)h}$ are functions of t, q, $\dot{q}$ for which the determinant $\Delta = |A_{hk}|$ $(h, k = 1, \ldots, s)$ is different from zero. We can choose such system of equations in an infinite number of ways. The variables $\delta\sigma_g$ in Eqs. (10.119) are arbitrary. Since $\Delta \neq 0$, we can solve the sets of equations (10.117) and (10.119) for δq_h, and obtain

$$\delta q_h = \sum_{g=1}^{m} a_{hg}\,\delta\sigma_g \qquad\qquad (10.120)$$

where a_{hg} is a minor of Δ corresponding to the element $A_{(\ell+g)h}$ divided by Δ; thus a_{hg} are specified functions of t, q, $\dot{q}$.

Substituting the values of δq_h from Eqs. (10.120) into the expression for d'Alembert's principle (10.118) we obtain another form of d'Alembert's principle, namely

$$\sum_g \delta\sigma_g \sum_h a_{hg}[T_h(q) - Q_h - \mathcal{R}_h - \mathcal{P}_h] = 0 \qquad\qquad (10.121)$$

Since the $\delta\sigma_g$'s are independent, Eq. (10.121) is equivalent to m second order equations

$$\sum_h a_{hg}[T_h(q) - Q_h - \mathcal{R}_h - \mathcal{P}_h] = 0 \qquad g = 1, 2, \ldots, m \qquad\qquad (10.122)$$

In this way the problem of the motion of nonholonomic system of N particles has been reduced to integration of s equations (10.114), (10.115), and (10.122).

Eqs. (10.122) are the most general equations of motion for nonholonomic systems.

PROBLEMS

10.1 A rough sphere lies inside a cylinder which rests upon a rough plane. If the cylinder is given a slight displacement, find the period of oscillations of the sphere.

10.2 Two particles of equal mass are connected by a weightless rod of length 2ℓ whose center moves along a circle of radius a as shown in Figure 10.1. Consider θ and ϕ as the generalized coordinates and write the expressions for (a) the potential energy of the system, and (b) the kinetic energy of the system.

Fig. 10.1

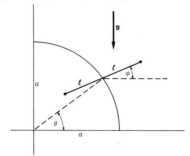

10.3 Two points A and B of masses $(M + m)$ and M respectively are suspended from the two ends of an inextensible cord passing over a smooth pulley (Fig. 10.2). A bug C of mass m climbs the string on the side where M is suspended. Determine the motion of the system of the three particles A, B, and C.

Fig. 10.2

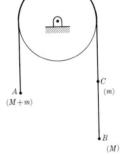

10.4 A pulley system is set up as shown in Figure 10.3, where the three masses have values 1, 2, 3. Find the resulting motion using Lagrange's equations.

Fig. 10.3

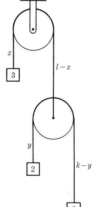

152

11 HAMILTON'S THEORY

We have been studying the Lagrangian formulation of classical dynamics. Apart from this approach there is another formulation due to Hamilton. *In Lagrange's procedure the generalized coordinates and generalized velocities were put on equal footing as a set of independent variables. In Hamilton's formulation the generalized coordinates and generalized momenta* (to be defined later) *serve as a set of independent variables.*

We will define the Hamiltonian or Hamilton's function H, and formulate a set of differential equations which will be called Hamilton's equations. Hamilton's equations are particularly useful in statistical mechanics and in some other branches of physics.

This chapter will conclude with a discussion of the case when the Hamiltonian does not include certain generalized coordinates.

11–1 *Generalized Momenta and the Hamiltonian*

Let

$$L = L(q, \dot{q}, t) \tag{11.1}$$

be the Lagrangian of some particular system; q and $\dot{q}$ stand for the whole set of the generalized coordinates $q_1, q_2, \ldots, q_n$ and the generalized velocities $\dot{q}_1, \dot{q}_2, \ldots, \dot{q}_n$ respectively. The *generalized momentum* p_k associated with the kth generalized coordinate q_k is defined as

$$p_k = \frac{\partial L}{\partial \dot{q}_k} \tag{11.2}$$

Every generalized momentum will be a function of the whole set of generalized coordinates and generalized velocities, i.e.

$$p_k = p_k(t, q, \dot{q}) \qquad k = 1, 2, \ldots, n \tag{11.3}$$

Under proper conditions this set of equations can be solved for the set of generalized velocities yielding

$$\dot{q}_i = \dot{q}_i(t, q, p) \qquad i = 1, 2, \ldots, n \tag{11.4}$$

The two sets of equations (11.3) and (11.4) establish *a one-to-one correspondence between the generalized momentum p_i and the generalized coordinate q_i* (i.e., between p_1 and q_1, p_2 and q_2, and so on).* It is said that p_i *and q_i are canonically conjugated quantities.***

We will now define the *Hamiltonian function H* as

$$H = \sum_{i=1}^{n} \dot{q}_i \frac{\partial L}{\partial \dot{q}_i} - L \tag{11.5}$$

We notice that H can be expressed as a function of the set q and the set p, i.e.

$$H = H(q, p, t) \tag{11.6}$$

In the case of a simple dynamical system

$$L = T(q, \dot{q}) - V(q) \tag{11.7}$$

and T is a homogeneous and quadratic function of the generalized velocities. By Euler's theorem for homogeneous functions

$$2T = \sum_{i=1}^{n} \dot{q}_i \frac{\partial T}{\partial \dot{q}_i} \tag{11.8}$$

Substituting this and $L = T - V$ in (11.5) we get

$$H = 2T - (T - V)$$

or

$$H = T + V \tag{11.9}$$

i.e.

$$H = E$$

where E is the total mechanical energy of the system. We see, therefore, that—whereas it may be difficult to assign a physical significance to the Lagrangian—we can assign quite a definite physical meaning to the Hamiltonian, viz., *for a simple dynamical system the Hamiltonian gives the total energy of the system.*

The Hamiltonian may also be introduced in the following way.*** Let us start with Lagrange's equations for a simple dynamical system, viz.

$$\frac{d}{dt} \frac{\partial T}{\partial \dot{q}_i} - \frac{\partial T}{\partial q_i} + \frac{\partial V}{\partial q_i} = 0 \qquad i = 1, 2, \ldots, n$$

---

* It might appear that the one-to-one correspondence between p_i and q_i follows from the definition of the generalized momentum. However, unless $\dot{q}_i$ can be expressed in terms of the set p and q alone, i.e., on the right-hand side of (11.4) there will be no other $\dot{q}$'s, then this one-to-one correspondence will not be established.
** Translating this into more common English one might say that p_i and q_i are fundamentally related.
*** L. Z. Pollara, *Am. J. Phys.* **26**, 195 (1958).

Multiplying by dq_i and adding all the equations gives

$$\sum_{i=1}^{n} \frac{d}{dt}\frac{\partial T}{\partial \dot{q}_i} dq_i - \sum_{i=1}^{n} \frac{\partial T}{\partial q_i} dq_i + \sum_{i=1}^{n} \frac{\partial L}{\partial q_i} dq_i = 0 \qquad (11.10)$$

Now $V = V(q)$, therefore

$$\sum_{i=1}^{n} \frac{\partial V}{\partial q_i} dq_i = dV \qquad (11.11)$$

Further

$$\sum_{i=1}^{n} \frac{d}{dt}\frac{\partial T}{\partial \dot{q}_i} dq_i = \sum_{i=1}^{n} \frac{d}{dt}\frac{\partial T}{\partial \dot{q}_i}\frac{dq_i}{dt} dt$$

$$= \sum_{i=1}^{n} \dot{q}_i \frac{d}{dt}\frac{\partial T}{\partial \dot{q}_i} dt$$

or

$$\sum_{i=1}^{n} \frac{d}{dt}\left(\frac{\partial T}{\partial \dot{q}_i}\right) dq_i = \sum_{i=1}^{n} \dot{q}_i d\left(\frac{\partial T}{\partial \dot{q}_i}\right) \qquad (11.12)$$

Substitution of (11.11) and (11.12) in (11.10) yields

$$\sum_{i} \dot{q}_i d\left(\frac{\partial T}{\partial \dot{q}_i}\right) - \sum_{i} \frac{\partial T}{\partial q_i} dq_i + dV = 0 \qquad (11.13)$$

We now integrate this equation and obtain

$$\sum_{i} \dot{q}_i \frac{\partial T}{\partial \dot{q}_i} - \int \sum_{i}\left[\frac{\partial T}{\partial \dot{q}_i} d\dot{q}_i + \frac{\partial T}{\partial q_i} dq_i\right] + V = \text{const.}$$

$$\sum_{i} \dot{q}_i \frac{\partial T}{\partial \dot{q}_i} - \int dT + V = \text{const.}$$

$$\sum_{i} \dot{q}_i \frac{\partial T}{\partial \dot{q}_i} - (T - V) = \text{const.}$$

or

$$\sum_{i} \dot{q}_i \frac{\partial T}{\partial \dot{q}_i} - L = H \qquad (11.14)$$

where the constant has been denoted by H.

11-2 Hamilton's Canonical Equations

In view of the definition of the generalized momentum, the Hamiltonian can be written as

$$H = \sum_{i=1}^{n} \dot{q}_i p_i - L \qquad (11.15)$$

Again let

$$L = L(\dot{q}, q, t)$$

We will now evaluate the variation δH of the Hamiltonian when q, $\dot{q}$, p, and t are all subjected to independent variations. Thus

$$\delta H = \sum_{i=1}^{n} p_i \, \delta \dot{q}_i + \sum_{i=1}^{n} \dot{q}_i \, \delta p_i - \sum_{i=1}^{n} \frac{\partial L}{\partial \dot{q}_i} \, \delta \dot{q}_i - \sum_{i=1}^{n} \frac{\partial L}{\partial q_i} \, \delta q_i - \frac{\partial L}{\partial t} \, \delta t$$

In this expression the first and the third term cancel, therefore

$$\delta H = \sum_{i=1}^{n} \dot{q}_i \, \delta p_i - \sum_{i=1}^{n} \frac{\partial L}{\partial q_i} \, \delta q_i - \frac{\partial L}{\partial t} \, \delta t \tag{11.16}$$

As stated above, the variations δp_i, δq_i and δt are independent, therefore

$$\frac{\partial H}{\partial q_i} = -\frac{\partial L}{\partial q_i} \tag{11.17a}$$

$$\frac{\partial H}{\partial p_i} = \dot{q}_i \tag{11.17b}$$

$$\frac{\partial H}{\partial t} = -\frac{\partial L}{\partial t} \tag{11.17c}$$

Now

$$\frac{d}{dt} \frac{\partial L}{\partial \dot{q}_i} - \frac{\partial L}{\partial q_i} = 0$$

from which

$$\frac{d}{dt} p_i = \frac{\partial L}{\partial q_i}$$

Thus (11.17a, b) can be written as

$$\frac{\partial H}{\partial p_i} = \dot{q}_i \qquad \frac{\partial H}{\partial q_i} = -\dot{p}_i \qquad i = 1, 2, \ldots, n \tag{11.18}$$

These are called *Hamilton's canonical equations.*

Example: The simple harmonic oscillator.

Let a particle m execute simple harmonic motion along the q axis. O is the position of equilibrium and k is the force constant. The kinetic and potential energy are given by

$$T = \tfrac{1}{2} m \dot{q}^2$$

and

$$V = \tfrac{1}{2} k q^2$$

The total energy of the particle is

$$E = \tfrac{1}{2} m \dot{q}^2 + \tfrac{1}{2} k q^2$$

We identify the total energy with the Hamiltonian. Thus

$$H = \tfrac{1}{2} m \dot{q}^2 + \tfrac{1}{2} k q^2$$

The generalized momentum of our particle is

$$p = \frac{\partial T}{\partial \dot{q}}$$

or

$$p = m\dot{q}$$

Substituting $\dot{q} = p/m$ in the Hamiltonian we get

$$H = \frac{1}{2m} p^2 + \frac{1}{2} kq^2$$

and this now is of the form $H = H(p, q)$.

The two Hamilton equations are

$$\frac{\partial H}{\partial p} = \dot{q} \qquad \frac{\partial H}{\partial q} = -\dot{p}$$

which in our case become

$$\frac{1}{m} p = \dot{q}$$

and

$$kq = -\dot{p}$$

Substitution of the first in the second yields

$$kq = -m\ddot{q}$$

or

$$\ddot{q} + (k/m)q = 0$$

This is the well known differential equation of the simple harmonic oscillator.

The Hamiltonian H is a function of the set p and q, and often of the time. Thus

$$H = H(p, q, t)$$

Evaluating the total time derivative we get

$$\frac{dH}{dt} = \sum_{i=1}^{n} \frac{\partial H}{\partial p_i} \dot{p}_i + \sum_{i=1}^{n} \frac{\partial H}{\partial q_i} \dot{q}_i + \frac{\partial H}{\partial t}$$

In view of Hamilton's equations (11.18) the two sums in the above equation cancel. Thus

$$\frac{dH}{dt} = \frac{\partial H}{\partial t} \tag{11.19}$$

11-3 The Routhian Procedure

When a generalized coordinate q_i, say, is absent from the Hamiltonian then

$$\frac{\partial H}{\partial q_i} = 0$$

It follows from the corresponding Hamilton equation that

$$\dot{p}_i = 0$$

or

$$p_i = \text{const.}$$

A coordinate which is absent from the Hamiltonian is called an ignorable or cyclic coordinate. We have just shown that *the generalized momentum conjugate to a cyclic coordinate is conserved.*

Let a certain system be described by n generalized coordinates. Of these let k generalized coordinates be ignorable. Arrange the coordinates in such a way that the first k will be ignorable. Thus the Lagrangian contains the following generalized coordinates and generalized velocities:

$$q_{k+1}, q_{k+2}, \ldots, q_n, \dot{q}_1, \dot{q}_2, \ldots, \dot{q}_k, \dot{q}_{k+1}, \ldots, \dot{q}_n$$

The generalized momenta conjugate to the cyclic coordinates will satisfy the following equations

$$
\begin{aligned}
p_1 &= c_1 \\
p_2 &= c_2 \\
&\vdots \\
p_k &= c_k
\end{aligned}
\tag{11.20}
$$

This set of equations contains the generalized velocities $\dot{q}_1, \dot{q}_2, \ldots, \dot{q}_k$. We can solve Eqs. (11.20) for these velocities and express all of them as functions of the set including only the following quantities

$$(\alpha) \equiv q_{k+1}, q_{k+2}, \ldots, q_n, c_1, c_2, \ldots, c_k, \dot{q}_{k+1}, \dot{q}_{k+2}, \ldots, \dot{q}_n \tag{11.21}$$

We now define the following function

$$R = L - \sum_{i=1}^{k} c_i \dot{q}_i \tag{11.22}$$

it is called the *Routhian function.* We express this function in terms of the quantities belonging to the set (α) only. Thus, the Lagrangian appearing in R will be of the form

$$L = L[q_{k+1}, q_{k+2}, \ldots, q_n; \dot{q}_1(\alpha), \dot{q}_2(\alpha), \ldots, \dot{q}_k(\alpha), \dot{q}_{k+1}, \dot{q}_{k+2}, \ldots, \dot{q}_n, t]$$

and similarly all the $\dot{q}_i$'s appearing in R for $i = 1, 2, \ldots, k$ will be expressed in terms of the quantities belonging to the set (α). Having done this we will evaluate the partial derivatives $\partial R / \partial q_j$ and $\partial R / \partial \dot{q}_j$ for $j > k$. Thus

$$
\begin{aligned}
\frac{\partial R}{\partial q_j} &= \frac{\partial L}{\partial q_j} + \frac{\partial L}{\partial \dot{q}_1} \frac{\partial \dot{q}_1}{\partial q_j} + \cdots + \frac{\partial L}{\partial \dot{q}_k} \frac{\partial \dot{q}_k}{\partial q_j} - c_1 \frac{\partial \dot{q}_1}{\partial q_j} - \cdots - c_k \frac{\partial \dot{q}_k}{\partial q_j} \\
&= \frac{\partial L}{\partial q_j} + \left(\frac{\partial L}{\partial \dot{q}_1} - c_1 \right) \frac{\partial \dot{q}_1}{\partial q_j} + \cdots + \left(\frac{\partial L}{\partial \dot{q}_k} - c_k \right) \frac{\partial \dot{q}_k}{\partial q_j}
\end{aligned}
$$

or

$$\frac{\partial R}{\partial q_j} = \frac{\partial L}{\partial q_j}$$

Also

$$\frac{\partial R}{\partial \dot{q}_j} = \frac{\partial L}{\partial \dot{q}_j} + \frac{\partial L}{\partial \dot{q}_1}\frac{\partial \dot{q}_1}{\partial \dot{q}_j} + \cdots + \frac{\partial L}{\partial \dot{q}_k}\frac{\partial \dot{q}_k}{\partial \dot{q}_j} - c_1\frac{\partial \dot{q}_1}{\partial \dot{q}_j} - \cdots - c_k\frac{\partial \dot{q}_k}{\partial \dot{q}_j}$$

$$= \frac{\partial L}{\partial \dot{q}_j} + \left(\frac{\partial L}{\partial \dot{q}_1} - c_1\right)\frac{\partial \dot{q}_1}{\partial \dot{q}_j} + \cdots + \left(\frac{\partial L}{\partial \dot{q}_k} - c_k\right)\frac{\partial \dot{q}_k}{\partial \dot{q}_j}$$

$$= \frac{\partial L}{\partial \dot{q}_j} \quad *$$

Thus

$$\frac{d}{dt}\frac{\partial R}{\partial \dot{q}_j} - \frac{\partial R}{\partial q_j} = 0 \qquad j = k+1, k+2, \ldots, n \qquad (11.23)$$

We notice therefore that *in the case of k cyclic coordinates the number of Lagrange's equations (which are the Routhian equations (11.23)) is reduced to $(n - k)$.*

Example: A particle of mass m is projected in the gravitational field of earth with an initial velocity v_o making an angle θ with the horizontal.

Let the Cartesian coordinates q_1 and q_2 be the two generalized coordinates of our particle. q_1 indicates the horizontal axis and q_2 the vertical one; thus q_2 is parallel to **g**, the acceleration due to gravity. The kinetic and potential energies of the particle are given by

$$T = \tfrac{1}{2}m(\dot{q}_1{}^2 + \dot{q}_2{}^2)$$

and

$$V = mgq_2$$

Thus the Lagrangian is

$$L = \tfrac{1}{2}m(\dot{q}_1{}^2 + \dot{q}_2{}^2) - mgq_2$$

and we see that q_1 is an ignorable coordinate. The generalized momentum conjugate to q_1 is then constant, i.e.

$$p_1 = c_1$$

The set (α) referred to above, Eq. (11.21), in our case is

$$(\alpha) \equiv q_2, c_1, \dot{q}_2$$

* The procedure of evaluating these partial derivatives follows the rules of partial differentiation of composite functions. Thus in the first case (i.e., in the evaluation of $\partial R/\partial q_j$) we first evaluate the explicit derivative of L with respect to the variable in question (q_j). Next we notice that $\dot{q}_1, \ldots, \dot{q}_k$ appearing in the Lagrangian are functions of the set (α) given by (11.21) and this set includes q_j; hence the next k terms in $\partial R/\partial q_j$. Finally we must differentiate the remaining k terms of R, again keeping in mind that $\dot{q}_s = \dot{q}_s(\alpha)$.

and the Routhian function, defined by Eq. (11.22), is

$$R = \tfrac{1}{2}m(\dot{q}_1{}^2 + \dot{q}_2{}^2) - mgq_2 - c_1\dot{q}_1$$

Now

$$p_1 = m\dot{q}_1$$

therefore

$$c_1 = m\dot{q}_1$$

or

$$\dot{q}_1 = c_1/m$$

Thus R expressed in terms of the set (α) becomes

$$R = \tfrac{1}{2}m\dot{q}_2{}^2 - mgq_2 + c_1{}^2/2m$$

The Routhian equation

$$\frac{d}{dt}\frac{\partial R}{\partial \dot{q}_2} - \frac{\partial R}{\partial q_2} = 0$$

becomes

$$m\ddot{q}_2 + mg = 0$$

or

$$\ddot{q}_2 + g = 0$$

This equation, together with $p_1 = c_1$ and the initial conditions solves the problem completely.

PROBLEMS

11.1   Obtain Hamilton's equations of motion in terms of spherical polar coordinates for the three-dimensional motion of a particle subject to no forces.

11.2   Using Hamilton's equations find the motion of a simple pulley with masses m_1 and m_2 at the ends of the string.

11.3   A flat plate moves in any manner in the vertical plane of the gravitational field of the earth. Obtain Hamilton's equations and their solutions for the resulting motion. (For the generalized coordinates choose the Cartesian coordinates of the center of mass of the plate and the angle θ that an arbitrary line in the plate makes with the vertical.)

11.4   In a problem defined by the Hamiltonian

$$H = q_1 p_1 - q_2 p_2 - aq_1{}^2 + bq_2{}^2$$

where a and b are constants, find q_1, q_2, p_1, p_2 as functions of time, and then show that

$$(p_1 - aq_1)(p_2 - bq_2) = \text{const.}$$

11.5 In a dynamical system with two degrees of freedom the kinetic energy is given by

$$T = \frac{\dot{q}_1{}^2}{2(a + bq_2)} + \tfrac{1}{2}q_2{}^2\dot{q}_2{}^2$$

and the potential energy is given by

$$V = c + dq_2$$

where a, b, c, d are constants. Show that the value of q_2 in terms of the time is given by an equation of the form

$$(q_2 - k)(q_2 - 2k)^2 = h(t - t_o)^2$$

11.6 Solve the problem of the motion of a projectile moving in a non-resistive medium in the gravitational field of earth using
  (a) Lagrange's method,
  (b) Hamilton's method, and
  (c) the Routhian procedure.

11.7 A particle of mass m moves in a plane under an acceleration μ/r^2 towards the origin. By ignoring the coordinate θ find the value of $\dot{r}$ in terms of r.

11.8 Two point masses m_1 and m_2 are fixed to the ends of a rigid weightless rod of length ℓ which is free to move in any manner. The system is put into a gravitational field which has a potential at each point P given by $V(P)$. Set up the Lagrangian and the Hamiltonian functions for this system in terms of m_1, m_2, ℓ, V, and some suitable coordinates. Write Hamilton's canonical equations for this system.

11.9 For an electron describing a plane orbit about a nucleus the Lagrangian is

$$L = -mc^2\sqrt{1 - \frac{v^2}{c^2}} + \frac{Ee}{r}$$

where v is the velocity of the electron, r its distance from the nucleus and m, c, E, e are constants. Find the Hamiltonian using plane polar coordinates r, θ and their associated momenta p_r, p_θ. Show that the equation of energy can be written in the form

$$p_r{}^2 + \frac{p_\theta{}^2}{r^2} = 2m\left[\omega + \frac{Ee}{r}\right] + \frac{[\omega + (Ee/r)]^2}{e^2}$$

where

$$H = mc^2 + \omega$$

and

$$\omega = \text{const.}$$

12 VARIATIONAL AND INTEGRAL PRINCIPLES. INTEGRATION OF EQUATIONS OF MOTION OF A SYSTEM OF PARTICLES

The applications of classical dynamics are manifold. Its results and methods are used in every branch of physics. Depending on the application of the dynamical results, the methods vary. When dealing with a given system, the starting procedure, in general, is to formulate appropriate differential equations of motion. Having obtained those we seek their solutions and investigate the properties of these solutions.

Quite often various properties of the motion of the system can be determined by examining the properties of the differential equations. *In some particular instance we may be satisfied with the investigations of some local properties of the motion which will apply to some limited interval of time. In such cases we will be satisfied with theorems stating the existence of solutions.*

In other systems we may want to investigate the properties of motion in an unlimited time. In this case one of the problems may be the investigation of the trajectories of the particles. Problems of this topological character interest contemporary physicists* and astronomers.

Another investigation concerns *the dependence of the sequence of motion of a system on changes of the initial state of the system, or on changes of some parameters entering into the equation of motion.* (These parameters are other than time and other than the coordinates of the system.) Here belong problems of stability or instability of motion in relation to the changes of the initial state of the system. Also, the so called *quasi-adiabatic processes* belong here; these processes occur when the external parameters are being changed extremely slowly.

Another important class of problems is that pertaining to *the perturbation of motion.* This is a vast set of problems important in classical and modern physics.

Many of the problems mentioned above are of importance in wave mechanics which is the last word in the present description of the atomic world.

There are many more special cases of applications of dynamics to some particular systems or particular situations. We will be able to touch upon only a few of them. Apart from basic principles of mechanics mastered so far, and to be discussed later, some more advanced aspects of mechanics are needed. Variational and integral principles and some basic approach to the problem of integration of dynamical equations are required.

---

* To this class of problems belong the ergodic and quasi-ergodic hypotheses which are of primary importance in statistical mechanics.

These will be discussed now, but only in the barest outline.*

12–1   Hamilton's Principle

Let us formulate the integral

$$\int_A^B L \, dt \qquad (12.1)$$

along the path AB which a given system describes. The integrand

$$L = L(q, \dot{q}) \qquad (12.2)$$

is the Lagrangian of the system. If the system has two degrees of freedom, and therefore is described by two generalized coordinates, then its path may look like the one shown in Figure 12.1. The space of the generalized coordinates, called the *configuration space*, is in this case two-dimensional. We

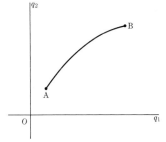

Fig. 12.1.
Path of a particle in
the configuration space.

may also form the *space of generalized velocities*. In it the system may describe a path which may look like that shown in Figure 12.2. We realize that as the system moves from state A to state B it simultaneously moves in both spaces.

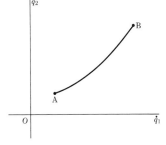

Fig. 12.2.
Path of a particle in
the velocity space.

Thus we may, if we wish, construct a *"product" four-dimensional space* in which every point has four coordinates $q_1, q_2, \dot{q}_1, \dot{q}_2$; we then speak of a trajectory of a point representing a system in this space.

---

* We admit with chagrin that thoroughness and rigor are absent in this chapter. Nevertheless, we feel that in this stage of our studies of mechanics at least some introduction to special and elegant dynamical methods should be given.

The parametric equations of trajectories are

$$q_1 = q_1(t) \qquad q_2 = q_2(t)$$
$$\dot{q}_1 = \dot{q}_1(t) \qquad \dot{q}_2 = \dot{q}_2(t) \tag{12.3}$$

Substitution in (12.2) yields

$$L = L(t) \tag{12.4}$$

and the integral (12.1) becomes

$$I = \int_{t_1}^{t_2} L(t)\, dt \tag{12.5}$$

Here t_1 and t_2 are the instances of time when the system is in state A and B respectively.

We now investigate a varied motion which will be a motion along a slightly different path. This new, slightly different trajectory, will be specified by equations

$$q_1' = q_1(t) + \epsilon_1(t)$$
$$q_2' = q_2(t) + \epsilon_2(t) \tag{12.6}$$

where ϵ_1 and ϵ_2 are small. From these we get $\dot{q}_1'$ and $\dot{q}_2'$ and substitute these together with q_1' and q_2' in Eq. (12.5). The integral then becomes

$$I' = \int L'(t)\, dt \tag{12.7}$$

We impose two restrictions concerning the motion of the system:
   (i) The varied path is AB, i.e., it starts at the point A and ends at B;
   (ii) The time of transit is the same.
   Let

$$\delta I = I' - I \tag{12.8}$$

Hamilton's principle states that the motion of the system proceeds in such a way that

$$\delta I = 0 \tag{12.9}$$

i.e., the integral $\int L(t)\, dt$ has a stationary value that is, the integral is either a maximum or a minimum.

Hamilton's principle can be taken as a fundamental principle of dynamics from which other principles and laws can be derived. Thus, for instance, it is possible to derive from it Lagrange's equations.

12-2   Principle of Least Action (Maupertuis Principle)

Let us again postulate a varied path but this time we stipulate that it must be such that the total mechanical energy E ($= T + V$) of the system along the varied path is the same as along the actual path. We introduce the integral

$$\int_A^B 2T \, dt \tag{12.10}$$

The principle of least action or Maupertuis principle, states that the system will move in such a way that

$$\delta \int_A^B 2T \, dt = 0 \tag{12.11}$$

Hamilton himself noticed the similarity between the Maupertuis principle and Fermat's principle. The latter is a principle of geometrical optics and its actual statement involves the index of refraction n of the medium. The principle states that a beam of light travels between two points A and B of a medium in such a way that

$$\delta \int_A^B n \, ds = 0 \tag{12.12}$$

Now n, the index of refraction of the medium, is inversely proportional to the wave velocity u in that medium. Therefore Fermat's principle can also be written as

$$\delta \int_A^B \frac{ds}{u} = 0 \tag{12.13}$$

or simply

$$\delta \int_A^B dt = 0 \tag{12.14}$$

This last form has a clear physical meaning because it states that the beam of light travels between two points A and B of the medium in such a way that the time taken has a stationary (usually minimum) value.

The similarity between Maupertuis and Fermat's principles can be seen by writing Eq. (12.11) as

$$\delta \int_A^B mv \, ds = 0 \tag{12.15}$$

or

$$\delta \int_A^B p \, ds = 0 \tag{12.16}$$

where we are assuming that our system is a single particle of mass m and linear momentum p. Now, the simplest thing to do is to invoke a result from modern physics which states that a particle travelling with linear momentum p is equivalent to a wave, the velocity u of which is inversely proportional to p.* Fermat's principle in the form of (12.13) then follows.

---

* Here we are talking about de Broglie's hypothesis. According to this hypothesis the linear momentum of the particle can be written as $p = h/\lambda$ where λ is the wavelength of the wave associated with the particle. The wavelength, in turn, is given by $\lambda = u/\nu$, where ν is the frequency of the wave.

12-3 Action or Hamilton's Characteristic Function

Consider a conservative system having kinetic energy T and total energy E.

The integral
$$A = \int_s 2T \, dt \qquad (12.17)$$

evaluated along the actual path s is called the *action of the system* between the initial and the final points of the path; it is also called *Hamilton's characteristic function*. This is the same integral which was used in the formulation of the Maupertuis principle.

Suppose the system is a particle of mass m described by Cartesian coordinates. Let
$$O \equiv (x_0, y_0, z_0)$$
and
$$P \equiv (x, y, z)$$

be the initial and final points of the path of the particle. Taking O as fixed, the action A will be a function of the coordinates of the end point and also of the total energy E, i.e.
$$A = A(x, y, z, E) \qquad (12.18)$$

Let t_o be the time of departure from O and t the time of arrival at P.

Fig. 12.3

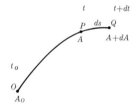

Consider now a small additional part PQ of the path (Fig. 12.3). Let the time it takes the particle to traverse this additional path be dt. Then at Q the action will be $A + dA$, and

$$\begin{aligned} dA &= 2T \, dt \\ &= mv^2 \, dt \\ &= mvv \, dt \\ &= p \, ds \end{aligned} \qquad (12.19)$$

where p is the linear momentum of the particle and $ds = PQ$. We can write the last relation as
$$dA = \mathbf{p} \cdot \mathbf{ds} \qquad (12.20)$$
or
$$dA = p_x \, dx + p_y \, dy + p_z \, dz \qquad (12.21)$$

If we retained the generalized coordinates then we would have had
$$2T = \sum_r p_r \dot{q}_r$$

and
$$2T \, dt = \sum_r p_r \, dq_r \qquad (12.22)$$

Eq. (12.21) suggests that we may write

$$\frac{\partial A}{\partial x} = p_x$$

and similar expressions for the other variables. This is actually the case and it can be proved rigorously. Here we will just state that the function A has the following properties

$$\left(\frac{\partial A}{\partial x}\right)_{y,z,E} = p_x \qquad \left(\frac{\partial A}{\partial y}\right)_{z,x,E} = p_y \qquad \left(\frac{\partial A}{\partial z}\right)_{x,y,E} = p_z$$

$$\left(\frac{\partial A}{\partial E}\right)_{x,y,z} = t - t_0 \qquad (12.23)$$

In order to see that the last property is valid we consider the action

$$A = \int_{t_0}^{t} 2T \, dt$$

together with the total energy

$$T + V = E$$

Then
$$A = \int_{t_0}^{t} (T + E - V) \, dt$$

or
$$A = \int_{t_0}^{t} (T - V) \, dt + \int_{t_0}^{t} E \, dt \qquad (12.24)$$

and from this expression the last property of Eqs. (12.23) follows.

12-4 Hamilton's Principal Function

The last relation (12.24) can be written as

$$A = \int L \, dt + E(t - t_0) \qquad (12.25)$$

The integral
$$S = \int L \, dt \qquad (12.26)$$

appearing in this last relation is called *Hamilton's principal function*. We met this integral when formulating Hamilton's principle. Eq. (12.25) can therefore be written as

$$S = A - E(t - t_0) \qquad (12.27)$$

and this gives the *relation between Hamilton's principal function S, the action A and the total energy E.* This relation suggests that Hamilton's principal function has similar properties to those of Hamilton's characteristic function, given by Eqs. (12.23). As before we will just state them without a proof. When the system is a single particle and Cartesian coordinates are used then

$$\frac{\partial S}{\partial x} = p_x \qquad \frac{\partial S}{\partial y} = p_y \qquad \frac{\partial S}{\partial z} = p_z \qquad \frac{\partial S}{\partial t} = -E \qquad (12.28)$$

12-5 General Remarks about Integration of Dynamical Equations of Motion

The differential equations of motion of a system of particles can be replaced by differential equations of the first order which are solved for the derivatives. These first order equations will be of the form

$$\dot{x}_i = X_i(t, x) \qquad i = 1, 2, \ldots, n \qquad (12.29)$$

Indeed, dynamical equations are linear equations of the second order and independent with respect to second derivatives of the generalized coordinates. Solving for the second derivatives we obtain equations of the type

$$\ddot{q}_k = Q_k(t, q, \dot{q}) \qquad (12.30)$$

where, as indicated by their arguments, the Q_k's, in general, are functions of time, of all the generalized coordinates and of the generalized velocities. Introducing new functions

$$\dot{q}_k = u_k \qquad (12.31)$$

we transform Eq. (12.30) into equations of the form

$$\dot{u}_k = Q_k(t, q, u) \qquad (12.32)$$

Lagrange's equations $\qquad \dfrac{d}{dt}\dfrac{\partial T}{\partial \dot{q}_i} - \dfrac{\partial T}{\partial q_i} = Q_i \qquad (12.33)$

can be transformed to first order equations in another way. Introducing the generalized momenta

$$p_i = \frac{\partial T}{\partial \dot{q}_i}$$

we obtain, as we have seen in Chapter 11, the first order equations

$$\dot{q}_i = \frac{\partial H}{\partial p_i} + Q_i \qquad \dot{p}_i = -\frac{\partial H}{\partial q_i} \qquad (12.34)$$

In seeking solutions of the differential equations of dynamics, several basic theorems of mathematical analysis are used. One basic but very general theorem is the following one: Let G and D denote domains in a space $E_{n+1}(t, x_1, x_2, \ldots, x_n)$ and another space $E_k(\alpha_1, \ldots, \alpha_k)$ respectively. At every point of these domains the functions

$$X_i(t, x, \alpha) \qquad i = 1, 2, \ldots, n$$

are specified. Then for every point $(\alpha_{10}, \ldots, \alpha_{k0})$ of D and for every point $(t_0, x_{10}, \ldots, x_{n0})$ of G there exists one and only one curve

$$x_i = \varphi_i(t, t_0, x_{h0}, \alpha_{j0}) \qquad i = 1, 2, \ldots, n \qquad (12.35)$$

which represents the integral of the differential equations

$$\dot{x}_i = X_i(t, x_h, \alpha_{j0})$$

and passes through the point (t_0, x_0); the end points of this curve lie at two points which lie on the boundary of G.

As stated above this is a basic theorem but it is so general that in many instances it is not sufficient for examination of the dynamical properties of some systems. Thus new formal methods of integration of dynamical equations of motion had to be devised. These methods utilized the fact that in most cases the equations of dynamics are variational equations.

Practically in all cases of integration of the differential equations of motion it is necessary to transform a given set of differential equations into another one. When doing so, care must be taken that this other set is independent. (We are assuming, of course, that the original set constituted an independent set.) No new solutions which are absent from the first set should be introduced into the second set.

Consider the first order dynamical differential equations

$$\dot{x}_i = X_i(t, x) \qquad i = 1, \ldots, h \qquad (12.36)$$

Let the functions $X_i(t, x)$ be defined in some domain G. Suppose that in the same domain there exist a function $f(t, x)$ such that if we substitute in it arbitrary solutions of Eqs. (12.36) then we will get identically

$$\frac{d}{dt} f[t, x(t)] = 0 \qquad (12.37)$$

From this relation we obtain $\qquad f(t, x) = C \qquad (12.38)$

where C is an arbitrary constant. We will call Eq. (12.38) the integral of the Eqs. (12.36). By Eq. (12.37), this integral will be satisfied by all solutions $x_i = x_i(t)$ of Eqs. (12.36). The function $f(t, x)$ is called the invariant of Eqs. (12.36). We will show that $f(t, x)$ satisfies a certain partial differential equation of the first order. In fact, we see that Eq. (12.37) can be written as

$$\frac{\partial f}{\partial t} + \sum_{i=1}^{h} \frac{\partial f}{\partial x_i} \dot{x}_i = 0 \qquad (12.39)$$

Realizing that this equation is satisfied by all solutions of Eqs. (12.36), we can rewrite it as

$$\frac{\partial f}{\partial t} + \sum_{i=1}^{h} X_i \frac{\partial f}{\partial x_i} = 0 \qquad (12.40)$$

We repeat that this last equation is satisfied by a function $f(t, x)$ when in this function we substitute for (t, x) the coordinates of an arbitrary point which lies on an arbitrary curve representing the integral of the set (12.36). However, by the theorem quoted above, only one curve representing the integral of the set (12.36) passes through every point of the domain. We are deducing, therefore, that the function $f(t, x)$ satisfies Eq. (12.40) in the whole domain G.

Equation (12.40) is satisfied by all invariants of Eqs. (12.36).

There can be only h integrals (12.38) which are independent with regard to x_i. It can be proved that any system of $h + 1$ integrals

$$f_1 = C_1 \qquad \cdots \qquad f_h = C_h \qquad f_{h+1} = C_{h+1}$$

of the set (12.36) forms a dependent set with regard to $t, x_1, \ldots, x_h$.

If, in a given domain, we determine h independent integrals of Eqs. (12.36), then the general solution of Eqs. (12.36) can be written as

$$x_i = x_i(t, C_1, \ldots, C_h) \qquad i = 1, \ldots, h \tag{12.41}$$

which will contain h arbitrary constants.

If the equations of the set (12.36) are the canonical equations

$$\dot{q}_i = \frac{\partial H}{\partial p_i} \qquad \dot{p}_i = -\frac{\partial H}{\partial q_i} \qquad i = 1, \ldots, s \tag{12.42}$$

then Eq. (12.40) takes the form

$$\frac{\partial f}{\partial t} + [H, f] = 0 \tag{12.43}$$

where the symbol $[H, f]$ is called a *Poisson bracket* and denotes the following function

$$[H, f] = \sum_{i=1}^{s} \left(\frac{\partial H}{\partial p_i} \frac{\partial f}{\partial q_i} - \frac{\partial H}{\partial q_i} \frac{\partial f}{\partial p_i} \right) \tag{12.44}$$

We have therefore shown that *the integration of the canonical equations, Eqs. (12.42), is equivalent to determining 2s independent solutions of Eq. (12.43)*.

The original dynamical equations may be written in the form

$$\ddot{q}_i = F_i(t, q, \dot{q}) \qquad i = 1, \ldots, s \tag{12.45}$$

The corresponding first order equations will then be of the form

$$\dot{q}_i = u_i \qquad \dot{u}_i = Q_i(t, q, u) \qquad i = 1, \ldots, s \tag{12.46}$$

The integrals of Eqs. (12.46) which contain at least one u_i, i.e., the integrals of the form

$$f(t, q, u) = C \tag{12.47}$$

or of the equivalent form $\qquad f(t, q, \dot{q}) = C \tag{12.48}$

are called the first integrals of Eqs. (12.45). These are, of course, first order equations which are satisfied by all the solutions of Eqs. (12.45). We will call the integrals, Eq. (12.48), independent if they are independent with respect to $\dot{q}_i$. There can only be s such independent first integrals.

12–6   Hamilton-Jacobi Differential Equation

When the dynamical equations of a system are variational equations, they can be integrated by a method given for the first time by Hamilton and developed independently by Jacobi. This Hamilton-Jacobi method is of great importance in modern physics.

We do not propose to discuss this method at any great length but limit ourselves to a few remarks only.

We have seen that we can identify the Hamiltonian H with the total energy E, i.e., we can write

$$H(p, q) = E \tag{12.49}$$

Using Eqs. (12.28) we can replace p by $\partial S/\partial q$ and E by $-\partial S/\partial t$, and obtain

$$H\left(\frac{\partial S}{\partial q}, q\right) + \frac{\partial S}{\partial t} = 0 \tag{12.50}$$

This is the Hamilton-Jacobi differential equation.

Example: A single particle moving in a potential $V(x, y, z)$.

The Hamiltonian of this particle is

$$H = 1/(2m)[p_x{}^2 + p_y{}^2 + p_z{}^2] + V(x, y, z)$$

and the Hamilton-Jacobi differential equation becomes

$$\frac{1}{2m}\left[\left(\frac{\partial S}{\partial x}\right)^2 + \left(\frac{\partial S}{\partial y}\right)^2 + \left(\frac{\partial S}{\partial z}\right)^2\right] + V(x, y, z) = \frac{\partial S}{\partial t} = 0$$

There is a strict relationship between the solution of the Hamilton-Jacobi equation and the solutions of Hamilton's as well as Lagrange's equations. This relationship was established for the first time by Hamilton in the case of geometrical optics, and then independently by Jacobi in his dissertations on dynamics.

We may start with a more general Hamilton-Jacobi equation, viz.

$$\frac{\partial S}{\partial t} + H\left(t, q, \frac{\partial S}{\partial q}\right) = 0 \tag{12.51}$$

We will call a solution

$$S = S(t, q, \alpha) \tag{12.52}$$

of Eq. (12.51) a complete solution if it depends on s parameters $\alpha_1, \ldots, \alpha_s$, and if it satisfies some special conditions.* The following theorem then holds:

The general solutions of Lagrange's equations

$$\frac{d}{dt}\frac{\partial L}{\partial \dot{q}_i} - \frac{\partial L}{\partial q_i} = 0 \qquad i = 1, \ldots, s \qquad (12.53)$$

are the solutions
$$q_i = q_i(t, \alpha, \beta) \qquad (12.54)$$

of the equations
$$\frac{\partial S(t, q, \alpha)}{\partial \alpha_k} = \beta_k \qquad (12.55)$$

where $S(t, q, \alpha)$ denote the complete solution of the corresponding Hamilton-Jacobi differential equation.

In addition, another equally important theorem is valid: *The general solutions of Hamilton's canonical equations*

$$\dot{q}_i = \frac{\partial H}{\partial p_i} \qquad \dot{p}_i = -\frac{\partial H}{\partial q_i} \qquad i = 1, \ldots, s \qquad (12.56)$$

are the solutions
$$q_i = q_i(t, \alpha, \beta) \qquad p_i = p_i(t, \alpha, \beta) \qquad (12.57)$$
of the equations

$$\frac{\partial S(t, q, \alpha)}{\partial \alpha_k} = \beta \qquad \frac{\partial S(t, q, \alpha)}{\partial q_k} = p_k \qquad k = 1, \ldots, s \qquad (12.58)$$

where again $S(t, q, \alpha)$ denotes the complete solution of the Hamilton-Jacobi differential equation.

Example: A particle falling in the gravitational field of earth.

Let the vertical coordinate be denoted by y. A particle of mass m is dropped from rest at $y = 0$. The Hamiltonian of the particle is

$$H = \frac{p_y{}^2}{2m} + V(y)$$

now,

$$V(y) = -mgy$$

therefore

$$H = \frac{p_y{}^2}{2m} - mgy$$

By one of the properties of Hamilton's principal function S, given by Eqs. (12.28)

$$\partial S/\partial y = p_y$$

---

* The function $S(t, q, \alpha)$ must belong to an appropriate class of functions, and the determinant $\Delta = \dfrac{\partial^2 S}{\partial q_i \, \partial \alpha_k}$ $(i, k = 1, \ldots, s)$ must be different from zero.

and so
$$H = \frac{1}{2m}\left(\frac{\partial S}{\partial y}\right)^2 - mgy$$

This we substitute in the equation
$$H + \frac{\partial S}{\partial t} = 0$$

and obtain
$$\frac{1}{2m}\left(\frac{\partial S}{\partial y}\right)^2 - mgy + \frac{\partial S}{\partial t} = 0$$

This is the Hamilton-Jacobi differential equation for a particle of mass m falling in the gravitational field of earth.

In order to solve it let
$$S = W(y) - \alpha t$$

then
$$\frac{1}{2m}\left(\frac{\partial W}{\partial y}\right)^2 - mgy - \alpha = 0$$

from which
$$W = \int \sqrt{2m(mgy + \alpha)}\, dy$$

and
$$S = \int \sqrt{2m(mgy + \alpha)}\, dy - \alpha t$$

According to Eq. (12.55) or Eqs. (12.58) another constant, β, enters, and this constant is obtained from
$$\beta = \frac{\partial S}{\partial \alpha}$$

In our case
$$\beta = \int \frac{\partial}{\partial \alpha}\, [2m(mgy + \alpha)]^{\frac{1}{2}}\, dy - t$$

or
$$\beta + t = \int m\, \frac{dy}{\sqrt{2m^2gy + 2m\alpha}}$$

from which
$$\beta + t = \frac{1}{mg}\, \sqrt{2m^2gy + 2m\alpha}$$

Now, by the last of Eqs. (12.28)
$$\frac{\partial S}{\partial t} = -E$$

i.e., $\alpha = E$, where E is the total energy. Let the particle start to move from rest with zero potential energy. At $t = 0$, therefore, the total energy will be zero, and will remain at this value for the rest of the motion. Thus $\alpha = 0$. The last equation now becomes
$$\beta + t = \frac{1}{mg}\, \sqrt{2m^2gy}$$

or

$$g(\beta + t)^2 = 2y$$

at $t = 0$, let $y = 0$, therefore $\beta = 0$. Thus

$$y = \tfrac{1}{2}gt^2$$

PROBLEMS

12.1   Prove that in the case of a particle under a central attraction μ/r^2, Hamilton's principal function is

$$S = -ht + \beta\theta + \int \left[\frac{2\mu}{r} + 2h - \frac{\beta^2}{r^2} \right]^{\frac{1}{2}} dr$$

Explain the meaning of the constants h and β.

12.2 A and B are two points in the gravitational field of the earth connected by a smooth wire, A being higher than B. A bead free to slide on the wire is then released from A. Show that the shape of the wire is given by

$$\left(\frac{dy}{dx} \right)^2 + 1 = \frac{\text{const.}}{y}$$

if the bead takes the shortest possible time to reach B.

12.3   Let

$$S \equiv \int_{x_0}^{x_1} f\left(\frac{dy}{dx}, y \right) dx$$

By considering two slightly different paths joining the points whose x coordinates are x_0 and x_1 show that

$$S = \left[\frac{\partial f}{\partial p} \, \delta y \right]_{x_0}^{x_1} + \int_{x_0}^{x_1} \left[\frac{\partial f}{\partial y} - \frac{d}{dx} \frac{\partial f}{\partial p} \right] \delta y \, dx$$

where

$$p \equiv \frac{dy}{dx}$$

If a necessary and sufficient condition for $\delta S = 0$ is $\partial f/\partial p = 0$ at both limits and

$$\frac{\partial f}{\partial y} - \frac{d}{dx} \frac{\partial f}{\partial p} = 0$$

at all intermediate values, show that f satisfies the differential equation

$$p \frac{\partial f}{\partial p} - f = \text{const.}$$

12.4   Consider a system of n particles

$$P_1(x_1, y_1, z_1), \ P_2(x_1, y_2, z_2), \ \ldots, \ P_n(x_n, y_n, z_n)$$

the motion of which is determined by the functions

$$x_i = x_i(t), \ y_i = y_i(t), \ z_i = z_i(t)$$

for

$$t_0 \le t \le t_1$$

and

$$i = 1, 2, \ldots, n$$

This motion may be consistent with the constraints of the system or it may not be, i.e., the motion is completely arbitrary.   Consider a function

$$F = F(x_1, \ldots, x_n, y_1, \ldots, y_n, z_1, \ldots, z_n, \dot{x}_1, \ldots, \dot{x}_n, \dot{y}_1, \ldots, \dot{y}_n, \dot{z}_1, \ldots, \dot{z}_n, t)$$

Write down the variation of this function for the motion under consideration. Obtain the relationships between the δx_i's and $\delta \dot{x}_i$'s which appear in your expression.

12.5   Show that the solutions $q_i = q_i(\alpha, \beta, t)$ of the equations

$$\frac{\partial S}{\partial \alpha_k} = \beta_k$$

are the general solutions of Lagrange's equations

$$\frac{d}{dt} \frac{\partial L}{\partial \dot{q}_i} - \frac{\partial L}{\partial q_i} = 0$$

The function $S(q, \alpha, t)$ is the general solution of the corresponding Hamilton-Jacobi differential equation.

12.6   Show that the solutions $q_i = q_i(\alpha, \beta, t)$ and $p_i = p_i(\alpha, \beta, t)$ of the equations

$$\frac{\partial S(q, \alpha, t)}{\partial \alpha_k} = \beta_k \qquad \frac{\partial S(q, \alpha, t)}{\partial q_k} = p_k$$

are the general solutions of Hamilton's canonical equations

$$\dot{q}_i = \frac{\partial H}{\partial p_i} \qquad \dot{p}_i = -\frac{\partial H}{\partial q_i}$$

The function $S(q, \alpha, t)$ denotes the general solution of the Hamilton-Jacobi differential equation.

13 $\quad$ THE KINEMATICAL THEORY OF RIGID BODY MOTION

13-1 $\quad$ The Number of Degrees of Freedom of a Rigid Body

In mechanics, a rigid body is defined as a collection of point masses in which the distance between any two points of the body remains constant. The position of all the points of such a body is uniquely determined if the positions of any three non-collinear points of the body are known.

All the points of a rigid body lying in a straight line or on a plane will continue to do so for any position of the body.

We will now determine the number of degrees of freedom of a free rigid body. We have stated above that the position of the rigid body is given if the positions of three of its points not lying in a straight line are known. Let us refer the position of the body to a Cartesian rectangular frame of reference K. Let

$$
\begin{aligned}
A_1 &\equiv (x_1, y_1, z_1) \\
A_2 &\equiv (x_2, y_2, z_2) \\
A_3 &\equiv (x_3, y_3, z_3)
\end{aligned}
\tag{13.1}
$$

be some three points of the body not lying in a straight line. The coordinates of these three points satisfy the following relations:

$$
\begin{aligned}
(x_1 - x_2)^2 + (y_1 - y_2)^2 + (z_1 - z_2)^2 &= R_{12}{}^2 \\
(x_2 - x_3)^2 + (y_2 - y_3)^2 + (z_2 - z_3)^2 &= R_{23}{}^2 \\
(x_3 - x_1)^2 + (y_3 - y_1)^2 + (z_3 - z_1)^2 &= R_{31}{}^2
\end{aligned}
\tag{13.2}
$$

where R_{12}, R_{23}, R_{31} are the distances between the various pairs of points. The original number of parameters determining the position of the rigid body is nine, and is given by the nine coordinates Eqs. (13.1). The set of relations (13.2) reduces this number by three. Thus *in general the number of degrees of freedom of a rigid body is six.*

When the number of degrees of freedom is less than six, we say that the rigid body is no longer free. Assume that one point of the body is fixed and let this point be denoted by A_1, say, the coordinates of which are known. In such a case only two more points are required to determine the position of the rigid body completely, i.e., we will need the six coordinates of the additional points A_2 and A_3 which are not collinear with A_1. As before, the relations (13.2) hold which reduce the number of degrees of freedom of the rigid body to three.

In the case where the rigid body has a fixed axis, this is equivalent to the assumption that two points A_1 and A_2 on this axis are fixed. It is therefore necessary to add the three coordinates of one more point A_3 which does not lie on the axis. Hence the last two relations (13.2) will now be satisfied and they will reduce the number of degrees of freedom by two, resulting in a single degree of freedom.

13-2 Axes Fixed in the Body. Eulerian Angles

It is always possible to specify a Cartesian frame of reference K' fixed in the rigid body. The coordinates x', y', z' of any point of the rigid body can, of course, be referred to this frame of reference. We will, in general, also have another frame of reference K with respect to which the rigid body will move. K will be considered a fixed frame of reference. Again, we may refer the coordinates x, y, z of any point of the rigid body to this frame. It is known that between the coordinates x, y, z and x', y', z' of one and the same point, the following relations hold

$$\begin{aligned}
x &= a + \alpha_1 x' + \beta_1 y' + \gamma_1 z' \\
y &= b + \alpha_2 x' + \beta_2 y' + \gamma_2 z' \\
z &= c + \alpha_3 x' + \beta_3 y' + \gamma_3 z'
\end{aligned} \tag{13.3}$$

where (a, b, c) are the coordinates of the origin O' of K' referred to the system K, and

$$\alpha_i, \beta_i, \gamma_i \qquad i = 1, 2, 3 \tag{13.4}$$

are the coefficients depending on the angles between the various coordinates axes. When K and K' are rectangular Cartesian axes, then (13.4) represent the cosines of the angles between the axes of K and those of K'. The meaning of these coefficients is clearly seen from the table

	x'	y'	z'
x	α_1	β_1	γ_1
y	α_2	β_2	γ_2
z	α_3	β_3	γ_3

Relations (13.3) can also be written in a matrix form as

$$\begin{bmatrix} x - a \\ y - b \\ z - c \end{bmatrix} = \begin{bmatrix} \alpha_1 & \beta_1 & \gamma_1 \\ \alpha_2 & \beta_2 & \gamma_2 \\ \alpha_3 & \beta_3 & \gamma_3 \end{bmatrix} \begin{bmatrix} x' \\ y' \\ z' \end{bmatrix} \tag{13.5}$$

From this we obtain

$$
\begin{bmatrix} x' \\ y' \\ z' \end{bmatrix} = \begin{bmatrix} \alpha_1 & \beta_1 & \gamma_1 \\ \alpha_2 & \beta_2 & \gamma_2 \\ \alpha_3 & \beta_3 & \gamma_3 \end{bmatrix}^{-1} \begin{bmatrix} x - a \\ y - b \\ z - c \end{bmatrix}
\tag{13.6}
$$

which will yield

$$
\begin{aligned}
x' &= a_1(x - a) + b_1(y - b) + c_1(z - c) \\
y' &= a_2(x - a) + b_2(y - b) + c_2(z - c) \\
z' &= a_3(x - a) + b_3(y - b) + c_3(z - c)
\end{aligned}
\tag{13.7}
$$

where the coefficients

$$
a_i, b_i, c_i \qquad i = 1, 2, 3
\tag{13.8}
$$

can be determined uniquely from (13.4).

It is also known that the following relations hold between the coefficients (13.4)

$$
\begin{aligned}
\alpha_i{}^2 + \beta_i{}^2 + \gamma_i{}^2 &= 1 \\
\alpha_i \alpha_k + \beta_i \beta_k + \gamma_i \gamma_k &= 0 \quad (i \neq k) \qquad i, k = 1, 2, 3
\end{aligned}
\tag{13.9}
$$

These are equivalent to the relations

$$
\sum_{i=1}^{3} \alpha_i{}^2 = \sum_{i=1}^{3} \beta_i{}^2 = \sum_{i=1}^{3} \gamma_i{}^2 = 1
$$

$$
\sum_{i=1}^{3} \alpha_i \beta_i = \sum_{i=1}^{3} \beta_i \gamma_i = \sum_{i=1}^{3} \gamma_i \alpha_i = 0
\tag{13.10}
$$

To determine the position of a rigid body during its motion we do not as a rule use the direction cosines $\alpha_i, \beta_i, \gamma_i$, but introduce a different set of angular coordinates which are called *Euler's angles*.

Consider the two Cartesian coordinate systems K and K' and let both of them have the same origin O but let them be oriented in an arbitrary way relative to each other as shown in Figure 13.1. We will call the line ON, which is common to the xy and $x'y'$ planes, the *line of nodes*. Consider the plane Ozz' which is perpendicular to the line of nodes. This plane will cut the planes Oxy, $Ox'y'$ along the lines OM and OM' respectively. We will direct the lines in such a way that they will form $90°$ angles with the line ON in the two planes Oxy and $Ox'y'$. *Euler's angles* can now be introduced in the following way:

(1) the precession angle ϕ between the axes Ox and ON, measured in the plane Oxy;

(2) the angle of nutation θ between the axes Oz and Oz', measured in the plane Ozz';

(3) the angle ψ of body's own rotation, as the angle between ON and Ox', measured in the plane $Ox'y'$.

178

parallel to one plane. The necessary and sufficient condition that such a motion will take place is that the velocities of three noncollinear points be parallel to a fixed plane. In such a case, the angular velocity vector of the body is always perpendicular to the fixed plane. At any moment the motion can be either translational or rotational, the more general motion being a combination of both.

There is still another special type of rigid body motion, that in which all the particles of the body describe helical paths about one axis. In this case the speed of every point of the body is constant and the velocity of any point on the axis of rotation is along that axis. This of course describes the motion of a screw. The importance of the latter type of motion stems from the fact that in the case of the most general type of motion, the rigid body at every instant has the above type of screw-like motion.

The general type of motion can also be interpreted in another way. Let O' be an arbitrarily chosen point of the rigid body, and A be any other point in the body; let

$$\overrightarrow{AO'} = \mathbf{r}'$$

The velocity of A with respect to a fixed frame of reference is then given by

$$\dot{\mathbf{r}}(t) = \dot{\mathbf{r}}'(t) + \mathbf{r}' \times \boldsymbol{\omega}(t) \tag{13.11}$$

where $\boldsymbol{\omega}(t)$ is the angular velocity of the rigid body. In the general case, therefore, the motion of the rigid body is the sum of translational and rotational motion. Eq. (13.11) is obtained in the following way: At a given instant let the body rotate with the angular velocity $\boldsymbol{\omega}$ about a certain instantaneous axis. Through O' draw a line parallel to this instantaneous axis. The perpendicular distance from A to this axis rotates with angular velocity $\boldsymbol{\omega}$ (as does any line in the body), and thus the linear velocity of A is $\mathbf{r}' \times \boldsymbol{\omega}$. The sum of this velocity and of the linear velocity of O' with respect to the fixed frame is the velocity of A.

13–4 The Components of the Velocity of Points of the Rigid Body in Fixed and Rotating Axes

Consider again two frames of reference: the fixed frame $K(Oxyz)$ and the frame $K'(O'x'y'z')$ which is rigidly attached to the rigid body. The position of O', the center of K' with respect to K, is given by the vector $\mathbf{r}_{O'} \equiv (a, b, c)$. The linear velocity of O' with respect to K is given by

$$\mathbf{v}_{O'} \equiv (\dot{a}, \dot{b}, \dot{c})$$

This vector can also be resolved along the $O'x'$, $O'y'$, $O'z'$ axes; the latter components will be denoted by

$$v_{O'x'}, v_{O'y'}, v_{O'z'}$$

Fig. 13.1.

The Eulerian angles.

Successive rotations to obtain
Euler's angles:
1. about z: ϕ
2. about LINE OF NODES: θ
3. about z': ψ
Oz', Oz, OM', OM are in one plane.

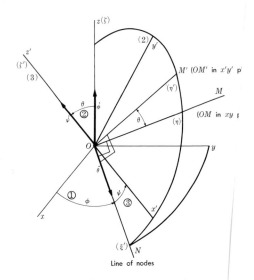

Line of nodes

To every position of the frame of reference K' there corresponds a uni[c]
of values of ϕ, θ, and ψ. (Here, of course, we are neglecting the multi[
of 2π.) Also, every set of values of Eulerian angles ϕ, θ, ψ determi[n]
position of the rigid body uniquely. This can be seen from the fa[c]
Eulerian angles can be introduced by three successive rotations of [
ordinate system with respect to another. Let us start with the set
$Ox'y'z'$ superimposed on $Oxyz$. (We recollect that the axes $Ox'y'z'$ are[
the body.) The three rotations are depicted in Figure 13.1. The tw[
mediate positions of the frame K' can be denoted by $O\xi'\eta\zeta$ and $O\xi$[
spectively. The first rotation of K' with respect to K is about the Oz ax[
angle ϕ. The frame K' in this position is denoted by $O\xi'\eta\zeta$. This first[
is followed by a rotation through an angle θ, about the axis $O\xi'$. The [
will now be denoted by $O\xi'\eta'\zeta'$. The last rotation is about the axi[
angle ψ. This is the final position of K' and here the axes will be[
by $Ox'y'z'$.

13-3 Special and General Motions of Rigid Body

When all the points of the rigid body have the same velocity, the[
the body is translational. When there is one line in the body whi[
at all times, the motion of the body is purely rotational. When[
these conditions is satisfied we say that the body is in a state of g[
tion. In the first two cases it is only necessary to study the mo[
representative point of the body. In the case of purely translatio[
the representative point moves with linear motion. In the second[
pure rotation, the representative point traces out a circle.

There are other special types of motion of the rigid body. On[
is the coplanar motion. This occurs when every point of the rigid [

The angular motion of the rigid body is described by the angular velocity vector

$$\boldsymbol{\omega} = \boldsymbol{\omega}(t)$$

In the K system

$$\boldsymbol{\omega} = (\omega_x, \omega_y, \omega_z)$$

and in the K' system

$$\boldsymbol{\omega} = (\omega_{x'}, \omega_{y'}, \omega_{z'})$$

Let $\alpha_i, \beta_i, \gamma_i$ ($i = 1, 2, 3$) again denote the cosines of the angles between the respective axes of K and K'. Then $(\omega_x, \omega_y, \omega_z)$ and $(\omega_{x'}, \omega_{y'}, \omega_{z'})$ are related by

$$\omega_x = \alpha_1 \omega_{x'} + \beta_1 \omega_{y'} + \gamma_1 \omega_{z'}$$
$$\omega_y = \alpha_2 \omega_{x'} + \beta_2 \omega_{y'} + \gamma_2 \omega_{z'} \qquad (13.12)$$
$$\omega_z = \alpha_3 \omega_{x'} + \beta_3 \omega_{y'} + \gamma_3 \omega_{z'}$$

and similarly $(\dot{a}, \dot{b}, \dot{c})$ and $(v_{O'x'}, v_{O'y'}, v_{O'z'})$ are connected by the relations

$$\dot{a} = \alpha_1 v_{O'x'} + \beta_1 v_{O'y'} + \gamma_1 v_{O'z'}$$
$$\dot{b} = \alpha_2 v_{O'x'} + \beta_2 v_{O'y'} + \gamma_2 v_{O'z'} \qquad (13.13)$$
$$\dot{c} = \alpha_3 v_{O'x'} + \beta_3 v_{O'y'} + \gamma_3 v_{O'z'}$$

Choose any point A of the rigid body; in the K system its coordinates are (x, y, z), and in the K' system they are (x', y', z'). The linear velocity of this point was shown to be

$$\mathbf{v}_A = \mathbf{v}_{O'} + \mathbf{r}' \times \boldsymbol{\omega} \qquad (13.14)$$

where $\mathbf{r}' = AO'$. The components of both sides of (13.14) along the fixed axes are

$$\dot{x} = \dot{a} + (b - y)\omega_z - (c - z)\omega_y$$
$$\dot{y} = \dot{b} + (c - z)\omega_x - (a - x)\omega_z \qquad (13.15a)$$
$$\dot{z} = \dot{c} + (a - x)\omega_y - (b - y)\omega_x$$

or

$$\dot{x} = \dot{a} + \omega_y(z - c) - \omega_z(y - b)$$
$$\dot{y} = \dot{b} + \omega_z(x - a) - \omega_x(z - c) \qquad (13.15b)$$
$$\dot{z} = \dot{c} + \omega_x(y - b) - \omega_y(x - a)$$

In (13.15a) we made use of the fact that in the system K

$$\mathbf{r}' \equiv [(a - x), (b - y), (c - z)]$$

If we want to project both sides of (13.14) onto the moving axes $O'x'$, $O'y'$, $O'z'$, then we denote the components of $\mathbf{v}_A$ along these axes by $(v_{x'}, v_{y'}, v_{z'})$ and we notice that the components of the vector $\mathbf{r}' = \overrightarrow{AO'}$ along the same axes are $(-x', -y', -z')$. We then get

$$v_{x'} = v_{O'x'} - y'\omega_{z'} + z'\omega_{y'}$$
$$v_{y'} = v_{O'y'} - z'\omega_{x'} + x'\omega_{z'} \tag{13.16a}$$
$$v_{z'} = v_{O'z'} - x'\omega_{y'} + y'\omega_{x'}$$

or

$$v_{x'} = v_{O'x'} + \omega_{y'}z' - \omega_{z'}y'$$
$$v_{y'} = v_{O'y'} + \omega_{z'}x' - \omega_{x'}z' \tag{13.16b}$$
$$v_{z'} = v_{O'z'} + \omega_{x'}y' - \omega_{y'}x'$$

The same type of relations as (13.12) or (13.13) hold between the components $(\dot{x}, \dot{y}, \dot{z})$ of the velocity vector $\mathbf{v}_A$ in the fixed coordinate system, and the components $(v_{x'}, v_{y'}, v_{z'})$ of the same velocity vector in the moving frame. Thus

$$\dot{x} = \alpha_1 v_{x'} + \beta_1 v_{y'} + \gamma_1 v_{z'}$$
$$\dot{y} = \alpha_2 v_{x'} + \beta_2 v_{y'} + \gamma_2 v_{z'} \tag{13.17}$$
$$\dot{z} = \alpha_3 v_{x'} + \beta_3 v_{y'} + \gamma_3 v_{z'}$$

The magnitude of $\boldsymbol{\omega}$ is given by

$$\omega^2 = \omega_x{}^2 + \omega_y{}^2 + \omega_z{}^2 \tag{13.18a}$$

or by

$$\omega^2 = \omega_{x'}{}^2 + \omega_{y'}{}^2 + \omega_{z'}{}^2 \tag{13.18b}$$

When, at a given moment, $\boldsymbol{\omega} = \mathbf{0}$ then

$$\omega_x = \omega_y = \omega_z = \omega_{x'} = \omega_{y'} = \omega_{z'} = 0$$

and the motion at this moment is translational. In this case Eqs. (13.15) and (13.16) become

$$\dot{x} = \dot{a} \qquad \dot{y} = \dot{b} \qquad \dot{z} = \dot{c} \tag{13.19}$$

and

$$v_{x'} = v_{O'x'} \qquad v_{y'} = v_{O'y'} \qquad v_{z'} = v_{O'z'} \tag{13.20}$$

When at a given moment $\mathbf{v}_{O'} = \mathbf{0}$, i.e., when momentarily the motion is purely rotational, then

$$\dot{a} = \dot{b} = \dot{c} = 0$$

and

$$v_{O'x'} = v_{O'y'} = v_{O'z'} = 0$$

From (13.15) and (13.16) we then obtain

$$\dot{x} = \omega_y(z - c) - \omega_z(y - b)$$
$$\dot{y} = \omega_z(x - a) - \omega_x(z - c) \tag{13.21}$$
$$\dot{z} = \omega_x(y - b) - \omega_y(x - z)$$

and

$$v_{x'} = \omega_{y'}z' - \omega_{z'}y'$$
$$v_{y'} = \omega_{z'}x' - \omega_{x'}z' \tag{13.22}$$
$$v_{z'} = \omega_{x'}y' - \omega_{y'}x'$$

13-4 The components of the velocity in fixed and rotating axes

Let us now consider the general type of motion of a rigid body. Given the kinematical law of motion of the rigid body, we wish to determine the components of the angular velocity vector $\boldsymbol{\omega}$. By this we mean that we want to find $\omega_x, \omega_y, \omega_z$ (and also $\omega_{x'}, \omega_{y'}, \omega_{z'}$) when the coordinates (a, b, c) of a certain point O' of the rigid body are known functions of time; in addition the nine cosines $(\alpha_i, \beta_i, \gamma_i; i = 1, 2, 3)$ of the angles between the axes of the two frames K and K' are known. The cosines satisfy the relations (13.9) of this chapter.

Choose three points M_1, M_2, M_3 of the rigid body and let their coordinates in the frame K' (fixed in the body) be

$$
\begin{aligned}
M_1 &\equiv (1, 0, 0) \\
M_2 &\equiv (0, 1, 0) \\
M_3 &\equiv (0, 0, 1)
\end{aligned}
\tag{13.23}
$$

The coordinates in the fixed frame of reference K are

$$
\begin{aligned}
M_1 &\equiv (a + \alpha_1, b + \alpha_2, c + \alpha_3) \\
M_2 &\equiv (a + \beta_1, b + \beta_2, c + \beta_3) \\
M_3 &\equiv (a + \gamma_1, b + \gamma_2, c + \gamma_3)
\end{aligned}
\tag{13.24}
$$

Substituting the coordinates of M_1, M_2, M_3 successively in (13.15b) we get

$$
\begin{aligned}
\dot{\alpha}_1 &= \omega_y \alpha_3 - \omega_z \alpha_2 \\
\dot{\alpha}_2 &= \omega_z \alpha_1 - \omega_x \alpha_3 \\
\dot{\alpha}_3 &= \omega_x \alpha_2 - \omega_y \alpha_1
\end{aligned}
\tag{13.25}
$$

$$
\begin{aligned}
\dot{\beta}_1 &= \omega_y \beta_3 - \omega_z \beta_2 \\
\dot{\beta}_2 &= \omega_z \beta_1 - \omega_x \beta_3 \\
\dot{\beta}_3 &= \omega_x \beta_2 - \omega_y \beta_1
\end{aligned}
\tag{13.26}
$$

$$
\begin{aligned}
\dot{\gamma}_1 &= \omega_y \gamma_3 - \omega_z \gamma_2 \\
\dot{\gamma}_2 &= \omega_z \gamma_1 - \omega_x \gamma_3 \\
\dot{\gamma}_3 &= \omega_x \gamma_2 - \omega_y \gamma_1
\end{aligned}
\tag{13.27}
$$

Let $\mathbf{i'}, \mathbf{j'}, \mathbf{k'}$ be unit vectors along the axes $O'x', O'y', O'z$, i.e.

$$
\mathbf{i'} = \overrightarrow{O'M}_1 \qquad \mathbf{j'} = \overrightarrow{O'M}_2 \qquad \mathbf{k'} = \overrightarrow{O'M}_3
$$

The coordinates of the end points of $\mathbf{i'}, \mathbf{j'}, \mathbf{k'}$ in the fixed frame of reference K, when O and O' coincide, are $(\alpha_1, \alpha_2, \alpha_3)$, $(\beta_1, \beta_2, \beta_3)$ and $(\gamma_1, \gamma_2, \gamma_3)$ respectively. It follows that (13.25), (13.26), (13.27) can be replaced by

$$
\frac{d\mathbf{i'}}{dt} = -\mathbf{i'} \times \boldsymbol{\omega} \qquad \frac{d\mathbf{j'}}{dt} = -\mathbf{j'} \times \boldsymbol{\omega} \qquad \frac{d\mathbf{k'}}{dt} = -\mathbf{k'} \times \boldsymbol{\omega} \tag{13.28}
$$

From (13.25), (13.26), (13.27), and using relations (13.9), we obtain*

$$\omega_x = \dot{\alpha}_3\alpha_2 + \dot{\beta}_3\beta_2 + \dot{\gamma}_3\gamma_2$$
$$\omega_y = \dot{\alpha}_1\alpha_3 + \dot{\beta}_1\beta_3 + \dot{\gamma}_1\gamma_3 \qquad (13.29)$$
$$\omega_z = \dot{\alpha}_2\alpha_1 + \dot{\beta}_2\beta_1 + \dot{\gamma}_2\gamma_1$$

Eqs. (13.29) give the components of the angular velocity vector ω along the fixed coordinate axes. In order to obtain the components of ω along the coordinate axes rotating with the body, we substitute the values of $\omega_x, \omega_y, \omega_z$ from (13.29) in (13.12).

13-6 The Components of the Angular Velocity along Fixed Axes in Terms of Euler's Angles

We will now express the components $\omega_x, \omega_y, \omega_z$ of the angular velocity vector ω in terms of Euler's angles. As a first step let us express the quantities

$$\alpha_1, \beta_1, \gamma_1$$
$$\alpha_2, \beta_2, \gamma_2$$
$$\alpha_3, \beta_3, \gamma_3$$

in terms of the Eulerian angles. Consider Figure 13.1 in which O and O' coincide. Again, let $\mathbf{i}', \mathbf{j}', \mathbf{k}'$ denote unit vectors along $O'x', O'y', O'z'$. The components of the three unit vectors along the three axes Ox, Oy, Oz will be

$$\alpha_1, \alpha_2, \alpha_3$$
$$\beta_1, \beta_2, \beta_3$$
$$\gamma_1, \gamma_2, \gamma_3$$

respectively (i.e., the components of $\mathbf{i}'$ along Ox is α_1, along Oy is α_2, along Oz is α_3, and so on). In Figure 13.1 the lines ON, OM' and OZ' are at right angles to each other. Let us find the orthogonal projections of $\mathbf{i}'$ on these three lines and let the projections be denoted by $\mathbf{u}_N$, $\mathbf{u}_{M'}$, $\mathbf{u}_{Z'}$ (which, of course, are not unit vectors.) Then, from the definition of Eulerian angles, the magnitudes of $\mathbf{u}_N$, $\mathbf{u}_{M'}$, $\mathbf{u}_{Z'}$ are

$$u_N = \cos\psi \qquad u_{M'} = \sin\psi \qquad u_{Z'} = 0$$

The vectors $\mathbf{u}_N$, $\mathbf{u}_{M'}$, $\mathbf{u}_{Z'}$ are the components of $\mathbf{i}'$ along ON, OM', OZ'. If we now project $\mathbf{u}_N$, $\mathbf{u}_{M'}$, $\mathbf{u}_{Z'}$ onto any axis, we obtain the components of $\mathbf{i}'$ along that axis. Let us therefore project everyone of these vectors onto the three mutually perpendicular axes ON, OM, OZ. We find that the magnitudes of the components of $\mathbf{i}'$ along these axes are

---

* Multiply the third equations of (13.25), (13.26), (13.27) by $\alpha_2, \beta_2, \gamma_2$ respectively and add; multiply the first equations of the same set by $\alpha_3, \beta_3, \gamma_3$ respectively and add; finally multiply the second equations by $\alpha_1, \beta_1, \gamma_1$ respectively and add. Apply (13.9) to these sums.

$$u_N = \cos \psi \qquad u_M = \sin \psi \cos \theta \qquad u_Z = \sin \psi \sin \theta$$

We must now find the magnitudes of the orthogonal projections of $\mathbf{u}_N$, $\mathbf{u}_M$, $\mathbf{u}_Z$ onto the axes Ox, Oy, Oz; their sums for the respective axes will produce the numbers α_1, α_2, α_3 which we are looking for. We find that

$$\alpha_1 = \cos \psi \cos \phi - \sin \psi \sin \phi \cos \theta$$
$$\alpha_2 = \cos \psi \sin \phi + \sin \psi \cos \phi \cos \theta \qquad (13.30)$$
$$\alpha_3 = \sin \psi \sin \theta$$

Proceeding in a similar way with the unit vectors $\mathbf{j}'$ and $\mathbf{k}'$ we also find that

$$\beta_1 = -\sin \psi \cos \phi - \cos \psi \sin \phi \cos \theta$$
$$\beta_2 = -\sin \psi \sin \phi + \cos \psi \cos \phi \cos \theta \qquad (13.31)$$
$$\beta_3 = \cos \psi \sin \theta$$

and

$$\gamma_1 = \sin \phi \sin \theta$$
$$\gamma_2 = -\cos \phi \sin \theta \qquad (13.32)$$
$$\gamma_3 = \cos \theta$$

We now take the values of β_i and γ_i from the last relations (13.31) and (13.32), substitute them in the third equations of the sets (13.26) and (13.27) and obtain

$$\omega_x(-\sin \psi \sin \phi + \cos \psi \cos \phi \cos \theta) + \omega_y(\sin \psi \cos \phi + \cos \psi \sin \phi \cos \theta)$$
$$= -\dot{\psi} \sin \psi \sin \theta + \dot{\theta} \cos \psi \cos \theta$$
$$\omega_x \cos \phi + \omega_y \sin \phi = \dot{\theta}$$

From these we get

$$\omega_x = \dot{\psi} \sin \phi \sin \theta + \dot{\theta} \cos \phi$$

and

$$\omega_y = -\dot{\psi} \cos \phi \sin \theta + \dot{\theta} \sin \phi \qquad (13.33)$$

Furthermore, substituting the values for ω_x, $\dot{\gamma}_1$, γ_2, γ_3 in the first equation of (13.27) we obtain

$$\omega_z = \dot{\phi} \cos \theta + \dot{\psi} \qquad (13.34)$$

13-7   The Angular Velocities of Precession, Nutation and Body's Own Rotation

Using methods similar to the ones used at the beginning of the last paragraph we find that

$$\cos (Ox, Oz') = \sin \phi \sin \theta$$
$$\cos (Ox, ON) = \cos \phi$$
$$\cos (Ox, Oz) = 0$$

$$\cos (Oy, Oz') = -\cos \phi \sin \theta$$
$$\cos (Oy, ON) = \sin \phi$$
$$\cos (Oy, Oz) = 0$$

$$\cos (Oz, Oz') = \cos \theta$$
$$\cos (Oz, ON) = 0$$
$$\cos (Oz, Oz) = 1$$

Using these relations we can rewrite (13.33) and (13.34) in the form

$$\omega_x = \omega \cos (Ox, \boldsymbol{\omega})$$
$$= \dot\psi \cos (Ox, Oz') + \dot\phi \cos (Ox, Oz) + \dot\theta \cos (Ox, ON)$$

$$\omega_y = \omega \cos (Oy, \boldsymbol{\omega})$$
$$= \dot\psi \cos (Oy, Oz') + \dot\phi \cos (Oy, Oz) + \dot\theta \cos (Oy, ON) \qquad (13.35)$$

$$\omega_z = \omega \cos (Oz, \boldsymbol{\omega})$$
$$= \dot\psi \cos (Oz, Oz') + \dot\phi \cos (Oz, Oz) + \dot\theta \cos (Oz, ON)$$

Let us place along the axes Oz', Oz, and the line of nodes ON, three vectors of magnitudes $\dot\psi$, $\dot\phi$, and $\dot\theta$. The right-hand sides of (13.35) represent the magnitudes of orthogonal projections of these vectors onto the fixed axes $Oxyz$. The left-hand sides of (13.35) are the components of the angular velocity vector. If $\mathbf{i}_{Z'}$, $\mathbf{i}_Z$ and $\mathbf{i}_N$ denote the unit vectors along Oz', Oz and ON respectively, we can write

$$\boldsymbol{\omega} = \dot\psi \mathbf{i}_{Z'} + \dot\phi \mathbf{i}_Z + \dot\theta \mathbf{i}_N \qquad (13.36)$$

We call the three angular velocity vectors $\dot\psi \mathbf{i}_{Z'}$, $\dot\phi \mathbf{i}_Z$, and $\dot\theta \mathbf{i}_N$ of a body rotation, precession and nutation respectively.

13–8 *The Components of the Angular Velocity Vector along the Rotating Axes in Terms of the Eulerian Angles*

As before, let $\mathbf{i}'$, $\mathbf{j}'$, $\mathbf{k}'$ denote unit vectors along the rotating axes Ox', Oy', Oz'. Then

$$\omega_{x'} = \mathbf{i}' \cdot \boldsymbol{\omega}$$
$$= \dot\psi \mathbf{i}_{Z'} \cdot \mathbf{i}' + \dot\theta \mathbf{i}_N \cdot \mathbf{i}' + \dot\phi \mathbf{i}_Z \cdot \mathbf{i}'$$

$$\omega_{y'} = \mathbf{j}' \cdot \boldsymbol{\omega}$$
$$= \dot\psi \mathbf{i}_{Z'} \cdot \mathbf{j}' + \dot\phi \mathbf{i}_Z \cdot \mathbf{j}' + \dot\theta \mathbf{i}_N \cdot \mathbf{j}'$$

$$\omega_{z'} = \mathbf{k}' \cdot \boldsymbol{\omega}$$
$$= \dot\psi \mathbf{i}_{Z'} \cdot \mathbf{k}' + \dot\phi \mathbf{i}_Z \cdot \mathbf{k}' + \dot\theta \mathbf{i}_N \cdot \mathbf{k}'$$

From these we get

$$\omega_{x'} = \dot{\phi} \sin \psi \sin \theta + \dot{\theta} \cos \psi$$
$$\omega_{y'} = \dot{\phi} \cos \psi \sin \theta - \dot{\theta} \sin \psi \qquad (13.37)$$
$$\omega_{z'} = \dot{\psi} + \dot{\phi} \cos \theta$$

These are the components of the angular velocity vector along the axes rotating with the body.

13-9   Acceleration of the Points of a Rigid Body

We will now investigate the accelerations of the points of a rigid body. Let A be any point of the rigid body. If O' is another point of the body, then, as we have seen, the linear velocity of A can be written as

$$\mathbf{v}_A(t) = \mathbf{v}_{O'}(t) + \mathbf{r}' \times \boldsymbol{\omega} \qquad (13.38)$$

where $\mathbf{r}' = \overrightarrow{AO'}$. We now differentiate this expression with respect to time and obtain

$$\mathbf{a}_A(t) = \mathbf{a}_{O'}(t) + \mathbf{r}' \times \frac{d\boldsymbol{\omega}}{dt} + [\mathbf{v}_{O'}(t) - \mathbf{v}_A(t)] \times \boldsymbol{\omega} \qquad (13.39)$$

where $\mathbf{v}_{O'}(t)$ and $\mathbf{v}_A(t)$ denote the velocities of the end points of the vector $\mathbf{r}'$. From (13.38) we have

$$\mathbf{v}_{O'}(t) - \mathbf{v}_A(t) = \boldsymbol{\omega} \times \mathbf{r}'$$

Thus (13.39) becomes

$$\mathbf{a}_A(t) = \mathbf{a}_{O'}(t) + \mathbf{r}' \times \frac{d\boldsymbol{\omega}}{dt} + (\boldsymbol{\omega} \times \mathbf{r}') \times \boldsymbol{\omega} \qquad (13.40)$$

Using the expression for the triple vector product* we find

$$\mathbf{a}_A(t) = \mathbf{a}_{O'}(t) + \mathbf{r}' \times \frac{d\boldsymbol{\omega}}{dt} + \mathbf{r}'\omega^2 - \boldsymbol{\omega}(\boldsymbol{\omega} \cdot \mathbf{r}') \qquad (13.41)$$

We may say that Eqs. (13.38) and (13.41) contain all the kinematical properties of the rigid body.

From (13.41) we see that *the acceleration vector $\mathbf{a}_A(t)$ of an arbitrary point A of a rigid body is the sum of the three vectors*

$$\mathbf{a}_{O'}(t) \qquad \mathbf{r}' \times \frac{d\boldsymbol{\omega}}{dt} \qquad \mathbf{r}'\omega^2 - \boldsymbol{\omega}(\mathbf{r}' \cdot \boldsymbol{\omega}) \qquad (13.42)$$

The first vector may be termed the linear acceleration of the rigid body. It is the same for all points of the rigid body and depends only on the choice of O'. The second vector is the moment of the vector $\dfrac{d\boldsymbol{\omega}}{dt}$ with respect to the point A; it may

* $\mathbf{a} \times (\mathbf{b} \times \mathbf{c}) = \mathbf{b}(\mathbf{a} \cdot \mathbf{c}) - \mathbf{c}(\mathbf{a} \cdot \mathbf{b})$

be termed the *rotational acceleration of the arbitrary point A.* The vector $\dfrac{d\boldsymbol{\omega}}{dt}$ is the *angular acceleration of the rigid body.* Consider now *the third vector, viz.*

$$\boldsymbol{\mathcal{P}} = \mathbf{r}'\omega^2 - \boldsymbol{\omega}(\mathbf{r}' \cdot \boldsymbol{\omega}) \tag{13.43}$$

This vector is a vector difference between the vector $\mathbf{r}'\omega^2$ lying along the $O'A$, and the vector $\boldsymbol{\omega}(\mathbf{r}' \cdot \boldsymbol{\omega})$ which lies along the angular velocity vector $\boldsymbol{\omega}$. $\boldsymbol{\mathcal{P}}$ is either zero or is perpendicular to $\boldsymbol{\omega}$, for scalar-multiplying Eq. (13.43) by $\boldsymbol{\omega}$ we get

$$\boldsymbol{\omega} \cdot \boldsymbol{\mathcal{P}} = \boldsymbol{\omega} \cdot \mathbf{r}'\omega^2 - (\mathbf{r}' \cdot \boldsymbol{\omega})\omega^2$$

or

$$\boldsymbol{\omega} \cdot \boldsymbol{\mathcal{P}} = 0 \tag{13.44}$$

Thus, if $\boldsymbol{\omega} \neq \mathbf{0}$ then $\boldsymbol{\mathcal{P}} \perp \boldsymbol{\omega}$. When $\boldsymbol{\omega} = \mathbf{0}$ then also $\boldsymbol{\mathcal{P}} = \mathbf{0}$. It is also possible that $\boldsymbol{\mathcal{P}} = \mathbf{0}$ when $\boldsymbol{\omega} \neq \mathbf{0}$ and A lies along the axis of $\boldsymbol{\omega}$. It can be shown that $\boldsymbol{\mathcal{P}}$ always points towards the axis of $\boldsymbol{\omega}$ and that

$$\boldsymbol{\mathcal{P}} = \rho\omega^2 \tag{13.45}$$

where ρ is the distance of A from the line of $\boldsymbol{\omega}$. *Vector $\boldsymbol{\mathcal{P}}$ can be termed the centripetal acceleration.*

13–10   The Components of the Acceleration Vector along Fixed and Rotating Axes

Consider the general expression (13.41) for the acceleration of any point A of the rigid body. As before, let

$$O' \equiv (a, b, c)$$

and

$$\boldsymbol{\omega} = \omega_x\mathbf{i} + \omega_y\mathbf{j} + \omega_z\mathbf{k}$$

Also

$$\frac{d\boldsymbol{\omega}}{dt} = \dot{\omega}_x\mathbf{i} + \dot{\omega}_y\mathbf{j} + \dot{\omega}_z\mathbf{k}$$

and

$$\mathbf{r}' \equiv (r_x', r_y', r_z')$$
$$= [-(x - a), -(y - b), -(z - c)]$$

Projecting both sides of (13.41) onto the fixed axes Ox, Oy, Oz we obtain

$$\ddot{x} = \ddot{a} + \dot{\omega}_y(z - c) - \dot{\omega}_z(y - b)$$
$$\qquad -\omega^2(x - a) + \omega_x[\omega_x(x - a) + \omega_y(y - b) + \omega_z(z - c)]$$

$$\ddot{y} = \ddot{b} + \dot{\omega}_z(x - a) - \dot{\omega}_x(z - c)$$
$$\qquad -\omega^2(y - b) + \omega_y[\omega_x(x - a) + \omega_y(y - b) + \omega_z(z - c)] \tag{13.46}$$

$$\ddot{z} = \ddot{c} + \dot{\omega}_x(y - b) - \dot{\omega}_y(x - a)$$
$$\qquad -\omega^2(z - c) + \omega_z[\omega_x(x - a) + \omega_y(y - b) + \omega_z(z - c)]$$

Before projecting the acceleration vector (13.41) onto the rotating axes $O'x', O'y', O'z'$, we notice that the components of $\mathbf{a}_{O'}(t)$ on these axes are

$$a_{O'x'} = \alpha_1 \ddot{a} + \alpha_2 \ddot{b} + \alpha_3 \ddot{c}$$
$$a_{O'y'} = \beta_1 \ddot{a} + \beta_2 \ddot{b} + \beta_3 \ddot{c}$$
$$a_{O'z'} = \gamma_1 \ddot{a} + \gamma_2 \ddot{b} + \gamma_3 \ddot{c}$$

Furthermore
$$\frac{d\boldsymbol{\omega}}{dt} = \dot{\omega}_{x'}\mathbf{i}' + \dot{\omega}_{y'}\mathbf{j}' + \dot{\omega}_{z'}\mathbf{k}'$$

Finally, the components of the vector $\mathbf{r}' = \overrightarrow{AO'}$ along the rotating axes are $-x', -y', -z'$. Taking all this into consideration we obtain for the components of the acceleration vector $\mathbf{a}_A(t)$ of any point A of the rigid body along the rotating axes the following expressions

$$a_{x'} = a_{O'x'} + \dot{\omega}_{y'}z' - \dot{\omega}_{z'}y' - \omega^2 x' + \omega_{x'}(\omega_{x'}x' + \omega_{y'}y' + \omega_{z'}z')$$
$$a_{y'} = a_{O'y'} + \dot{\omega}_{z'}x' - \dot{\omega}_{x'}z' - \omega^2 y' + \omega_{y'}(\omega_{x'}x' + \omega_{y'}y' + \omega_{z'}z') \qquad (13.47)$$
$$a_{z'} = a_{O'z'} + \dot{\omega}_{x'}y' - \dot{\omega}_{y'}x' - \omega^2 z' + \omega_{z'}(\omega_{x'}x' + \omega_{y'}y' + \omega_{z'}z')$$

In these expressions $a_{O'x'}$, $a_{O'y'}$, $a_{O'z'}$ are the components of the linear acceleration of the rigid body; the following two terms of (13.47) are the components of the angular acceleration; finally, the remaining terms are the components of the centripetal acceleration.

PROBLEM

If a system of rectangular coordinate axes $K'(x', y')$ is rotated with respect to the system $K(x, y)$ by an angle θ, then the coordinates (x', y') and (x, y) of one and the same point are related by

$$\begin{bmatrix} x' \\ y' \end{bmatrix} = \begin{bmatrix} \cos\theta & \sin\theta \\ -\sin\theta & \cos\theta \end{bmatrix} \begin{bmatrix} x \\ y \end{bmatrix}$$

If ϕ, θ, ψ are the Eulerian angles, show that the transition from $K(x, y, z)$ to $K'(x', y', z')$ is accomplished by three rotations represented by the matrices

$$\mathbf{M}_\phi = \begin{bmatrix} \cos\phi & \sin\phi & 0 \\ -\sin\phi & \cos\phi & 0 \\ 0 & 0 & 1 \end{bmatrix} \qquad \mathbf{M}_\theta = \begin{bmatrix} 1 & 0 & 0 \\ 0 & \cos\theta & \sin\theta \\ 0 & -\sin\theta & \cos\theta \end{bmatrix}$$

$$\mathbf{M}_\psi = \begin{bmatrix} \cos\psi & \sin\psi & 0 \\ -\sin\psi & \cos\psi & 0 \\ 0 & 0 & 1 \end{bmatrix}$$

Write down the overall transformation.

14

GENERAL DYNAMICAL PRINCIPLES OF RIGID BODY MOTION

14–1 Mass of the Rigid Body

With every rigid body S we can associate a nonnegative, additive and continuous function called its mass which is given by

$$M(S) = \iiint_S \rho(P)\, dV \tag{14.1}$$

where $\rho(P)$ is the density of the rigid body at the position of the point P. The mass does not depend on the position of the rigid body in space, nor does it depend on time.

When ρ is a constant, the rigid body is homogeneous.

If the rigid body is geometrically divided into n parts then

$$M(S) = \sum_{i=1}^{n} M(S_i)$$

or

$$M(S) = \sum_{i=1}^{n} \iiint_{S_i} \rho\, dV \tag{14.2}$$

This is a useful expression for evaluating the mass of those rigid bodies which have complicated geometrical shapes.

14–2 Auxiliary Expressions

With every point P of the rigid body let us associate a vector $\mathbf{r}(P, \alpha)$ which is dependent on a certain parameter α. If this vector function $\mathbf{r}(P, \alpha)$ is integrable over the whole rigid body S, then we can introduce another vector function

$$R(\alpha) = \iiint \rho(P)\mathbf{r}(P, \alpha)\, dV \tag{14.3}$$

If, in addition, the function $\mathbf{r}(P, \alpha)$ has derivatives $\dfrac{d\mathbf{r}(P, \alpha)}{d\alpha}$ at all points P and if these derivatives are integrable over the entire rigid body, then the function $\mathbf{R}(\alpha)$ has a derivative with respect to α given by

$$\frac{d\mathbf{R}(\alpha)}{d\alpha} = \iiint \rho(P) \frac{d\mathbf{r}(P, \alpha)}{d\alpha} \, dV \qquad (14.4)$$

This reasoning, appropriately generalized, applies to cases when more parameters than one α are involved.

We have seen in Section 2–10 that if we refer a vector $\mathbf{H}(t)$ to two frames of reference $K(x, y, z)$ and $K'(x', y', z')$, such that the second rotates with respect to the first with angular velocity ω, then the time rate of change of the vector evaluated by two observers placed respectively in the two frames, are related by

$$\frac{d_s \mathbf{H}(t)}{dt} = \frac{d_r \mathbf{H}(t)}{dt} + \omega \times \mathbf{H}(t) \qquad (14.5)$$

Consider now the position vector $\mathbf{r}(P, t)$ associated with the point P of the rigid body. The same vector referred to K' will be denoted by $\mathbf{r}'(P, t)$. Then, as stated above, we can define the two functions

$$\mathbf{R}(t) = \iiint \rho(P)\mathbf{r}(P, t) \, dV \qquad (14.6)$$

and

$$\mathbf{R}'(t) = \iiint \rho(P)\mathbf{r}'(P, t) \, dV \qquad (14.7)$$

Further

$$\frac{d_r \mathbf{R}'(t)}{dt} = \iiint \rho(P) \frac{d\mathbf{r}'(P, t)}{dt} \, dV \qquad (14.8)$$

and

$$\frac{d_r \mathbf{R}'(t)}{dt} = \iiint \rho(P) \left[\frac{d_s \mathbf{r}(P, t)}{dt} - \omega \times \mathbf{r}'(P, t) \right] dV \qquad (14.9)$$

or

$$\frac{d_r \mathbf{R}'(t)}{dt} = \iiint \rho(P) \frac{d_s \mathbf{r}(P, t)}{dt} \, dV - \omega \times \iiint \rho(P)\mathbf{r}'(P, t) \, dV$$

Using Eqs. (14.6) and (14.7), this last expression can be written as

$$\frac{d_s \mathbf{R}(t)}{dt} = \frac{d_r \mathbf{R}(t)}{dt} + \omega \times \mathbf{R}(t) \qquad (14.10)$$

The results obtained above will be applied many times in this chapter.

14–3   The Center of Mass

In Section 6–1 we have already defined the center of mass of a system of particles. Now, we wish to introduce the concept of *the center of mass* of a rigid body. Consider a rigid body S of mass M and density $\rho(P)$. Let O be any point, moving or fixed, and let $\overrightarrow{OP} = \mathbf{r}_P$. Then a unique point Q of the rigid body S can be defined by

$$M\bar{\mathbf{r}} = \iiint \rho(P)\mathbf{r}_P \, dV \qquad (14.11)$$

where $\bar{\mathbf{r}} = \overrightarrow{OQ}$.

The position of the point Q does not depend on the choice of the point O. In fact it does not change its position in the rigid body. Q is the center of mass of the rigid body.

Let O be a fixed point. Then

$$\dot{\mathbf{r}}_P = \frac{d\mathbf{r}_P}{dt} \quad \text{and} \quad \dot{\bar{\mathbf{r}}}_Q = \frac{d\bar{\mathbf{r}}}{dt}$$

give the velocities of P and Q respectively. Differentiating Eq. (14.11) with respect to time we obtain

$$M\dot{\bar{\mathbf{r}}} = \iiint \rho(P)\dot{\mathbf{r}}_P \, dV \tag{14.12}$$

and if we differentiate a second time we have

$$M\ddot{\bar{\mathbf{r}}} = \iiint \rho(P)\ddot{\mathbf{r}}_P \, dV \tag{14.13}$$

The last two expressions give the velocity and the acceleration of the center of the mass of the rigid body.

Let O be the origin of the fixed Cartesian frame of reference $K(x, y, z)$. In this frame let

$$\mathbf{r}_P = (x, y, z)$$

and

$$\bar{\mathbf{r}} = (\bar{x}, \bar{y}, \bar{z})$$

Further, let the system $K'(x', y', z')$ be rigidly attached to the body. In this system the point P will have coordinates (x', y', z'). Then

$$M\bar{x} = \iiint \rho(x', y', z')x \, dV$$

$$M\bar{y} = \iiint \rho(x', y', z')y \, dV \tag{14.14}$$

$$M\bar{z} = \iiint \rho(x', y', z')z \, dV$$

Of course, when evaluating the above integrals, x, y, z have to be expressed as functions of x', y', z'.

If K and K' coincide then

$$M\bar{x} = \iiint \rho(x', y', z')x' \, dV$$

$$M\bar{y} = \iiint \rho(x', y', z')y' \, dV \tag{14.15}$$

$$M\bar{z} = \iiint \rho(x', y', z')z' \, dV$$

In these equations we have made use of triple integrals. These will occur only when the rigid body fills a three-dimensional space. When the rigid body fills two- or one-dimensional space then, correspondingly, the integrals will be double or single.

It should be noticed that in Eqs. (14.14) x, y, and z are functions of time, whereas in Eqs. (14.15) time does not enter.

14-4 The Moment of Inertia of a Rigid Body

The moment of inertia plays a most important role in the rotation of rigid bodies. In the case of rotation about a fixed axis, the moment of inertia is a constant scalar. It plays the same role as mass in the linear motion.* For a general rotation, the moment of inertia varies and it is not a scalar.

Consider the rigid body as a system of particles such that the distances between any two particles remain constant. At a particular instant of time, the body will rotate about some instantaneous axis with an angular velocity $\boldsymbol{\omega}$. If the position vector of the i-th particle, measured from a fixed origin, is $\mathbf{r}_i$, then the linear velocity of this particle is

$$\dot{\mathbf{r}}_i = \boldsymbol{\omega} \times \mathbf{r}_i \tag{14.16}$$

and its angular momentum is

$$\mathbf{h}_i = \mathbf{r}_i \times m_i(\boldsymbol{\omega} \times \mathbf{r}_i) \tag{14.17}$$

The resultant angular momentum of the whole rigid body is

$$\mathbf{h} = \sum_i \mathbf{r}_i \times m_i(\boldsymbol{\omega} \times \mathbf{r}_i) \tag{14.18}$$

Expanding the right-hand side we obtain

$$\begin{aligned}
h_x &= I_{xx}\omega_x + I_{xy}\omega_y + I_{xz}\omega_z \\
h_y &= I_{yx}\omega_x + I_{yy}\omega_y + I_{yz}\omega_z \\
h_z &= I_{zx}\omega_x + I_{zy}\omega_y + I_{zz}\omega_z
\end{aligned} \tag{14.19}$$

where

$$I_{xx} = \sum_i m_i(y_i^2 + z_i^2) \quad I_{xy} = -\sum_i m_i x_i y_i \quad I_{xz} = -\sum_i m_i x_i z_i$$

$$I_{yx} = -\sum_i m_i y_i x_i \quad I_{yy} = \sum_i m_i(x_i^2 + z_i^2) \quad I_{yz} = -\sum_i m_i y_i z_i$$

$$I_{zx} = -\sum_i m_i z_i x_i \quad I_{zy} = -\sum_i m_i z_i y_i \quad I_{zz} = \sum_i m_i(x_i^2 + y_i^2)$$

$$\tag{14.20}$$

* One might say that mass is a quantitative measure of the resistance that a body offers to translational motion. If so, then the moment of inertia of the body rotating about a fixed axis is the quantitative measure of the resistance offered by the body to rotational motion.

We may write Eqs. (14.19) in matrix form as

$$
\begin{bmatrix} h_x \\ h_y \\ h_z \end{bmatrix} = \begin{bmatrix} I_{xx} & I_{xy} & I_{xz} \\ I_{yx} & I_{yy} & I_{yz} \\ I_{zx} & I_{zy} & I_{zz} \end{bmatrix} \begin{bmatrix} \omega_x \\ \omega_y \\ \omega_z \end{bmatrix} \tag{14.21}
$$

or, more concisely still, as

$$
\mathbf{h} = \mathbf{I}\boldsymbol{\omega} \tag{14.22}
$$

where $\mathbf{h}$ and $\boldsymbol{\omega}$ are column vectors and $\mathbf{I}$ stands for the three-by-three matrix of Eq. (14.21). We will call $\mathbf{I}$ the *inertia tensor*. We notice that it has two types of components. The diagonal components I_{xx}, I_{yy}, I_{zz} are the familiar *moments of inertia* of the body about the three axes Ox, Oy, Oz respectively. The components having mixed subscripts are called *products of inertia*.* If we denote the components of the moment of inertia tensor by I_{ij}, then I_{ii} are the moments of inertia and $I_{ij}(i \neq j)$ are the products of inertia. We notice that

$$
I_{ij} = I_{ji} \tag{14.23}
$$

There are therefore only three independent products of inertia.

In the case of a continuous distribution of matter, the moments and products of inertia are written as integrals

$$
I_{xx} = \iiint \rho(y^2 + z^2)\, dV \qquad I_{yy} = \iiint \rho(z^2 + x^2)\, dV
$$

$$
I_{zz} = \iiint \rho(x^2 + y^2)\, dV \tag{14.24}
$$

and

$$
I_{xy} = -\iiint \rho xy\, dV \qquad I_{yz} = -\iiint \rho yz\, dV \qquad I_{zx} = -\iiint \rho zx\, dV
$$

The inertia tensor $\mathbf{I}$ has been introduced above as the system of coefficients I_{ij}. From Eq. (14.21) or (14.22) we see that it plays a role of an operator. Operating on $\boldsymbol{\omega}$ with $\mathbf{I}$ yields the angular momentum vector $\mathbf{h}$. In general, therefore, $\mathbf{h}$ will not be parallel to $\boldsymbol{\omega}$.

The components of the inertia tensor can also be introduced in another way. Let us again consider the rigid body as a collection of point masses m_i and consider an axis passing through point O. Along the axis draw a unit vector $\mathbf{c}$ and let the position vector of the particle m_i be $\mathbf{r}_i$. If the line which we just introduced is the axis of rotation then the moment of inertia of the i-th particle about this axis is $m_i(\mathbf{r}_i \times \mathbf{c})^2$, because $(\mathbf{r}_i \times \mathbf{c})^2$ is the square of the distance from m_i to the axis (Fig. 14.1). For the entire rigid body

$$
I_{\mathbf{c}} = \sum_i m_i(\mathbf{r}_i \times \mathbf{c})^2 \tag{14.25}
$$

* Some authors define the products of inertia with a plus sign in front of the summation sign; then Eqs. (14.19) will have negative signs in front of the products of inertia.

14-4 The moment of inertia of a rigid body

Fig. 14.1

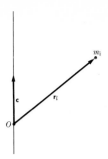

If α, β, γ are the direction cosines of the axis **c**, then the last expression can be expanded as

$$I_c = \sum_i m_i \{(y_i\gamma - z_i\beta)^2 + (z_i\alpha - x_i\gamma)^2 + (x_i\beta - y_i\alpha)^2\}$$

or

$$I_c = \sum_i m_i(y_i^2 + z_i^2)\alpha^2 + \sum_i m_i(z_i^2 + x_i^2)\beta^2 + \sum_i m_i(x_i^2 + y_i^2)$$
$$- 2\sum_i m_i y_i z_i \beta\gamma - 2\sum_i m_i z_i x_i \gamma\alpha - 2\sum_i m_i x_i y_i \alpha\beta \qquad (14.26)$$

We see that I has been expressed as a quadratic function in α, β, γ. The coefficients of this quadratic expression are the moments and products of inertia, I_{ij}.

We notice that the moment of inertia I, just evaluated, is the ordinary moment of inertia of the rigid body about the axis specified by the unit vector **c**.* If the rigid body rotates instantaneously about the axis **c** then the angular velocity vector lies along this axis and I given by Eq. (14.25) is the moment of inertia of the body. However, in the dynamical theory of the rotation of rigid bodies the moment of inertia in this form is hardly ever considered. Instead, as we shall see, the moments and products of inertia I_{ij} are used.

There is a very useful procedure which permits the evaluation of the moment of inertia I for any direction. From O draw a radius vector **R** in the direction about which the moment of inertia is to be evaluated. Let the length of this radius vector be given by

$$R = \frac{1}{\sqrt{I}} \qquad (14.27)$$

If the end point of **R** has coordinates x, y, z, then

$$\alpha = \frac{x}{R} \qquad \beta = \frac{y}{R} \qquad \gamma = \frac{z}{R}$$

or

$$\alpha = \sqrt{I}\,x \qquad \beta = \sqrt{I}\,y \qquad \gamma = \sqrt{I}\,z$$

* Its meaning is completely different from that of the inertia tensor introduced above.

Substitution into Eq. (14.26) yields

$$I_{xx}x^2 + I_{yy}y^2 + I_{zz}z^2 - 2I_{xy}xy - 2I_{yz}yz - 2I_{zx}zx = 1 \qquad (14.28)$$

This is an equation of an ellipsoid, called the *ellipsoid of inertia*. We have thus shown that the locus of end points of **R** is an ellipsoid.

As we know, there is a special system x', y', z' of coordinate axes for which the equation of an ellipsoid takes a particularly simple form. This happens when the principal axes of the ellipsoid lie along the coordinate axes. For these axes Eq. (14.28) becomes

$$I_1 x'^2 + I_2 y'^2 + I_3 z'^2 = 1 \qquad (14.29)$$

This particular system of axes is called the set of *principal axes of the rigid body* and we notice that in this system the products of inertia are absent and only the moments of inertia, denoted here by I_1, I_2, I_3 are left. These are called the *principal moments of inertia*. Once the principal moments of inertia and the principal axes are known, the ellipsoid of inertia can be obtained. The moment of inertia about any direction is then given by

$$I = \frac{1}{R^2} \qquad (14.30)$$

In general, as we have already stated, the angular momentum vector is not parallel to the angular velocity vector. In order that **h** be parallel to **ω** we must have
$$\frac{h_x}{h} = \frac{\omega_x}{\omega} \qquad \frac{h_y}{h} = \frac{\omega_y}{\omega} \qquad \frac{h_z}{h} = \frac{\omega_z}{\omega}$$

or
$$h_x = \frac{h}{\omega}\omega_x \qquad h_y = \frac{h}{\omega}\omega_y \qquad h_z = \frac{h}{\omega}\omega_z \qquad (14.31)$$

Here h_x/h, h_y/h, h_z/h are the direction cosines of **h**, and ω_x/ω, ω_y/ω, ω_z/ω are the direction cosines of **ω**. We see therefore that if **h** is to be parallel to **ω** then

$$h_x \propto \omega_x \qquad h_y \propto \omega_y \qquad h_z \propto \omega_z$$

with the same proportionality constant h/ω.

We repeat that in general **h** is not parallel to **ω**. Let us find out whether it is possible to realize some special rotations of the rigid body such that **ω** will be parallel to **h**. Choose any system of axes and evaluate the components of the moment of inertia tensor **I**. Then

$$\mathbf{h} = \mathbf{I}\boldsymbol{\omega}$$

This last equation, written in full, is given by Eq. (14.19). In addition, from Eq. (14.31), denoting h/ω by I, we have

$$h_x = I\omega_x$$
$$h_y = I\omega_y \qquad (14.32)$$
$$h_z = I\omega_z$$

Equating the right hand sides of Eq. (14.19) to (14.32) we obtain

$$I_{xx}\omega_x + I_{xy}\omega_y + I_{xz}\omega_z = I\omega_x$$
$$I_{yx}\omega_x + I_{yy}\omega_y + I_{yz}\omega_z = I\omega_y$$
$$I_{zx}\omega_x + I_{zy}\omega_y + I_{zz}\omega_z = I\omega_z$$

or

$$(I_{xx} - I)\omega_x + I_{xy}\omega_y + I_{xz}\omega_z = 0$$
$$I_{yx}\omega_x + (I_{yy} - I)\omega_y + I_{yz}\omega_z = 0 \qquad (14.33)$$
$$I_{zx}\omega_x + I_{zy}\omega_y + (I_{zz} - I)\omega_z = 0$$

This is a set of homogeneous equations. The unknowns are the required values of ω_x, ω_y, ω_z. In order that the set of equations have any solutions at all, the determinant of the coefficients of ω_x, ω_y, and ω_z must vanish. Thus we have

$$\begin{vmatrix} (I_{xx} - I) & I_{xy} & I_{xz} \\ I_{yx} & (I_{yy} - I) & I_{yz} \\ I_{zx} & I_{zy} & (I_{zz} - I) \end{vmatrix} = 0 \qquad (14.34)$$

This is an equation for the proportionality constant I. Actually it is a cubic and has three roots which we may denote by I_1, I_2, I_3. We now substitute each one of them in turn into the set of homogeneous equations (14.33). Since the equations are homogeneous, only the ratios ω_x/ω_z and ω_y/ω_z can be determined. Hence, all that we can determine is the directions in the rigid body such that if $\boldsymbol{\omega}$ is placed along them, (i.e., if the body rotates about these special directions) the angular momentum of the rigid body will be parallel to the angular velocity vector. In this case we can therefore write

$$h_{x'} = I_1\omega_{x'}$$
$$h_{y'} = I_2\omega_{y'} \qquad (14.35)$$
$$h_{z'} = I_3\omega_{z'}$$

where we have identified Ox', Oy', Oz' with the special directions.

If we want to write Eqs. (14.35) in the matrix form then we will obtain

$$\begin{bmatrix} h_{x'} \\ h_{y'} \\ h_{z'} \end{bmatrix} = \begin{bmatrix} I_1 & 0 & 0 \\ 0 & I_2 & 0 \\ 0 & 0 & I_3 \end{bmatrix} \begin{bmatrix} \omega_{x'} \\ \omega_{y'} \\ \omega_{z'} \end{bmatrix} \qquad (14.36)$$

We notice that *the moment of inertia matrix is now diagonal in form* and thus the products of inertia are absent.*

Returning to the ellipsoid of inertia we can express the same result as obtained above by saying that if the body rotates about any of its principal axes then the angular momentum will be parallel to the axis of rotation.

---

* Mathematically, therefore, the problem is solved by diagonalizing the moment of inertia matrix.

14-5 The Linear and Angular Momentum of Rigid Body

We have already discussed the linear and angular momentum in the case of a system of particles, and—when introducing the moment of inertia—carried over the expression for the angular momentum to the case of a rigid body. Let us reintroduce these concepts treating the rigid body as a continuous distribution of matter. Let us again consider a rigid body S, the density of which at any point P is given by $\rho(P)$.

The linear momentum of the rigid body is

$$\mathbf{p} = \iiint \rho(P)\dot{\mathbf{r}}_P \, dV \tag{14.37}$$

where $\dot{\mathbf{r}}_P$ is the velocity of the point P, and the integration, as always, extends over the entire rigid body.

The angular momentum of the rigid body about a point O is

$$\mathbf{h}_O = \iiint \rho(P)\mathbf{r}_P \times \dot{\mathbf{r}}_P \, dV \tag{14.38}$$

where $\mathbf{p}$ and $\mathbf{h}_O$ are vector functions of time.

Given two points O and O', the relation between $\mathbf{h}_O$ and $\mathbf{h}_{O'}$ is given by

$$\mathbf{h}_{O'} = \mathbf{h}_O - \mathbf{c} \times \mathbf{p} \tag{14.39}$$

where $\mathbf{c} = \overrightarrow{OO'}$.

Comparing (14.37) with (14.12) we find that

$$\mathbf{p} = M\dot{\mathbf{r}} \tag{14.40}$$

Thus the linear momentum of the rigid body is equal to the linear momentum of a point mass placed at and moving with the center of mass.

Let us determine the time derivatives of the linear and angular momenta. For the time derivative of the linear momentum we have, from Eq. (14.37)

$$\dot{\mathbf{p}} = \iiint \rho(P)\ddot{\mathbf{r}}_P \, dV \tag{14.41}$$

and from (14.40)

$$\dot{\mathbf{p}} = M\ddot{\mathbf{r}} \tag{14.42}$$

Therefore

$$M\ddot{\mathbf{r}} = \iiint \rho(P)\ddot{\mathbf{r}}_P \, dV \tag{14.43}$$

For the time derivative of the angular momentum, from Eq. (14.38), we obtain

$$\dot{\mathbf{h}}_O = \iiint \rho(P)[\dot{\mathbf{r}}_P \times \dot{\mathbf{r}}_P + \mathbf{r}_P \times \ddot{\mathbf{r}}_P] \, dV \tag{14.44}$$

or

$$\dot{\mathbf{h}}_O = \iiint \rho(P)\mathbf{r}_P \times \ddot{\mathbf{r}}_P \, dV \tag{14.45}$$

This is the result when O is fixed.

Let us now consider a moving origin O'. Its position with respect to the fixed origin will be denoted by the vector $\mathbf{c}$ (Fig. 14.2). Then

$$\mathbf{r}_{P}' = \mathbf{r}_{P} - \mathbf{c}$$

and

$$\dot{\mathbf{r}}_{P}' = \dot{\mathbf{r}}_{P} - \dot{\mathbf{c}}$$

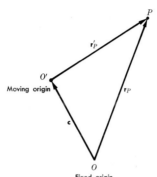

Fig. 14.2

The angular momentum of the rigid body about O'^{*} will now be

$$\mathbf{h}_{O'} = \iiint \rho(P)\mathbf{r}_{P'} \times \dot{\mathbf{r}}_{P} \, dV \tag{14.46}$$

or

$$\mathbf{h}_{O'} = \iiint \rho(P)(\mathbf{r}_{P} - \mathbf{c}) \times \dot{\mathbf{r}}_{P} \, dV$$

Time differentiation yields

$$\dot{\mathbf{h}}_{O'} = \iiint \rho(P)(\dot{\mathbf{r}}_{P} - \dot{\mathbf{c}}) \times \dot{\mathbf{r}}_{P} \, dV + \iiint \rho(P)(\mathbf{r}_{P} - \mathbf{c}) \times \ddot{\mathbf{r}}_{P} \, dV$$

In the second integral we substitute back $\mathbf{r}_{P} - \mathbf{c} = \mathbf{r}_{P}'$. Then

$$\dot{\mathbf{h}}_{O'} = -\mathbf{c} \times \iiint \rho(P)\dot{\mathbf{r}}_{P} \, dV + \iiint \rho(P)\mathbf{r}_{P}' \times \ddot{\mathbf{r}}_{P} \, dV$$

or, using Eq. (14.37)

$$\dot{\mathbf{h}}_{O'} + \dot{\mathbf{c}} \times \mathbf{p} = \iiint \rho(P)\mathbf{r}_{P}' \times \ddot{\mathbf{r}}_{P} \, dV \tag{14.47}$$

If O' becomes the center of mass, Q, then

$$\dot{\mathbf{h}}_{Q} = \iiint \rho(P)\mathbf{r}_{Q}' \times \ddot{\mathbf{r}}_{P} \, dV \tag{14.48}$$

* The angular momentum of the rigid body given by Eq. (14.46) is such that every element of integration in Eq. (14.46) is the moment about O' of momentum of $\rho(P) \, dV$ relative to O. A thorough discussion of this point for the case of a system of particles can be found in Section 6–4.

where $\mathbf{r}_Q' = \overrightarrow{QP}$. In this case the second term on the left in Eq. (14.47) vanishes in view of Eq. (14.40).

14-6   The Kinetic Energy

The kinetic energy of a rigid body is given by

$$T = \tfrac{1}{2} \iiint \rho(P) \dot{\mathbf{r}}_P{}^2 \, dV \qquad (14.49)$$

If O' is an arbitrary point of the rigid body and $\boldsymbol{\omega}$ is the angular velocity of the body then

$$\dot{\mathbf{r}}_P = \dot{\mathbf{c}} + \boldsymbol{\omega} \times \mathbf{r}_P' \qquad (14.50)$$

From this we have

$$\dot{\mathbf{r}}_P{}^2 = \dot{\mathbf{c}}^2 + 2\dot{\mathbf{c}} \cdot \boldsymbol{\omega} \times \mathbf{r}_P' + (\boldsymbol{\omega} \times \mathbf{r}_P')^2$$

Since $\mathbf{c}$ and $\boldsymbol{\omega}$ do not depend on the variables of integration

$$T = \tfrac{1}{2}\dot{\mathbf{c}}^2 \iiint \rho(P) \, dV + \dot{\mathbf{c}} \cdot \boldsymbol{\omega} \times \iiint \rho(P)\mathbf{r}_P' \, dV + \tfrac{1}{2} \iiint \rho(P)(\boldsymbol{\omega} \times \mathbf{r}_P')^2 \, dV$$

Now

$$\iiint \rho(P) \, dV = M$$

$$\iiint \rho(P)\mathbf{r}_P' \, dV = M\bar{\mathbf{r}}'$$

and

$$\iiint \rho(P)(\boldsymbol{\omega} \times \mathbf{r}_P')^2 \, dV = \omega^2 \iiint \rho(P){r_\perp}^2 \, dV$$

$$= I_{O'}\omega^2$$

where $r_\perp$ is the distance of P from the line parallel to the instantaneous axis of rotation and passing through O'; $I_{O'}$ is the moment of inertia about this axis; $\bar{\mathbf{r}}'$ is $\overrightarrow{O'Q}$, i.e., it is the position vector of the center of mass Q with respect to O'. In view of these last relations

$$T = \tfrac{1}{2}M\dot{\mathbf{c}}^2 + M\dot{\mathbf{c}} \cdot \boldsymbol{\omega} \times \bar{\mathbf{r}}' + \tfrac{1}{2}I_{O'}\omega^2 \qquad (14.51)$$

If $O' \equiv Q$, then $\bar{\mathbf{r}}' = \mathbf{0}$ and

$$T = \tfrac{1}{2}M\dot{\mathbf{r}}_Q{}^2 + \tfrac{1}{2}I_Q\omega^2 \qquad (14.52)$$

Equation (14.52) states that *the kinetic energy of the rigid body of mass M is equal to the kinetic energy of a point mass M placed at and moving with the center of mass Q, plus the kinetic energy of rotation of the body about an axis passing through the center of mass.*

200

We will now discuss the dynamical principles of the unconstrained motion of a rigid body. As we know, an unconstrained rigid body has six degrees of freedom. The laws governing the motion of a rigid body are generalizations of Newton's laws. They are the idealized results of experiments and observations performed on material rigid bodies. Formally, the laws can be made identical with those for a system of particles but it must be realized that they cannot be derived from them without additional postulates.

Some particular motion of a rigid body is caused by a certain system of forces acting on it. We can easily see, however, that from the studies of the motion, the system of forces cannot be determined uniquely. Indeed, every system of forces causing the rigid body to move in a certain way can be replaced by another equivalent system resulting in the same motion. *The important quantities which at a particular time have unique values are the linear and the angular momenta of the rigid body.*

Let us first consider a closed system consisting of n rigid bodies $S_1, S_2, \ldots$, S_n. A closed system consisting of a single rigid body is called an isolated body. *An isolated rigid body moves in such a way that the time rates of change of both the linear and angular momenta are zero*, i.e.

$$\dot{\mathbf{p}} = \mathbf{0} \tag{14.53}$$

and
$$\dot{\mathbf{h}}_{O'} + \dot{\mathbf{c}} \times \mathbf{p} = \mathbf{0} \tag{14.54}$$

where $\mathbf{c}$ is the velocity of the origin O' with respect to which both momenta are evaluated. The two equations (14.53) and (14.54) can also be written as

$$\iiint \rho(P)\ddot{\mathbf{r}}_P \, dV = \mathbf{0} \tag{14.55}$$

and
$$\iiint \rho(P)\mathbf{r}_{P'} \times \ddot{\mathbf{r}}_P = \mathbf{0} \tag{14.56}$$

A closed system consisting of two rigid bodies S_1 and S_2 moves in such a way that at every moment the linear momenta $\mathbf{p}_1$ and $\mathbf{p}_2$ and the angular momenta $\mathbf{h}_{O'1}$ and $\mathbf{h}_{O'2}$ satisfy the equations

$$\dot{\mathbf{p}}_1 + \dot{\mathbf{p}}_2 = \mathbf{0} \tag{14.57}$$

and
$$\dot{\mathbf{h}}_{O'1} + \dot{\mathbf{h}}_{O'2} + \dot{\mathbf{c}} \times \mathbf{p}_1 + \dot{\mathbf{c}} \times \mathbf{p}_2 = \mathbf{0} \tag{14.58}$$

Again, these can be replaced by

$$\iiint_{S_1} \rho(P_1)\ddot{\mathbf{r}}_1 \, dV_1 + \iiint_{S_2} \rho(P_2)\ddot{\mathbf{r}}_2 \, dV_2 = \mathbf{0} \tag{14.59}$$

and
$$\iiint \rho(P_1)\mathbf{r}_{1'} \times \ddot{\mathbf{r}}_1 \, dV_1 + \iiint \rho(P_2)\mathbf{r}_{2'} \times \ddot{\mathbf{r}}_2 \, dV_2 = \mathbf{0} \tag{14.60}$$

In a closed system consisting of a finite number of material rigid bodies, any rigid body acts on another one as if the two constituted a closed system.

A closed system consisting of n rigid bodies moves in such a way that the following set of equations is valid

$$\dot{\mathbf{p}}_k = \mathbf{F}_k \qquad (14.61)$$

and $$\dot{\mathbf{h}}_{O'k} + \dot{\mathbf{c}} \times \mathbf{p}_k = \mathbf{G}_{O'k} \qquad (k = 1, 2, \ldots, n) \qquad (14.62)$$

where $\mathbf{p}_k$ and $\mathbf{h}_{O'k}$ are linear and angular momenta of the k-th rigid body and $\mathbf{F}_k$ and $\mathbf{G}_{O'k}$ are the resultant force and torque in the k-th body. Every equation is equivalent to three scalar equations, yielding altogether $6n$ scalar equations, from which the $6n$ parameters describing the n rigid bodies can be obtained.

14-8   Rigid Body Referred to Frames Which Move with Respect to Each Other

We will now consider two frames of reference $K(x, y, z)$ and $K_1(x_1, y_1, z_1)$. Let $\boldsymbol{\omega}_1$ denote the angular velocity of K_1 with respect to K. We will assume that Newton's laws are valid in the system K. Variables with no subscripts will refer to K and those with subscript 1, to the K_1 frame. Thus any point P of our rigid body S will have velocity and acceleration $\mathbf{v}$ and $\mathbf{a}$ when referred to K, and velocity $\mathbf{v}_1$ and acceleration $\mathbf{a}_1$, when referred to K_1. We know from the kinematical theory that these velocities and accelerations are related by

$$\mathbf{v} = \mathbf{v}_1 + \mathbf{v}_e \qquad (14.63)$$

and $$\mathbf{a} = \mathbf{a}_1 + \mathbf{a}_c + \mathbf{a}_e \qquad (14.64)$$

where $$\mathbf{v}_e = \mathbf{v}_Q + \boldsymbol{\omega}_1 \times \mathbf{r}_1 \qquad (14.65)$$

Here $\mathbf{r}_1 = \overrightarrow{QP}$ and Q is an arbitrary point which belongs to the space K_1. Further, $\mathbf{a}_c$ is the Coriolis acceleration given by

$$\mathbf{a}_c = 2\boldsymbol{\omega}_1 \times \mathbf{v}_1 \qquad (14.66)$$

and finally $$\mathbf{a}_e = \mathbf{a}_Q + \mathbf{r}_1 \times \frac{d\boldsymbol{\omega}_1}{dt} + \boldsymbol{\omega}_1 \times (\boldsymbol{\omega}_1 \times \mathbf{r}_1) \qquad (14.67)$$

Let $\mathbf{p}_1$ and $\mathbf{h}_{O1}$ denote the linear and angular momenta of the rigid body in its motion in the space K_1. Then

$$\dot{\mathbf{p}}_1 = \iiint \rho \mathbf{a}_1 \, dV \qquad (14.68)$$

and $$\dot{\mathbf{h}}_{O1} + (\mathbf{v}_O)_1 \times \mathbf{p}_1 = \iiint \rho \mathbf{r} \times \mathbf{a}_1 \, dV \qquad (14.69)$$

Here $\mathbf{r} = \overrightarrow{OP}$ and $(\mathbf{v}_O)_1$ is the velocity of O measured in K_1.

Let $\mathbf{p}$ and $\mathbf{h}_O$ denote the linear and angular momenta of the same rigid body but referred to the space K. Then by (14.63) and (14.64)

$$\mathbf{p} = \iiint \rho \mathbf{v}_1 \, dV + \iiint \rho \mathbf{v}_e \, dV \tag{14.70}$$

$$\dot{\mathbf{p}} = \iiint \rho \mathbf{a}_1 \, dV + \iiint \rho \mathbf{a}_e \, dV + \iiint \rho \mathbf{a}_c \, dV \tag{14.71}$$

and

$$\dot{\mathbf{h}}_O + \mathbf{v}_O \times \mathbf{p} = \iiint \rho \mathbf{r} \times \mathbf{a}_1 \, dV + \iiint \rho \mathbf{r} \times \mathbf{a}_e \, dV + \iiint \rho \mathbf{r} \times \mathbf{a}_c \, dV \tag{14.72}$$

The vector equations of motion of the rigid body S in the frame K are

$$\dot{\mathbf{p}} = \mathbf{F}$$

and

$$\dot{\mathbf{h}} + \mathbf{v}_O \times \mathbf{p} = \mathbf{G}$$

where $\mathbf{F}$ and $\mathbf{G}$ are the net force and the net torque acting on the rigid body as measured by an observer in K. On the basis of Eqs. (14.68)–(14.72), the equations of motion of S in the frame K_1

$$\dot{\mathbf{p}}_1 = \dot{\mathbf{p}} - \iiint \rho \mathbf{a}_c \, dV - \iiint \rho \mathbf{a}_e \, dV \tag{14.73}$$

and

$$\dot{\mathbf{h}}_{O1} + (\mathbf{v}_O)_1 \times \mathbf{p}_1 = \dot{\mathbf{h}}_O + \mathbf{v}_O \times \mathbf{p} - \iiint \rho \mathbf{r} \times \mathbf{a}_c \, dV - \iiint \rho \mathbf{r} \times \mathbf{a}_c \, dV \tag{14.74}$$

We can now write these results as

$$\dot{\mathbf{p}}_1 = \mathbf{F}_1 + \mathbf{F}_c + \mathbf{F}_e \tag{14.75}$$

and

$$\dot{\mathbf{h}}_{O1} + (\mathbf{v}_O)_1 \times \mathbf{p}_1 = \mathbf{G}_{O1} + \mathbf{G}_{Oc} + \mathbf{G}_{Oe} \tag{14.76}$$

where $\mathbf{F}_c$ and $\mathbf{F}_e$ are given by

$$\mathbf{F}_c = - \iiint \rho \mathbf{a}_c \, dV \tag{14.77}$$

and

$$\mathbf{F}_e = - \iiint \rho \mathbf{a}_e \, dV$$

respectively, with

$$\mathbf{G}_{Oc} = - \iiint \rho \mathbf{r} \times \mathbf{a}_c \, dV$$

and $\hspace{8cm}$ (14.78)

$$\mathbf{G}_{Oe} = - \iiint \rho \mathbf{r} \times \mathbf{a}_e \, dV$$

We will now summarize the results which we have just obtained. We are given two frames of reference K and K_1 which have common time. *In order* to pass from the equations of motion of a rigid body S in system K to the system K_1 we have to add in the linear momentum equation the Coriolis and the lifting ($\mathbf{F}_e$) forces, and in the angular momentum equations, we must add the torques caused by these two fictitious forces.

14–9 D'Alembert's Principle for Rigid Bodies

The equations of unconstrained motion of a rigid body are of the form

$$\mathbf{F} - \dot{\mathbf{p}} = \mathbf{0} \tag{14.79}$$

and
$$\dot{\mathbf{h}}_{O'} + \dot{\mathbf{c}} \times \mathbf{p} - \mathbf{G}_{O'} = \mathbf{0} \tag{14.80}$$

where $\mathbf{F}$ is the resultant force acting on the rigid body, $\mathbf{G}_{O'}$ is the resultant torque and $\mathbf{c}$ is the position vector of the moving origin O'. Let us scalar-multiply the first equation by an arbitrary vector $\mathbf{B}$, and the second equation by an arbitrary vector $\mathbf{A}$. Adding the resulting two equations we obtain

$$(\mathbf{F} - \dot{\mathbf{p}}) \cdot \mathbf{B} + (\dot{\mathbf{h}}_O + \dot{\mathbf{c}} \times \mathbf{p} - \mathbf{G}_{O'}) \cdot \mathbf{A} = 0 \tag{14.81}$$

This identity represents *D'Alembert's principle of a rigid body moving under no constraints.*

As we know, a rigid body has six degrees of freedom, therefore to describe its motion we need six generalized coordinates $q_i (i = 1, 2, \ldots, 6)$. We can associate with every point of the rigid body a function which will be a point function of all six generalized coordinates. The motion of the rigid body is completely determined if the q_i's are determined as functions of time.

Let (x', y', z') be a frame of reference fixed in the rigid body, and let the angular velocity vector referred to this frame be given by

$$\boldsymbol{\omega} = \omega_{x'}\mathbf{i}' + \omega_{y'}\mathbf{j}' + \omega_{z'}\mathbf{k}' \tag{14.82}$$

where $\mathbf{i}'$, $\mathbf{j}'$, $\mathbf{k}'$ are unit vectors along the axes x', y', z'. On the basis of Euler's theorem for homogeneous functions we can write

$$\boldsymbol{\omega} = \sum_{i=1}^{6} \frac{\partial \boldsymbol{\omega}}{\partial \dot{q}_i} \dot{q}_i \tag{14.83}$$

where $\partial \boldsymbol{\omega}/\partial \dot{q}_i$ does not depend on $\dot{q}_i$.* Let O' and P be two points fixed in the rigid body. The linear velocities of P and O' are related by

$$\dot{\mathbf{r}}_P = \dot{\mathbf{c}} + \boldsymbol{\omega} \times \mathbf{r}_P' \tag{14.84}$$

where all the symbols are shown in Figure 14.2. Now

$$\frac{d\mathbf{r}_P}{dt} = \sum \frac{\partial \mathbf{r}_P}{\partial q_i} \dot{q}_i \qquad \frac{d\mathbf{c}}{dt} = \sum \frac{\partial \mathbf{c}}{\partial q_i} \dot{q}_i \tag{14.85}$$

---

* The angular velocity vector $\boldsymbol{\omega}$ is a function of the generalized coordinates q_i and of the generalized velocities $\dot{q}_i$. Equation (14.83) follows from the fact that $\boldsymbol{\omega}$ is a linear function of the generalized velocities $\dot{q}_i$.

Using these and (14.83) we can write (14.84) in the form

$$\sum_{i=1}^{6}\left[\frac{\partial \mathbf{r}_P}{\partial q_i} - \frac{\partial \mathbf{c}}{\partial q_i} - \frac{\partial \boldsymbol{\omega}}{\partial \dot{q}_i} \times \mathbf{r}_{P'}\right]\dot{q}_i = \mathbf{0} \qquad (14.86)$$

This relation is true for any motion of the rigid body, therefore it is true for any $\dot{q}_i$. Thus we obtain

$$\frac{\partial \mathbf{r}_P}{\partial q_i} - \frac{\partial \mathbf{c}}{\partial q_i} - \frac{\partial \boldsymbol{\omega}}{\partial \dot{q}_i} \times \mathbf{r}_{P'} = \mathbf{0} \qquad i = 1, 2, \ldots, 6 \qquad (14.87)$$

Let us now introduce the following two vector quantities

$$\delta \boldsymbol{\gamma} = \sum_{i=1}^{6} \frac{\partial \boldsymbol{\omega}}{\partial \dot{q}_i}\, \delta q_i \qquad \delta \mathbf{c} = \sum_{i=1}^{6} \frac{\partial \mathbf{c}}{\partial q_i}\, \delta q_i \qquad (14.88)$$

where δq_i are arbitrary numbers. The meaning of $\delta \mathbf{c}$ is clear: it is the virtual displacement of the point O' of Figure 14.2. $\delta \boldsymbol{\gamma}$ is a vector field which we might term the angular virtual displacement. In fact, if we use the Eulerian angles, ϕ, ψ, θ, as three of the generalized coordinates q_i, then, using Eqs. (13.37) in the right-hand side of

$$\delta \boldsymbol{\gamma} = \sum \frac{\partial \boldsymbol{\omega}}{\partial \dot{q}_i}\, \delta q_i$$

we obtain $\qquad\qquad \delta \boldsymbol{\gamma} \equiv (\delta \gamma_{x'}, \delta \gamma_{y'}, \delta \gamma_{z'})$

where
$$\delta \gamma_{x'} = \sin \psi \sin \theta \; \delta \phi + \cos \psi \; \delta \theta$$
$$\delta \gamma_{y'} = \cos \psi \sin \theta \; \delta \phi - \cos \psi \; \delta \theta$$
$$\delta \gamma_{z'} = \delta \psi + \cos \theta \; \delta \phi$$

from which the meaning of $\delta \boldsymbol{\gamma}$ can be seen more clearly.

We will put
$$\mathbf{A} = \delta \boldsymbol{\gamma} \qquad \text{and} \qquad \mathbf{B} = \delta \mathbf{c} \qquad (14.89)$$

and substitute these into the expression for d'Alembert's principle. Into this expression we will also put

$$\dot{\mathbf{p}} = \iiint \rho \ddot{\mathbf{r}}_P \, dV$$

and

$$\dot{\mathbf{h}}_{O'} + \dot{\mathbf{c}} \times \mathbf{p} = \iiint \rho \mathbf{r}' \times \ddot{\mathbf{r}}_P \, dV$$

D'Alembert's principle for rigid body then takes the form

$$\sum_i \delta q_i \iiint \rho \left[\ddot{\mathbf{r}}_P \cdot \frac{\partial \mathbf{c}}{\partial q_i} + \ddot{\mathbf{r}}_P \times \mathbf{r}_{P'} \cdot \frac{\partial \boldsymbol{\omega}}{\partial \dot{q}_i}\right] dV = \sum_i \left[\mathbf{F} \cdot \frac{\partial \mathbf{c}}{\partial q_i} + \mathbf{G}_{O'} \cdot \frac{\partial \boldsymbol{\omega}}{\partial \dot{q}_i}\right] \delta q_i$$

$$= \mathbf{F} \cdot \delta \mathbf{c} + \mathbf{G}_{O'} \cdot \delta \boldsymbol{\gamma} \qquad (14.90)$$

In the last equation the δq_i's are completely arbitrary, thus we obtain the following six equations

$$\iiint \rho \left[\ddot{\mathbf{r}}_P \cdot \frac{\partial \mathbf{c}}{\partial q_i} + \ddot{\mathbf{r}}_P \times \mathbf{r}_{P'} \cdot \frac{\partial \boldsymbol{\omega}}{\partial \dot{q}_i} \right] dV = \mathbf{F} \cdot \frac{\partial \mathbf{c}}{\partial q_i} + \mathbf{G}_{O'} \cdot \frac{\partial \boldsymbol{\omega}}{\partial \dot{q}_i}$$

$$i = 1, 2, \ldots, 6 \qquad (14.91)$$

Using the identity (14.87) we arrive at

$$\ddot{\mathbf{r}}_P \cdot \frac{\partial \mathbf{c}}{\partial q_i} + \ddot{\mathbf{r}}_P \times \mathbf{r}_{P'} \cdot \frac{\partial \boldsymbol{\omega}}{\partial \dot{q}_i} = \ddot{\mathbf{r}}_P \cdot \left[\frac{\partial \mathbf{c}}{\partial q_i} + \mathbf{r}' \times \frac{\partial \boldsymbol{\omega}}{\partial \dot{q}_i} \right] = \ddot{\mathbf{r}}_P \cdot \frac{\partial \mathbf{r}_P}{\partial \dot{q}_i} \qquad (14.92)$$

In deriving Lagrange's equations for particles we have used identities which we called cancellation of dots and interchanging of d and ∂. In the case of a rigid body* these are

$$\frac{\partial \mathbf{r}_P}{\partial q_i} = \frac{\partial \dot{\mathbf{r}}_P}{\partial \dot{q}_i} \qquad \frac{d}{dt} \frac{\partial \mathbf{r}_P}{\partial q_i} = \frac{\partial \dot{\mathbf{r}}_P}{\partial q_i} \qquad (14.93)$$

Using these we get

$$\ddot{\mathbf{r}}_P \cdot \frac{\partial \mathbf{r}_P}{\partial q_i} = \frac{d}{dt} \left(\dot{\mathbf{r}}_P \cdot \frac{\partial \mathbf{r}_P}{\partial q_i} \right) - \dot{\mathbf{r}}_P \frac{d}{dt} \frac{\partial \mathbf{r}_P}{\partial q_i}$$

$$= \frac{d}{dt} \left(\dot{\mathbf{r}}_P \cdot \frac{\partial \dot{\mathbf{r}}_P}{\partial \dot{q}_i} \right) - \dot{\mathbf{r}}_P \cdot \frac{\partial \dot{\mathbf{r}}_P}{\partial q_i} \qquad (14.94)$$

Thus Eq. (14.91) can be written as

$$\iiint \rho \frac{d}{dt} \left(\dot{\mathbf{r}}_P \cdot \frac{\partial \dot{\mathbf{r}}_P}{\partial \dot{q}_i} \right) dV - \iiint \rho \dot{\mathbf{r}}_P \cdot \frac{\partial \dot{\mathbf{r}}_P}{\partial q_i} dV$$

$$= \frac{d}{dt} \iiint \rho \dot{\mathbf{r}}_P \cdot \frac{\partial \dot{\mathbf{r}}_P}{\partial \dot{q}_i} dV - \iiint \rho \dot{\mathbf{r}}_P \cdot \frac{\partial \dot{\mathbf{r}}_P}{\partial q_i} dV \qquad (14.95)$$

$$= \mathbf{F} \cdot \frac{\partial \mathbf{c}}{\partial q_i} + \mathbf{G}_{O'} \cdot \frac{\partial \boldsymbol{\omega}}{\partial \dot{q}_i}$$

We notice that

$$\iiint \rho \dot{\mathbf{r}}_P \cdot \frac{\partial \dot{\mathbf{r}}_P}{\partial \dot{q}_i} dV = \frac{1}{2} \iiint \rho \frac{\partial \dot{\mathbf{r}}_P{}^2}{\partial \dot{q}_i} dV$$

$$= \frac{\partial}{\partial \dot{q}_i} \frac{1}{2} \iiint \rho \dot{\mathbf{r}}_P{}^2 dV \qquad (14.96)$$

$$= \frac{\partial T}{\partial \dot{q}_i}$$

* These relations should be derived using a similar procedure as before, (see Sec. 8–1).

and

$$\iiint \rho \dot{\mathbf{r}}_P \cdot \frac{\partial \dot{\mathbf{r}}_P}{\partial q_i} \, dV = \frac{1}{2} \iiint \rho \frac{\partial \dot{\mathbf{r}}_P^2}{\partial q_i} \, dV$$

$$= \frac{\partial}{\partial q_i} \frac{1}{2} \iiint \rho \dot{\mathbf{r}}_P^2 \, dV \qquad (14.97)$$

$$= \frac{\partial T}{\partial q_i}$$

where T is the kinetic energy. Eqs. (14.95) can now be written as

$$\frac{d}{dt} \frac{\partial T}{\partial \dot{q}_i} - \frac{\partial T}{\partial q_i} = \mathbf{F} \cdot \frac{\partial \mathbf{c}}{\partial q_i} + \mathbf{G}_{O'} \cdot \frac{\partial \boldsymbol{\omega}}{\partial \dot{q}_i} \qquad i = 1, 2, \ldots, 6 \qquad (14.98)$$

These are Lagrange's equations for a rigid body under the influence of no constraints. The right-hand sides of these equations, viz.

$$Q_i = \mathbf{F} \cdot \frac{\partial \mathbf{c}}{\partial q_i} + \mathbf{G}_{O'} \cdot \frac{\partial \boldsymbol{\omega}}{\partial \dot{q}_i} \qquad (14.99)$$

are the generalized forces.

D'Alembert's principle can therefore be written as

$$\sum_{i=1} \left[\frac{d}{dt} \frac{\partial T}{\partial \dot{q}_i} - \frac{\partial T}{\partial \dot{q}_i} - Q_i \right] \delta q_i = 0 \qquad (14.100)$$

If the generalized forces are derivable from a potential independent of the generalized velocities $\dot{q}_i$, i.e., if

$$Q_i = - \frac{\partial V(t, q)}{\partial q_i} \qquad (14.101)$$

then Lagrange's equations take the form

$$\frac{d}{dt} \frac{\partial L}{\partial \dot{q}_i} - \frac{\partial L}{\partial q_i} = 0 \qquad i = 1, 2, \ldots, 6 \qquad (14.102)$$

where

$$L = T - V$$

is the Lagrangian of the rigid body.

The right hand side of the second Eq. (14.90), viz., the quantity

$$\mathbf{F} \cdot \delta \mathbf{c} + \mathbf{G}_{O'} \cdot \delta \boldsymbol{\gamma}$$

represents the virtual work performed on the body corresponding to $\delta \mathbf{c}$ and to $\delta \boldsymbol{\gamma}$.

This statement might require some clarification. Examining Figure 14.2 we see that the virtual displacement $\delta \mathbf{r}_P$ of the point P (with respect to the fixed origin O) expressed in terms of generalized coordinates is

$$\delta \mathbf{r}_P = \sum_{i=1}^{6} \frac{\partial \mathbf{r}_P}{\partial q_i} \delta q_i$$

Using Eqs. (14.87) we find that

$$\delta \mathbf{r}_P = \sum_{i=1}^{6} \left(\frac{\partial \mathbf{c}}{\partial q_i} + \frac{\partial \boldsymbol{\gamma}}{\partial \dot{q}_i} \times \mathbf{r}_P' \right) \delta q_i$$

which in view of Eqs. (14.88) yields

$$\delta \mathbf{r}_P = \delta \mathbf{c} + \delta \boldsymbol{\gamma} \times \mathbf{r}_P'$$

Thus the virtual displacement $\delta \mathbf{r}_P$ of the point P has been expressed as the sum of the virtual displacement $\delta \mathbf{c}$ of the point O' and the virtual displacement of the point P with respect to the point O'.

Let a force $\mathbf{F}_k$ act on the point P. Scalar-multiplying both sides of the last equation by $\mathbf{F}_k$ we obtain

$$\mathbf{F}_k \cdot \delta \mathbf{r}_P = \mathbf{F}_k \cdot \delta \mathbf{c} + \mathbf{F}_k \cdot \delta \boldsymbol{\gamma} \times \mathbf{r}_P'$$

Using the permutation property of the triple scalar product we have

$$\mathbf{F}_k \cdot \delta \mathbf{r}_P = \mathbf{F}_k \cdot \delta \mathbf{c} + \delta \boldsymbol{\gamma} \cdot \mathbf{r}_P' \times \mathbf{F}_k$$

or $\qquad \mathbf{F}_k \cdot \delta \mathbf{r}_P = \mathbf{F}_k \cdot \delta \mathbf{c} + \delta \boldsymbol{\gamma} \cdot \mathbf{G}_{O'k}$

where now $\mathbf{G}_{O'k}$ is the moment of the force $\mathbf{F}_k$ about the point O'.

The virtual work

$$\mathbf{F} \cdot \delta \mathbf{c} + \mathbf{G}_{O'} \cdot \delta \boldsymbol{\gamma}$$

is also given by $\sum_{i=1}^{6} Q_i \, \delta q_i$; thus

$$\mathbf{F} \cdot \delta \mathbf{c} + \mathbf{G}_{O'} \cdot \delta \boldsymbol{\gamma} = \sum_{i=1}^{6} Q_i \, \delta q_i \qquad (14.103)$$

In order to write down Lagrange's equations for a rigid body, we must first calculate the kinetic energy T of the rigid body and then evaluate the virtual work Eq. (14.103) performed on the body during the virtual displacements $\delta \mathbf{c}$ and $\delta \boldsymbol{\gamma}$. Lagrange's equations then become

$$\frac{d}{dt} \frac{\partial T}{\partial \dot{q}_i} - \frac{\partial T}{\partial q_i} = Q_i \qquad (14.104)$$

Let $\mathbf{i}, \mathbf{j}, \mathbf{k}$ be unit vectors along the coordinate axes of any rectangular frame of reference. In this frame let

$$
\begin{aligned}
\delta \mathbf{c} &\equiv (\delta c_x, \, \delta c_y, \, \delta c_z) \\
\delta \boldsymbol{\gamma} &\equiv (\delta \gamma_x, \, \delta \gamma_y, \, \delta \gamma_z) \\
\mathbf{F} &\equiv (X, Y, Z) \\
\mathbf{G}_{O'} &\equiv (G_x, G_y, G_z)
\end{aligned}
\qquad (14.105)
$$

The virtual work is then given by

$$
\begin{aligned}
\mathbf{F} \cdot \delta \mathbf{c} + \mathbf{G}_{O'} \cdot \delta \boldsymbol{\gamma} &= (X\mathbf{i} + Y\mathbf{j} + Z\mathbf{k}) \cdot (\delta c_x \mathbf{i} + \delta c_y \mathbf{j} + \delta c_z \mathbf{k}) \\
&\quad + (G_x \mathbf{i} + G_y \mathbf{j} + G_z \mathbf{k}) \cdot (\delta \gamma_x \mathbf{i} + \delta \gamma_y \mathbf{j} + \delta \gamma_z \mathbf{k}) \\
&= X \, \delta c_x + Y \, \delta c_y + Z \, \delta c_z + G_x \, \delta \gamma_x + G_y \, \delta \gamma_y + G_z \, \delta \gamma_z
\end{aligned}
$$
$$(14.106)$$

The last expression can be rendered more general by considering two rectangular Cartesian frames of reference K and K', specified by unit vectors **i**, **j**, **k** and **i'**, **j'**, **k'** respectively. Let **F** and $\delta\mathbf{c}$ be specified in K as

$$\mathbf{F} = X\mathbf{i} + Y\mathbf{j} + Z\mathbf{k}$$

and
$$\delta\mathbf{c} = \delta c_x\mathbf{i} + \delta c_y\mathbf{j} + \delta c_z\mathbf{k} \tag{14.107}$$

and $\mathbf{G}_{O'}$ and $\delta\boldsymbol{\gamma}$ in K' as

$$\mathbf{G}_{O'} = G_{x'}\mathbf{i'} + G_{y'}\mathbf{j'} + G_{z'}\mathbf{k'}$$

and
$$\delta\boldsymbol{\gamma} = \delta\gamma_{x'}\mathbf{i'} + \delta\gamma_{y'}\mathbf{j'} + \delta\gamma_{z'}\mathbf{k'} \tag{14.108}$$

Then

$$\mathbf{F} \cdot \delta\mathbf{c} + \mathbf{G}_{O'} \cdot \delta\boldsymbol{\gamma} = X\,\delta c_x + Y\,\delta c_y + Z\,\delta c_z + G_{x'}\,\delta\gamma_{x'} + G_{y'}\,\delta\gamma_{y'} + G_{z'}\,\delta\gamma_z \tag{14.109}$$

For the angular velocity we can also write[*]

$$\boldsymbol{\omega} = \dot{\psi}\mathbf{u}_{z'} + \dot{\phi}\mathbf{u}_z + \dot{\theta}\mathbf{u}_N \tag{14.110}$$

where $\mathbf{u}_{z'}$ is the unit vector along the body axis, $\mathbf{u}_z$ that along the space axis, and $\mathbf{u}_N$ is the unit vector along the line of nodes.[**] From (14.110)

$$\delta\boldsymbol{\gamma} = \mathbf{u}_{z'}\,\delta\psi + \mathbf{u}_z\,\delta\phi + \mathbf{u}_N\,\delta\theta \tag{14.111}$$

Thus

$$\mathbf{F} \cdot \delta\mathbf{c} + \mathbf{G}_{O'} \cdot \delta\boldsymbol{\gamma} = \mathbf{F} \cdot \delta\mathbf{c} + (\mathbf{G}_{O'} \cdot \mathbf{u}_{z'})\,\delta\psi + (\mathbf{G}_{O'} \cdot \mathbf{u}_z)\,\delta\phi + (\mathbf{G}_{O'} \cdot \mathbf{u}_N)\,\delta\phi$$
$$= X\,\delta c_x + Y\,\delta c_y + Z\,\delta c_z + G_{z'}\,\delta\psi + G_z\,\delta\phi + G_N\,\delta\theta \tag{14.112}$$

where $G_{z'}$, G_z, G_N are the components along Oz', Oz, ON of the moments of the forces acting on the rigid body.

For the first three generalized coordinates we can choose x, y, z of the center of mass Q of the rigid body referred to a fixed Cartesian frame of reference $K(x, y, z)$. Let x', y', z' be the set of principal axes of the rigid body (and therefore fixed in the body). Let the Eulerian angles ϕ, ψ, θ which specify the position of the principal axes x', y', z', serve as the remaining set of generalized coordinates. Then from expressions derived previously (Sec. 13–8).

$$\omega_{x'} = \dot{\phi}\sin\psi\sin\theta + \dot{\theta}\cos\psi$$
$$\omega_{y'} = \dot{\phi}\cos\psi\sin\theta - \dot{\theta}\sin\psi \tag{14.113}$$
$$\omega_{z'} = \dot{\psi} + \dot{\phi}\cos\theta$$

Using these expressions and the set of generalized coordinates introduced

---

[*] See Section 13–7.
[**] The body axis is an axis fixed in the rigid body. If the body is symmetrical then the axis of symmetry is usually chosen as the body axis. The space axis is an axis fixed in space.

above, the kinetic energy of the rigid body can be written as

$$T = \tfrac{1}{2}M(\dot{\bar{x}}^2 + \dot{\bar{y}}^2 + \dot{\bar{z}}^2) + \tfrac{1}{2}[I_1(\dot{\phi}\sin\psi\sin\theta + \dot{\theta}\cos\psi)^2$$
$$+ I_2(\dot{\phi}\cos\psi\sin\theta - \dot{\theta}\sin\psi)^2 + I_3(\dot{\psi} + \dot{\phi}\cos\theta)^2]$$

(14.114)

Lagrange's equations then become

$$M\ddot{\bar{x}} = X$$
$$M\ddot{\bar{y}} = Y$$
$$M\ddot{\bar{z}} = Z$$

$$\frac{d}{dt}\frac{\partial T}{\partial\dot{\psi}} - \frac{\partial T}{\partial\psi} = G_{Qz'}$$

$$\frac{d}{dt}\frac{\partial T}{\partial\dot{\phi}} = G_{Qz}$$

(14.115)

$$\frac{d}{dt}\frac{\partial T}{\partial\dot{\theta}} - \frac{\partial T}{\partial\theta} = G_{QN}$$

Here X, Y, Z are the components along the fixed axes x, y, z of the net force $\mathbf{F}$ acting on the body, and $G_{Qz'}, G_{Qz}, G_{QN}$ are the components of the net torque acting on the body along the body axis Qz', the fixed space axis Qz and the line of nodes QN respectively.

14–11 Constrained Motion of Rigid Bodies

We will now consider the motion of a rigid body subject to constraints. Let the constraints be specified by the equations

$$f_1 = 0 \qquad f_2 = 0 \qquad \ldots \qquad f_s = 0 \qquad (14.116)$$

The number s of the equations cannot be greater than five. As in the case of particles, *the constraints introduce new forces which are called reactions.* Then, *if the reactions are added to the applied forces, the motion of the rigid body can be treated as non-constrained.*

Thus D'Alembert's principle for constrained motion of a rigid body takes the form

$$\sum_{i=1}^{6}\left[\frac{d}{dt}\frac{\partial T}{\partial\dot{q}_i} - \frac{\partial T}{\partial q_i} - Q_i - R_i\right]\delta q_i = 0 \qquad (14.117)$$

where Q_i and R_i are the components of the generalized forces corresponding to the applied forces and to the reactions respectively, and the δq_i's are arbitrary displacements. From (14.117) we obtain

$$\frac{d}{dt}\frac{\partial T}{\partial\dot{q}_i} - \frac{\partial T}{\partial q_i} = Q_i + R_i \qquad i = 1, 2, \ldots, 6 \qquad (14.118)$$

We remember that the unknown functions q_i not only satisfy the above equations but also Eqs. (14.116) which specify the constraints.

In this way we have reduced the problem of the rigid body motion to the formally identical problem of the motion of a system of particles.

14–12 Motion of a Rigid Body under Holonomic Constraints

Let us consider the case when the constraints are homonomic, i.e., when the constraining equations are of the form

$$f_h(t, q) = 0 \qquad h = 1, 2, \ldots \qquad (14.119)$$

We are assuming that using the above equations we can express all the q_i's as functions of $6 - h = s$ parameters r_j, thus obtaining

$$q_i = q_i(t, r)$$

Then

$$\delta q_i = \sum_{j=1}^{s} \frac{\partial q_i}{\partial r_j} \delta r_j \qquad (14.120)$$

where the δr_j's are (arbitrary) virtual displacements.

In addition let us assume that the physical constraints are perfect, i.e., no work is done by the reactions along the virtual displacements. Substitution of Eq. (14.120) in (14.117), and considerations of the fact that the δr_j's are independent, yields

$$\sum_{i=1}^{6} \frac{\partial q_i}{\partial r_j} \left[\frac{d}{dt} \frac{\partial T}{\partial \dot{q}_i} - \frac{\partial T}{\partial q_i} \right] = \sum_{i=1}^{6} \frac{\partial q_i}{\partial r_j} Q_i \qquad (14.121)$$

We also must have

$$\sum_{i=1}^{6} \frac{\partial q_i}{\partial r_j} \left[\frac{d}{dt} \frac{\partial T}{\partial \dot{q}_i} - \frac{\partial T}{\partial q_i} \right] = \frac{d}{dt} \sum_{i=1}^{6} \frac{\partial T}{\partial \dot{q}_i} \frac{\partial q_i}{\partial r_j} - \sum_{i=1}^{6} \left[\frac{\partial T}{\partial \dot{q}_i} \frac{d}{dt} \frac{\partial q_i}{\partial r_j} + \frac{\partial T}{\partial q_i} \frac{\partial q_i}{\partial r_j} \right]$$

$$= \frac{d}{dt} \sum_{i=1}^{6} \frac{\partial T}{\partial \dot{q}_i} \frac{\partial \dot{q}_i}{\partial r_j} - \sum_{i=1}^{6} \left[\frac{\partial T}{\partial \dot{q}_i} \frac{\partial \dot{q}_i}{\partial r_j} + \frac{\partial T}{\partial q_i} \frac{\partial q_i}{\partial r_j} \right] \qquad (14.122)$$

$$= \frac{d}{dt} \frac{\partial}{\partial \dot{r}_j} T(t, r, \dot{r}) - \frac{\partial}{\partial r_j} T(t, r, \dot{r})$$

Denoting

$$\overline{T} = T(t, r, \dot{r}) \qquad (14.123)$$

and also denoting by K_j the right hand side of Eq. (14.121) expressed in terms of $t, r, \dot{r}$, we obtain

$$\frac{d}{dt} \frac{\partial \overline{T}}{\partial \dot{r}_j} - \frac{\partial \overline{T}}{\partial r_j} = K_j \qquad j = 1, 2, \ldots, s \qquad (14.124)$$

These are Lagrange's equations for a rigid body moving under holonomic constraints which are realized by perfect physical constraints.

The kinetic energy of the rigid body is

$$T = \tfrac{1}{2} \iiint \rho \dot{\mathbf{r}}_P{}^2 \, dV \qquad (14.125)$$

Let O' and P be any two points of the rigid body. Then

$$\frac{dT}{dt} = \iiint \rho \dot{\mathbf{r}}_P \cdot \ddot{\mathbf{r}}_P \, dV$$

$$= \iiint \rho \dot{\mathbf{r}}_P \cdot [\dot{\mathbf{c}} + \boldsymbol{\omega} \times \mathbf{r}'] \, dV \qquad (14.126)$$

or

$$\frac{dT}{dt} = \dot{\mathbf{c}} \cdot \iiint \rho \ddot{\mathbf{r}}_P \, dV + \boldsymbol{\omega} \cdot \iiint \rho \mathbf{r}' \times \ddot{\mathbf{r}}_P \, dV$$

Now, the equations of motion of a rigid body are

$$\dot{\mathbf{p}} = \iiint \rho \ddot{\mathbf{r}}_P \, dV$$

and

$$\dot{\mathbf{h}}_{O'} + \dot{\mathbf{c}} \times \mathbf{p} = \iiint \rho \mathbf{r}' \times \ddot{\mathbf{r}}_P \, dV$$

or

$$\mathbf{h}_{O'} + \dot{\mathbf{c}} \times \mathbf{p} = \mathbf{G}_{O'}$$

Using these we obtain

$$\frac{dT}{dt} = \mathbf{F} \cdot \dot{\mathbf{c}} + \mathbf{G}_{O'} \cdot \boldsymbol{\omega} \qquad (14.127)$$

Since $\dot{\mathbf{c}} \, dt = d\mathbf{c}$

$$dT = \mathbf{F} \cdot d\mathbf{c} + \mathbf{G}_{O'} \cdot \boldsymbol{\omega} \, dt \qquad (14.128)$$

Let $\mathbf{F}_k (k = 1, 2, \ldots, n)$ be a set of n forces acting on the body, and P_k be the points of the rigid body where the forces are applied. Then

$$\mathbf{F} = \sum_{k=1}^{n} \mathbf{F}_k$$

and

$$\mathbf{G}_{O'} = \sum \mathbf{r}_k' \times \mathbf{F}_k$$

where

$$\mathbf{r}_k' = \overrightarrow{O'P_k}$$

Using the last two relations we get

$$\mathbf{F} \cdot \dot{\mathbf{c}} + \mathbf{G}_{O'} \cdot \boldsymbol{\omega} = \sum_{k} [\mathbf{F}_k \cdot \dot{\mathbf{c}} + \mathbf{r}_k' \times \mathbf{F}_k \cdot \boldsymbol{\omega}]$$

Let $\dot{\mathbf{r}}_K$ denote the linear velocity of the point P_k. We can write

$$\mathbf{r}_k' \times \mathbf{F}_k \cdot \boldsymbol{\omega} = \mathbf{F}_k \cdot \boldsymbol{\omega} \times \mathbf{r}_k'$$

and

$$\dot{\mathbf{r}}_k = \dot{\mathbf{c}} + \boldsymbol{\omega} \times \mathbf{r}_k'$$

Thus the law of energy expressed by (14.127) can also be written in the form

$$\frac{dT}{dt} = \sum_{k=1}^{n} \mathbf{F}_k \cdot \dot{\mathbf{r}}_k \tag{14.129}$$

or

$$dT = \sum_{k=1}^{n} \mathbf{F}_k \cdot d\mathbf{r}_k \tag{14.130}$$

The first of these equations states that *the time derivative of the kinetic energy of the rigid body is equal to the resultant power due to all the forces acting on the body at any given instant.*

14–14   The Energy Integral

Let us again denote by $\mathbf{F}$ the resultant of all the forces acting on the rigid body and let $\mathbf{G}_{O'}$ be the resultant torque. The forces acting on the body may depend on time, on the coordinates q which determine the position of the rigid body, and on the generalized velocities $\dot{q}$. Thus the resultant power $\mathbf{F} \cdot \dot{\mathbf{c}} + \mathbf{G}_{O'} \cdot \boldsymbol{\omega}$ may also depend on all of these arguments. Using Eq. (14.90) we can write

$$\mathbf{F} \cdot \dot{\mathbf{c}} + \mathbf{G}_{O'} \cdot \boldsymbol{\omega} = \sum_{i} \left[\mathbf{F} \cdot \frac{\partial \mathbf{c}}{\partial q_i} + \mathbf{G}_{O'} \cdot \frac{\partial \boldsymbol{\omega}}{\partial \dot{q}_i} \right] \dot{q}_i$$

$$= \sum Q_i \dot{q}_i$$

where Q_i's are the generalized forces.

If the power is the total derivative of a certain function $V(t, q)$, then from the law of energy Eq. (14.129) we must have

$$\frac{dT}{dt} = -\frac{dV(t, q)}{dt} \tag{14.131}$$

from which we obtain the energy integral

$$T + V = d \tag{14.132}$$

where d is constant.

If, in a particular case, the power generated by all the forces is zero then the energy integral takes the form

$$T = d \tag{14.133}$$

In all cases where the energy integral exists, we say that the motion proceeds with conservation of energy.

PROBLEMS

14.1 Find the center of mass of (a) a hemispherical shell and (b) a solid hemisphere.

14.2 (a) Find the coordinates of the centroid of the area bounded by the curve $y = x^2$, the x axis and ordinate $x = 1$.

(b) If the curve is rotated about the x axis find the coordinates of the centroid of the volume of revolution generated by the area.

14.3 (a) Find the coordinates of the centroid of the area formed by the curve $y^2 = 4ax$, the x axis and ordinate $x = 1$.

(b) If the area is rotated about x axis through an angle 2π find the centroid of the resulting volume of revolution.

14.4 A dumbbell with two equal spheres of radii r each and equal masses M, rotates with constant angular velocity ω about an axis perpendicular to the slim rod joining the two spheres. The distance between the centers of the two spheres is $2a$ ($> 2r$). Find the moment of inertia of the dumbbell for any position of the axis, and also the position of the axis for maximum angular momentum.

14.5 A solid is formed by joining the flat surface of a hemisphere to the base of a right circular cone of the same material. The height of the cone is the same as the diameter of the base and also the same as the diameter of the hemisphere. Find the centroid of the solid so formed, assuming a uniform density ρ.

14.6 An arc AB is rotated about an axis by an angle 2π. Prove that the area of the resulting surface of revolution is equal to the length of the arc multiplied by the length of the path described by the centroid of the arc AB. (This is called the first theorem of Pappus.)

14.7 An area A is rotated about an axis by an angle 2π. Show that the volume of the resulting solid of revolution is equal to the product of the area A and the length of the path described by the centroid of the area A. (This is the second theorem of Pappus.)

14.8 Find the location of the centroid of a semicircular arc and also of a semicircular area of the same radius.

14.9 Find the surface area and the volume of the anchor ring obtained by rotating a circle of radius a about a line at a distance b from its center (Fig. 14.3). The distance b is greater than a and the line lies in the plane of the circle.

Fig. 14.3

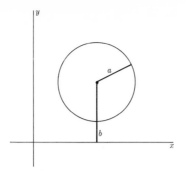

14.10 Find the moments of inertia of the following solids:

(a) A rectangle of lengths $2a$ and $2b$ about the two symmetry axes.

(b) A circular disc of internal radius a about a symmetry axis perpendicular to the disc.

(c) A spherical shell (find the polar moment of inertia first).

(d) A solid sphere.

14.11 Consider a right circular cone of height h and base radius a.

(a) Show that the moment of inertia about the axis of the cone is $(3/10)Ma^2$.

(b) Find the moment of inertia about a line through the vertex, perpendicular to the axis.

(c) Find the moment of inertia about a line parallel to the line of (b), and passing through the mass center.

14.12 Prove that the moment of inertia of a thin uniform plate about an axis perpendicular to the plate is equal to the sum of the moments of inertia about two axes perpendicular to each other lying in the plane of the plate, and passing through the trace of the first axis in the plate. (Thus for the situation shown in Figure 14.4 you are to prove that $I_{zz} = I_{xx} + I_{yy}$.)

Fig. 14.4

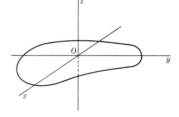

14.13 (a) Consider a system of point masses spread in the xy plane. Show that the moment of inertia about a line 1 (Fig. 14.5) passing through O is given by

$$I = I_{xx} \cos^2 \alpha + I_{yy} \sin^2 \alpha + I_{xy} \sin 2\alpha.$$

(The product of inertia $I_{xy} = -\sum_i m_i x_i y_i$ may be termed the moment of deviation of the system with respect to the x and y axes.)

Fig. 14.5

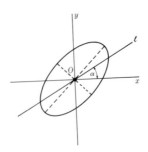

(b) The ellipsoid of inertia now becomes an ellipse of inertia. Obtain the equation of the ellipse of inertia referred to the x, y axes, and also to the principal axes.

14.14 A wheel of mass M, radius a and moment of inertia $\frac{1}{2}Ma^2$ about its mass center has a simple pendulum of mass M and length $\frac{1}{2}a$ attached to its axle. It starts to roll down the plane with the pendulum initially vertical. Obtain Lagrange's equations of motion.

14.15 (a) Consider the motion of a bar. Show that if we draw the velocity vectors of all the points of the bar then the ends of the velocity vectors lie in a straight line.

(b) Hence prove that if we draw the velocity vectors of every point of a moving plane then their ends will form a plane. (Before proving this theorem for all the points of the plane it might be advisable to show that the velocity of a rigid body is completely determined if the velocities of three of its non-collinear points are known. An equivalent theorem should be proved for the bar.)

14.16 Let a thin uniform plate move in any manner in the xy plane. Show that the instantaneous axis can be found

(a) if the linear velocities of two of its points are known, or

(b) if the linear velocity of one point is known together with the angular velocity of any line of the plate.

14.17 Two bars OA and OB jointed at O move in a plane. The velocities of A and B (Fig. 14.6) are given. Find the velocity of O.

Fig. 14.6

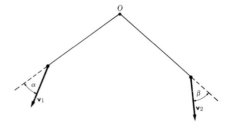

14.18   A sphere $x^2 + y^2 + z^2 = 1$ rotates around its center O. At a certain instant of time t, we are given the velocity $\mathbf{v}$ of the point $A(1, 0, 0)$ and the direction of the velocity $\mathbf{w}$ of the point $B(0, 1, 0)$. Determine the instantaneous axis of rotation, the angular velocity and the velocity $\mathbf{w}$.

14.19   A uniform circular disc is constrained to move in a vertical plane along the inner side of the circle shown in Figure 14.7 and under the gravitational attraction of the earth. The mass of the disc is m and its moment of inertia about an axis perpendicular to the plane of the disc and passing through the center of mass is I. Determine the motion of the disc in the case when
   (a) there is no friction, and
   (b) the surfaces of contact are perfectly rough.

Fig. 14.7

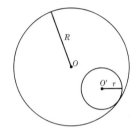

14.20   Derive the laws of motion of a physical pendulum. (This is a rigid body capable of oscillating about a fixed horizontal axis not passing through its center of mass.)

14.21   A sphere of radius a rolls down a fixed sphere of radius b. It starts from rest when the common radius through the point of contact makes an angle α with the vertical.
   (a) If, at time t, the common radius makes an angle θ with the vertical, show that
$$(7/5)(a + b)\dot{\theta} = 2g(\cos \alpha - \cos \theta)$$
   (b) In the case when $\alpha \neq 0$, find the value of θ where the rolling sphere leaves the fixed sphere.

14.22   A uniform circular disc of radius a is rolling without slipping along a horizontal plane with velocity $\mathbf{v}$, when the highest point is suddenly fixed. Show that the disc will make a complete revolution about the fixed point if $v^2 > 24ag$.

14.23   Two rigid weightless rods of length l are welded together at their midpoints at an angle ψ. One rod has equal particles of mass m at each end and the system is rotated at a constant angular velocity ω about the other rod as an axis in bearings as shown in Figure 14.8.
   (a) Find the components of the angular momentum of the system in a suitable set of coordinates (ω along the space z axis).

Fig. 14.8

(b) Write all the moments and products of inertia for the set of coordinates chosen in (a).

(c) Find a possible set of principal axes by inspection and verify your choice. Write all the components of moment of inertia for these axes.

(d) Is the angular momentum in (a) constant? If not, give the bearing reactions.

14.24 A slim uniform rod of length L is constrained to rotate in the manner shown in Figure 14.9. The rod always points towards the center O of the circle of radius R. One end of the rod moves along the circle with uniform speed v.

Fig. 14.9

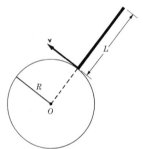

(a) Determine the kinetic energy of the rod by treating the motion as purely rotational about O. (The moment of inertia of the rod about O will have to be evaluated.)

(b) Check your result by reevaluating the kinetic energy as the sum of translational and rotational kinetic energy.

15

SOME PARTICULAR CASES OF RIGID BODY MOTION

In general, the motion of rigid bodies is very complicated. In this chapter we will only deal with some special and relatively simple cases.

15-1 Various Forms of the Equations of Motion of Rigid Bodies

Let a rigid body move in a certain space E. The motion is governed by two vector equations

$$\dot{\mathbf{p}} = \mathbf{F} \tag{15.1}$$

and

$$\dot{\mathbf{h}}_{O'} + \dot{\mathbf{c}} \times \mathbf{p} = \mathbf{G}_{O'} \tag{15.2}$$

where—as stated in the last chapter—$\mathbf{p}$ and $\mathbf{h}$ are the linear and angular momenta and $\mathbf{c}$ is the position vector of the moving point O' with respect to some fixed point O, i.e., $\mathbf{c} = \overrightarrow{OO'}$. The momentum $\mathbf{p}$ is evaluated relative to O and $\mathbf{h}_{O'}$ is the moment about O' of the momentum $\mathbf{p}$; $\mathbf{F}$ is the resultant force and $G_{O'}$ is the torque acting on the body.

Let there be another space E_1 moving with respect to the space E with an angular velocity ω^*. If $\mathbf{A}(t)$ is a vector function differentiable in E, then it will also be a specified vector function $\mathbf{A}_1(t)$ in E_1, and—as we know—

$$\frac{d\mathbf{A}}{dt} = \frac{d\mathbf{A}_1}{dt} + \omega^* \times \mathbf{A} \tag{15.3}$$

In view of this, Eqs. (15.1) and (15.2) can be written as

$$\dot{\mathbf{p}}_1 + \omega^* \times \mathbf{p} = \mathbf{F} \tag{15.4}$$

and

$$(\dot{\mathbf{h}}_{O'})_1 + \dot{\mathbf{c}} \times \mathbf{p} + \omega^* \times \mathbf{h}_{O'} = \mathbf{G}_{O'} \tag{15.5}$$

In these equations $\mathbf{p}_1$ and $(\mathbf{h}_{O'})_1$ are the linear and angular momenta respectively of the rigid body moving in space E but considered as functions of time in space E_1.

Let O' be a point of the rigid body, then*

$$\dot{\mathbf{c}} = \mathbf{v}_{O'r} + \mathbf{v}_{O'e} \tag{15.6}$$

---

* See Section 2–10.

where $\mathbf{v}_{O'r}$ is the velocity of O' related to E_1 and $\mathbf{v}_{O'e}$ is what (following the terminology of Section 2.10), we may call the lift velocity; the latter is the velocity in E with which O' is lifted by E_1.

Using Eq. (15.6), the equations of motion Eqs. (15.4) and (15.5) can be written as

$$\dot{\mathbf{p}}_1 + \boldsymbol{\omega}^* \times \mathbf{p} = \mathbf{F} \tag{15.7}$$

and

$$(\dot{\mathbf{h}}_{O'})_1 + \mathbf{v}_{O'r} \times \mathbf{p} + \mathbf{v}_{O'e} \times \mathbf{p} + \boldsymbol{\omega}^* \times \mathbf{h}_{O'} = \mathbf{G}_{O'} \tag{15.8}$$

These equations are the most general equations of motion for the rigid body in space E, referred to the space E_1 which is moving in an arbitrary manner in E.

If E_1 is a space permanently connected with the rigid body then $\boldsymbol{\omega}^* = \boldsymbol{\omega}$, where $\boldsymbol{\omega}$ is the angular velocity of the rigid body, and now, of course, $\mathbf{v}_{O'r} = \mathbf{0}$.

We should add that Eqs. (15.7) and (15.8) are equally valid for unconstrained and constrained motion of the rigid body. In the latter case the reactions will enter into the expressions for the resultant force and the resultant torque.

Let us now choose for O' the center of mass Q of the rigid body. Then $\dot{\mathbf{c}} = \mathbf{v}_Q$, and

$$\mathbf{v}_Q \times \mathbf{p} = (\mathbf{v}_{Qr} + \mathbf{v}_{Qe}) \times \mathbf{p} \tag{15.9}$$

(because $\mathbf{p} = M\mathbf{v}_Q$, where M is the mass of the rigid body). Eqs. (15.7) and (15.8) now take the form

$$\dot{\mathbf{p}}_1 + \boldsymbol{\omega}^* \times \mathbf{p} = \mathbf{F} \tag{15.10}$$

and

$$(\dot{\mathbf{h}}_Q)_1 + \boldsymbol{\omega}^* \times \mathbf{h}_Q = \mathbf{G}_Q \tag{15.11}$$

Consider again a general moving point O'. Let $\boldsymbol{\omega}$ denote the angular velocity of the rigid body in the space E and $\boldsymbol{\omega}_1$ that in E_1. Then

$$\boldsymbol{\omega} = \boldsymbol{\omega}^* + \boldsymbol{\omega}_1$$

Thus Eqs. (15.7) and (15.8) can also be written as

$$\dot{\mathbf{p}}_1 + (\boldsymbol{\omega} - \boldsymbol{\omega}_1) \times \mathbf{p} = \mathbf{F} \tag{15.12}$$

and

$$(\dot{\mathbf{h}}_{O'})_1 + \dot{\mathbf{c}} \times \mathbf{p} + (\boldsymbol{\omega} - \boldsymbol{\omega}_1) \times \mathbf{h}_{O'} = \mathbf{G}_{O'} \tag{15.13}$$

Let us now introduce still another space denoted by E_2 and let $\boldsymbol{\omega}^{**}$ be the angular velocity with which E_2 rotates with respect to E. The equations of motion can now be written as

$$\dot{\mathbf{p}}_1 + \boldsymbol{\omega}^* \times \mathbf{p} = \mathbf{F} \tag{15.14}$$

and

$$(\dot{\mathbf{h}}_{O'})_2 + \dot{\mathbf{c}} \times \mathbf{p} + \boldsymbol{\omega}^{**} \times \mathbf{h}_{O'} = \mathbf{G}_{O'} \tag{15.15}$$

Here again $(\mathbf{h}_{O'})_2$ is the angular momentum $\mathbf{h}_{O'}$ but considered as a vector function of time in space E_2.

Most often the space E_1 and E are identical and E_2 is permanently connected with the rigid body. Then $\boldsymbol{\omega}^* = \mathbf{0}$, $\boldsymbol{\omega}^{**} = \boldsymbol{\omega}$, where $\boldsymbol{\omega}$ is the angular velocity of the body. Choosing the various spaces in this manner, and identifying O' with the center of mass Q, Eqs. (15.14) and (15.15) can be written as

$$\dot{\mathbf{p}} = \mathbf{F} \tag{15.16}$$

and
$$\dot{\mathbf{h}}_Q + \boldsymbol{\omega} \times \mathbf{h}_Q = \mathbf{G}_Q \tag{15.17}$$

These latter vector equations of a rigid body are used quite often, but in practice they must be broken down into scalar component forms.

Eq. (15.16) is equivalent to the three scalar equations

$$\begin{aligned}
M\ddot{\xi} &= X \\
M\ddot{\eta} &= Y \\
M\ddot{\zeta} &= Z
\end{aligned} \tag{15.18}$$

which are the *equations of motion of the center of mass of the rigid body.*

The scalar equations equivalent to Eq. (15.17), slightly transformed, constitute an important set of equations of motion of a rigid body which are referred to as the Euler equations. Before obtaining them we will expand our discussion of the kinetic energy of the rigid body given in the last chapter.

15–2   The Kinetic Energy of a Rigid Body. Euler's Equations

Let us consider a fixed coordinate system K. Through an arbitrary point O' of the rigid body let us draw three axes of another frame K' in such a way that the corresponding axes of K and K' will be parallel. Let the point O' move with a velocity the components of which in both frames of reference are

$$v_{O'x} \qquad v_{O'y} \qquad v_{O'z}$$

Furthermore let (ξ, η, ζ) denote the coordinates of the center of mass of the rigid body in the K' frame and $(\omega_{x'}, \omega_{y'}, \omega_{z'})$ be the components of the angular velocity vector in the K' frame. In addition, let α, β, γ be the direction cosines of the angular velocity vector $\boldsymbol{\omega}$ of the rigid body in K' and $I_{x'x'}, I_{y'y'}, I_{z'z'}, I_{y'z'}, I_{z'x'}, I_{x'y'}$ be the moments and products of inertia of the rigid body with respect to K'. Then

$$\omega_{x'} = \omega\alpha \qquad \omega_{y'} = \omega\beta \qquad \omega_{z'} = \omega\gamma \tag{15.19}$$

and by Eq. (14.26)

$$I_{O'\omega} = I_{x'x'}\alpha^2 + I_{y'y'}\beta^2 + I_{z'z'}\gamma^2 - 2I_{y'z'}\beta\gamma - 2I_{z'x'}\gamma\alpha - 2I_{x'y'}\alpha\beta \tag{15.20}$$

We now return to Eq. (14.51) which gives the kinetic energy of the rigid body. In this expression $\dot{\mathbf{c}}$ is the velocity of O'. The triple scalar product appearing in (14.51) can be written in the form of a determinant. Thus, in the present case, (14.51) takes the form:

$$T = \tfrac{1}{2}M(v_{O'}{}^2{}_x + v_{O'}{}^2{}_y + v_{O'}{}^2{}_z) - M \begin{vmatrix} v_{O'x} & v_{O'y} & v_{O'z} \\ \xi & \eta & \zeta \\ \omega_{x'} & \omega_{y'} & \omega_{z'} \end{vmatrix}$$

$$+ \tfrac{1}{2}(I_{x'x'}\omega_{x'}{}^2 + I_{y'y'}\omega_{y'}{}^2 + I_{z'z'}\omega_{z'}{}^2 \tag{15.21}$$

$$- 2I_{y'z'}\omega_{y'}\omega_{z'} - 2I_{z'x'}\omega_{z'}\omega_{x'} - 2I_{x'y'}\omega_{x'}\omega_{y'})$$

If the frame K' is not attached to the rigid body permanently then the moments and products of inertia are functions of time. If, however, the axes of K' are permanently attached to the body then $I_{i'j'}$ are constants. If O' becomes the center of mass Q of the rigid body then

$$T = \tfrac{1}{2}M(v_{Qx'}{}^2 + v_{Qy'}{}^2 + v_{Qz'}{}^2) + \tfrac{1}{2}(I_{x'x'}\omega_{x'}{}^2 + \cdots - 2I_{x'y'}\omega_{x'}\omega_{y'}) \tag{15.22}$$

According to Eq. (14.49) the kinetic energy of the rigid body can be written as

$$T = \tfrac{1}{2} \iiint \rho(P)\dot{\mathbf{r}}_P{}^2 \, dV \tag{15.23}$$

From this expression we can obtain the components of the linear momentum $\mathbf{p}$ *and the angular momentum* $\mathbf{h}$ *of the rigid body along the axes* $O'x'$, $O'y'$, $O'z'$, *where* O' *is an arbitrary point of the body.*

Let $\mathbf{i}'$, $\mathbf{j}'$, $\mathbf{k}'$ be unit vectors along $O'x'$, $O'y'$, $O'z'$ and let $\dot{\mathbf{c}}$, as usual, denote the velocity of O', and let $\boldsymbol{\omega}$ be the angular velocity of the rigid body; then

$$\dot{\mathbf{c}} = v_{O'x'}\mathbf{i}' + v_{O'y'}\mathbf{j}' + v_{O'z'}\mathbf{k}'$$

and

$$\boldsymbol{\omega} = \omega_{x'}\mathbf{i}' + \omega_{y'}\mathbf{j}' + \omega_{z'}\mathbf{k}' \tag{15.24}$$

Using these expressions in conjunction with Eq. (14.50) we find that

$$\frac{\partial \dot{\mathbf{r}}_P}{\partial v_{O'x'}} = \frac{\partial \dot{\mathbf{c}}}{\partial v_{O'x'}} = \mathbf{i}' \qquad \frac{\partial \dot{\mathbf{r}}_P}{\partial v_{O'y'}} = \mathbf{j}' \qquad \frac{\partial \dot{\mathbf{r}}_P}{\partial v_{O'z'}} = \mathbf{k}'$$

and

$$\frac{\partial \dot{\mathbf{r}}_P}{\partial \omega_{x'}} = \frac{\partial \boldsymbol{\omega}}{\partial \omega_{x'}} \times \mathbf{r}_{P'} = \mathbf{i}' \times \mathbf{r}_{P'}$$

$$\frac{\partial \dot{\mathbf{r}}_P}{\partial \omega_{y'}} = \frac{\partial \boldsymbol{\omega}}{\partial \omega_{y'}} \times \mathbf{r}_{P'} = \mathbf{j}' \times \mathbf{r}_{P'} \tag{15.25}$$

$$\frac{\partial \dot{\mathbf{r}}_P}{\partial \omega_{z'}} = \frac{\partial \boldsymbol{\omega}}{\partial \omega_{z'}} \times \mathbf{r}_{P'} = \mathbf{k}' \times \mathbf{r}_{P'}$$

Now, let us partially differentiate both sides of (15.23) with respect to $v_{O'x'}$; we then obtain

$$\frac{\partial T}{\partial v_{O'x'}} = \iiint \rho(P)\dot{\mathbf{r}}_P \frac{\partial \dot{\mathbf{r}}_P}{\partial v_{O'x'}}\, dV$$

$$= \mathbf{i}' \cdot \iiint \rho(P)\dot{\mathbf{r}}_P\, dV$$

$$= \mathbf{i}' \cdot \mathbf{p}$$

and similar expressions for the other derivatives. Thus

$$\frac{\partial T}{\partial v_{O'x'}} = \mathbf{p}\cdot\mathbf{i}' \qquad \frac{\partial T}{\partial v_{O'y'}} = \mathbf{p}\cdot\mathbf{j}' \qquad \frac{\partial T}{\partial v_{O'z'}} = \mathbf{p}\cdot\mathbf{k}' \qquad (15.26)$$

It therefore follows that

$$\mathbf{p} = \frac{\partial T}{\partial v_{O'x'}}\mathbf{i}' + \frac{\partial T}{\partial v_{O'y'}}\mathbf{j}' + \frac{\partial T}{\partial v_{O'z'}}\mathbf{k}' \qquad (15.27)$$

Partially differentiating Eq. (15.23) with respect to $\omega_{x'}$ we obtain the further result that

$$\frac{\partial T}{\partial \omega_{x'}} = \iiint \rho(P)\dot{\mathbf{r}}_P \frac{\partial \dot{\mathbf{r}}_P}{\partial \omega_{x'}}\, dV$$

$$= \iiint \rho(P)\dot{\mathbf{r}}_P \cdot \mathbf{i}' \times \mathbf{r}_{P'}\, dV$$

Now, $$\dot{\mathbf{r}}_P \cdot \mathbf{i}' \times \mathbf{r}_{P}' = \mathbf{i}' \cdot \mathbf{r}_{P}' \times \dot{\mathbf{r}}_P$$

so the last expression can be written in the form

$$\frac{\partial T}{\partial \omega_{x'}} = \mathbf{i}' \cdot \iiint \rho(P)\mathbf{r}_{P}' \times \dot{\mathbf{r}}_P\, dV$$

or $$\frac{\partial T}{\partial \omega_{x'}} = \mathbf{h}_{O'} \cdot \mathbf{i}'$$

In a similar manner we obtain expressions for the other derivatives:

$$\frac{\partial T}{\partial \omega_{x'}} = \mathbf{h}_{O'}\cdot\mathbf{i}' \qquad \frac{\partial T}{\partial \omega_{y'}} = \mathbf{h}_{O'}\cdot\mathbf{j}' \qquad \frac{\partial T}{\partial \omega_{z'}} = \mathbf{h}_{O'}\cdot\mathbf{k}' \qquad (15.28)$$

from which $$\mathbf{h}_{O'} = \frac{\partial T}{\partial \omega_{x'}}\mathbf{i}' + \frac{\partial T}{\partial \omega_{y'}}\mathbf{j}' + \frac{\partial T}{\partial \omega_{z'}}\mathbf{k}' \qquad (15.29)$$

If the axes K' were attached to the rigid body, and if—in addition—these axes were the principal axes of the body, then Eq. (15.22) for the kinetic energy would become

$$T = \tfrac{1}{2}M(\dot{\xi}^2 + \dot{\eta}^2 + \dot{\zeta}^2) + \tfrac{1}{2}M(I_1\omega_1{}^2 + I_2\omega_2{}^2 + I_3\omega_3{}^2) \qquad (15.30)$$

where I_1, I_2, I_3 are the principal moments of inertia and $(\omega_1, \omega_2, \omega_3)$ are the components of the angular velocity $\boldsymbol{\omega}$ of the rigid body along the principal axes.

15–2 The kinetic energy of a rigid body. Euler's equations

The components of the angular momentum $\mathbf{h}_Q$ are given by Eq. (15.29) and in the present case are

$$\frac{\partial T}{\partial \omega_1} = I_1 \omega_1 \qquad \frac{\partial T}{\partial \omega_2} = I_2 \omega_2 \qquad \frac{\partial T}{\partial \omega_3} = I_3 \omega_3 \qquad (15.31)$$

We are now ready to write the scalar equations equivalent to Eq. (15.17), namely

$$\begin{aligned}
I_1 \dot{\omega}_1 + (I_3 - I_2)\omega_2 \omega_3 &= G_1 \\
I_2 \dot{\omega}_2 + (I_1 - I_2)\omega_3 \omega_1 &= G_2 \\
I_3 \dot{\omega}_3 + (I_2 - I_1)\omega_1 \omega_2 &= G_3
\end{aligned} \qquad (15.32)$$

These are *Euler's equations.* G_1, G_2, G_3 are the components of the torque along the principal axes of the body.

Euler's equations can also be obtained in a much quicker way if we make use of certain results obtained previously. We start by resolving Eq. (15.17) along the principal axes and obtain

$$\begin{aligned}
G_1 &= \dot{h}_1 + \omega_2 h_3 - \omega_3 h_3 \\
G_2 &= \dot{h}_2 + \omega_3 h_1 - \omega_1 h_3 \\
G_3 &= \dot{h}_3 + \omega_1 h_2 - \omega_2 h_1
\end{aligned} \qquad (15.33)$$

where h_1, h_2, h_3 are the components of the angular momentum along the principal axes of the body and $\dot{h}_1, \dot{h}_2, \dot{h}_3$ their time derivatives. Now, by Eq. (14.35)

$$h_1 = I_1 \omega_1 \qquad h_2 = I_2 \omega_2 \qquad h_3 = I_3 \omega_3 \qquad (15.34)$$

and

$$\dot{h}_1 = I_1 \dot{\omega}_1 \qquad \dot{h}_2 = I_2 \dot{\omega}_2 \qquad \dot{h}_3 = I_3 \dot{\omega}_3 \qquad (15.35)$$

Substituting these into Eq. (15.33) yields Euler's equations (15.32).

15-3   *The Complete Set of Equations of Motion of a Rigid Body*

We will now collect a complete set of equations of motion of a rigid body. It will consist of Eqs. (15.18), (15.32) and also of Eqs. (13.37). Thus, consider a rigid body of mass M moving in any manner. Let its center of mass have coordinates ξ, η, ζ; let its principal axes be denoted by subscripts 1, 2, 3 and the Eulerian angles be ϕ, ψ, θ. The resultant force acting on the body has components X, Y, Z and the resultant torque resolved along the principal axes is G_1, G_2, G_3. *The complete set of equations of motion for the rigid body is*

$$\begin{aligned}
M\ddot{\xi} &= X \\
M\ddot{\eta} &= Y \\
M\ddot{\zeta} &= Z
\end{aligned} \qquad (15.36)$$

$$I_1\dot{\omega}_1 + (I_3 - I_2)\omega_3\omega_2 = G_1$$
$$I_2\dot{\omega}_2 + (I_1 - I_3)\omega_3\omega_1 = G_2 \qquad (15.37)$$
$$I_3\dot{\omega}_3 + (I_2 - I_1)\omega_1\omega_2 = G_3$$

$$\omega_1 = \dot{\phi}\sin\psi\sin\theta + \dot{\theta}\cos\psi$$
$$\omega_2 = \dot{\phi}\cos\psi\sin\theta - \dot{\theta}\sin\psi \qquad (15.38)$$
$$\omega_3 = \dot{\psi} + \dot{\phi}\cos\theta$$

These are nine equations of motion in nine unknown functions ξ, η, ζ, ω_1, ω_2, ω_3, ϕ, ψ, θ, where the equations in ξ, η, ζ are of the second order and the remaining ones are of the first order.

As we know, a general type of a motion may be considered as the superposition of translational and rotational motions. Eqs. (15.36) represent the translational motion and Eqs. (15.37) the rotational motion.

15–4 A Free Motion of Rigid Body

We will now consider a rigid body moving under the influence of no forces. More exactly, we are considering the case when the resultant force and the resultant torque acting on the body vanish, i.e., when

$$\mathbf{F} = \mathbf{0}$$
and
$$\mathbf{G}_{O'} = \mathbf{0}$$

Applying Eqs. (15.4) and (15.5) to this case with $\boldsymbol{\omega}^* = \mathbf{0}$ and $O' \equiv Q$ (the center of gravity), we obtain

$$\dot{\mathbf{p}} = \mathbf{0}$$
and
$$\dot{\mathbf{h}}_Q = \mathbf{0} \qquad (15.39)$$

It follows that in this case

$$\mathbf{p} = \mathbf{A}$$
and
$$\mathbf{h}_Q = \mathbf{L} \qquad (15.40)$$

where $\mathbf{A}$ and $\mathbf{L}$ are constant vectors.

Equations (15.36) now yield

$$\dot{\xi} = a_1 \qquad \dot{\eta} = a_2 \qquad \dot{\zeta} = a_3 \qquad (15.41)$$

from which we obtain

$$\xi = a_1 t + b_1 \qquad \eta = a_2 t + b_2 \qquad \zeta = a_3 t + b_3 \qquad (15.42)$$

where a_i, b_i are constants of integration. Therefore *in a free motion, the center of mass of the rigid body moves uniformly along a straight line*. Of course, if initially the center of mass Q is at rest then it will remain at rest and the motion will be a pure rotational motion about the center of mass.

Let us turn now to the rotational part of the motion which is described by Euler's equations (15.37). In the case of free motion these become

$$I_1\dot{\omega}_1 + (I_3 - I_2)\omega_2\omega_3 = 0$$
$$I_2\dot{\omega}_2 + (I_1 - I_3)\omega_1\omega_3 = 0 \qquad (15.43)$$
$$I_3\dot{\omega}_3 + (I_2 - I_1)\omega_1\omega_2 = 0$$

From these equations $\omega_1, \omega_2, \omega_3$ can be determined as functions of time. These we substitute in Eqs. (15.38) from which the Eulerian angles ϕ, ψ, and θ can be determined.

As stated above, in the case of the free motion of the rigid body the angular momentum vector $\mathbf{h}_Q$ is constant. This permits the determination of the three integrals of Eqs. (15.43) and also of the integrals of Eqs. (15.38).

The components of $\mathbf{h}_Q$ along the fixed axes are also constant. Let $\alpha_i, \beta_i, \gamma_i$ denote the cosines of the angles between the fixed and the moving axes, where the latter are the principal axes of the body. The three integrals of (15.43) will yield $\omega_1, \omega_2, \omega_3$. Having obtained these, we form the products $I_1\omega_1, I_2\omega_2, I_3\omega_3$ which—as we know—are the components h_1, h_2, h_3 of the angular momentum vector along the principal axes. As stated before, the components of the angular momentum vector along the fixed axes are constants. Thus for the three components of the angular momentum along the fixed axes we can write

$$I_1\omega_1\alpha_1 + I_2\omega_2\beta_1 + I_3\omega_3\gamma_1 = \ell_1$$
$$I_1\omega_1\alpha_2 + I_1\omega_1\beta_2 + I_3\omega_3\gamma_2 = \ell_2 \qquad (15.44)$$
$$I_1\omega_1\alpha_3 + I_2\omega_2\beta_3 + I_3\omega_3\gamma_3 = \ell_3$$

where ℓ_1, ℓ_2, ℓ_3 are constants. The relationship between $\alpha_i, \beta_i, \gamma_i$ and the Eulerian angles is given by Eqs. (13.30), (13.31) and (13.32). The constants ℓ_1, ℓ_2, ℓ_3 are determined by the initial conditions to which the rigid body is subjected.

Squaring Eqs. (15.44) and adding we obtain

$$I_1{}^2\omega_1{}^2 + I_2{}^2\omega_2{}^2 + I_3{}^2\omega_3{}^2 = \ell^2 \qquad (15.45)$$

where

$$\ell^2 = \ell_1{}^2 + \ell_2{}^2 + \ell_3{}^2$$

Eq. (15.45) expresses the fact that *the magnitude of the angular momentum* $\mathbf{h}_Q$ *is constant*. This equation is satisfied by all the values of $\omega_1, \omega_2, \omega_3$ which satisfy Eqs. (15.43). Thus Eq. (15.45) is an integral of Eqs. (15.43). We may call it *the integral of the moments*.

We have seen in Section 14–14 that, for the type of motion considered here, there exists the energy integral

$$T = d \qquad (15.46)$$

where T is the kinetic energy, and is given by Eq. (15.30) which—in view of Eq. (15.41)—becomes

15–4 A free motion of rigid body

$$T = \tfrac{1}{2}(I_1\omega_1{}^2 + I_2\omega_2{}^2 + I_3\omega_3{}^2) \qquad (15.47)$$

Thus Eq. (15.46) can be written as

$$I_1\omega_1{}^2 + I_2\omega_2{}^2 + I_3\omega_3{}^2 = c \qquad (15.48)$$

where c is a constant of integration. Of course, Eq. (15.48) is also an integral of Eqs. (15.43). We will call it *the energy integral*.

To render the integral of the moments and the energy integral more symmetrical we will introduce two new constants δ and μ by the relations

$$c = \delta\mu^2 \qquad \ell = \delta\mu$$

Eqs. (15.45) and (15.48) then become

$$I_1{}^2\omega_1{}^2 + I_2{}^2\omega_2{}^2 + I_3{}^2\omega_3{}^2 = \delta^2\mu^2$$

and
$$I_1\omega_1{}^2 + I_2\omega_2{}^2 + I_3\omega_3{}^2 = \delta\mu^2 \qquad (15.49)$$

Eliminating μ from the two equations we obtain the homogeneous equation

$$I_1(I_1 - \delta)\omega_1{}^2 + I_2(I_2 - \delta)\omega_2{}^2 + I_3(I_3 - \delta)\omega_3{}^2 = 0 \qquad (15.50)$$

This equation—in the same way as Eqs. (15.49)—is satisfied by all the solutions of Eqs. (15.43). Every particular solution will contain its own constant of integration δ.

In the previous chapter we have introduced the ellipsoid of inertia. When referred to the principal axes, its equation is

$$I_1 x'^2 + I_2 y'^2 + I_3 z'^2 = 1 \qquad (15.51)$$

In general the axes of the ellipsoid will all be different; in some cases two will be equal and in special cases all will be equal. In the first case we will assume that $I_1 > I_2 > I_3$, in the second that $I_1 = I_2$, and in the last case, of course, that $I_1 = I_2 = I_3$.

In this last case the ellipsoid of inertia is a sphere. Eqs. (15.43) yield

$$\omega_1 = (\omega_1)_0 \qquad \omega_2 = (\omega_2)_0 \qquad \omega_3 = (\omega_3)_0$$

where $(\omega_1)_0$, $(\omega_2)_0$, $(\omega_3)_0$ are constants which in turn means that ω is constant. Eqs. (15.34) in this special case become

$$h_1 = I\omega_1$$
$$h_2 = I\omega_2 \qquad (15.52)$$
$$h_3 = I\omega_3$$

where we have denoted $I_1 = I_2 = I_3 = I$. This means that the resultant constant angular momentum lies along the constant axis of rotation given by ω. We can say, therefore, that *in the case when the ellipsoid of inertia is a sphere, the most general type of free motion of a rigid body consists of uniform translation of the center of mass of the body and a uniform rotation about an axis which has constant direction in the body and in space.*

15–5 Integration of Equations of Free Motion of an Asymmetric Rigid Body

The equations of free motion of a rigid body are given by Eqs. (15.43). When the body is asymmetric then $I_1 \neq I_2 \neq I_3$. We will now indicate how the equations of motion are integrated in this case. As before, we are assuming that $I_1 > I_2 > I_3$.

We notice that in the case when all the principal moments of inertia are different, the number $(I_1 - \delta)$ and $(I_3 - \delta)$ in Eq. (15.50) cannot have the same sign. It follows therefore that

$$I_1 \geq \delta \geq I_3 \qquad (15.53)$$

Let us first assume that $I_1 > \delta > I_3$. From Eq. (15.50) we obtain

$$\omega_1{}^2 = a^2(\alpha^2 - \omega_2{}^2) \qquad \omega_3{}^2 = b^2(\beta^2 - \omega_2{}^2) \qquad (15.54)$$

where
$$a^2 = \frac{I_2(I_2 - I_3)}{I_1(I_1 - I_3)} \qquad \alpha^2 = \frac{\delta(\delta - I_3)}{I_2(I_2 - I_3)}\,\mu^2$$

$$b^2 = \frac{I_2(I_1 - I_2)}{I_3(I_1 - I_3)} \qquad \beta^2 = \frac{\delta(I_1 - \delta)}{I_2(I_1 - I_2)}\,\mu^2 \qquad (15.55)$$

We can assume that a, b, α, β are positive.

Using Eqs. (15.54) we can write the second of Eqs. (15.43) in the form

$$\dot{\omega}_2{}^2 = (1/I_2{}^2)(I_1 - I_3)a^2b^2(\alpha^2 - \omega_2{}^2)(\beta^2 - \omega_2{}^2) \qquad (15.56)$$

There are three cases to consider depending on whether $\alpha > \beta$, $\alpha < \beta$, or $\alpha = \beta$. These are equivalent to the cases when $\delta > I_2$, $\delta < I_2$ and when $\delta = I_2$. In the first two cases integration of Eq. (15.56) shows that $\omega_1(t)$, $\omega_2(t)$, $\omega_3(t)$ are elliptic functions. We will not deal with these cases.

Consider the case when $\alpha = \beta$, i.e., when $\delta = I_2$. Eq. (15.56) now becomes

$$\dot{\omega}_2{}^2 = (1/I_2{}^2)(I_1 - I_3)a^2b^2(\alpha^2 - \omega_2{}^2)^2 \qquad (15.57)$$

Integrating this equation we obtain

$$\omega_2(t) = \frac{\alpha(e^{\mp n(t-t_0)} - 1)}{\gamma e^{\mp n(t-t_0)} + 1} \qquad (15.58)$$

where
$$\gamma = \frac{\alpha - (\omega_2)_0}{a + (\omega_2)_0}$$

and
$$n = \frac{2\alpha(I_1 - I_3)ab}{I_2}$$

when $(\omega_1)_0(\omega_3)_0 > 0$ the upper sign in Eq. (15.58) is to be used, and when

$(\omega_1)_0(\omega_3)_0 < 0$ the lower sign is to be taken. This result holds when the initial value of ω_2 is different than $\pm\alpha$, i.e., when $(\omega_2)_0 \neq \alpha$.

When $(\omega_2)_0 = \pm\alpha$, then at all times

$$\omega_2 = \pm\alpha$$

so that

$$\omega_1 = \omega_3 = 0$$

Thus, in the case when $\alpha = \beta$ which will occur when $\delta = I_2$, and when $(\omega_2)_0 = \alpha$, the rigid body will rotate about the y' axis, which is the intermediate axis of the ellipsoid of inertia. The components of the angular momentum in this case are 0, $I_2\omega_2$, 0 and so the axis of rotation is also the line containing the angular momentum. In addition, this line does not change its direction in the fixed space.

We have yet to examine the two remaining cases when $\delta = I_1$ and when $\delta = I_3$. When $\delta = I_1$, Eq. (15.50) takes the form

$$I_2(I_2 - I_1)\omega_2{}^2 + I_3(I_3 - I_1)\omega_3{}^2 = 0 \tag{15.59}$$

According to our assumption $I_2 - I_1 < 0$ and $I_3 - I_1 < 0$, therefore at all times we must have

$$\omega_2 = \omega_3 = 0$$

which means that in this case the body will always rotate about the shortest axis of inertia.

Similarly, when $\delta = I_3$ the body will constantly rotate about the greatest axis of the momental ellipsoid. The angular momentum in the two respective cases will have components $I_1\omega_1$, 0, 0 and 0, 0, $I_3\omega_3$.

These results can be summarized by saying that when the momental ellipsoid of the rigid body has three unequal ellipsoidal axes, a body which is initially rotating about one of these axes will continue to rotate about the same axis, and the axis will not change its orientation in space.

So far, for the case $I_1 > I_2 > I_3$, we have obtained five integrals of Eqs. (15.43) and of Eqs. (15.38), namely the three integrals (15.44) of which one can be replaced by the integral given by Eq. (15.45) or by the first of Eqs. (15.49); the fourth integral is the energy integral (the second of Eqs. (15.49); the fifth integral is given by Eq. (15.58).*

We must now evaluate one more integral in order to complete the solution of the problem. Because the direction of the angular momentum is constant in fixed space, we will choose for the axis containing this angular momentum the (fixed) space axis Qz. In this case, in the integrals of moments, Eqs. (15.44), we will have

$$\ell_1 = \ell_2 = 0$$
$$\ell_3 = \ell = \delta\mu$$

* As stated before, this integral is obtained for the case when $\alpha = \beta$. When this is not so the integral will involve elliptical functions. We have not written out this integral.

Projecting this on the three rotating axes we have

$$I_1\omega_1 = \delta\mu\alpha_3 \qquad I_2\omega_2 = \delta\mu\beta_3 \qquad I_3\omega_3 = \delta\mu\gamma_3$$

These, using Eqs. (13.32) can be rewritten as

$$\begin{aligned} I_1\omega_1 &= \delta\mu \sin\phi \sin\theta \\ I_2\omega_2 &= -\delta\mu \cos\phi \sin\theta \\ I_3\omega_3 &= \delta\mu \cos\theta \end{aligned} \qquad (15.60)$$

from which the angles θ and ψ can be evaluated. We find quite simply that

$$\sin\theta = \pm \frac{\sqrt{I_1{}^2\omega_1{}^2 + I_2{}^2\omega_2{}^2}}{\delta\mu} \qquad (15.61)$$

and

$$\cos\theta = \frac{I_3\omega_3}{\delta\mu}$$

Knowing θ we can obtain the angle ϕ from the first two Eqs. (15.60).

The angle of precession ϕ is determined in the following way: From the equations

$$\omega_1 = \dot\phi \sin\theta \sin\psi + \dot\theta \cos\psi$$

and

$$\omega_2 = \dot\phi \sin\theta \cos\psi - \dot\theta \sin\psi$$

we find that

$$\dot\phi = \frac{\omega_1 \sin\psi + \omega_2 \cos\psi}{\sin\theta} \qquad (15.62)$$

Using (15.60), the numerator of this last relation can be written as

$$\omega_1 \sin\psi + \omega_2 \cos\psi = \frac{I_1\omega_1{}^2 + I_2\omega_2{}^2}{\delta\mu \sin\theta}$$

Thus, making use of (15.49) we obtain

$$\begin{aligned} \dot\phi &= \frac{I_1\omega_1{}^2 + I_2\omega_2{}^2}{\delta\mu \sin^2\theta} \\ &= \frac{I_1\omega_1{}^2 + I_2\omega_2{}^2}{\delta\mu(1 - \cos^2\theta)} \\ &= \frac{\delta\mu\,(I_1\omega_1{}^2 + I_2\omega_2{}^2)}{\delta^2\mu^2 - I_3{}^2\omega_3{}^2} \\ &= \delta\mu\,\frac{I_1\omega_1{}^2 + I_2\omega_2{}^2}{I_1{}^2\omega_1{}^2 + I_2{}^2\omega_2{}^2} \end{aligned} \qquad (15.63)$$

Considering the fact that the functions $\omega_1(t)$ and $\omega_2(t)$ have already been determined (and are not simultaneously equal to zero), we see that $\dot\phi$ is always positive. Thus the Qzz' plane at all times rotates in the positive direction about the space axis Qz. From Eq. (15.63) we find the sixth integral, viz.

$$\phi - \phi_0 = \delta\mu \int_{t_0}^{t} \frac{I_1\omega_1{}^2 + I_2\omega_2{}^2}{I_1{}^2\omega_2{}^2 + I_2{}^2\omega_2{}^2}\, dt \qquad (15.64)$$

We will now consider the case of the free motion of a rigid body for which the ellipsoid of inertia has two equal axes, say

$$I_1 = I_2 \neq I_3 \tag{15.65}$$

where I_3 can be either smaller or greater than I_1. It follows from the third of Eqs. (15.43) that in this case $\omega_3 = (\omega_3)_0$, where $(\omega_3)_0$ is constant. The energy integral given by Eq. (15.48) can in the present case be written as

$$I_1(\omega_1^2 + \omega_2^2) + I_3\omega_3^2 = a$$

and we see that $(\omega_1^2 + \omega_2^2)$ is a constant of motion. Thus $\omega^2 = \omega_1^2 + \omega_2^2 + \omega_3^2$ is constant, i.e., *the magnitude of the angular velocity vector ω is constant.*

Furthermore, Eqs. (15.60) now take the form

$$I_1\omega_1 = \delta\mu \sin \phi \sin \theta$$
$$I_1\omega_2 = -\delta\mu \cos \phi \sin \theta \tag{15.66}$$
$$I_3(\omega_3)_0 = \delta\mu \cos \theta$$

It follows that $\theta = \theta_0$, i.e., *the motion proceeds with constant nutation.*

Eq. (15.63), from which the angle of precession is determined, now becomes

$$\dot{\phi} = \frac{\delta\mu I_1(\omega_1^2 + \omega_2^2)}{I_1^2(\omega_1^2 + \omega_2^2)}$$
$$= \frac{\delta\mu}{I_1} \tag{15.67}$$

and the latter quantity is constant. This in turn means that *the precession of the body is proportional to time.*

Finally, the third of Eqs. (15.38) takes the form

$$(\omega_3)_0 = \dot{\phi} \cos \theta_0 + \dot{\psi} \tag{15.68}$$

and we see from it that ψ *also varies proportionally to time.*

As we know from the kinematical theory of rigid body motion, the instantaneous angular velocity of the body consists of three components: $\dot{\theta}$, along the line of nodes, $\dot{\phi}$, along the fixed space axis Qz, and $\dot{\psi}$ along the body axis Qz'. In the present case $\dot{\theta} = 0$ and $\dot{\phi}$ and $\dot{\psi}$ are both constant; thus the angle θ between the directions of these two components ($\dot{\phi}$ and $\dot{\psi}$) also remains constant. Therefore, we see again that *the magnitude of the angular velocity is constant and the angular motion is uniform.*

When viewed in the fixed space, the axis of rotation of the rigid body describes a circular cone about the space axis Qz, and when viewed by an observer attached to the body, the axis of rotation describes a cone about the body axis Qz'.

The homogeneous equation (15.50) now takes the form

$$I_1(I_1 - \delta)(\omega_1{}^2 + \omega_2{}^2) + I_3(I_3 - \delta)\omega_3{}^2 = 0 \qquad (15.69)$$

We see from this equation that δ should lie between I_1 and I_3. When $I_1 > I_3$ then $I_1 \geq \delta \geq I_3$. δ can become equal to I_1 only when at all times $\omega_3 = 0$, and this will happen when $(\omega_3)_0 = 0$, i.e., when at $t = 0$ the body rotates about one of the axes perpendicular to the axis of symmetry of the body. The components of the angular momentum in this case are $I_1\omega_1, I_1\omega_2, 0$ and the angular momentum lies along the instantaneous axis of rotation; thus the axis of rotation will not change its direction in space. From the first and the second of Eqs. (15.43) we see that when $\omega_3 = 0$, the axis of rotation will also not change its direction in the rigid body.

When $\delta = I_3$ we deduce from Eq. (15.69) that at all times

$$\omega_1 = \omega_2 = 0$$

and this will occur only when

$$(\omega_1)_0 = (\omega_2)_0 = 0$$

Thus, as before, once the body is started rotating about its principal axis, it will continue to do so, and this axis will not change its position in space.

The central axis which has constant direction in space and in the body, and about which the body in its free motion can rotate permanently, may be termed the axis of constant rotation. We have shown that the principal axes of inertia may become axes of constant rotation.

15–7   Poinsot's Geometrical Interpretation of the Free Motion of Rigid Body

The analytical results for the motion of the rigid body under the influence of no forces have been given a clear geometrical interpretation by Poinsot. Let us first determine the surface on which the axes of rotation in the motion which we are now discussing must always lie. As before, we will take the principal axes of inertia x_1, y_1, z_1 as the axes fixed in the body. The equation of the instantaneous axis of rotation in this system is

$$\frac{x_1}{\omega_1} = \frac{y_1}{\omega_2} = \frac{z_1}{\omega_3} \qquad (15.70)$$

Eliminating the variables $\omega_1, \omega_2, \omega_3$ between this equation and Eq. (15.50) we obtain the equation of the required surface

$$I_1(I_1 - \delta)x_1{}^2 + I_2(I_2 - \delta)y_1{}^2 + I_3(I_3 - \delta)z_1{}^2 = 0 \qquad (15.71)$$

This is the equation of a cone.

When $I_1 > I_2 > I_3$, and in addition if $I_1 = \delta$, then Eq. (15.71) reduces to

$$I_2(I_2 - I_1)y_1{}^2 + I_3(I_3 - I_1)z_1{}^2 = 0$$

The only real solution of this equation is

$$y_1 = z_1 = 0$$

and this represents the x_1 axis. We notice the agreement with the results of our previous discussion.

When $I_3 = \delta$, the cone becomes the z_1 axis.

When $I_2 = \delta$, Eq. (15.71) takes the form

$$I_1(I_1 - I_2)x_1{}^2 + I_3(I_3 - I_2)z_1{}^2 = 0$$

Because of the inequalities

$$I_1 - I_2 > 0 \qquad I_3 - I_2 < 0$$

we can write this last equation as

$$\left(\sqrt{I_1(I_1 - I_2)}\, x_1 + \sqrt{I_3(I_2 - I_3)}\, z_1\right)$$
$$\times \left(\sqrt{I_1(I_1 - I_2)}\, x_1 - \sqrt{I_3(I_2 - I_3)}\, z_1\right) = 0$$

In this case, therefore, the cone reduces to two planes

$$\sqrt{I_1(I_1 - I_2)}\, x_1 + \sqrt{I_3(I_2 - I_3)}\, z_1 = 0$$

and

$$\sqrt{I_1(I_1 - I_2)}\, x_1 + \sqrt{I_3(I_2 - I_3)}\, z_1 = 0$$

which will contain the y_1 axis, then it will continue to rotate about this axis.

In the case of the rotational ellipsoid of inertia, the cone constituting the surface which always contains the rotational axes becomes a circular cone and its equation is

$$I_1(I_1 - \delta)(x_1{}^2 + y_1{}^2) + I_3(I_3 - \delta)z_1{}^2 = 0$$

When $I_1 = \delta$ the cone reduces to the plane $z_1 = 0$, and when $I_3 = \delta$ it reduces to the z_1 axis.

Let us return to the discussion of the moment of inertia given in Section 14-4. The distance between the center of the momental ellipsoid and the point of intersection of the instantaneous axis with the ellipsoid was denoted by R. We may call this point of intersection the *instantaneous pole of the ellipsoid*. Its coordinates can be written as

$$x_1 = R\,\frac{\omega_1}{\omega} \qquad y_1 = R\,\frac{\omega_2}{\omega} \qquad z_1 = R\,\frac{\omega_3}{\omega} \qquad (15.72)$$

Substituting these into the equation of the ellipsoid of inertia, viz., into the equation

$$I_1 x_1{}^2 + I_2 y_1{}^2 + I_3 z_1{}^2 = 1$$

we obtain

$$R^2(I_1\omega_1{}^2 + I_2\omega_2{}^2 + I_3\omega_3{}^2) = \omega^2$$

Now, the kinetic energy of the body rotating about its center of mass is given by

$$T = \tfrac{1}{2}(I_1\omega_1^2 + I_2\omega_2^2 + I_3\omega_3^2)$$

which can be written as

$$T = \frac{1}{2}\frac{\omega^2}{R^2} \tag{15.73}$$

This result, of course, follows quite readily from our consideration in Section 14–4.

The above result is general. In the case of a free motion of the rigid body the kinetic energy is constant and relation (15.73) takes the form

$$\omega = \delta\mu R \tag{15.74}$$

This shows that *in a free motion the angular velocity at every instant is proportional to the distance between the center of the ellipsoid of inertia and the instantaneous pole.*

Using Eqs. (15.72) and (15.73) we can write the coordinates of the instantaneous pole as

$$x_0 = \frac{\omega_1}{\sqrt{2T}} \qquad y_0 = \frac{\omega_2}{\sqrt{2T}} \qquad z_0 = \frac{\omega_3}{\sqrt{2T}} \tag{15.75}$$

The equation of the plane tangent to the ellipsoid of inertia at the instantaneous pole is

$$I_1\omega_1 x_1 + I_2\omega_2 y_1 + I_3\omega_3 z_1 - \sqrt{2T} = 0 \tag{15.76}$$

We notice that this plane is perpendicular to the vector $(I_1\omega_1, I_2\omega_2, I_3\omega_3)$, i.e., to the angular momentum vector about the center of mass Q. We have just shown that *in any motion of the rigid body, the plane tangent at the instantaneous pole to the ellipsoid of inertia referred to its principal axes is at every instant perpendicular to the corresponding angular momentum about the center of mass.*

In the case of free motion the angular momentum has a fixed direction in space and hence the plane tangent to the ellipsoid vector at the instantaneous pole will never change its inclination. We may restate this result by saying that *in the free motion of a rigid body, the planes tangent at the pole to the ellipsoid of inertia never change their inclinations; they always remain perpendicular to the fixed direction of the angular momentum vector evaluated about the center of mass.* The equation of the tangent plane in this latter case has the form

$$I_1\omega_1 x_1 + I_2\omega_2 y_1 + I_3\omega_3 z_1 - \mu\sqrt{\delta} = 0 \tag{15.77}$$

The distance between the center of mass of the rigid body (also the center of the ellipsoid of inertia) to the plane tangent at the instantaneous pole is

$$D = \frac{\sqrt{2T}}{\sqrt{I_1^2\omega_1^2 + I_2^2\omega_2^2 + I_3^2\omega_3^2}} \tag{15.78}$$

or
$$D = \frac{\sqrt{2T}}{h_Q}$$

because
$$h_Q{}^2 = (I_1\omega_1)^2 + (I_2\omega_2)^2 + (I_3\omega_3)^2$$

In the case of free motion
$$2T = \delta\mu^2$$

and
$$h_Q = \delta\mu$$

therefore
$$D = \frac{1}{\sqrt{\delta}} = \text{const.} \qquad (15.79)$$

We can reformulate our result by stating that *in a free motion of a rigid body the ellipsoid of inertia referred to the principal axes of the rigid body is at all times tangent to a certain plane which is rigidly connected to the center of mass and which does not change its inclination in the fixed space. The point of tangency is the instantaneous pole.*

This result can take another form yet, and this is the form of Poinsot's theorem. It states that *in a motion of a rigid body for which the resultant force and the resultant torque is zero, the ellipsoid of inertia, referred to the principal axes of inertia, rolls without slipping on a certain plane attached rigidly to the center of mass of the body and perpendicular to the angular momentum vector of the body evaluated about the center of mass.* The equation of this plane is given by Eq. (15.77).

This interpretation of the free motion of a rigid body is purely geometrical because it does not contain the dependence of the angular velocity and of the position of the body on time.

The geometrical locus of the instantaneous poles on the ellipsoid of inertia is called the polhode. This, of course, is the intersection of the cone which is the locus of axes of rotation with the ellipsoid of inertia. Thus the equation of the polhode is given by

$$I_1 x_1{}^2 + I_2 y_1{}^2 + I_3 z_1{}^2 = 1$$
$$I_1(I_1 - \delta)x_1{}^2 + I_2(I_2 - \delta)y_1{}^2 + I_3(I_3 - \delta)z_1{}^2 = 0 \qquad (15.80)$$

Actually the two equations denote a curve consisting of two branches: one is the polhode and the other is a curve symmetrical to the polhode with respect to the center of the momental ellipsoid. Indeed, every generator of the cone

$$I_1(I_1 - \delta)x_1{}^2 + I_2(I_2 - \delta)y_1{}^2 + I_3(I_3 - \delta)z_1{}^2 = 0 \qquad (15.81)$$

will intersect the ellipsoid of inertia in two points of which only one constitutes the instantaneous pole.

In Eq. (15.81), the coefficient of $x_1{}^2$ is always nonnegative and that of $z_1{}^2$ nonpositive. When $I_1 = \delta$ the cone degenerates into the x_1 axis and the polhode becomes a single point, viz. the point of intersection of the x_1 axis with the momental ellipsoid.

When $I_1 > \delta > I_2$ then the coefficients of $y_1{}^2$ and $z_1{}^2$ in the equation of the cone are negative; the cone therefore surrounds the x_1 axis. In this case the polhode is a closed curve surrounding one of the ends of the ellipsoid namely that end which lies near the x_1 axis.

When $I_2 = \delta$, the cone (15.81) reduces to two planes intersecting along the median axis of the ellipsoid. The polhode in this case is an ellipse because it is the intersection of the ellipsoid with one of the planes.

When $I_2 > \delta > I_3$ the polhode is a closed curve and surrounds the z_1 axis. The polhode becomes a point of intersection of the z_1 axis with the ellipsoid when $\delta = I_3$.

When the ellipsoid of inertia rolls over the plane given by Eq. (15.77) then the point of tangency of the ellipsoid traces out a curve on this plane. This curve has a special name; it is called the *herpolhode. At every instant the polhode and the herpolhode have one common point which is the instantaneous pole. At this point the two curves are tangent to each other.*

15-8 Unconstrained Motion of Rigid Body in the Gravitational Field

It is known that in a small region of space near the earth the acceleration due to gravity has a constant value g and that the gravitational forces acting on a rigid body of mass M are equivalent to a single force Mg acting through the center of mass Q. With a proper choice of the coordinate axes the equations of motion of the center of mass, given by Eqs. (15.36), become

$$\ddot{\xi} = 0 \qquad \ddot{\eta} = 0 \qquad \ddot{\zeta} = g \qquad (15.82)$$

The resultant torque about the center of mass is zero, therefore the equations of the rotational motion about the center, given by Eqs. (15.37), take the form

$$I_1\dot{\omega}_1 + (I_3 - I_2)\omega_2\omega_3 = 0$$
$$I_2\dot{\omega}_2 + (I_1 - I_3)\omega_3\omega_1 = 0 \qquad (15.83)$$
$$I_3\dot{\omega}_3 + (I_2 - I_1)\omega_1\omega_2 = 0$$

These equations are identical with Eqs. (15.43) for a motion of the body under no forces. Eqs. (15.83) have the two integrals (15.49) but the second is not an energy integral now. This is because the kinetic energy is

$$T = \tfrac{1}{2}M(\dot{\xi}^2 + \dot{\eta}^2 + \dot{\zeta}^2) + \tfrac{1}{2}(I_1\omega_1{}^2 + I_2\omega_2{}^2 + I_3\omega_3{}^2) \qquad (15.84)$$

or $\qquad T = mg\zeta + d$

where d is a constant of integration.

Integration of Eqs. (15.82) gives

$$\xi = \alpha_1 t + \beta_1$$
$$\eta = \alpha_2 t + \beta_2 \qquad (15.85)$$
$$\zeta = -\tfrac{1}{2}gt^2 + \alpha_3 t + \beta_3$$

where $\alpha_i \beta_i$ are constants of integration. These are now the equations of motion of the center of mass of the rigid body.

The rotational motion of the body about the center of mass will have all the characteristics of the free rotational motion discussed previously.

15–9 Motion of the Rigid Body with One Point Fixed

We will now consider certain cases of the constrained motion of a rigid body. As before, in such a case we introduce the postulate of reactions as a result of which all the equations of motion of the rigid body discussed in Section 15–1 are valid when on the right hand sides of the various equations we replace the resultant force $\mathbf{F}$ and the resultant torque $\mathbf{G}_{O'}$ by $\mathbf{F} + \mathbf{R}$ and $\mathbf{G}_{O'} + \mathbf{H}_{O'}$ respectively, where $\mathbf{R}$ is the resultant force of reaction and $\mathbf{H}_{O'}$ is the resultant moment of all the reactions.

In what follows we will consider perfect constraints, i.e., ones for which the forces of reactions do not do any work during virtual displacements of the rigid body.

We will start our investigation of the constrained motion by discussing the motion of a rigid body when one point of the rigid body is fixed. We will denote this fixed point by O'. We can show that in this case all the reactions have a resultant passing through the point O'. The moment of these reactions about O' is zero. The equations of motion applicable to the non-constrained motion are Eqs. (15.4) and (15.5). In the present special case, these equations become

$$\dot{\mathbf{p}}_1 + \boldsymbol{\omega}^* \times \mathbf{p} = \mathbf{F} + \mathbf{R} \qquad (15.86)$$

and

$$(\dot{\mathbf{h}}_{O'})_1 + \boldsymbol{\omega}^* \times \mathbf{h}_{O'} = \mathbf{G}_{O'} \qquad (15.87)$$

The latter equation does not contain reactions. It will serve to determine the angular position of the body. The angular position will then be given in terms of Eulerian angles, and from Eq. (15.86) the resultant reaction $\mathbf{R}$ can be determined.

As in Section 15–1, let the space E_1 be permanently connected with the rigid body and let the angular velocity of the rigid body be $\boldsymbol{\omega}$. In Eqs. (15.86) and (15.87) we will thus set $\boldsymbol{\omega}^* = \boldsymbol{\omega}$. For the frame of axes fixed in the body we will choose the principal axes of inertia of the body referred to the point O'. As before, the components referred to these axes will be denoted by subscripts 1, 2, 3.

We first obtain the kinetic energy of the rigid body and the components of the linear and angular momenta along the principal axes of the body. Thus

$$T = \tfrac{1}{2}(I_1\omega_1{}^2 + I_2\omega_2{}^2 + I_3\omega_3{}^2) \tag{15.88}$$

$$p_1 = M(\omega_2\zeta - \omega_3\eta) \qquad p_2 = M(\omega_3\xi - \omega_1\zeta) \qquad p_3 = M(\omega_1\eta - \omega_2\xi) \tag{15.89}$$

$$h_1 = I_1\omega_1 \qquad h_2 = I_2\omega_2 \qquad h_3 = I_3\omega_3 \tag{15.90}$$

In Eq. (15.89) ξ, η, ζ are the coordinates of the center of mass of the rigid body. The scalar equations equivalent to Eq. (15.86) are

$$M(\zeta\dot{\omega}_2 - \eta\dot{\omega}_3) + M\omega_1(\omega_1\xi + \omega_2\eta + \omega_3\zeta) - M\xi\omega^2 = X + R_x$$
$$M(\xi\dot{\omega}_3 - \zeta\dot{\omega}_1) + M\omega_2(\omega_1\xi + \omega_2\eta + \omega_3\zeta) - M\eta\omega^2 = Y + R_y \tag{15.91}$$
$$M(\eta\dot{\omega}_1 - \xi\dot{\omega}_2) + M\omega_3(\omega_1\xi + \omega_2\eta + \omega_3\zeta) - M\zeta\omega^2 = Z + R_z$$

and the scalar equations equivalent to (15.87) are

$$I_1\dot{\omega}_1 + (I_3 - I_2)\omega_2\omega_3 = G_1$$
$$I_2\dot{\omega}_2 + (I_1 - I_3)\omega_3\omega_1 = G_2 \tag{15.92}$$
$$I_3\dot{\omega}_3 + (I_2 - I_1)\omega_1\omega_2 = G_3$$

These are Euler's equations. The components G_1, G_2, G_3 of the torque may be functions of t, ϕ, ψ, θ, $\dot{\phi}$, $\dot{\psi}$, $\dot{\theta}$.

The two sets of Eqs. (15.91) and (15.92) have to be supplemented by Eqs. (15.38).

The problem of this type of motion can be solved by integrating six first order equations (15.92) and (15.38) which will furnish the six unknown functions ω_1, ω_2, ω_3, $\dot{\phi}$, $\dot{\psi}$, $\dot{\theta}$, or by integrating three second order equations in order to obtain the three unknown functions ϕ, ψ, θ; the three second order equations can be obtained by eliminating ω_1, ω_2, ω_3 from Eqs. (15.92), and (15.38).

So far in this chapter we have not made any use of Lagrange's equations. In principle, as was pointed out in the last chapter, Lagrange's equations can always be used; however, in many actual cases they may be difficult to solve. To obtain the equations we first express the kinetic energy given by Eq. (15.88) in terms of ϕ, ψ, θ, $\dot{\phi}$, $\dot{\psi}$, $\dot{\theta}$, and then write Lagrange's equations in the form

$$\frac{d}{dt}\frac{\partial T}{\partial \dot{\psi}} - \frac{\partial T}{\partial \psi} = G_{O'z'}$$

$$\frac{d}{dt}\frac{\partial T}{\partial \dot{\phi}} - \frac{\partial T}{\partial \phi} = G_{O'z} \tag{15.93}$$

$$\frac{d}{dt}\frac{\partial T}{\partial \dot{\theta}} - \frac{\partial T}{\partial \theta} = G_{O'N}$$

where $G_{O'z'}$, $G_{O'z'}$, $G_{O'N}$ are the components of the torque along the axis $O'z'$ fixed in the body, the axis $O'z$ fixed in space and the line of nodes $O'N$ respectively.

We will now consider the special case of the motion of a rigid body on which the force of gravity is acting alone and when one of its points is fixed. We will choose O' (which is not the center of mass) as the fixed point. Let $O'z$ be a fixed axis directed vertically upwards. Then, since the gravitational force acts vertically downward, the moment of this force about the vertical fixed axis $O'z$ remains constant. Hence we deduce that one of the integrals of the set (15.44) exists, namely

$$I_1\omega_1\alpha_3 + I_2\omega_2\beta_3 + I_3\omega_3\gamma_3 = a \qquad (15.94)$$

where a is a constant of integration and $\alpha_3, \beta_3, \gamma_3$ are given by the last of the three sets of Eqs. (13.30), (13.31) and (13.32). Furthermore, the gravitational force has the potential energy function $Mg\zeta$, where ζ is the z coordinate of the center of mass in the fixed coordinate system. Thus we can write the energy integral as

$$2T = I_1\omega_1{}^2 + I_2\omega_2{}^2 + I_3\omega_3{}^2 \qquad (15.95)$$
$$= -2Mg\zeta + d$$

where d denotes a constant of integration.

The coordinate ζ can be expressed in terms of the coordinates ξ_1, η_1, ζ_1 of the center of mass in the rotating frame and in terms of the Eulerian angles.

The motion will be determined when $\omega_1, \omega_2, \omega_3, \phi, \psi, \theta$ will be found as functions of time. For this we need six equations. The first two are the Eqs. (15.94) and (15.95) written above, the third one is the third Euler equation, which in this case is of the form

$$I_3\dot{\omega}_3 + (I_2 - I_1)\omega_1\omega_2 = 0 \qquad (15.96)$$

the last three are Eqs. (15.38).

The laws of motion which we are now considering can also be obtained from Lagrange's equations. We start with the expression for the kinetic energy

$$T = \tfrac{1}{2}(I_1\omega_1{}^2 + I_2\omega_2{}^2 + I_3\omega_3{}^2)$$

which, when Eqs. (15.38) are used, becomes

$$T = \tfrac{1}{2}[I_1(\dot{\phi}\sin\theta\sin\psi + \dot{\theta}\cos\psi)^2 + I_2(\dot{\phi}\sin\theta\cos\psi - \dot{\theta}\sin\psi)^2 + I_3(\dot{\phi}\cos\theta + \dot{\psi})^2] \qquad (15.97)$$

Remembering that the derivative of T with respect to $\dot{\phi}$ is equal to the component of the angular momentum about the fixed axis $O'z$, we can write the integral of moments given by Eq. (15.94) as

$$\frac{\partial T}{\partial \dot{\phi}} = a \qquad (15.98)$$

Next substituting the value of T from Eq. (15.97) into Eq. (15.95) we obtain another integral of the corresponding Lagrange equations. Both this latter integral and the integral Eq. (15.98) will be differential equations of the first order with respect to the Eulerian angles. Finally, for the last equation we could take

$$\frac{d}{dt}\frac{\partial T}{\partial \dot{\psi}} - \frac{\partial T}{\partial \psi} = G_{z'}$$

or

$$\frac{d}{dt}[I_3(\dot{\phi}\cos\theta + \dot{\psi})] - \frac{\partial T}{\partial \psi} = G_{z'} \qquad (15.99)$$

where $G_{z'}$ is the moment of the gravitational force about the moving axis $O'z'$.

We will consider in some detail the case when the ellipsoid of inertia of the rigid body is a rotational ellipsoid about the point O' and when the center of mass of the rigid body lies on the rotational axis of symmetry. For this axis we will choose the z_1 axis to be directed from the fixed origin O' towards the center of mass Q. With this choice $I_1 = I_2$ and $G_3 = 0$. In this case Eq. (15.99) which is a second order differential equation can be replaced by the first order equation

$$\omega_3 = \dot{\phi}\cos\theta + \dot{\psi} = (\omega_3)_0 \qquad (15.100)$$

where $(\omega_3)_0$ is the initial angular velocity about the symmetry axis of the body. If $O'Q = \bar{\zeta}$ then the z coordinate of Q in the fixed frame is given by

$$\zeta = \bar{\zeta}\cos\theta \qquad (15.101)$$

The kinetic energy as given by Eq. (15.97), in this case becomes

$$T = \tfrac{1}{2}[I_1(\dot{\phi}^2\sin^2\theta + \dot{\theta}^2) + I_3(\dot{\phi}\cos\theta + \dot{\psi})^2] \qquad (15.102)$$

We can now evaluate $\partial T/\partial \dot{\phi}$ and substitute the result into Eq. (15.98). If we also make use of Eq. (15.100) we then obtain

$$I_1\dot{\phi}\sin^2\theta + I_3(\omega_3)_0\cos\theta = a \qquad (15.103)$$

Using Eqs. (15.100), (15.101) and (15.102) we can write the energy integral (15.95) as

$$\dot{\phi}^2\sin^2\theta + \dot{\theta}^2 = \lambda^2(\alpha - \cos\theta) \qquad (15.104)$$

where

$$\lambda^2 = \frac{2Mg\bar{\zeta}}{I_1} > 0$$

$$\qquad (15.105)$$

and

$$\alpha = \frac{d - I_3(\omega_3)_0{}^2}{2Mg\bar{\zeta}}$$

Let us draw a sphere of unit radius and denote by N the point where the symmetry axis of the rigid body pierces the sphere. The motion of the rigid body will be established if the coordinates of N and the angle ψ are known at any time. Indeed, for the coordinates of N we can take the angles ϕ and θ. Thus if the coordinates of N and the angle ψ were known then we would have determined the Eulerian angles as functions of time.

We can consider the motion of N as the sum of two motions: the first will be the motion along the meridian which lies in the vertical plane, and the second will be the rotational motion of the plane containing the meridian about the fixed space axis $O'z$. The first motion will determine the nutational changes of θ and the second the precessional change of ϕ.

We will consider two cases, namely when the initial velocity about the body axis is different than zero and when it is zero, i.e., when $(\omega_3)_0 \neq 0$ and when $(\omega_3)_0 = 0$.

Consider first the case when $(\omega_3)_0 \neq 0$. Solving Eq. (15.103) for $\dot{\phi} \sin^2 \theta$ we obtain

$$\dot{\phi} \sin^2 \theta = \frac{a}{I_1} - \frac{I_3(\omega_3)_0}{I_1} \cos \theta$$

or

$$\dot{\phi} \sin^2 \theta = B(A - \cos \theta) \tag{15.106}$$

where

$$B = \frac{I_3(\omega_3)_0}{I_1} \neq 0 \qquad A = \frac{a}{BI_1} \tag{15.107}$$

Let us assume that at a given instant N is not at the point where the space axis pierces the unit sphere, i.e., $\sin \theta \neq 0$. Then, during some interval of time $\sin \theta$ will remain different than zero. Eliminating $\dot{\phi}$ from Eqs. (15.104) and (15.106) we obtain

$$\dot{\theta}^2 = 1/(\sin^2 \theta)[\lambda^2(\alpha - \cos \theta) \sin^2 \theta - B^2(A - \cos \theta)^2]$$

Introducing a new variable u defined as

$$u = \cos \theta$$

we transform the last equation to

$$\dot{u}^2 = \lambda^2(\alpha - u)(1 - u^2) - B^2(A - u)^2 = f(u) \tag{15.108}$$

Consider now the case when $(\omega_3)_0 = 0$. Instead of Eq. (15.106) we obtain

$$\dot{\phi} \sin^2 \theta = \frac{a}{I_1} = \rho \tag{15.109}$$

Eliminating $\dot{\phi}$ between this equation and Eq. (15.104) we have

$$\dot{\theta}^2 = (1/\sin^2 \theta)[\lambda^2(\alpha - \cos \theta) \sin^2 \theta - \rho^2] \tag{15.110}$$

which in terms of the new variable u takes the form

$$\dot{u}^2 = \lambda^2(\alpha - u)(1 - u^2) - \rho^2 = f(u) \tag{15.111}$$

Investigations of the properties of Eqs. (15.108) and (15.111) yield some properties of the type of motion which we are considering here, namely the motion of a rigid body on which only the force of gravitational attraction is acting and which has one fixed point.*

* In this section we have touched upon the vast subject of the motion of a spinning top. For further development of this subject special monographs should be consulted. For a brief discussion Rutherford's book *Classical Mechanics* may, for instance, be used and for a somewhat wider discussion Goldstein's *Classical Mechanics* should be examined.

Fig. 15.1

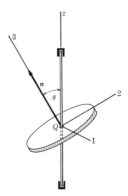

Example: A thin homogeneous disc of mass M and radius R is rigidly attached to an axle AB (Fig. 15.1). A torque is applied which rotates the assembly with constant angular velocity ω. The normal to the disc makes a constant angle θ with the axle.

(a) Evaluate the principal moments of inertia of the disc.

(b) Using Euler's equations determine the components of the torque along the principal axes.

(c) Find the components of the angular momentum along the principal axes.

(d) Determine the resultant angular momentum and its inclination to the body axis.

(e) Find the Eulerian components of the generalized momentum.

(f) What relation would be used to obtain the components G_θ, G_ϕ, G_ψ of the torque along the line of nodes, the axle and the body axis respectively?

(a). We first evaluate the moment of inertia, I_3, about the axis perpendicular to the plate and passing through its center. For the element of mass we choose the ring of radius r and thickness dr (Fig. 15.2); its mass is

$$dm = 2\pi r \rho t \, dr$$

Fig. 15.2

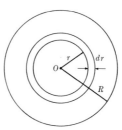

The moment of inertia of this elementary ring is

$$dI_3 = r^2 \, dm$$

or

$$dI_3 = r^2 \rho t 2\pi r \, dr$$

where ρ is the density of the disc and t is its thickness. The moment of inertia of the whole disc is

$$I_3 = \int_0^R 2\pi\rho t r^3 \, dr$$

or

$$I_3 = \tfrac{2}{4}\pi\rho t R^4$$

Now the mass of the ring is

$$M = \rho t \pi R^2$$

Therefore

$$I_3 = \tfrac{1}{2}MR^2$$

This is the moment of inertia about one of the principal axes of the disc.

The other two principal axes are any two axes 1 and 2 in the plane of the disc and perpendicular to each other. By the theorem stated in Problem 4.12:

$$I_3 = I_1 + I_2$$

But in our case

$$I_1 = I_2$$

Therefore

$$2I_1 = I_3$$

or

$$I_1 = I_2 = \tfrac{1}{2}I_3$$

Thus

$$I_1 = I_2 = \tfrac{1}{4}MR^2$$

(b). Euler's equations are

$$G_1 = I_1\dot{\omega}_1 + (I_3 - I_2)\omega_3\omega_2$$
$$G_2 = I\dot{\omega}_2 + (I_1 - I_3)\omega_1\omega_3$$
$$G_3 = I\dot{\omega}_3 + (I_2 - I_1)\omega_2\omega_1$$

where the subscripts refer to the axes 1, 2, 3, fixed in the body. In our case the axle and the disc form a rigid body. A convenient system of axes fixed in the body will be the axes 1, 2 and 3 shown in Figure 15.1. The axis 2 will be in the plane of the axle and the axis 3. The axis 1 will be perpendicular to both axes 2 and 3. The angular velocity vector $\boldsymbol{\omega}$ is constant and lies along the space axis. Its components along the three principal axes are

$$\omega_1 = 0 \qquad \omega_2 = \omega \sin\theta \qquad \omega_3 = \omega \cos\theta$$

All these components are constant.

By the third Euler equation

$$G_3 = I_2\dot{\omega}_3$$

because $I_1 = I_2$. Since ω_3 is constant therefore

$$G_3 = 0$$

By the second Euler equation

$$G_2 = 0$$

because $\dot{\omega}_2 = 0$ and $\omega_1 = 0$

The only non-zero component of the torque is G_1 which is obtained from the first Euler equation

$$G_1 = (I_3 - I_2)\omega_3\omega_2$$

or $\qquad G_1 = (\tfrac{1}{2}MR^2 - \tfrac{1}{4}MR^2)\omega^2 \cos\theta \sin\theta$

which becomes $\qquad G_1 = \tfrac{1}{4}MR^2\omega^2 \sin\theta \cos\theta$

(c). The three components of the angular momentum along the principal axes are

$$h_1 = I_1\omega_1 \qquad h_2 = I_2\omega_2 \qquad h_3 = I_3\omega_3$$

or in our case

$$h_1 = 0 \qquad h_2 = \tfrac{1}{4}MR^2\omega \sin\theta \qquad h_3 = \tfrac{1}{2}MR^2\omega \cos\theta$$

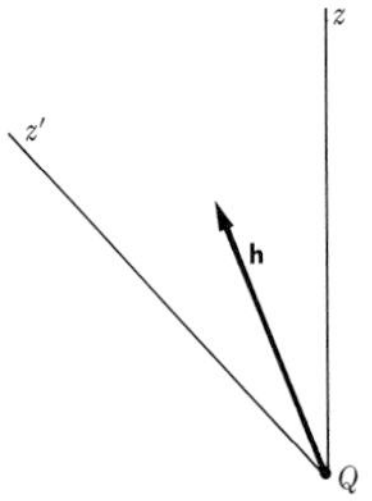

Fig. 15.3

(d). The resultant angular momentum lies in the plane of the body axis and the space axis (Fig. 15.3), and its magnitude is given by

$$h^2 = (\tfrac{1}{4})^2(MR^2)^2\omega^2 \sin^2\theta + \tfrac{1}{4}(MR^2)^2\omega^2 \cos^2\theta$$

or

$$h = \tfrac{1}{2}MR^2\omega\sqrt{\tfrac{1}{4}\sin^2\theta + \cos^2\theta}$$

Its inclination to the body axis is given by

$$\tan\alpha = \frac{h_2}{h_3}$$

or

$$\tan\alpha = \frac{\tfrac{1}{4}MR^2\omega \sin\theta}{\tfrac{1}{2}MR^2\omega \cos\theta}$$

Thus

$$\tan\alpha = \tfrac{1}{2}\tan\theta$$

or

$$\alpha = \text{arc tan}\,(\tfrac{1}{2}\tan\theta)$$

(e). The Eulerian components p_θ, p_ϕ, and p_ψ of the generalized momentum are the components of the angular momentum vector along the line of nodes,

244

the space axis and the body axis respectively. Thus in our case

$$p_\theta = 0$$
$$p_\phi = \tfrac{1}{2}MR^2\omega\sqrt{\tfrac{1}{4}\sin^2\theta + \cos^2\theta}\,\sin\alpha$$
$$p_\psi = \tfrac{1}{2}MR^2\omega\sqrt{\tfrac{1}{4}\sin^2\theta + \cos^2\theta}\,\cos\alpha$$

(f). Having determined G_1, G_2 and G_3 the three required components of the torque are obtained from

$$\begin{bmatrix} G_\theta \\ G_\phi \\ G_\psi \end{bmatrix} = \begin{bmatrix} \cos\psi & -\sin\psi & 0 \\ \cos\psi\sin\theta & \cos\psi\sin\theta & \cos\theta \\ 0 & 0 & 1 \end{bmatrix} \begin{bmatrix} G_1 \\ G_2 \\ G_3 \end{bmatrix}$$

In our case G_2 and G_3 are both zero.

PROBLEMS

15.1 Prove that the principal axes are the only axes about which a rigid body in its free motion can rotate with constant angular velocity.

15.2 When, in a free motion, a body rotates about one of its principal axes, then at every instant the angular momentum vector lies along the axis of rotation. Discuss analytically the only other case when this is possible.

15.3 Prove that in order that a rigid body can be moved with a purely translational motion, it is necessary and sufficient that the resultant force acting on the body passed through the center of mass and that the initial angular velocity of the body is zero.

15.4 Show that the energy integral for the motion of a rigid body in the gravitational field of the earth can be written as

$$\dot\zeta^2 + g\zeta = a$$

where ζ is the z coordinate of the center of mass of the body, g is the acceleration due to gravity and a is a constant of integration.

15.5 A solid uniform sphere has rigidly attached to it a light rod which passes through the sphere's center. This rod is joined to a fixed vertical axis so that the angle θ between the rod and the axis may change but the rod must turn with the axis. (Fig. 15.4.) If the vertical axis revolved with constant velocity show that the equation of motion is of the form:

$$\dot\theta^2 = n^2(\cos\theta - \cos\beta)(\cos\alpha - \cos\theta)$$

Fig. 15.4

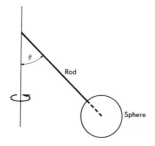

15.6 (a) The moments and the products of inertia of a rigid body are given by $I_{xx} = I_{yy} = I_{zz} = a$, and $I_{yz} = I_{zx} = I_{xy} = b$. Determine the principal moments of inertia.

A rigid body with the above moments of inertia rotates in such a way that its axis of symmetry makes a constant angle θ with the space axis O. The angular velocity vector is constant and lies along O.

(b) Determine the components of the angular momentum vector along the principal axes of the body.

(c) Find the kinetic energy of the body.

15.7 There is a very special case of the motion of a rigid body with one fixed point when the resultant of all the forces acting on the body passes through the fixed point O'. Write Euler's equations for this case. Discuss the ellipsoid of inertia, Poinsot's plane [given by Eq. (15.78)], and the locus of the axes of rotation.

16 SMALL OSCILLATIONS

As we have seen, the general motion of rigid bodies is quite complicated, but we are able to formulate procedures by means of which any problem of rigid body motion can, in principle, be solved. By this we mean that in general we can write down the equations of motion for a rigid body but quite often we may have great difficulties in solving the equations.

We next want to consider a system of rigid bodies which are interconnected in some way. The situation still remains relatively simple when all the members of the system including the linkages are rigid bodies. We will not study such systems. What we want to consider is systems which consist of particles or rigid bodies connected by non-rigid linkages. There are many different types of such linkages. One example of such systems, shown in Figure 16.1, consists of a series of point masses connected by springs. If we

Fig. 16.1

disturb such a system by compressing some springs and extending others, and, in addition, displace the masses perpendicular to the horizontal direction, then the resulting motion will be very complicated indeed. In some cases there are no actual linkages but there exist constraints which permit certain types of motion only. An example of this type is shown in Figure 16.2. It

Fig. 16.2

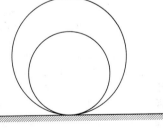

consists of a hollow cylinder which can roll on a rough plane with another cylinder inside.

It will be important for us to be able to attack problems of this sort, because systems of the type quoted above can serve as models for atomic or molecular systems. In solid state physics we have to deal with crystals which consist of regular arrangements of atoms or molecules. Interatomic forces are present, and it is of interest to know their nature and to find their magnitudes. Be-

247

Fig. 16.3

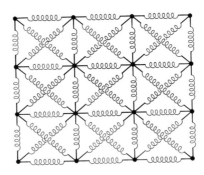

cause of these forces, atoms are in a continuous state of vibration about their positions of equilibrium. Figure 16.3 shows a model of a two-dimensional crystal in which the atoms are arranged in a square pattern. We assume that in this model the forces acting between the atoms can be replaced by springs of suitable force constants. In Figure 16.4 we have picked one atom and shown the forces (replaced by springs) which result from nearest neighbor interactions only. Every atom in the crystal is subjected to such forces.

Fig. 16.4

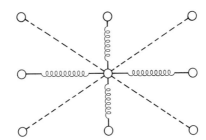

Situations are more complicated, of course, if in addition next to the nearest atoms interact with every atom.

As already mentioned, atoms execute oscillations about their positions of equilibrium. We shall study oscillations of mechanical systems about their positions of equilibrium of which we shall only consider small oscillations. Even in such a case the resulting motion of the system is rather complicated and at first sight it would seem impossible to describe it analytically. However, there exist methods which permit the untangling of such motion. Such methods will be discussed presently. Their power will be appreciated if the complexity of the motion of such coupled systems is realized. Consider once more the case of masses connected with springs (Fig. 16.1). Suppose that we displace the masses in the vertical directions only. At time $t = 0$, let every mass be displaced by a different amount either above or below the horizontal line, and then released. In the resulting general motion the particles will not vibrate independently but will influence each other through the springs.

We will first solve a simple problem belonging to this category by methods which are already available to us. In obtaining the solutions, we will introduce new concepts which will be of importance later when the general theory of small oscillations will be formulated.

16–1 *Two Particles on a Stretched Elastic String*

We will now consider two particles, each of mass m, attached to a stretched elastic string which is fixed at both ends. The equilibrium position is shown in Figure 16.5. In this position the distance between the particles is b and

Fig. 16.5

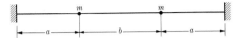

the distance between the particle and the end of the string is a for each particle. Let both particles be displaced slightly in the vertical direction in one plane, and released. Small oscillations will result. We will assume that the tension in the string remains constant in magnitude even when the particles oscillate.

(*a*) *The Use of Newton's Equations.*

Let the positions of the two particles in the displaced positions be y_1 and y_2 respectively. There are two forces **P** acting on each particle, as shown in Figure 16.6 but only their vertical components contribute towards the

Fig. 16.6

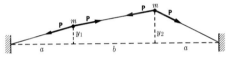

accelerations of the particles. We will neglect the effects of gravitational attraction. Thus, for small oscillations, the equations of motion are

$$m\ddot{y}_1 = -P\frac{y_1}{a} + P\frac{y_2 - y_1}{b}$$

and

$$m\ddot{y}_2 = -P\frac{y_2}{a} - P\frac{y_2 - y_1}{b}$$

or

$$m\ddot{y}_1 = -P\frac{a+b}{ab}y_1 + \frac{P}{b}y_2$$

and

$$m\ddot{y}_2 = \frac{P}{b}y_1 - P\frac{a+b}{ab}y_2 \qquad (16.1)$$

Dividing these equations by m and denoting

$$\frac{1}{m}\frac{P(a+b)}{ab} = \alpha \qquad \frac{1}{m}\frac{P}{b} = \beta \qquad (16.2)$$

we obtain

$$\ddot{y}_1 = -\alpha y_1 + \beta y_2$$
$$\ddot{y}_2 = \beta y_1 - \alpha y_2 \qquad (16.3)$$

Adding the two equations gives

$$\ddot{y}_1 + \ddot{y}_2 = (\beta - \alpha)(y_1 + y_2) \qquad (16.4)$$

Subtraction yields

$$\ddot{y}_1 - \ddot{y}_2 = (\alpha + \beta)(y_2 - y_1) \qquad (16.5)$$

The last two equations can be rewritten as

$$\frac{d^2}{dt^2}(y_1 + y_2) + (\alpha - \beta)(y_1 + y_2) = 0 \tag{16.6}$$

and

$$\frac{d^2}{dt^2}(y_1 - y_2) + (\alpha + \beta)(y_1 - y_2) = 0 \tag{16.7}$$

It is very suggestive to introduce new coordinates defined by

$$\bar{y} = y_1 + y_2 \tag{16.8}$$

and

$$\bar{y}_2 = y_1 - y_2 \tag{16.9}$$

If we also let

$$\omega_1 = \sqrt{\alpha - \beta}$$

and

$$\omega_2 = \sqrt{\alpha + \beta} \tag{16.10}$$

Equations (16.6) and (16.7) then take the form

$$\ddot{\bar{y}}_1 + \omega_1{}^2 \bar{y}_1 = 0 \tag{16.11}$$

and

$$\ddot{\bar{y}}_2 + \omega_2{}^2 \bar{y}_2 = 0$$

Their solutions can be written immediately as

$$\bar{y}_1 = a_1 \cos(\omega_1 + \epsilon_1) \tag{16.12}$$

and

$$\bar{y}_2 = a_2 \cos(\omega_2 + \epsilon_2) \tag{16.13}$$

These are the complete solutions of our problem; they involve four constants $a_1, a_2, \epsilon_1, \epsilon_2$ which can be determined from the initial conditions.

We have obtained a few significant results which form the essence of the theory of small oscillations. First, we notice from Eqs. (16.12) and (16.13) that *the system vibrates with two frequencies ω_1 and ω_2* which, using Eqs. (16.10) and (16.2), can be expressed in terms of physical constants of the system and in terms of the tension P as

$$\omega_1 = \sqrt{\frac{P}{ma}} \tag{16.14}$$

and

$$\omega_2 = \sqrt{\frac{P}{m}\frac{2a + b}{ab}} \tag{16.15}$$

These are the frequencies with which the coordinates $\bar{y}_1$ and $\bar{y}_2$ vibrate.

The original coordinates of the system are y_1 and y_2. Solving Eqs. (16.8) and (16.9) for y_1 and y_2 we obtain

$$y_1 = (1/2)(\bar{y}_1 + \bar{y}_2)$$

and

$$y_2 = (1/2)(\bar{y}_1 - \bar{y}_2) \tag{16.16}$$

Substitution of Eqs. (16.12) and (16.13) into (16.16) yields

$$y_1 = (1/2)a_1 \cos(\omega_1 t + \epsilon_1) + (1/2)a_2 \cos(\omega_2 t + \epsilon_2) \tag{16.17}$$

and $$y_2 = (1/2)a_1 \cos(\omega_1 t + \epsilon_1) - (1/2)a_2 \cos(\omega_2 t + \epsilon_2) \qquad (16.18)$$

These are the general solutions of our problem for the original coordinates. Although, in general, both y_1 and y_2 vibrate in some complicated way and with some resultant frequencies, we notice that the solutions contain only the two frequencies ω_1 and ω_2; we call these *normal frequencies* of the system.

Let us now turn to the coordinates $\bar{y}_1$ and $\bar{y}_2$. We assert that *it is possible to disturb the system at $t = 0$ in such a way that only one of these coordinates is nonzero* (and the other will be permanently zero). Indeed, from Eq. (16.8) we see that if $\bar{y}_1$ is to be zero then

$$y_1 + y_2 = 0$$

or $$y_1 = -y_2 \qquad (16.19)$$

The system will then vibrate with one normal frequency, viz., ω_2 in this case. Similarly we can initially disturb the system in such a way that $\bar{y}_2 = 0$. From Eq. (16.9) we see that this will require

$$y_1 - y_2 = 0$$

or $$y_1 = y_2 \qquad (16.20)$$

In this case the system will vibrate with the normal frequency ω_1 only.

These two vibrations are of a special type. We call them *normal modes of vibrations. One of the characteristics of normal modes is that when the system vibrates in one of them, then it does so with only one of the normal frequencies.*

The behavior of the original coordinates y_1 and y_2 when the system vibrates in one of its normal modes can be obtained from Eqs. (16.16) in conjunction with Eqs. (16.12) and (16.13). When $\bar{y}_1 = 0$ then

$$y_1 = (1/2)\bar{y}_2$$

and $$y_2 = -(1/2)\bar{y}_2$$

or

$$y_1 = (1/2)a_2 \cos(\omega_2 t + \epsilon_2)$$

and $$y_2 = -(1/2)a_2 \cos(\omega_2 t + \epsilon_2) \qquad (16.21)$$

Similarly when $\bar{y}_2 = 0$ then

$$y_1 = (1/2)\bar{y}_1$$

and $$y_2 = (1/2)\bar{y}_1$$

or

$$y_1 = (1/2)a_1 \cos(\omega_1 t + \epsilon_1) \qquad (16.22)$$

and $$y_2 = (1/2)a_1 \cos(\omega_1 t + \epsilon_1)$$

We notice that in both cases *not only is the frequency in a particular mode the same, but also the epoch angle is the same.* This is another characteristic of the normal modes.

16–1 Two particles on a stretched elastic string

Fig. 16.7a

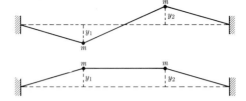

Fig. 16.7b

Figures 16.7(a) and (b) show the two normal modes of vibration of our system.

We can now summerize our results. We have been considering *a system with two degrees of freedom.* We found that *it has two normal frequencies.* In general *both coordinates* (y_1 and y_2) *involve both normal frequencies.* However, *it is possible to find a set of coordinates, each of which oscillate with only one of the normal frequencies. Such a set of coordinates constitute normal coordinates of the system.* When only one mode is excited the other normal coordinate is permanently zero. This latter fact allows us to examine *the nature of the normal mode.* For a general motion, *the original coordinates are linear combinations of the normal coordinates.* When the system vibrates in one of its normal modes the behavior of the original coordinates can easily be determined by suppression of the other normal coordinate. We have seen that, *when the system vibrates in either of its normal modes, both original coordinates have the same frequency and the same epoch angle, i.e., they have the same phase.*

In the above development cosine solutions were used. This permitted us to follow all the physical implications of the theory of normal modes. Should we be interested in a little shorter and simpler method of obtaining solutions then we should start with the differential equations (16.1) and assume exponential solutions

$$y_1 = Ae^{i\omega t}$$

and

$$y_2 = Be^{i\omega t} \tag{16.23}$$

Substitution in the differential equation yields a determinental equation from which the same normal frequencies are obtained. The relations between the constants A and B are, of course, also the same. The final form of the general solutions is

$$y_1 = A_1 e^{i\omega_1 t} + A_1' e^{-i\omega_1 t} + A_2 e^{i\omega_2 t} + A_2' e^{-i\omega_2 t}$$

$$y_2 = A_1 e^{i\omega_1 t} + A_1' e^{-i\omega_1 t} - A_2 e^{i\omega_2 t} - A_2' e^{-i\omega_2' t} \tag{16.24}$$

These were obtained by assuming that both y_1 and y_2 are superpositions of exponential solutions which contain both positive and negative angular frequencies. The search for normal coordinates and normal modes of vibrations should then follow.

(b) The Use of Lagrange's Equations.

To form the Lagrangian function of our system we need the kinetic and potential energy. The potential energy is the elastic potential energy of the string. We will consider the three portions of the string separately and

252

Fig. 16.8

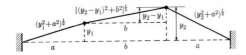

evaluate the potential energy stored in them. For every portion we will calculate its extension and multiply it by the tension P. Thus for the left-most portion of the string (Fig. 16.8) the extension is given by

$$(a^2 + y_1^2)^{1/2} - a = a\left(1 + \frac{y_1^2}{a^2}\right)^{1/2} - a$$

$$= a\left(1 + \frac{1}{2}\frac{y_1^2}{a^2}\right) - a$$

$$= a + \frac{1}{2}\frac{y_1^2}{a} - a = \frac{1}{2}\frac{y_1^2}{a}$$

In the binomial expansion, only the first two terms have been retained. Similarly for the middle and the right-most portions, the extensions are given respectively by

$$\frac{1}{2b}(y_2 - y_1)^2 \quad \text{and} \quad \frac{1}{2}\frac{y_2^2}{a}$$

Thus the total potential energy is[*]

$$V = \frac{P}{2}\left[\frac{y_1^2}{a} + \frac{(y_2 - y_1)^2}{b} + \frac{y_2^2}{a}\right] \tag{16.25}$$

The kinetic energy of the system is

$$T = \tfrac{1}{2}m(\dot{y}_1^2 + \dot{y}_2^2) \tag{16.26}$$

Thus the Lagrangian function becomes

$$L = \tfrac{1}{2}m\dot{y}_1^2 + \tfrac{1}{2}m\dot{y}_2^2 - \tfrac{1}{2}P\left[\frac{y_1^2}{a} + \frac{1}{b}(y_2^2 - 2y_1y_2 + y_1^2) + \frac{y_2^2}{a}\right] \tag{16.27}$$

[*] It might be illuminating to evaluate the potential energy in two different ways. This can be done by applying the definition of the potential energy as the negative of the work done against the forces of the field. However, caution has to be exercised. Let us treat the two particles as two free bodies. The net vertical force acting on the left particle, Figure 16.9, is $F_1 = -P\frac{y_1}{a} + P\frac{y_2 - y_1}{b}$ and that on the right particle is $F_2 = -P\frac{y_2 - y_1}{b} - P\frac{y_2}{a}$. If we evaluate the potential energy from the relation

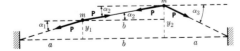

Fig. 16.9

$V = -\int_0^{y_1} F_1\, dy_1 - \int_0^{y_2} F_2\, dy_2$, the correct expression for V will not be obtained. This is so because the system is coupled, i.e., the motion of one particle influences the

The two Lagrangian equations are

$$\frac{d}{dt}\left(\frac{\partial L}{\partial \dot{y}_1}\right) - \frac{\partial L}{\partial y_1} = 0 \qquad (16.28)$$

and

$$\frac{d}{dt}\left(\frac{\partial L}{\partial \dot{y}_2}\right) - \frac{\partial L}{\partial y_2} = 0$$

After substitution of all the partial derivatives we obtain differential equations which are identical with those obtained previously (Eqs. 16.1).

(c) *The Use of Hamilton's Equations.*

Since the system is conservative, the Hamiltonian function is

$$H = T + V$$

Now, the total energy $E(= T + V)$ of our system is

$$E = \tfrac{1}{2}m\dot{y}_1^2 + \tfrac{1}{2}m\dot{y}_2^2 + \tfrac{1}{2}P\left[\frac{y_1^2}{a} + \frac{1}{b}(y_2^2 - 2y_1y_2 + y_1^2) + \frac{y_2^2}{a}\right]$$

Expressing it in terms of the generalized momenta

$$p_1 = m\dot{y}_1 \qquad \text{and} \qquad p_2 = m\dot{y}_2$$

we obtain

$$H = \frac{1}{2m}p_1^2 + \frac{1}{2m}p_2^2 + \frac{1}{2}P\left[\frac{y_1^2}{a} + \frac{1}{b}(y_2^2 - 2y_1y_2 + y_1^2) + \frac{y_2^2}{a}\right]$$

$$(16.29)$$

motion of the other. In spite of this latter fact the coordinates y_1 and y_2 are still independent. The interdependence of the two particles can be seen from the fact that if we push the right particle to the final position y_2 (Fig. 16.10(a)) then no work has been

Fig. 16.10a

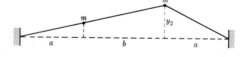

Fig. 16.10b

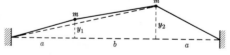

done on the left particle because the forces acting on it are at all times equal and oppositely directed. The proper procedure to calculate the potential energy would then be to move the right particle to the final position y_2 and calculate the work done in this process. This particle should then be held fixed and the left particle moved to the final position y_1 (Fig. 16.10(b)). It will be found that in this way the correct expression for the potential energy is obtained.

16-1   Two particles on a stretched elastic string

The four Hamilton equations are

$$\dot{y}_1 = \frac{\partial H}{\partial p_1} \qquad \dot{p}_1 = -\frac{\partial H}{\partial y_1}$$

$$\dot{y}_2 = \frac{\partial H}{\partial p_2} \qquad \dot{p}_2 = -\frac{\partial H}{\partial y_2} \qquad (16.30)$$

Two of these are trivial because they reintroduce the momenta, but the other two become the set of differential equations of motion obtained twice before.

16–2 Introduction to the Theory of Small Oscillations

We will now present the formal theory of free small oscillations of coupled rigid bodies about a position of equilibrium. When confronted with any problem belonging to this category we can always try to use any of the methods applied to the example considered before. There are, however, methods which yield solutions, together with all the normal quantities, in a straightforward way. These procedures, based on some results of linear algebra,* will now be outlined.

The whole method is based on the possibility of the simultaneous reduction of quadratic forms to sums of squares. In our case, the two quadratic forms are the potential and kinetic energies of the system. *This reduction leads to normal coordinates, normal frequencies and normal modes of vibrations.* This is the way in which we will first develop the theory of small oscillations. We will later demonstrate, however, that *the entire procedure is actually based on the principal axis transformation,* somewhat similar to, but more general than, the transformation to the principal axes of rotation for rigid bodies; the latter was a particular case of a similarity transformation.**

It is first necessary to demonstrate that *both the kinetic and potential energies of systems executing small vibrations about the positions of equilibrium are quadratic in form with constant coefficients.*

16–3 The Potential and Kinetic Energy

Consider a system of n degrees of freedom which is describable by n generalized coordinates

$$q_1, q_2, \ldots, q_n$$

We now assume that the system has an equilibrium position and we choose

---

* All the necessary parts of linear algebra and matrix analysis are discussed in detail in Appendix B. The reader who has not had any contact with linear algebra and matrices should study this appendix now.
** Discussed at length in Appendix B.

a coordinate system in such a way that the equilibrium configuration corresponds to the value of zero for every coordinate. Thus, when the system is at equilibrium,

$$q_1 = q_2 = \cdots = q_n = 0$$

We also assume that the potential energy of the system is a function of all the generalized coordinates; thus

$$V = V(q_1, q_2, \ldots, q_n)$$

At the equilibrium position

$$V = V(0, 0, \ldots, 0)$$

and since the zero potential energy is always arbitrary, we may choose this value to be zero. The system executes small oscillations and so, in every displaced position, the values of the coordinates will be quite close to zero. It is therefore possible to expand the potential energy in Taylor's series about the equilibrium position.* Thus

$$V(q_1, q_2, \ldots, q_n)$$

$$= V(0, 0, \ldots, 0) + q_1 \left[\frac{\partial V(q_1, \ldots, q_n)}{\partial q_1} \right]_0$$

$$+ q_2 \left[\frac{\partial V(q_1, \ldots, q_n)}{\partial q_2} \right]_0 + \cdots + q_n \left[\frac{\partial V(q_1, \ldots, q_n)}{\partial q_n} \right]_0$$

$$+ \tfrac{1}{2} q_1{}^2 \left[\frac{\partial^2 V(q_1, \ldots, q_n)}{\partial q_1{}^2} \right]_0 + \cdots + q_1 q_2 \left[\frac{\partial^2 V(q_1, \ldots, q_n)}{\partial q_1 \, \partial q_2} \right]_0 + \cdots + o(3)$$

$$(16.31)$$

In this expression the zero subscripts indicate that the derivatives are all evaluated at $(0, 0, \ldots, 0)$; $o(3)$ indicates all the higher order terms. Now, at the point $(0, 0, \ldots, 0)$ the system is at equilibrium for which the condition is that all the first derivatives evaluated there vanish. In addition we have chosen

$$V(0, 0, \ldots, 0) = 0$$

Further, in $o(3)$ all the terms contain either cubes and higher power of the generalized coordinates or their triple and higher products. For small oscillations we feel justified in neglecting them. We are therefore left with

$$V(q_1, q_2, \ldots, q_n)$$

$$= \frac{1}{2} \left\{ \left[\frac{\partial^2 V(q_1, \ldots, q_n)}{\partial q_1{}^2} \right]_0 q_1{}^2 + \cdots + 2 \left[\frac{\partial^2 V(q_1, \ldots, q_n)}{\partial q_1 \, \partial q_2} \right]_0 q_1 q_2 + \cdots \right\}$$

* The meaning of Taylor's expansion should be clearly understood. In this case the potential $V(q_1, q_2, \ldots, q_n)$ is a function of several variables. We know its value at one point, in our case at $(0, 0, \ldots, 0)$, and also all its derivatives at this point. The value of $V(q_1, q_2, \ldots, q_n)$ at a neighboring point can be expressed in terms of $V(0, 0, \ldots, 0)$ and the derivatives of $V(q_1, q_2, \ldots, q_n)$ evaluated at $(0, 0, \ldots, 0)$. Taylor's expansion gives this value. Incidentally, in the case when the expansion takes place about the origin, the theorem is called Maclaurin's expansion.

which is of the form

$$V(q_1, q_2, \ldots, q_n) = \tfrac{1}{2}(b_{11}q_1{}^2 + b_{22}q_2{}^2 + \cdots + 2b_{12}q_1q_2 + \cdots) \qquad (16.32)$$

where
$$b_{ij} = \left[\frac{\partial^2 V(q_1, \ldots, q_n)}{\partial q_i \, \partial q_j}\right]_0 \qquad (16.33)$$

and, of course, the b_{ij} are numbers.

We have just demonstrated that the potential energy function is a quadratic form in generalized coordinates with constant coefficients.

The kinetic energy is a homogeneous quadratic function in generalized velocities. Thus it is of the form

$$T = \tfrac{1}{2}(a_{11}\dot{q}_1{}^2 + a_{22}\dot{q}_2{}^2 + \cdots + 2a_{12}\dot{q}_1\dot{q}_2 + \cdots) \qquad (16.34)$$

but the coefficients are, in general, functions of generalized coordinates, i.e.

$$a_{ij} = a_{ij}(q_1, q_2, \ldots, q_n)$$

Again we can expand every coefficient in terms of Taylor's series. Thus

$$a_{ij} = a_{ij}(0, 0, \ldots, 0) + o(1)$$

Here $o(1)$ stands for the sum of all the other terms of the Taylor series. If every coefficient is to be constant then all the terms included in $o(1)$ should be discarded. We are assuming that in the case of small oscillations such an approximation is valid. Thus we set

$$a_{ij}(q_1, q_2, \ldots, q_n) = a_{ij}(0, 0, \ldots, 0) \qquad (16.35)$$

The kinetic energy, given by Eq. (16.34) becomes then a quadratic form with constant coefficients. In addition, the kinetic energy is always positive. For this reason the kinetic energy T is positive definite.*

The kinetic and potential energies can also be written in the matrix form as

$$T = \tfrac{1}{2}\dot{\mathbf{q}}'\mathbf{A}\dot{\mathbf{q}} \qquad (16.36)$$

and
$$V = \tfrac{1}{2}\mathbf{q}'\mathbf{B}\mathbf{q} \qquad (16.37)$$

respectively, where
$$\mathbf{A} = [a_{ij}] \quad \text{and} \quad \mathbf{B} = [b_{ij}] \qquad (16.38)$$

are matrices of the coefficients of the kinetic and potential energies, $\mathbf{q}$ and $\dot{\mathbf{q}}$ are column vectors of the generalized coordinates and generalized velocities respectively and $\mathbf{q}'$ and $\dot{\mathbf{q}}'$ are their transposes.**

Examining the actual forms of the kinetic and potential energies of coupled systems we will see that the coefficients a_{ij} of the kinetic energy contain the

---

* This is a requirement which one of the quadratic forms must fulfill in order that both can simultaneously be reduced to sums of squares.
** In Appendix B we have demonstrated how a quadratic form can be expressed in matrix notation.

inertial properties of the system and the coefficients b_{ij} describe the elastic properties, i.e., a_{ij} contain masses and moments of inertia and b_{ij} contain the force constants of the elastic linkages. For this reason **A** is sometimes called the inertia matrix and **B** the elastic matrix.

16-4 Reduction of Kinetic and Potential Energy to Sum of Squares

Given two quadratic forms

$$Q_1 = \sum_i \sum_j a_{ij} x_i x_j \tag{16.39}$$

and

$$Q_2 = \sum_i \sum_j b_{ij} x_i x_j \tag{16.40}$$

in which the coefficients a_{ij} and b_{ij} are constant and symmetric, and Q_1 is positive definite, it is possible to reduce them to the following forms:*

$$Q_1 = y_1{}^2 + y_2{}^2 + \cdots + y_n{}^2 \tag{16.41}$$

$$Q_2 = \lambda_1 y_1{}^2 + \lambda_2 y_2{}^2 + \cdots + \lambda_n y_n{}^2 \tag{16.42}$$

In the case of small oscillations we have two such quadratic forms, namely

$$2T = \sum_i \sum_j a_{ij} \dot{q}_i \dot{q}_j \tag{16.43}$$

and

$$2V = \sum_i \sum_j b_{ij} q_i q_i \tag{16.44}$$

It is now possible to find a linear transformation

$$\mathbf{q} = \mathbf{C}\bar{\mathbf{q}} \tag{16.45}$$

where **C** is a transformation matrix, which will reduce the two quadratic forms to

$$2T = \dot{\bar{q}}_1{}^2 + \dot{\bar{q}}_2{}^2 + \cdots + \dot{\bar{q}}_n{}^2 \tag{16.46}$$

and

$$2V = \lambda_1 \bar{q}_1{}^2 + \lambda_2 \bar{q}_2{}^2 + \cdots + \lambda_n \bar{q}_n{}^2 \tag{16.47}$$

The λ's are the roots of the determinantal equation**

---

* See Appendix B for a detailed demonstration of how this can be done. Here we will just apply this theorem.

** A word of explanation is necessary here. In the two forms $Q_1 = \sum_i \sum_j a_{ij} x_i x_j$ and $Q_2 = \sum_i \sum_j b_{ij} x_i x_j$ the coordinates x_i are the same and only the coefficients a_{ij} and b_{ij} are different. This is not the case in the two forms for the kinetic and potential energy, viz., $2T = \sum_i \sum_j a_{ij} \dot{q}_i \dot{q}_j$ and $2V = \sum_i \sum_j b_{ij} q_i q_j$; in the latter, the generalized coordinates appear and in the former, their time derivatives. But this presents no difficulty. The actual process concerns the simultaneous diagonalization of the two matrices **A** and **B**. The old and new coordinates are related by $\mathbf{q} = \mathbf{C}\bar{\mathbf{q}}$, which is valid for the velocities $\dot{\mathbf{q}}$ as well, i.e., $\dot{\mathbf{q}} = \mathbf{C}\dot{\bar{\mathbf{q}}}$.

$$\begin{vmatrix} \lambda a_{11} - b_{11} & \lambda a_{12} - b_{12} & \cdots & \lambda a_{1n} - b_{1n} \\ \lambda a_{21} - b_{21} & \cdots\cdots\cdots\cdots & & \lambda a_{2n} - b_{2n} \\ \lambda a_{n1} - b_{n1} & \cdots\cdots\cdots\cdots & & \lambda a_{nn} - b_{nn} \end{vmatrix} = 0 \qquad (16.48)$$

The set

$$\bar{q}_1, \bar{q}_2, \ldots, \bar{q}_n$$

can now be used as a new set of coordinates. Although they have been introduced here through a definition, we will soon see that they correspond to the normal coordinates of the system. We will later present a method of finding them.

16–5 Lagrange's Equations in Terms of Normal Coordinates

In terms of normal coordinates the kinetic and the potential energies are given by

$$T = \tfrac{1}{2}(\dot{\bar{q}}_1{}^2 + \dot{\bar{q}}_2{}^2 + \cdots + \dot{\bar{q}}_n{}^2)$$

and

$$V = \tfrac{1}{2}(\lambda_1 \bar{q}_1{}^2 + \lambda_2 \bar{q}_2{}^2 + \cdots + \lambda_n \bar{q}_n{}^2)$$

The Lagrangian function is therefore

$$L = \tfrac{1}{2}(\dot{\bar{q}}_1{}^2 + \dot{\bar{q}}_2{}^2 + \cdots + \dot{\bar{q}}_n{}^2 - \lambda_1 \bar{q}_1{}^2 - \lambda_2 \bar{q}_2{}^2 - \cdots - \lambda_n \bar{q}_n{}^2)$$

and Lagrange's equations are

$$\ddot{\bar{q}}_s + \lambda_s \bar{q}_s = 0 \qquad s = 1, 2, \ldots, n \qquad (16.49)$$

The solutions of these equations are

$$\bar{q}_s = A_s \cos\left(\sqrt{\lambda_s}\, t + \epsilon_s\right) \qquad (16.50)$$

We thus see that all *the normal coordinates vibrate with simple harmonic motion* and therefore we can identify the λ's as the squares of the normal frequencies of the system.

So far we have found the behavior of the normal coordinates. The behavior of the original set of coordinates can be found if we substitute the $\bar{q}_s$'s in the linear transformation

$$\mathbf{q} = \mathbf{C}\bar{\mathbf{q}} \qquad (16.51)$$

Before we can do this we must write out the matrix equation in full. We thus have

$$\begin{bmatrix} q_1 \\ q_2 \\ \vdots \\ q_n \end{bmatrix} = \begin{bmatrix} c_{11} & c_{12} & \cdots & c_{1n} \\ c_{21} & \cdots\cdots\cdots & & c_{2n} \\ c_{n1} & \cdots\cdots\cdots & & c_{nn} \end{bmatrix} \begin{bmatrix} \bar{q}_1 \\ \bar{q}_2 \\ \vdots \\ \bar{q}_n \end{bmatrix} \qquad (16.52)$$

and we have to matrix-multiply out the right hand side. We will then see that the i-th generalized coordinate is given by

$$q_i = \sum_{s=1}^{n} c_{is}\bar{q}_s \qquad (16.53)$$

In this we substitute the expression for $\bar{q}_s$ from Eq. (16.50) and obtain

$$q_i = \sum_{s=1}^{n} c_{is}A_s \cos{(\sqrt{\lambda_s}t + \epsilon_s)} \qquad i = 1, 2, \ldots, n \qquad (16.54)$$

This is a rather significant result. It states that *every generalized coordinate of the system is a linear superposition of the normal coordinates. The same set of normal coordinates enters into the linear superposition for every generalized coordinate. Associated with every normal coordinate there is one normal frequency. Again the same set of normal frequencies enters into the linear superposition of which every generalized coordinate is made up.* It is through the set of normal coordinates that the complicated resultant motion of the system can be untangled. The set of normal frequencies affords the physical insight into the problem.

16–6   Normal Modes of Vibration

All of the normal coordinates of the set

$$\bar{q}_1, \bar{q}_2, \ldots, \bar{q}_n$$

are independent.* Within the limits of small vibrations they can be varied independently of each other. In particular, we can set all of them to zero, except one; thus we may have

$$\bar{q}_1 = \bar{q}_2 = \cdots = \bar{q}_{s-1} = \bar{q}_{s+1} = \cdots = \bar{q}_n = 0$$

In this case we say that we have excited one mode of vibration,** and suppressed all the others. When the system is vibrating in its s-th mode, the vibration is completely described by the equation

$$\bar{q}_s = A_s \cos{(\sqrt{\lambda_s}t + \epsilon_s)} \qquad (16.55)$$

If we wish to describe the behavior of the original coordinates for this mode, then we must revert to Eqs. (16.54). Only one mode is excited, therefore the summation sign has to be dropped and we get

$$q_i = c_{is}A_s \cos{(\sqrt{\lambda_s}t + \epsilon_s)} \qquad i = 1, 2, \ldots, n \qquad (16.56)$$

* The normal coordinates are independent only if $\mathbf{c}^{-1}$ exists; the q's are assumed to be independent.
** The expression "mode of vibration" really signifies "type of vibration."

This expression gives the behavior of every generalized coordinate when the system vibrates in its s-th mode. We see that *in this case every generalized coordinate vibrates with the same angular frequency and the same epoch angle, i.e., every generalized coordinate has the same phase.*

16–7 Determination of Normal Coordinates

There still remains the problem of finding the normal coordinates. In principle they can be found from

$$\mathbf{q} = \mathbf{C}\bar{\mathbf{q}}$$

once the matrix $\mathbf{C}$ is obtained, because we simply would have

$$\bar{\mathbf{q}} = \mathbf{C}^{-1}\mathbf{q}$$

where $\mathbf{C}^{-1}$ is the matrix inverse to $\mathbf{C}$. We will follow this method later, but at this moment we will obtain the normal coordinates in a different way.

Consider again the case when the system vibrates in its s-th normal mode. The i-th generalized coordinate then varies with time according to Eq. (16.56). Differentiating this equation twice with respect to time we obtain

$$\ddot{\bar{q}}_i + \lambda_s \bar{q}_i = 0 \tag{16.57}$$

The Lagrangian function of the system in terms of the original generalized coordinates is

$$L = \tfrac{1}{2} \sum_i \sum_j (a_{ij}\dot{q}_i\dot{q}_j - b_{ij}q_iq_j) \tag{16.58}$$

and Lagrange's equations

$$\frac{d}{dt}\left(\frac{\partial L}{\partial \dot{q}_j}\right) - \frac{\partial L}{\partial q_j} = 0 \qquad j = 1, 2, \ldots, n$$

become $\quad \displaystyle\sum_i (a_{ij}\ddot{q}_i + b_{ij}q_i) = 0 \qquad j = 1, 2, \ldots, n \tag{16.59}$

When the system vibrates in its s-th normal mode, then, from Eq. (16.57)

$$\ddot{q}_i = -\lambda_s q_i \tag{16.60}$$

Substituting this into Eq. (16.59) gives

$$\sum_i (\lambda_s a_{ij} - b_{ij})q_i = 0 \qquad j = 1, 2, \ldots, n \tag{16.61}$$

This is a set of homogeneous equations for the generalized coordinates. There will be one such set of equations for every mode of vibration. These equations are useful because they permit the investigation of the nature of the various normal modes. The nature of a particular normal mode will be known when the ratios of the generalized coordinates for this mode are known; these ratios can be determined from the last equations.

We have previously stated that

$$\bar{\mathbf{q}} = \mathbf{C}^{-1}\,\mathbf{q} \tag{16.62}$$

from which we see that the normal coordinates are linear functions of the original coordinates. We will write this linear relationship as

$$\bar{q}_s = \sum_{i,j} e_i a_{ij} q_j \tag{16.63}$$

When the e_i's are known, the normal coordinates can be found.*

Now, every normal coordinate vibrates with simple harmonic motion according to the relation

$$\ddot{\bar{q}}_s + \lambda_s \bar{q}_s = 0 \tag{16.64}$$

Therefore

$$\ddot{\bar{q}}_s = -\lambda_s \bar{q}_s$$

$$= -\lambda_s \sum_i \sum_j e_i a_{ij} q_j$$

$$= -\sum_i \sum_j e_i \lambda_s a_{ij} q_j$$

From Lagrange's equations

$$\sum_j \lambda_s a_{ij} q_j = \sum_j b_{ij} q_j$$

and so

$$\ddot{\bar{q}}_s = -\sum_{i,j} e_i b_{ij} q_j$$

Comparing the two end expressions for $\ddot{\bar{q}}_s$ we get

$$\sum_i \sum_j e_i \lambda_s a_{ij} q_j = \sum_i \sum_j e_i b_{ij} q_j$$

This is true for every q_j of the set

$$q_1, q_2, \ldots, q_n$$

of the independent generalized coordinates. Therefore

$$\sum_i (\lambda_s a_{ij} - b_{ij}) e_i = 0 \qquad j = 1, 2, \ldots, n \tag{16.65}$$

If we compare this relation with Eq. (16.61) we notice that the coefficients e_i obey the same relations as the generalized coordinates when the system vibrates in the s-th normal mode. The last set, Eq. (16.65), constitutes a set of n homogeneous equations. Once they are solved for the e_i's, or strictly speaking for their ratios, then the normal coordinates can be determined from Eq. (16.63).

Summarizing the procedure which we outlined above, we see that, for a particular system executing small oscillations, we should choose suitable gen-

* In the form given by Eq. (16.63), the various normal coordinates $\bar{q}_s$ are distinguished by a different set of coefficients e_i for which a better notation would be e_{is}.

16-7 Determination of normal coordinates

eralized coordinates and construct expressions for the kinetic and potential energies.* These have to be quadratic in form with constant coefficients. The coefficients should be symmetrical or should be symmetrized.** The final forms of the kinetic and potential energies are

$$T = \tfrac{1}{2} \sum_i \sum_j a_{ij} \dot{q}_i \dot{q}_j$$

and

$$V = \tfrac{1}{2} \sum_i \sum_j b_{ij} q_i q_j$$

These forms reduce to

$$T = \tfrac{1}{2}(\dot{\bar{q}}_1{}^2 + \dot{\bar{q}}_2{}^2 + \cdots + \dot{\bar{q}}_n{}^2)$$

and

$$V = \tfrac{1}{2}(\lambda_1 \bar{q}_1{}^2 + \lambda_2 \bar{q}_2{}^2 + \cdots + \lambda_n \bar{q}_n{}^2)$$

where the λ's are the roots of the determinantal equation

$$|\lambda a_{ij} - b_{ij}| = 0$$

and the normal coordinates are evaluated from

$$\bar{q}_s = \sum_{i,j} e_i a_{ij} q_j$$

once the e_i's are obtained from the homogeneous equations

$$\sum_i (\lambda_s a_{ij} - b_{ij}) e_i = 0 \qquad j = 1, 2, \ldots, n$$

The latter equations are also satisfied by the generalized coordinates (q_i) when the system vibrates in any of its normal modes. Thus, using the same set of equations, we can determine the behavior of the system for the various normal modes. These equations, being homogeneous, will not furnish more than the ratios of the coordinates, but this is enough to see how the system will behave. The actual behavior of the generalized coordinates, when all modes are excited, is given by

$$q_i = \sum_{s=1}^{n} c_{is} A_s \cos (\sqrt{\lambda_s} t + \epsilon_s) \qquad i = 1, 2, \ldots, n$$

* The only place where difficulties are encountered in solving problems of small oscillations is in obtaining the expressions for the potential and kinetic energies.
** The coefficients a_{ij} are symmetric if $a_{ij} = a_{ji}$. If $a_{ij} \neq a_{ji}$ then we can symmetrize them. We notice that in the quadratic form they occur in the terms $a_{ij} x_i x_j + a_{ji} x_j x_i$. For this we can write $a_{ij} x_i x_j + a_{ji} x_j x_i = \tfrac{1}{2}(a_{ij} + a_{ji}) x_i x_j + \tfrac{1}{2}(a_{ji} + a_{ij}) x_j x_i = b_{ij} x_i x_j + b_{ji} x_j x_i$, where $b_{ij} = \tfrac{1}{2}(a_{ij} + a_{ji})$ are the new symmetric coefficients.
Often, having obtained the expression for the potential and kinetic energies, we seem to be missing some of the coefficients, e.g., we have a_{ij} but do not have a_{ji}. In this case we simply split the coefficients into two, viz., $a_{ij} x_i x_j = \tfrac{1}{2} a_{ij} x_i x_j + \tfrac{1}{2} a_{ji} x_j x_i$.

When only the s-th mode is excited, then

$$q_i = c_{is} A_s \cos (\sqrt{\lambda_s} t + \epsilon_s) \qquad\qquad i = 1, 2, \ldots, n$$

16–8 Principal Axis Transformation for Small Oscillations

It is possible to treat the whole problem of normal modes of vibrations as an eigenvalue problem, very similar to the one of determining the principal moments of inertia and principal axes of rotation.* It should be stressed here that this is really the basic approach to the theory of small oscillations and for this reason we shall now discuss it.

Consider again a system of n degrees of freedom, which is therefore describable by n generalized coordinates

$$q_1, q_2, \ldots, q_n$$

executing small free oscillations about a position of stable equilibrium. The kinetic and potential energies are given by Eqs. (16.43) and (16.44), and therefore the Lagrangian of the system is

$$L = \tfrac{1}{2} \sum_i \sum_j (a_{ij} \dot{q}_i \dot{q}_j - b_{ij} q_i q_j) \tag{16.66}$$

and Lagrange's equations are

$$\sum_j (a_{ij} \ddot{q}_j + b_{ij} q_j) = 0 \qquad i = 1, 2, \ldots, n \tag{16.67}$$

Again, knowing that the system executes small oscillations we may assume solutions of the form

$$q_i = l_i e^{i\omega t} \tag{16.68}$$

Substitution in Lagrange's equations yields

$$\sum_j (\omega^2 a_{ij} - b_{ij}) l_j = 0 \qquad i = 1, 2, \ldots, n \tag{16.69}$$

or, denoting

$$\lambda = \omega^2$$

$$\sum_j (\lambda a_{ij} - b_{ij}) l_j = 0 \qquad i = 1, 2, \ldots, n \tag{16.70}$$

This is a set of homogeneous equations in the l_i's and therefore for non-trivial solutions

$$|\lambda a_{ij} - b_{ij}| = 0 \tag{16.71}$$

from which, as before, the set of the squares of the characteristic frequencies

$$\lambda_1, \lambda_2, \ldots, \lambda_n$$

is obtained.

---

* Some general aspects of the eigenvalue problem are mentioned in Appendix B. See also Chapter 19 on Eigenphysics.

We now go back to the homogeneous equations and substitute into them, in turn, every value of λ from the above set. We thus obtain n sets of n homogeneous equations. We then solve these for the ratios of the unknown l_i's. If these ratios are denoted by c_i then we can write

$$l_i = Ac_i \tag{16.72}$$

where A is arbitrary. Therefore, for a particular value of λ, say λ_s, the solutions of Lagrange's equations are

$$\begin{aligned}
q_1^{(s)} &= c_{1s}A_s e^{i\omega_s t} \\
q_2^{(s)} &= c_{2s}A_s e^{i\omega_s t} \\
&\vdots \\
q_n^{(s)} &= c_{ns}A_s e^{i\omega_s t}
\end{aligned} \tag{16.73}$$

All the c_{is}'s still include an arbitrary multiplication constant. This arbitrary factor may be removed by setting the first non-zero c equal to unity.

Let us denote

$$\bar{q}_s = A_s e^{i\omega_s t} \tag{16.74}$$

The most general solutions of Lagrange's equations must contain all frequencies, and therefore the i-th generalized coordinate will be of the form

$$q_i = c_{i1}\bar{q}_1 + c_{i2}\bar{q}_2 + \cdots + c_{in}\bar{q}_n \tag{16.75}$$

All the solutions can be written in the matrix form

$$\mathbf{q} = \mathbf{C}\bar{\mathbf{q}} \tag{16.76}$$

where $\mathbf{q}$ and $\bar{\mathbf{q}}$ are column matrices and $\mathbf{C}$ is the matrix $[c_{ij}]$. From the definition of the set

$$\bar{q}_1, \bar{q}_2, \ldots, \bar{q}_n$$

we recognize it as the set of normal coordinates. We notice that for any normal coordinate, say $\bar{q}_s$, we can replace Eq. (16.74) by

$$\bar{q}_s = A_s \cos(\omega_s t + \epsilon_s) \tag{16.77}$$

Of course, only in the case when the system vibrates in the s-th mode, is the behavior in the s-th mode given by Eq. (16.77).

Let us now turn to the eigenvalue problem. We recall that, in terms of matrices, an eigenvalue equation is of the form

$$\mathbf{Ax} = \lambda\mathbf{x}$$

where $\mathbf{A}$ is a matrix, $\mathbf{x}$ is a column vector and λ is a constant. The essence of the eigenvalue equation lies in the fact that operating on the vector $\mathbf{x}$ with the matrix $\mathbf{A}$ does not change the direction of $\mathbf{x}$ but simply its length. We can easily see the physical meaning of an eigenvalue equation in the case of two- and three-dimensional vectors; nevertheless we extend the procedure to n-dimensional space. In our case of a system with n degrees of freedom, the n generalized coordinates can form components of an n-dimensional vector.

Any other set of independent coordinates could also serve as components of such a vector. Let us return to our homogeneous equations (16.70). Assume for a moment that

$$a_{ij} = \delta_{ij} \tag{16.78}$$

where δ_{ij} is the Kronecker delta. In this case the kinetic energy is

$$T = \tfrac{1}{2}(\dot{q}_1{}^2 + \dot{q}_2{}^2 + \cdots + \dot{q}_n{}^2) \tag{16.79}$$

The homogeneous equations then become

$$\sum_j b_{ij}l_j = \lambda l_i \tag{16.80}$$

or in matrix form

$$\mathbf{Bl} = \lambda \mathbf{l} \tag{16.81}$$

and this is in the form of an eigenvalue equation. In this case* it is possible to find a matrix $\mathbf{C}$ such that the matrix $\mathbf{\Lambda}$ given by

$$\mathbf{\Lambda} = \mathbf{C}^{-1}\mathbf{BC} \tag{16.82}$$

will be similar to $\mathbf{B}$ and diagonal. The elements of the diagonal matrix $\mathbf{\Lambda}$ will be the eigenvalues of the problem, and the columns of $\mathbf{C}$ will determine the principal axes of the matrix $\mathbf{B}$. In our case, the eigenvalues are the squares of the normal frequencies, and the principal axes lead to normal coordinates.

Consider the homogeneous equations (16.70). In these we can replace the l_i's by the c_i's; thus

$$\sum_j (\lambda a_{ij} - b_{ij})c_j = 0 \qquad i = 1, 2, \ldots, n \tag{16.83}$$

In matrix form these are

$$(\lambda \mathbf{A} - \mathbf{B})\mathbf{c} = \mathbf{0}$$

or

$$\mathbf{Bc} = \lambda \mathbf{Ac} \tag{16.84}$$

This matrix equation is not in the form of an eigenvalue equation because operating on $\mathbf{c}$ with the matrix $\mathbf{B}$ is not equivalent to multiplying $\mathbf{c}$ by a constant. However, let us premultiply both sides by $\mathbf{A}^{-1}$; then

$$\mathbf{A}^{-1}\mathbf{Bc} = \mathbf{A}^{-1}\lambda \mathbf{Ac}$$
$$= \lambda \mathbf{A}^{-1}\mathbf{Ac}$$

or

$$(\mathbf{A}^{-1}\mathbf{B})\mathbf{c} = \lambda \mathbf{c} \tag{16.85}$$

* See Appendix B.

and this is an eigenvalue equation. In this case, therefore, there exists a matrix $\mathbf{C}$ such that the similar matrix

$$\boldsymbol{\Lambda} = \mathbf{C}^{-1}(\mathbf{A}^{-1}\mathbf{B})\mathbf{C} \tag{16.86}$$

will be diagonal. The diagonal elements will constitute the set of eigenvalues

$$\lambda_1, \lambda_2, \ldots, \lambda_n$$

To see that this is so in our case, we write Lagrange's equations (16.67) in matrix form as

$$\mathbf{A}\ddot{\mathbf{q}} + \mathbf{B}\mathbf{q} = \mathbf{0} \tag{16.87}$$

Now
$$\mathbf{q} = \mathbf{C}\bar{\mathbf{q}}$$

therefore
$$\mathbf{A}\mathbf{C}\ddot{\bar{\mathbf{q}}} + \mathbf{B}\mathbf{C}\bar{\mathbf{q}} = \mathbf{0}$$

Premultiplying this by $(\mathbf{A}\mathbf{C})^{-1}$ we get

$$(\mathbf{A}\mathbf{C})^{-1}\mathbf{A}\mathbf{C}\ddot{\bar{\mathbf{q}}} + (\mathbf{A}\mathbf{C})^{-1}\mathbf{B}\mathbf{C}\bar{\mathbf{q}} = \mathbf{0}$$

Now,
$$(\mathbf{A}\mathbf{C})^{-1}\mathbf{A}\mathbf{C} = \mathbf{I}$$

and
$$(\mathbf{A}\mathbf{C})^{-1} = \mathbf{C}^{-1}\mathbf{A}^{-1}$$

thus
$$\ddot{\bar{\mathbf{q}}} + \mathbf{C}^{-1}\mathbf{A}^{-1}\mathbf{B}\mathbf{C}\bar{\mathbf{q}} = \mathbf{0} \tag{16.88}$$

and this is of the form

$$\ddot{\bar{\mathbf{q}}} + \boldsymbol{\Lambda}\bar{\mathbf{q}} = \mathbf{0} \tag{16.89}$$

The normal coordinates forming the vector $\bar{\mathbf{q}}$ satisfy the equations

$$\ddot{\bar{q}}_1 + \lambda_1\bar{q}_1 = 0$$
$$\ddot{\bar{q}}_2 + \lambda_2\bar{q}_2 = 0$$
$$\vdots$$
$$\ddot{\bar{q}}_n + \lambda_n\bar{q}_n = 0 \tag{16.90}$$

which can be written in matrix form as

$$\begin{bmatrix} \ddot{\bar{q}}_1 \\ \ddot{\bar{q}}_2 \\ \vdots \\ \ddot{\bar{q}}_n \end{bmatrix} + \begin{bmatrix} \lambda_1 & & & \mathbf{O} \\ & \lambda_2 & & \\ & & \ddots & \\ \mathbf{O} & & & \lambda_n \end{bmatrix} \begin{bmatrix} \bar{q}_1 \\ \bar{q}_2 \\ \vdots \\ \bar{q}_n \end{bmatrix} = \mathbf{0}$$

Therefore appearing in Eq. (16.89) is the diagonal matrix

$$\boldsymbol{\Lambda} = \begin{bmatrix} \lambda_1 & & & \mathbf{O} \\ & \lambda_2 & & \\ & & \ddots & \\ \mathbf{O} & & & \lambda_n \end{bmatrix} \tag{16.91}$$

We can see the relation of this treatment to the simultaneous diagonalization of the matrices **A** and **B** from the following procedure. Consider the matrix equation

$$\mathbf{A}\mathbf{C}\ddot{\bar{q}} + \mathbf{B}\mathbf{C}\bar{q} = \mathbf{0}$$

Premultiplying by **C'** we obtain

$$\mathbf{C}'\mathbf{A}\mathbf{C}\ddot{\bar{q}} + \mathbf{C}'\mathbf{B}\mathbf{C}\bar{q} = \mathbf{0}$$

We want

$$\mathbf{C}'\mathbf{A}\mathbf{C} = \mathbf{I}$$

and

$$\mathbf{C}'\mathbf{B}\mathbf{C} = \Lambda$$

simultaneously. Then

$$\ddot{\bar{q}} + \Lambda\bar{q} = \mathbf{0}$$

The last few lines contain perhaps the most concise summary of the theory of small oscillations, but to realize this we have to understand clearly the whole analytical procedure in terms of which the theory is formulated.

16-9   The Two Particles on a Stretched String

We shall now apply the theory to our example of two particles on a stretched elastic string, Fig. 16.9. The kinetic energy is given by

$$T = \tfrac{1}{2}m\dot{y}_1{}^2 + \tfrac{1}{2}m\dot{y}_2{}^2$$

and the potential energy, given by Eq. (16.25) can be written as

$$V = \tfrac{1}{2}P\left[\frac{a+b}{ab}\,y_1{}^2 - \frac{1}{b}\,y_1 y_2 - \frac{1}{b}\,y_2 y_1 + \frac{a+b}{ab}\,y_2{}^2\right]$$

In matrix form

$$2T = [\dot{y}_1 \quad \dot{y}_2]\begin{bmatrix} m & 0 \\ 0 & m \end{bmatrix}\begin{bmatrix} \dot{y}_1 \\ \dot{y}_2 \end{bmatrix}$$

and

$$2V = [y_1 \quad y_2]\begin{bmatrix} P\dfrac{a+b}{ab}, & -\dfrac{P}{b} \\[2ex] -\dfrac{P}{b}, & P\dfrac{a+b}{ab} \end{bmatrix}\begin{bmatrix} y_1 \\ y_2 \end{bmatrix}$$

These are of the form

$$2T = \dot{y}'\mathbf{A}\dot{y}$$

and

$$2V = y'\mathbf{B}y$$

therefore

$$\mathbf{A} = \begin{bmatrix} m & 0 \\ 0 & m \end{bmatrix}$$

and

$$
\mathbf{B} = \begin{bmatrix} P\dfrac{a+b}{ab}, & -\dfrac{P}{b} \\[2ex] -\dfrac{P}{b}, & P\dfrac{a+b}{ab} \end{bmatrix}
$$

The eigenvalues of the problem are determined from

$$
\begin{vmatrix} \lambda m - P\dfrac{a+b}{ab}, & \dfrac{P}{b} \\[2ex] \dfrac{P}{b}, & \lambda m - P\dfrac{a+b}{ab} \end{vmatrix} = 0
$$

which, as before, yields

$$
\lambda_1 = \frac{P}{m}\frac{2a+b}{ab}
$$

and

$$
\lambda_2 = \frac{P}{m}\frac{1}{a}
$$

Equations (16.65) for $\lambda = \lambda_1$ and $i, j, = 1, 2,$ are

$$
(\lambda_1 a_{11} - b_{11})e_1 + (\lambda_1 a_{21} - b_{21})e_2 = 0
$$
$$
(\lambda a_{12} - b_{12})e_1 + (\lambda_1 a_{22} - b_{22})e_2 = 0
$$

In our case these become

$$
\left[\frac{P}{m}\frac{2a+b}{ab}m - P\frac{a+b}{ab}\right]e_1 + \left[\frac{P}{b}\right]e_2 = 0
$$
$$
\frac{P}{b}e_1 + \left[\frac{P}{m}\frac{2a+b}{ab}m - P\frac{a+b}{ab}\right]e_2 = 0
$$

Both equations yield

$$
e_1 + e_2 = 0
$$

With $\lambda = \lambda_2$, Eqs. (16.65) give

$$
e_1 - e_2 = 0
$$

As we have shown, the last two equations contain two useful results. First, we have seen from Eqs. (16.61) and (16.65) that the e_i's behave in the same way as the generalized coordinates when the system vibrates in one of its normal modes. Thus for $\lambda = \lambda_1$

$$
q_1 + q_2 = 0
$$

and for $\lambda = \lambda_2$

$$
q_1 - q_2 = 0
$$

Of course, we identify the λ's with ω^2, the normal angular frequencies. Thus, when the system is so excited that only

$$\omega_1 = \sqrt{\frac{P}{m} \frac{2a + b}{a + b}}$$

is present, then

$$y_1 = -y_2$$

and when only

$$\omega_2 = \sqrt{\frac{P}{m} \frac{1}{a}}$$

is present,

$$y_1 = y_2$$

From these, the nature of the two normal modes is evident.

The normal coordinates are obtained from Eq. (16.63). For $i, j = 1, 2$, these are

$$\bar{y}_1 = e_1 a_{11} y_1 + e_2 a_{21} y_1 + e_1 a_{12} y_2 + e_2 a_{22} y_2$$

For the first normal mode

$$e_1 = -e_2$$

therefore

$$\bar{y}_1 = (a_{11} y_1 - a_{21} y_1 + a_{12} y_2 - a_{22} y_2) e_1$$

or in our case

$$\bar{y}_1 = m(y_1 + y_2) e_1$$

Now, Eqs. (16.65) determine the ratios of e_2 to e_1 only; thus e_1 is arbitrary. Setting $e_1 = 1/m$, we get

$$\bar{y}_1 = y_1 + y_2$$

In a similar way we get

$$\bar{y}_2 = y_2 - y_1$$

We are not rewriting the form of the kinetic and potential energies in terms of the normal coordinates. These are identical for any problem. The same applies to the Lagrangian function and Lagrange's equations in terms of normal coordinates.

We can treat this problem in a slightly more formal way as one of a transformation to a set of principal axes. In our case the matrices **A** and **B** are symmetric and T is positive definite, therefore there exists a transformation

$$\mathbf{y} = \mathbf{C}\bar{\mathbf{y}}$$

such that

$$\mathbf{C'AC} = \mathbf{I}$$

and simultaneously

$$\mathbf{C'BC} = \Lambda$$

Λ furnishes the eigenvalues, and the column vectors of $\mathbf{C}$, which are obtained from

$$(\lambda \mathbf{A} - \mathbf{B})\mathbf{c} = \mathbf{0}$$

determine the eigenvectors. The last equation is identical with Eq. (16.83). For $\lambda = \lambda_1$ we get

$$(\lambda_1 a_{11} - b_{11})c_{11} + (\lambda_1 a_{21} - b_{21})c_{21} = 0$$
$$(\lambda_1 a_{12} - b_{12})c_{11} + (\lambda_1 a_{22} - b_{22})c_{21} = 0$$

For $\lambda = \lambda_2$ we get

$$(\lambda_2 a_{11} - b_{11})c_{12} + (\lambda_2 a_{21} - b_{21})c_{22} = 0$$
$$(\lambda_2 a_{12} - b_{12})c_{12} + (\lambda_2 a_{22} - b_{22})c_{22} = 0$$

We see that the c_{ij}'s are identical with the e_i's, determined previously. Thus

$$c_{11} + c_{21} = 0$$

and

$$c_{12} - c_{22} = 0$$

Let

$$c_{11} = \frac{1}{\sqrt{2m}}, \qquad \text{then} \qquad c_{21} = -\frac{1}{\sqrt{2m}} \;;$$

also let

$$c_{12} = \frac{1}{\sqrt{2m}}, \qquad \text{then} \qquad c_{22} = \frac{1}{\sqrt{2m}}$$

Therefore

$$\mathbf{C} = \frac{1}{\sqrt{2m}} \begin{bmatrix} 1 & 1 \\ -1 & 1 \end{bmatrix}$$

Now

$$\bar{\mathbf{y}} = \mathbf{C}^{-1}\mathbf{y}$$

We find that

$$\mathbf{C}^{-1} = \sqrt{\frac{m}{2}} \begin{bmatrix} 1 & -1 \\ 1 & 1 \end{bmatrix}$$

Therefore

$$\begin{bmatrix} \bar{y}_1 \\ \bar{y}_2 \end{bmatrix} = \sqrt{\frac{m}{2}} \begin{bmatrix} 1 & -1 \\ 1 & 1 \end{bmatrix} \begin{bmatrix} y_1 \\ y_2 \end{bmatrix}$$

$$= \sqrt{\frac{m}{2}} \begin{bmatrix} y_1 - y_2 \\ y_1 + y_2 \end{bmatrix}$$

So,

$$\bar{y}_1 = \sqrt{\frac{m}{2}} (y_1 - y_2)$$

and

$$\bar{y}_2 = \sqrt{\frac{m}{2}} (y_1 + y_2)$$

When the system does not vibrate in any of its normal modes, but executes general (small) vibrations, the solutions are obtained from

$$\mathbf{y} = \mathbf{C}\mathbf{\bar{y}}$$

Thus

$$y_1 = \sum_{s=1}^{2} c_{1s}\bar{y}_s$$

and

$$y_2 = \sum_{s=1}^{2} c_{2s}\bar{y}_s$$

where

$$\bar{y}_s = A_s \cos\left(\sqrt{\lambda_s}\, t + \epsilon_s\right)$$

[See Eq. (16.77)].

The general solution to our problem is therefore contained in the two equations

$$y_1 = A_1 \cos\left(\sqrt{\lambda_1}\, t + \epsilon_1\right) - A_2 \cos\left(\sqrt{\lambda_2}\, t + \epsilon_2\right)$$

and

$$y_2 = A_1 \cos\left(\sqrt{\lambda_1}\, t + \epsilon_1\right) + A_2 \cos\left(\sqrt{\lambda_2}\, t + \epsilon_2\right)$$

PROBLEMS

16.1 Find the normal modes of small vibrations for the system shown in Figure 16.11. Consider the motion to take place in the vertical plane only.

Fig. 16.11

(This is a system of three degrees of freedom: two oscillations, one of the rod and the other of the spring, and the elongation of the spring.)

16.2 Two particles m and $4m$ are attached to a stretched wire under tension P as shown in Figure 16.12. The mass of the wire is negligible. The wire

Fig. 16.12

makes small oscillations in one plane during which P remains constant.

(a) Show that the frequencies of the normal modes of oscillations are $(\frac{1}{4}\pi)\sqrt{P/(ma)}$ and $(\frac{1}{4}\pi)\sqrt{(P/m)(1/a + 5/b)}$.

272

(b) Write the normal coordinates in terms of the coordinates of the particles.

(c) Find the Lagrangian function in terms of the normal coordinates of the particles.

16.3 A uniform rod AB of length $2a$ is suspended from a fixed point O by a string OC of length $(5/6)a$ attached to a point C of the rod such that $AC = (2/3)a$. Find the periods of the normal modes of oscillation in the vertical plane.

16.4 One point of a uniform circular loop of mass M and radius a is fixed, and the loop is free to move in a vertical plane through this fixed point. A bead of mass m slides on the loop without friction. Let the system execute small oscillations. Prove that the periods of the normal oscillations about the position of stable equilibrium are given by

$$\tau_1 = 2\pi\sqrt{\frac{2a}{g}} \qquad \tau_2 = 2\pi\sqrt{\frac{M}{M+m}\frac{a}{g}}$$

16.5 Two equal point masses are coupled by springs of equal spring constants k in the manner shown in Figure 16.13.

Fig. 16.13

(a) Introduce generalized coordinates for one-dimensional oscillations in the x direction and obtain the potential and kinetic energies of the system.

(b) Obtain the normal frequencies of the system.

(c) Obtain the normal coordinates of the system.

(d) Write down the Lagrangian and Lagrange's equations in terms of the normal coordinates.

16.6 Three heavy beads of mass m, m, and M respectively are free to slide on a smooth, circular wire loop placed in a horizontal plane. The beads are connected by three identical springs of negligible mass and spring constant k. When the masses are distributed symmetrically, the springs are unstressed (Fig. 16.14).

Fig. 16.14

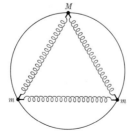

(a) Find the periods of the normal modes of small oscillations about this configuration.

(b) Describe the behavior of the system in each of its normal modes.

(c) Write the Lagrangian for this system in terms of generalized coordinates and then in terms of normal coordinates.

(d) Name the ignorable coordinates of this system and discuss their significance.

(e) What are the generalized momenta in this problem in the original generalized coordinates and in the normal coordinates.

(f) Write down the Hamiltonian for this system in the generalized and in the normal coordinates.

(g) Write Hamilton's equations in the generalized coordinates and in the normal coordinates.

Fig. 16.15

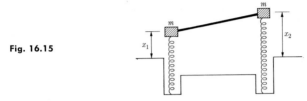

16.7 Two point masses, each of mass m, rest on the top of two springs. The unstretched lengths of the springs are equal and both have equal spring constants, $k = 2$. The point masses are connected by an extensible rod in such a manner that the coupling can be expressed by a potential energy term of the form $x_1 x_2$, where x_1 and x_2 are the generalized coordinates of the two point masses (Fig. 16.15). The two springs execute small oscillations in vertical directions. Neglect the gravitational potential energy.

(a) Find the normal period of oscillations, and

(b) Determine the normal coordinates.

17

PRINCIPLES OF THE THEORY OF RELATIVITY

The theory of relativity is the physical theory of relative motion. The theory considers two frames of reference which are moving with respect to each other, and it attempts to correlate the results of physical measurements made on the same physical processes by observers who are stationary in each of the two moving frames. The special theory of relativity deals with the case when the frames move with a uniform velocity with respect to each other, while the general theory of relativity deals with frames which are uniformly accelerated with respect to each other.

We shall concern ourselves mostly with the special theory but we shall precede this by a discussion of the classical principle of relativity.

17–1   The Newtonian Principle of Relativity

Consider two fixed rectangular frames of reference of common origin, rotated with respect to each other by a constant angle θ, as shown in Figure 17.1. The

Fig. 17.1

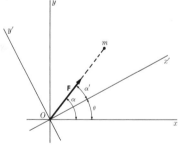

particle m shown in that figure is acted on by a force **F**. For an observer who refers his observations to the Oxy frame of reference, Newton's second law will be of the form

$$\mathbf{F} = m\ddot{\mathbf{r}} \tag{17.1}$$

which is equivalent to two scalar equations

$$F_x = m\ddot{x}$$
$$F_y = m\ddot{y} \tag{17.2}$$

We wish to find the form of Newton's second law when all the quantities, i.e., the components of the force and of the acceleration are referred to the $Ox'y'$ system. We know that the coordinates (x, y) and (x', y') of one and the same point are connected by the relations

$$x = x' \cos \theta - y' \sin \theta$$
$$y = x' \sin \theta + y' \cos \theta$$
(17.3)

From these we obtain

$$x' = x \cos \theta + y \sin \theta$$
$$y' = -x \sin \theta + y \cos \theta$$
(17.4)

and, differentiating twice with respect to time, we get

$$\ddot{x}' = \ddot{x} \cos \theta + \ddot{y} \sin \theta$$
$$\ddot{y}' = -\ddot{x} \sin \theta + \ddot{y} \cos \theta$$
(17.5)

Multiplying the first equation of (17.5) by m we have

$$m\ddot{x}' = m\ddot{x} \cos \theta + m\ddot{y} \sin \theta$$
(17.6)

Using (17.2) we obtain

$$m\ddot{x}' = F_x \cos \theta + F_y \sin \theta$$
(17.7)

But, with reference to the Oxy axes we have

$$F_x = F \cos \alpha$$
$$F_y = F \sin \alpha$$
(17.8)

Substitution in (17.7) yields

$$m\ddot{x}' = F \cos \alpha \cos \theta + F \sin \alpha \sin \theta$$

or

$$m\ddot{x}' = F \cos (\alpha - \theta)$$
(17.9)

Since

$$\alpha - \theta = \alpha'$$

therefore

$$m\ddot{x}' = F \cos \alpha'$$
(17.10a)

In a similar way we obtain

$$m\ddot{y}' = F \sin \alpha'$$
(17.10b)

Now, referring to $Ox'y'$ we have

$$F_{x'} = F \cos \alpha'$$

and

$$F_{y'} = F \sin \alpha'$$
(17.11)

thus (17.10a, b) become

$$F_{x'} = m\ddot{x}'$$

and

$$F_{y'} = m\ddot{y}'$$
(17.12)

Equation (17.12) is of exactly the same form as Eq. (17.2). We infer that Newton's second law is the same for both observers. We may say that Newton's second law is invariant with respect to rotation of axes through a constant angle.

Consider now the case when two frames of reference $\Sigma(Oxy)$ and $\Sigma'(O'x'y')$ are moving with respect to each other with uniform velocity **v** as shown in Fig. 17.2. Referring to the unprimed system, Newton's second law is

Fig. 17.2

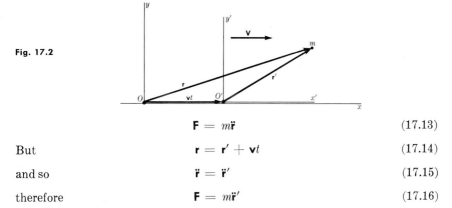

$$\mathbf{F} = m\ddot{\mathbf{r}} \qquad (17.13)$$

But
$$\mathbf{r} = \mathbf{r}' + \mathbf{v}t \qquad (17.14)$$

and so
$$\ddot{\mathbf{r}} = \ddot{\mathbf{r}}' \qquad (17.15)$$

therefore
$$\mathbf{F} = m\ddot{\mathbf{r}}' \qquad (17.16)$$

In going over from Eq. (17.13) to (17.16) we have used the transformation of coordinates, and we have also assumed that the time scale is the same for both observers. All this is contained in what are called *Galilean transformations* which, applied to our case, are of the form

$$
\begin{aligned}
x &= x' + vt \\
y &= y' \\
z &= z' \\
t &= t'
\end{aligned}
\qquad (17.17)
$$

The result obtained above may best be stated by saying that the form of *Newton's second law is invariant with respect to Galilean transformations.*

Inherent in classical physics was the assumption of the existence of absolute space to which all phenomena could be referred, and of absolute time, the same for observers in different frames of reference. Both these assumptions have been subjected to severe tests. These will be described now.

17–2 The Michelson-Morley Experiment

It was realized for a long time that the earth moves with high velocities with respect to stars which apparently are fixed. Michelson and Morley set themselves the task to detect this motion through absolute space. At the time when their experiment was performed (the end of 19th century), there was a common belief that there existed a weightless, all pervading, yet perfectly elastic substance which served as the medium in which the electromagnetic waves could propagate. It was called the luminiferous ether (meaning the "light carrying" ether). Michelson and Morley were actually checking for motion with respect to the ether. For that purpose they used Michelson's interferometer shown in Figure 17.3. Light coming from the source S is split

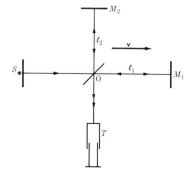

Fig. 17.3
Michelson interferometer.

by the beam splitter O (a half silvered mirror) so that part travels to the mirror M_1 and back, and another part travels to the mirror M_2 and back. On the return path, part of each beam goes to the telescope T. Along OT, two coherent beams are superimposed, and interference occurs. When the two mirrors M_1 and M_2 are at right angles, circular fringes will be observed.*

Let the interferometer be oriented in the manner shown in Figure 17.3; $\mathbf{v}$ denotes the absolute velocity of the earth and is parallel to OM_1. Using purely classical reasoning, we find that the time for a beam of light to cover the distance OM_1O is

$$t_1 = \frac{l_1}{c - v} + \frac{l_1}{c + v}$$

$$= \frac{2l_1 c}{c^2 - v^2}$$

$$= \frac{2l_1}{c(1 - v^2/c^2)}$$

or

$$t_1 = \frac{2l_1}{c} \beta^2 \qquad (17.18)$$

where

$$\beta = \frac{1}{\sqrt{1 - \dfrac{v^2}{c^2}}} \qquad (17.19)$$

and c is the speed of light. (In certain texts β stands for v/c.) The time t_2

* The formation of the fringes in the Michelson interferometer should be studied. Usually the virtual fringes are utilized. These are described in standard optics books such as Jenkins and White *Fundamentals of Optics* Third edition, McGraw-Hill, New York (1957), p. 246.

Fig. 17.4

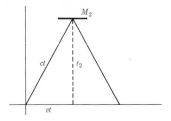

for the beam of light to travel the distance OM_2O can be obtained from Figure 17.4. If $t(= \frac{1}{2}t_2)$ is the time for the light to go the distance OM_2, then

$$c^2t^2 = v^2t^2 + l_2{}^2$$

from which

$$t = \frac{l_2}{c}\beta$$

and

$$t_2 = \frac{2l_2\beta}{c} \tag{17.20}$$

Comparing Eq. (17.18) with (17.20) we see that even if $l_1 = l_2$, $t_1 \neq t_2$.
  In general

$$t_1 - t_2 = \frac{2}{c}(l_1\beta^2 - l_2\beta) \tag{17.21}$$

and when $l_1 = l_2 = l$, then

$$t_1 - t_2 = \frac{2l}{c}(\beta^2 - \beta) \tag{17.22}$$

Assuming that $v \ll c$ and using the bionomial expansion for β^2 and β in which only the lowest order terms are retained, we get

$$t_1 - t_2 = \frac{1}{c}\frac{v^2}{c^2} \tag{17.23}$$

If we take $v = 30$ km/sec and $l = 30$ m, then

$$t_1 - t_2 = 10^{-15} \text{ sec}$$

($l = 30$ m is a typical value of later experiments. Michelson and Morley used $l \approx 12$ m). This is the time difference for the beams of light travelling in the two interferometer arms. As small as it is, it can still be detected if the light vibrations themselves are used for this measurement. Suppose that monochromatic light of wavelength $\lambda = 6000$ Å is used. Let us place ourselves at any point in the path of the beam and count the number of wavelengths which will pass this point. One wavelength will pass in the time τ equal to the period of the light wave. The number N of wavelengths passing during the time Δt will be

$$N = (\Delta t)\nu \tag{17.24}$$

In our case

$$\Delta t = t_1 - t_2$$

$$= 10^{-15} \text{ sec}$$

and

$$\tau = \frac{\lambda}{c} \qquad\qquad (17.25)$$

Using the given numbers we find

$$N = \tfrac{1}{2}$$

Thus half a wavelength will pass in the time interval Δt.

Let us assume that it would be possible to stop the earth. Let us further assume that with the earth stationary, the configuration of the interferometer is such that the path difference corresponds to two wavelengths.* This is shown in Figure 17.5(a).** We will place the cross-hair of the telescope in the center between two dark fringes, as shown in Figure 17.6(a). Let us now impart the velocity of 30 km/sec to the earth parallel to OM_1. Now the beam of light will cover the distance OM_1O in a time 10^{-15} sec longer than previously, and the path OM_1 will be able to accommodate half of the wavelength more than before. The path difference 2λ will now change to $(2 + \tfrac{1}{2})\lambda$, and at the cross-hair a dark band will now appear. The path difference will be longer than before and the whole pattern will shift towards the center as shown in Figure 17.6(b).

Let us again start with the earth stationary but have the interferometer turned 90° in clockwise direction. Now, in this situation, impart to the earth the same velocity which will now be parallel to the arm OM_2 [Fig. 17.5(c)]. This arm will now be able to accommodate $\tfrac{1}{2}\lambda$ more than before. The path difference $2(OM_1 - OM_2)$ will now be $(2 - \tfrac{1}{2})\lambda$. At the cross-hair of the telescope a dark band will occur, but, since the path difference is less than in the stationary case, the pattern of the fringes will expand.

It is impossible to stop the earth but it is possible to rotate the interferometer. For 90° rotation, one whole fringe shift should be observed.

In their experiment, Michelson and Morley did not observe any fringe shift. The experiment was repeated by many observers amongst whom we may mention G. Joos who had at his disposal the optical plant of Zeiss in Jena, Germany, where he was able to construct a very accurate interferometer. Such was the accuracy of this instrument, that he could detect a fringe shift of 10^{-3} of a fringe. Again he did not observe any shift.***

* We are thus departing slightly from Michelson and Morley's configuration, but, we feel this will clarify the argument which we are about to present.
** The diagram is highly unrealistic. Actually one 30 meter arm will accommodate some 50,000,000 wavelengths, and then the other, in our case, 50,000,001 wavelengths.
*** George Joos, *Theoretical Physics*, Blackie, London and Glasgow (1934), Chapter 10.

Fig. 17.5

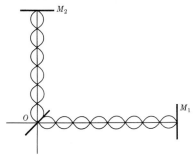

(a) The earth stationary

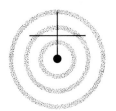

Fig. 17.6

(a) The earth stationary

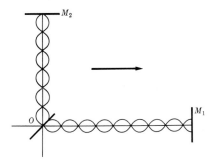

(b) The earth moving parallel to OM₁

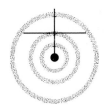

(b) The earth moving parallel to OM₁

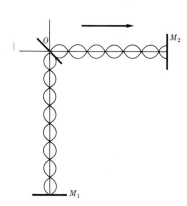

(c) The earth moving parallel to OM₂

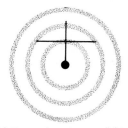

(c) The earth moving parallel to OM₂

17-3 First Explanation of the Null Result of Michelson-Morley Experiment

Of the many attempts to explain the null result of Michelson-Morley experiment, the most plausible was the Fitzgerald-Lorentz contraction hypothesis. Taking the null result of the experiment to be correct, we have to write

$$t_1 - t_2 = 0$$

or

$$t_1 = t_2$$

Then, from (17.21) we obtain

$$l_1\beta^2 = l_2\beta$$

or

$$l_1 = \frac{1}{\beta} l_2$$

When at rest $l_1 = l_2 = l_0$; denoting the length of the moving arm by l, we get

$$l = \frac{1}{\beta} l_0 \tag{17.26}$$

This result contains the *Fitzgerald-Lorentz contraction hypothesis*. It states that if a rod travels with a velocity **v** parallel to its length, this length is altered by the ratio $\frac{1}{\beta}$. Briefly, we may say that moving rods contract.

17-4 The Kennedy-Thorndike Experiment

In 1932 Kennedy and Thorndike repeated the Michelson-Morley experiment for which they assumed the validity of the Fitzgerald-Lorentz contraction hypothesis. In their experiment $l_1 \neq l_2$. The original expression for the time difference of the two beams of light travelling along OM_1O and OM_2O was given by Eq. (17.21), viz.

$$t_1 - t_2 = \frac{2\beta}{c} (l_1\beta - l_2)$$

Assuming the validity of the contraction hypothesis, however, we must replace l_1 by $\frac{1}{\beta} l_1$ (if the velocity of the interferometer is parallel to the OM_1 arm). The time difference therefore becomes

$$t_1 - t_2 = \frac{2\beta}{c} (l_1 - l_2) \tag{17.27}$$

No fringe shift should now be expected because the contraction hypothesis is in operation. Nevertheless $t_1 - t_2$, which we may denote by Δt, is a function of the velocity, i.e.

$$\Delta t = f(v) \tag{17.28}$$

the functional dependence coming through β in Eq. (17.27). Thus, when the velocity changes, the time difference will change accordingly, and hence a fringe shift should again be observed. In this case the interferometer arms are not going to be interchanged; they are going to be left in the same position and the observer will wait until $\mathbf{v}$ changes. Now, $\mathbf{v}$ can change because of diurnal variations and also because of annual variations. For maximum change in the two respective cases the observer has to wait either 12 hours or six months. Using Eq. (17.24) we again have

$$N = (\Delta t)\nu \tag{17.29}$$

or, substituting Eq. (17.27), we get

$$N = \frac{2(l_1 - l_2)}{c\left(1 - \dfrac{v^2}{c^2}\right)^{\frac{1}{2}}} \nu \tag{17.30}$$

In the Kennedy-Thorndike experiment $2(l_1 - l_2) = 31.8\text{ cm}$ and $\lambda = 5461\text{ Å}$. Substituting in Eq. (17.30), and neglecting $(v/c)^2$, we obtain

$$N = 5.8 \times 10^5$$

Considering N as a function of v we find

$$dN = \frac{2(l_1 - l_2)}{c} \nu \left(1 - \frac{v^2}{c^2}\right)^{-\frac{3}{2}} \frac{v^2}{c^2}\, dv$$

therefore

$$\frac{dN}{N} = \frac{\dfrac{v\, dv}{c^2}}{1 - \dfrac{v^2}{c^2}}$$

or

$$v\, dv = (c^2 - v^2)\, dN/N \tag{17.31}$$

Neglecting v^2 we obtain

$$v\, dv = c^2\, dN/N \tag{17.32}$$

The procedure used in the experiment was to wait for a change dv in the velocity of the earth, measure the appropriate fringe shift dN, and from Eq. (17.32), calculate the absolute velocity of the earth. The absolute velocity of any point on the surface of the earth can be considered to be the resultant of the absolute velocity of the sun, the linear velocity of the earth resulting from the orbital motion around the sun, and the linear velocity resulting from the rotation of the earth around its axis. These three velocity components and the resultant are shown in Figure 17.7.

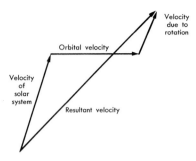

Fig. 17.7
The component
and the resultant
earth velocities.

Velocity
due to
rotation

Orbital velocity

Velocity
of
solar
system

Resultant velocity

For diurnal variation, the change of the velocity of the earth is

$$\Delta v_d = 1 \text{ km/sec}$$

and for the annual variation

$$\Delta v_a = 60 \text{ km/sec}$$

The actual velocities which were determined in the Kennedy-Thorndike experiment were: v_β, the component of the absolute velocity of the earth parallel to the equatorial plane, and v_α, the component of the absolute velocity of the earth parallel to the orbital plane. The values obtained from the measurements of the fringe shifts in the respective cases were

$$v_\beta = (24 \pm 19) \text{ km/sec}$$

and

$$v_\alpha = (15 \pm 4) \text{ km/sec}$$

The resultant absolute velocity of the earth was thus estimated to be

$$v = (10 \pm 10) \text{ km/sec}$$

This result must be treated as an experimental error, especially if we take into account the fact that the relative velocities of some of the nebulae are of the order of 1000 km/sec. Thus the Kennedy-Thorndike experiment also produced a null result.

17-5   *First Explanation of the Null Result of the Kennedy-Thorndike Experiment*

The null result of the Kennedy-Thorndike experiment proves that it is not enough to accept the Fitzgerald-Lorentz contraction hypothesis. Examining Eq. (17.30) for the order of interference we may say that

$$\nu\beta = \text{const.} \tag{17.33}$$

because it was proved experimentally that N did not change. In Eq. (17.33) ν is the frequency of the light emitted by atoms moving with velocity **v**. Let ν_0 refer to the frequency of the light emitted by atoms at rest; then

$\beta = 1$ and (17.33) can be written as

$$\nu = \frac{1}{\beta} \nu_0 \qquad (17.34)$$

In terms of the period of the emitted light

$$\tau = \beta \tau_0 \qquad (17.35)$$

We notice that $\tau > \tau_0$. This result is referred to as *time dilatation*. An atom emitting monochromatic light is the best possible clock that nature can produce. The period of the light wave can be taken as the unit of time. We have just shown that *moving clocks go slow*.

17–6 The Lorentz Transformations

Physical measurements in the end consist of measurements of distance and measurements of time. Rods are used for measuring distances, and for measuring time, the best clock—as already stated above—is an atom emitting monochromatic light. It is therefore of utmost importance to consider the results of the experiments described above in great detail, draw proper deductions from them, and modify the statements of the laws of physics accordingly.

Let us start with the question of synchronization of clocks in two frames $\Sigma(Oxyz)$ and $\Sigma'(O'x'y'z')$ moving with respect to each other with uniform velocity **v**. Suppose that Σ is stationary. Place an atom clock at O and another clock at the end of a rod at Q (both are in the frame Σ). A beam of light leaves the observer O at $t = 0$, arrives at Q at t_1, is reflected there and returns to O at t_2; both t_1 and t_2 are measured from $t = 0$. We will say that the clocks at O and Q are synchronized if $t_1 = (1/2)t_2$.* Here, of course, we are assuming that space is isotropic.

Consider now the moving frame of reference. Let O' have a similar atom clock and a similar measuring rod. For the observer at O the rod belonging to Σ' will be contracted and he will observe time dilatation. Suppose that both observers commence the time measurements when O and O' coincide; thus both observers start from the instants

$$t = 0 \qquad \text{and} \qquad t' = 0$$

If O' calls the distance $O'A$, in his frame, l', then O calls the same distance $l = (1/\beta)l'$. According to O the signal originating at O' reaches A at the

---

* It is always possible to synchronize the clocks at O and Q so that they will satisfy this definition of synchronization. The observer at O registers the time of departure and the time of arrival of the signal and the observer at Q registers the time of reflection of the signal. The observer at O communicates to the observer at Q the fact that for synchronization the time of reflection should be $t_1 = (1/2)t_2$. Q should set his clock according to this communication. In the same manner any number of clocks could be synchronized. When this has been done, we say that coordinate time has been established.

instant $t_1 = l/(c - v)$, (because $ct_1 = l + vt_1$), and the same signal covers the distance AO' in time $\bar{t}_2 = l/(c + v)$ (because $c\bar{t}_2 = l - v\bar{t}_2$). The total distance $O'AO'$ is covered in time $t_2 = l/(c - v) + l/(c + v)$. At the same instant the clock of O' registers the time $t_2' = 2l'/c$.

Consider now the instant of time when the light reaches some point between O' and A, say B (Fig. 17.8), upon returning from A. O will call this

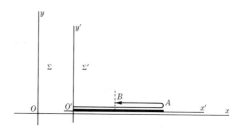

instant t and O' will call it t'. The time necessary to travel the distance AB as measured by O is

$$t - l/(c - v) = t - l'/[\beta(c - v)]$$

The same time measured by O' will be

$$\frac{1}{\beta}\left\{t - \frac{l'}{\beta(c - v)}\right\}$$

The total time for the light to go the distance $O'AB$ will be

$$t' = \frac{l'}{c} + \frac{1}{\beta}\left\{t - \frac{l'}{\beta(c - v)}\right\}$$

or

$$t' = \frac{t}{\beta} - \frac{l'v}{c^2}$$

Putting $x' = l'$ and solving for t we get

$$t = \beta\left[t' + \frac{vx'}{c^2}\right] \tag{17.36}$$

The observer O' considers the end of the rod of length l' to be at x', i.e., for him

$$x' = l'$$

For O, however, the same distance is

$$x = l + vt$$

or

$$x = \frac{l'}{\beta} + vt$$

i.e.

$$x' = (x - vt)\beta \tag{17.37}$$

Substituting this in (17.36) and solving for t' we obtain

$$t' = \beta\left(t - \frac{vx}{c^2}\right) \tag{17.38}$$

As far as the distances perpendicular to the direction of motion are concerned, both O and O' agree that they are the same, i.e.

$$y' = y \qquad z' = z$$

The relations

$$x' = \beta(x - vt)$$
$$y' = y$$
$$z' = z \tag{17.39}$$
$$t' = \beta\left(t - \frac{vx}{c^2}\right)$$

are called *Lorentz transformations*.

When Eqs. (17.39) are solved for the coordinates of the Σ system, we get

$$x = \beta(x' + vt')$$
$$y = y'$$
$$z = z' \tag{17.40}$$
$$t = \beta\left(t' + \frac{vx'}{c^2}\right)$$

We notice that Eqs. (17.39) and (17.40) are identical with the exception that $-v$ is replaced by $+v$. Therefore, *in considering the two systems Σ and Σ' which are in uniform motion relative to each other we may either consider Σ as fixed and Σ' as moving with velocity v, or consider Σ' fixed and Σ moving with velocity $-v$.*

17–7 Successive Lorentz Transformations

Consider one stationary system Σ and systems Σ_1 and Σ_2 which move with velocities v_1 and v_2 with respect to Σ parallel to the x-axis. We can apply Lorentz transformations to systems Σ and Σ_1 and obtain

$$\begin{Bmatrix} x \\ y \\ z \\ t \end{Bmatrix} = \begin{Bmatrix} x_1 \\ y_1 \\ z_1 \\ t_1 \end{Bmatrix} \tag{17.41}$$

Similarly for the systems Σ and Σ_2 we would get

$$\left\{\begin{matrix} x \\ y \\ z \\ t \end{matrix}\right\} = \left\{\begin{matrix} x_2 \\ y_2 \\ z_2 \\ t_2 \end{matrix}\right\} \tag{17.42}$$

Both Eqs. (17.41) and (17.42) are of the form given by Eqs. (17.40). Consider the x and t transformations only. From Eqs. (17.41) and (17.42) we can eliminate x, t, and t_2 and obtain*

$$x_2 = \frac{x_1 - Vt_1}{\sqrt{1 - \dfrac{V}{c^2}}} \tag{17.43}$$

where

$$V = \frac{v_2 - v_1}{1 - \dfrac{v_1 v_2}{c^2}} \tag{17.44}$$

V, given by Eq. (17.44) is the relative velocity of O_2 with respect to O_1. That this is so can be seen from the following argument. Take any point on the x_2 axis in Σ_2. Its coordinate in Σ_2 will be x_2, in Σ_1, x_1 and in Σ, x. dx_1/dt_1 will be the velocity of O_2 relative to O_1; thus

$$V = \frac{dx_1}{dt_1}$$

and the velocity of O_2 with respect to O is

$$v_2 = \frac{dx}{dt}$$

The Lorentz transformations in the differential form are

$$dx_1 = (dx - v_1 \, dt)\beta_1$$

and

$$dt_1 = \left(dt - v_1 \frac{dx}{c^2}\right)\beta_1$$

Therefore

$$\frac{dx_1}{dt_1} = \frac{dx - v_1 \, dt}{dt - v_1 \dfrac{dx}{c^2}}$$

$$= \frac{\dfrac{dx}{dt} - v_1}{1 - v_1 \dfrac{dx}{dt} \dfrac{1}{c^2}}$$

*Starting with Eqs. (17.41) and (17.42), which are of the same form as Eq. (17.40), write out all the steps leading to Eq. (17.43).

17-7 Successive Lorentz transformations

or
$$V = \frac{v_2 - v_1}{1 - \dfrac{v_1 v_2}{c^2}}$$

The main result of the successive Lorentz transformations from which Eq. (17.43) was obtained, is that we will not be able to determine which system is stationary (when we are either in Σ_1 or Σ_2). We can generalize this result by saying that *no experiment can detect which system is stationary.*

17-8 Modification of Length

Let O_2 in the system Σ_2 have a measuring rod with its ends at $x_2{}^{(1)}$ and $x_2{}^{(2)}$. Let O_1 measure the length of this rod. Using Lorentz transformations we have

$$x_2{}^{(2)} - x_2{}^{(1)} = \frac{(x_1{}^{(2)} - Vt_1) - (x_1{}^{(1)} - Vt_1)}{\left(1 - \dfrac{V^2}{c^2}\right)^{\frac{1}{2}}}$$

where V is the velocity of O_2 relative to O_1. This last relation reduces to

$$x_2{}^{(2)} - x_2{}^{(1)} = \frac{x_1{}^{(2)} - x_1{}^{(1)}}{\sqrt{1 - \dfrac{V^2}{c^2}}}$$

or, if $x_1{}^{(2)} - x_1{}^{(1)} = l_1$ and $x_2{}^{(2)} - x_2{}^{(1)} = l_2$, then

$$l_1 = l_2 \sqrt{1 - \frac{V^2}{c^2}} \tag{17.45}$$

This relation indicates that when the rod is measured by O_1 it will appear to him that it contracts by the factor $\sqrt{1 - (V^2/c^2)}$. Thus *Fitzgerald-Lorentz contraction follows directly from the Lorentz transformations* and these —as we have seen—depend on how the time scales for the two observers are set.

17-9 Time Dilatation

Let $t_2{}^{(1)}$ and $t_2{}^{(2)}$ be the times registered by a clock fixed in Σ_2 at x_2, and let $t_1{}^{(1)}$ and $t_1{}^{(2)}$ be the corresponding instants registered by a clock fixed in Σ_1. Then

$$t_1{}^{(1)} = \beta[t_2{}^{(1)} + V(x_2/c^2)]$$

and
$$t_1{}^{(2)} = \beta[t_2{}^{(2)} + V(x_2/c^2)]$$

Upon subtraction
$$t_1{}^{(2)} - t_1{}^{(1)} = \beta(t_2{}^{(2)} - t_2{}^{(1)})$$

which may be written in the form

$$\Delta t_1 = \beta \, \Delta t_2 \tag{17.46}$$

This result contains the *time dilatation and it again follows from the Lorentz transformations.*

Both Eqs. (17.45) and (17.46) apply to two systems in relative motion. *No mention is made of any system which is absolutely at rest.*

17–10   *The Principles of the Special Theory of Relativity*

Einstein summarized all the results, discussed above, in two statements. The first pertains to the velocity of light as measured by different observers moving with respect to each other. Michelson and Morley were not able to detect any difference in the velocity of light whether the light travelled parallel or perpendicular to the velocity of the observer. Einstein was quick to realize that the velocity is the same whether measured by a stationary or a moving observer. More exactly, *the velocity of light is the same when measured by two observers moving relative to each other.*

The second principle pertains to the relation between the validity of physical laws and the choice of frames in which the laws are formulated. The most important type of frames in classical mechanics are *the inertial frames.* By definition, inertial frames have three characteristics:

(i) Events occurring in space follow the rules of Euclidean geometry,

(ii) Coordinate time can be established for the whole frame, which means that the whole frame will have one and the same universal time,

(iii) Newton's first law is valid, i.e., a point remains at rest or in uniform motion in that frame unless acted on by a force.

A practical frame which fulfills all these requirements quite well is the frame of fixed stars.

The second principle of relativity enunciated by Einstein states that *it is impossible to detect relative motion of one frame with respect to an inertial frame.* Thus it follows that the former is also an inertial frame; and further, if physical laws are valid in one frame, they are equally valid in the other.

Of course, *when working in different frames we have to transform from one to another.*

We started our discussion of the theory of relativity by introducing the classical principle of relativity which stated that Newton's second law is invariant with respect to Galilean transformations. Einstein changed this statement by replacing the Galilean transformations with Lorentz transformations. He asserted that the laws of all physical phenomena are the same in all inertial frames. *The transformations which have to be used between the various inertial systems in order to render the laws the same, are the Lorentz transformations.*

To summarize, we can say that

All laws of physical phenomena are the same in all inertial systems, and

The velocity of light is the same in all places, in all directions and in all inertial frames.

It has been stated at the beginning of this chapter that the theory of relativity is "the physical theory of relative motion." From what we have learned so far, and from what we will learn in the next chapter, the statement in quotation marks gives a rather poor description of the theory of relativity. Actually the theory includes several other aspects which affect all branches of physics. Nevertheless, the fact remains that the primary object of the theory of relativity is to relate the results of observations of two observers moving with respect to each other.

So far we have been investigating the case when two frames in which the two observers are placed move with respect to each other with uniform motion. It is natural to extend these considerations to the case of two frames moving relative to each other with accelerated motion.

Consider the following physical situation. Let there be two Cartesian frames $\Sigma(Oxyz)$ and $\Sigma'(O'x'y'z')$. At zero time the two frames coincide and then Σ' starts moving with constant acceleration along the negative direction of the z axis (Fig. 17.9). Let there be a point mass P the position of which

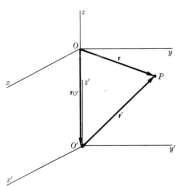

Fig. 17.9

in Σ is $\mathbf{r} = \overrightarrow{OP}$, and in Σ', $\mathbf{r}' = \overrightarrow{O'P}$. If $\overrightarrow{OO'} = \mathbf{r}_{O'}$ then

$$\mathbf{r} = \mathbf{r}' + \mathbf{r}_{O'}$$

Differentiating this relation twice with respect to time, we obtain

$$\ddot{\mathbf{r}} = \ddot{\mathbf{r}}' + \ddot{\mathbf{r}}_{O'} \tag{17.47}$$

If a is the magnitude of the constant acceleration of Σ' with respect to Σ and $\mathbf{k}$ is unit vector along the Oz axis, then

$$\ddot{\mathbf{r}}_{O'} = -a\mathbf{k} \tag{17.48}$$

and Eq. (17.47) becomes $\qquad \ddot{\mathbf{r}} = \ddot{\mathbf{r}}' - a\mathbf{k} \tag{17.49}$

Multiplying both sides by the mass m of the particle we get

$$m\ddot{\mathbf{r}} = m\ddot{\mathbf{r}}' - ma\mathbf{k} \tag{17.50}$$

Now, $m\ddot{\mathbf{r}}$ is the product of the mass and the acceleration measured in the Σ frame. Let this frame be one in which Newton's laws hold. Thus we know that

$$\mathbf{F} = m\ddot{\mathbf{r}} \tag{17.51}$$

where $\mathbf{F}$ is the actual force acting on m. This is not the force that an observer in Σ' sees, for—solving Eq. (17.50) for $m\ddot{\mathbf{r}}'$—he obtains

$$m\ddot{\mathbf{r}}' = \mathbf{F} + ma\mathbf{k} \tag{17.52}$$

Therefore, in addition to $\mathbf{F}$ the observer in Σ' experiences another force $ma\mathbf{k}$.

Notice that if $\mathbf{F} = \mathbf{O}$, i.e., when the observer in Σ does not see any force, the observer in Σ' gets

$$m\ddot{\mathbf{r}}' = ma\mathbf{k} \tag{17.53}$$

Suppose that Σ' moves with respect to Σ with a constant acceleration $a = g$ (numerically equal to acceleration due to gravity), along the positive Oz direction. Let $\mathbf{F} = \mathbf{O}$ which—again—means that an observer in Σ does not experience any force. Then (17.49) becomes

$$\ddot{\mathbf{r}}' = -g\mathbf{k} \tag{17.54}$$

Thus the observer in Σ' will find that the particle P "falls down" with an acceleration g.

We have just shown that the gravitational force of attraction has been "created" by accelerating one system with respect to another.

Einstein discussed these results in the following way. Starting from the experimental evidence that all objects fall with the same acceleration in a uniform gravitational field he pointed out that *an object falling freely in such a field is physically equivalent to the same object at rest in a field free space. Also, an object at rest in such a gravitational field is physically equivalent to the same object being uniformly accelerated in a field free space.* The two instances indicate *the equivalence of gravitational fields and accelerating coordinate systems. Einstein extended this equivalence to include gravitational and acceleration effects on all physical processes and called the resulting statement the principle of equivalence.* That is to say, *physical processes take place in identical fashion whether at rest in a gravitational field or in an accelerating coordinate system in a field free space;* also, *any physical process takes place in the same way whether at rest in field free space or falling freely in a gravitational field.*

The general theory of relativity is so constructed as to have this principle built in. We must realize that the validity of the principle of equivalence is based on the assumption that *the inertial mass entering into Newton's second law is equivalent to the gravitational mass which enters in Newton's law of universal attraction.* This is the first time that we distinguish between these two types of masses. We have occasionally referred to mass as the quantitative measure of resistance that a body offers against linear motion. Now, the character of mass entering in Newton's law of universal gravitation, viz.

$$F = G\,\frac{m_1 m_2}{r^2} \qquad (17.55)$$

is different. Here (for the same r) the magnitudes of m_1 and m_2 will determine the strength of gravitational attraction between them. It is by no means obvious that the masses appearing in this law and those appearing in Newton's second law are equal. However, it was assumed that the two types of masses are equal. This assumption has been born out by very intensive experiments.*

The principle of equivalence forms the starting point of the general theory of relativity. The actual purpose of the theory is to find the structure of the space-time continuum which will contain gravitational and other forces. To obtain this goal geometrical methods are used. However, since we are dealing here with the four-dimensional space-time continuum which for non-uniform fields is non-Euclidean, a new type of geometry must be introduced and applied. Such geometry had already been formulated by Gauss and by Riemann long before Einstein conceived the theory of relativity. Einstein made use of it to describe physical reality.

Any further development of the theory would involve some knowledge of specialized mathematical formalism and for that reason we will limit our discussion of the general theory of relativity to the few remarks made above.

Instead, we will consider some more details of the development of the special theory of relativity.

* Mention must be made here of the pioneering experiments performed by Eötvös. (R. v. Eötvös, D. Pekár and E. Fekete, *Ann Physik* **68**, 11 (1922).) The importance of these experiments has recently been discussed by L. I. Schiff, "On Experimental Tests of the General Theory of Relativity," *Am. J. Physics* **28**, 340 (1960) and also by R. H. Dicke, "Eötvös Experiment and the Gravitational Red Shift," *Am. J. Physics* **28**, 344 (1960).

18

RELATIVITY MECHANICS

Having introduced the principles of the special theory of relativity we want to find out what are the forms of the physical laws which are consistent with this theory. All parts of physics have to be modified. Thus optics, electromagnetic theory, modern physics and also—of course—the principles of mechanics, have to be modified. Since—at present—mechanics is the object of our studies, we will only consider the impact of the special theory of relativity on this branch of physics, and we will only examine some very elementary aspects thereof.

18–1   The Relativistic Invariant

We have seen that the Lorentz transformations apply not only to space coordinates but also to time. Time is therefore not an absolute quantity (as was indicated by Galilean transformations) but belongs to a particular frame in the same way as the space coordinates. Thus, when we speak about two systems, we should indicate the space coordinates and the time for both of them.

Let two systems $\Sigma(x, y, z, t)$ and $\Sigma'(x', y', z', t')$ coincide at

$$t = 0$$

i.e., also at

$$t' = 0$$

Let a signal of light be sent out from the two coinciding origins. After an interval of time t the light signal reaches a sphere

$$x^2 + y^2 + z^2 - c^2t^2 = 0 \tag{18.1}$$

Let the systems Σ and Σ' move with respect to each other with uniform velocity. Applying the Lorentz transformations to Eq. (18.1), we find that

$$x^2 + y^2 + z^2 - c^2t^2 = x'^2 + y'^2 + z'^2 - c^2t'^2 \tag{18.2}$$

We call the expression $(x^2 + y^2 + z^2 - c^2t^2)$ a *relativistic invariant*.

From our studies of the theory of relativity it is evident that there is a connection between time measurements. As we stated above, in order to specify a particular system of reference we must designate the space and the time coordinates. Space and time cannot be considered as two independent continua. We therefore merge them into one four-dimensional continuum. From the mathematical point of view—as we shall see—this presents no difficulty. In addition, the whole formalism of the special theory of relativity can be incorporated in a four-dimensional analysis quite simply.

We will thus introduce a four-dimensional space in which three directions will correspond to space directions and the fourth one to time. It is seen immediately that in this four-dimensional hyperspace the four directions are not equivalent, for the fourth direction connected with time is not interchangeable with any of the space directions.

In a three-dimensional space the position of a point is specified by its three coordinates. If $\mathbf{i}_1, \mathbf{i}_2, \mathbf{i}_3$ are the three coordinate unit vectors, the space-position vector of the particle is

$$\mathbf{r} = x\mathbf{i}_1 + y\mathbf{i}_2 + z\mathbf{i}_3 \tag{18.3}$$

In the four-dimensional space we will need four coordinates x, y, z, w to specify the position of a point. We will also have to extend the set of unit vectors to four, viz.: $\mathbf{i}_1, \mathbf{i}_2, \mathbf{i}_3, \mathbf{i}_4$. It will be assumed that they form an orthogonal set. The position vector of a point located in a four-dimensional space is now written as*

$$\mathscr{R} = x\mathbf{i}_1 + y\mathbf{i}_2 + z\mathbf{i}_3 + w\mathbf{i}_4 \tag{18.4}$$

We should like to attach a physical meaning to the four-vector $\mathscr{R}$ when the fourth dimension corresponds to time. First, we want to find a proper fourth coordinate w. The form of the relativistic invariant gives us a hint as to its form. If

$$\mathscr{R}^2 = x^2 + y^2 + z^2 + w^2 \tag{18.5}$$

is to correspond to the relativistic invariant then we can choose

$$w = ict \tag{18.6}$$

We see that $\mathscr{R}$ designates a point at an instant of time; we say that it designates an event.

There is no difficulty in forming the Lorentz transformations for the variables

$$x, \ y, \ z, \ ict$$

* We will denote all four-vectors by script letters.

If V is the relative velocity of two systems then the Lorentz transformations take the form

$$x' = \frac{x - (V/ic)ict}{\sqrt{1 + (V/ic)^2}}$$

$$y' = y$$

$$z' = z \qquad (18.7)$$

$$ict' = \frac{(V/ic)x + ict}{\sqrt{1 + (V/ic)^2}}$$

Let us define an imaginary angle θ in the manner shown in Figure 18.1; thus

$$\theta = \text{arc tan } (V/ic) \qquad (18.8)$$

Fig. 18.1

The new Lorentz transformations can then be written in the form

$$x' = x \cos \theta - w \sin \theta$$

$$w' = x \sin \theta + w \cos \theta$$

$$y' = y \qquad (18.9)$$

$$z' = z$$

where we have put $w = ict$ and $w' = ict'$.

The first two equations just give a rotational transformation of the x and w axes (Fig. 18.2). We say that this transformation is accomplished about the yz plane and that it affects an event (x, y, z, t).

Fig. 18.2

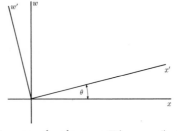

Consider now three frames of reference $\Sigma(x, y, z, t)$, $\Sigma_1(x_1, y_1, z_1, t_1)$ and $\Sigma_2(x_2, y_2, z_2, t_2)$. Let Σ_1 move with velocity v_1 and Σ_2 with v_2, both with respect to Σ. The transformation from Σ to Σ_1 can be accomplished by a rotation of the (x, w) axes to the (x_1, w_1) axes. The angle of rotation will be

$$\theta_1 = \text{arc tan } (v_1/ic) \qquad (18.10)$$

18–2 The four-dimensional space of Minkowski

Similarly the transformation from Σ to Σ_2 will be performed by means of a rotation through an angle

$$\theta_2 = \text{arc tan } (v_2/ic) \qquad (18.11)$$

The two rotations are shown in Figure 18.3.

Fig. 18.3

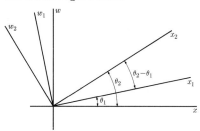

If we want to obtain the transformation from Σ_1 to Σ_2 by the same procedure, then this will be done by a rotation through the angle

$$\theta_2 - \theta_1 = \text{arc tan } (V/ic) \qquad (18.12)$$

Where V is the velocity of Σ_2 with respect to Σ_1. From the last equation we can write

$$V = ic \tan (\theta_2 - \theta_1) \qquad (18.13)$$

Now,

$$\tan \theta_1 = v_1/(ic) \qquad \tan \theta_2 = v_2/(ic)$$

and

$$\tan (\theta_2 - \theta_1) = \frac{\tan \theta_2 - \tan \theta_1}{1 + \tan \theta_1 \tan \theta_2}$$

Therefore

$$\tan (\theta_2 - \theta_1) = \frac{v_2/(ic) - v_1/(ic)}{1 + v_1 v_2/(i^2 c^2)} \qquad (18.14)$$

$$= \frac{1}{ic} \frac{v_2 - v_1}{1 - v_1 v_2/c^2}$$

Thus finally

$$V = \frac{v_2 - v_1}{1 - v_1 v_2/c^2} \qquad (18.15)$$

According to the principle of relativity all physical laws are invariant with respect to Lorentz transformations. On the basis of the discussion just completed, we may state this principle in another way, viz.: *The forms of all physical laws are invariant with respect to rotation in the four-dimensional space.*

18-3 *Four-Dimensional Velocity. Proper Time*

In a three-dimensional space referred to fixed axes, the velocity vector of a point P situated at $\mathbf{r}$ is given by

$$\dot{\mathbf{r}} = \frac{dx}{dt} \mathbf{i}_1 + \frac{dy}{dt} \mathbf{i}_2 + \frac{dz}{dt} \mathbf{i}_3 \qquad (18.16)$$

i.e., if **r** in matrix notation is

$$\mathbf{r} = (x \ y \ z)$$

then

$$\dot{\mathbf{r}} = \left(\frac{dx}{dt} \ \frac{dy}{dt} \ \frac{dz}{dt} \right) \tag{18.17}$$

We have seen above that $x^2 + y^2 + z^2 + w^2$ is a relativistic invariant. We will write it in the differential form and denote it as $-c^2\, d\tau^2$. Thus we will have

$$dx^2 + dy^2 + dz^2 + dw^2 = -c^2\, d\tau^2 \tag{18.18}$$

τ is called the proper time, and is an invariant. In terms of the relativistic element of length

$$d\Re^2 = dx^2 + dy^2 + dz^2 + dw^2 \tag{18.19}$$

the proper time is defined as

$$d\tau^2 = -\frac{d\Re^2}{c^2} \tag{18.20}$$

We now define the *four-dimensional velocity* as

$$\mathfrak{v} = \left(\frac{dx}{d\tau} \ \frac{dy}{d\tau} \ \frac{dz}{d\tau} \ \frac{dw}{d\tau} \right) \tag{18.21}$$

In order to find the relation between dt and $d\tau$ we start with

$$v^2 = \frac{dx^2}{dt^2} + \frac{dy^2}{dt^2} + \frac{dz^2}{dt^2} \tag{18.22}$$

from which

$$dx^2 + dy^2 + dz^2 = v^2\, dt^2$$

Substituting this and $dw^2 = -c^2\, dt^2$ in Eq. (18.18) we obtain

$$v^2\, dt^2 - c^2\, dt^2 = -c^2\, d\tau^2$$

or

$$d\tau^2 = dt^2 \left(1 - \frac{v^2}{c^2} \right) \tag{18.23}$$

In the above expressions v is the Newtonian velocity measured in the Σ system. (We are considering two systems Σ and Σ'.) We will denote

$$\gamma = \frac{1}{\sqrt{1 - \dfrac{v^2}{c^2}}} \tag{18.24}$$

and reserve β for

$$\beta = \frac{1}{\sqrt{1 - \dfrac{V^2}{c^2}}} \tag{18.25}$$

where V is the relative velocity of the two systems. The relation between the two time elements dt and $d\tau$ can now be written as

$$dt = \gamma \, d\tau \tag{18.26}$$

Suppose that the particle is at rest in the Σ' system. In general we have

$$dx'^2 + dy'^2 + dz'^2 + dw'^2 = -c^2 \, d\tau^2 \tag{18.27}$$

When the particle is at rest in Σ' then

$$dx' = dy' = dz' = 0$$

and

$$d\tau = dt' \tag{18.28}$$

This provides us with some physical meaning for τ.

If we start with the relation between dt and $d\tau$ given by Eq. (18.26), we can write

$$\frac{dx}{d\tau} = \gamma \, \frac{dx}{dt} \tag{18.29}$$

and this is the same as

$$\mathcal{V}_x = \gamma v_x \tag{18.30}$$

Similar relations obtain for other components. We thus find that

$$\mathcal{V} = (\gamma v_x \;\; \gamma v_y \;\; \gamma v_z \;\; \gamma \, dw/dt) \tag{18.31}$$

which more concisely can be written as

$$\mathcal{V} = (\gamma \mathbf{v} \;\; \gamma \, dw/dt) \tag{18.32}$$

or

$$\mathcal{V} = (\gamma \mathbf{v} \;\; \gamma ic) \tag{18.33}$$

We are now in the position to investigate the relations between the velocities of one and the same particle measured by two observers who move relative to each other. The relations which we will obtain will be referred to as velocity transformations. Again, consider two systems Σ and Σ' which move with respect to each other with velocity v along the x axis. The point which is moving is P and its velocity measured by an observer in Σ' is $\mathbf{v}'$ and that measured by an observer in Σ is $\mathbf{v}$. The Galilean transformations for the velocities are

$$v_x' = v_x - V \qquad v_y' = v_y \qquad v_z' = v_z \tag{18.34}$$

In order to obtain the Lorentz transformations of velocity we start with

$$x' = \frac{x - (V/ic)ict}{\sqrt{1 + \left(\dfrac{V}{ic}\right)^2}} \qquad y' = y \qquad z' = z \tag{18.35}$$

We differentiate both sides of the first transformation with respect to τ; thus

$$\frac{dx'}{d\tau} = \frac{d}{d\tau}\left[\frac{x - (V/ic)ict}{\sqrt{1 + \left(\dfrac{V}{ic}\right)^2}}\right] \tag{18.36}$$

which gives

$$\mathcal{U}_x' = [\mathcal{U}_x - (V/ic)\mathcal{U}_w]\beta \tag{18.37}$$

This in turn can be written as

$$\gamma'v_x' = [\gamma v_x - (V/ic)\gamma ic]\beta \tag{18.38}$$

or

$$v_x' = [v_x - V]\frac{\gamma}{\gamma'}\beta \tag{18.39}$$

Now

$$d\tau = \frac{dt}{\gamma}$$

and also

$$d\tau = \frac{dt'}{\gamma'}$$

therefore

$$\frac{\gamma'}{\gamma} = \frac{dt'}{dt} \tag{18.40}$$

$$= \frac{(dt - (V/c^2)\,dx)\beta}{dt}$$

$$= \left(1 - \frac{V}{c^2}\frac{dx}{dt}\right)\beta$$

or

$$\frac{\gamma'}{\gamma} = \left(1 - \frac{Vv_x}{c^2}\right)\beta \tag{18.41}$$

Substituting this in Eq. (18.39) we obtain

$$v_x' = \frac{v_x - V}{1 - \dfrac{Vv_x}{c^2}} \tag{18.42}$$

For the y and z components we have

$$\mathcal{U}_y' = \mathcal{U}_y \qquad \mathcal{U}_z' = \mathcal{U}_z \tag{18.43}$$

In terms of Newtonian components these last relations become

$$\gamma'v_y' = \gamma v_y \qquad \gamma'v_z' = \gamma v_z \tag{18.44}$$

Using (18.41) we can write

$$v_y' = \frac{v_y}{\left(1 - \dfrac{Vv_x}{c^2}\right)\beta} \qquad v_z' = \frac{v_z}{\left(1 - \dfrac{Vv_x}{c^2}\right)\beta} \tag{18.45}$$

18–3 Four-dimensional velocity. Proper time

These, together with Eq. (18.42), constitute the Lorentz transformations of velocity.

As we would expect, the Galilean transformations for velocities are, in general, not valid. The proper relations between components of velocities of one and the same point measured by observers in two different frames are given by the Lorentz transformations for velocities.

18–4 Relativistic Momentum. Relativistic Mass

In Newtonian mechanics the mass m_0 of a particle is constant and its linear momentum is

$$\mathbf{p} = m_0\mathbf{v} \tag{18.46}$$

where $\mathbf{v}$ is the velocity. When the resultant force acting on the particle is zero then the linear momentum within a particular frame is conserved. Any component of the momentum is likewise conserved.

We define the *four-dimensional momentum* of the particle as

$$\mathcal{P} = m_0\mathbf{\mathcal{U}} \tag{18.47}$$

We will postulate that *with no resultant force acting on the particle, the four-dimensional momentum is conserved.* Any component of $\mathcal{P}$ will also be conserved. The x component of the four-momentum will be

$$\mathcal{P}_x = m_0\frac{dx}{d\tau}$$

or

$$\mathcal{P}_x = m_0\gamma\frac{dx}{dt} \tag{18.48}$$

Denoting

$$m = m_0\gamma \tag{18.49}$$

we have

$$\mathcal{P}_x = m\frac{dx}{dt} \tag{18.50}$$

We see that if the postulate of conservation of the four-momentum is satisfied, the mass of the particle will change. The mass is the quantity m given by Eq. (18.49); we call it the *relativistic mass* of the particle.

The fourth component of the four-momentum is

$$\mathcal{P}_w = m_0\mathcal{U}_w$$

$$= m_0\frac{dw}{d\tau}$$

$$= m_0\gamma\frac{dw}{dt} \tag{18.51}$$

$$= m_0\gamma ic$$

Thus

$$\mathcal{P}_w = mic \tag{18.52}$$

If we have a system of particles on which no resultant force is acting, the total four-momentum is conserved. If, for instance, the system undergoes a collision, then

$$\sum (\mathbf{P})_i = \sum (\mathbf{P})_f \qquad (18.53)$$

where the subscripts i and f refer to the state of the system before and after the collision. In this relation $\mathbf{P}$ stands for the four-vector; thus Eq. (18.53) is equivalent to four scalar relations

$$\sum (\mathcal{P}_x)_i = \sum (\mathcal{P}_x)_f \qquad \sum (\mathcal{P}_y)_i = \sum (\mathcal{P}_y)_f$$

$$\sum (\mathcal{P}_z)_i = \sum (\mathcal{P}_z)_f \qquad \sum (\mathcal{P}_w)_i = \sum (\mathcal{P}_w)_f \qquad (18.54)$$

In view of the form of $\mathcal{P}_w$ as given by Eq. (18.52) the last relation states that

$$\sum (m)_i = \sum (m)_f$$

i.e., Σm is conserved. Thus, *although the mass of particular particles of the system of colliding particles changes, the sum of the relativistic masses of the whole system does not change.*

The four-dimensional momentum

$$\mathbf{P} = \mathcal{P}_x \mathbf{i}_1 + \mathcal{P}_y \mathbf{i}_2 + \mathcal{P}_z \mathbf{i}_3 + \mathcal{P}_w \mathbf{i}_4$$

was defined as

$$\mathbf{P} = m_0 \mathbf{\mathcal{V}}$$

Using Eq. (18.50) (with similar expressions for the y and z components), and also Eq. (18.52), we can write

$$\mathbf{P} = m_0(\gamma \mathbf{v} \; \gamma ic)$$

$$= (m\mathbf{v} \; mic) \qquad (18.55)$$

$$= \left(m\mathbf{v} \; - \frac{mc^2}{ic} \right)$$

or

$$\mathbf{P} = (\mathbf{p} \; -E/ic) \qquad (18.56)$$

where use has been made of the relation $E = mc^2$, discussed in Section 18–7. We can take this last relation as expressing the fact that the three-dimensional momentum $\mathbf{p}$ (in which the relativistic mass enters) is the spatial component of the four-momentum, and its fourth component is the energy.

18–5 Force

We define the *four-dimensional force* as

$$\mathfrak{F} = \frac{d}{d\tau} (m_0 \mathbf{\mathcal{V}}) \qquad (18.57)$$

302

We can also write

$$\mathfrak{F} = m_0 \frac{d^2 \mathfrak{R}}{d\tau^2} \qquad (18.58)$$

The x component of $\mathfrak{F}$ is

$$\mathfrak{F}_x = m_0 \frac{d^2 x}{d\tau^2}$$

$$= m_0 \frac{d}{d\tau}\left(\frac{dx}{d\tau}\right)$$

$$= m_0 \gamma \frac{d}{dt}\left(\gamma \frac{dx}{dt}\right)$$

$$= \gamma \frac{d}{dt}(m_0 \gamma v_x)$$

$$= \gamma \frac{d}{dt}(m v_x)$$

or

$$\mathfrak{F}_x = \gamma F_x \qquad (18.59)$$

Similarly

$$\mathfrak{F}_y = \gamma F_y \qquad \mathfrak{F}_z = \gamma F_z$$

where

$$\mathbf{F} = (F_x \ F_y \ F_z)$$

We see that

$$F_x = \frac{d}{dt}(m v_x) \qquad F_y = \frac{d}{dt}(m v_y) \qquad F_z = \frac{d}{dt}(m v_z) \qquad (18.60)$$

We call $\mathbf{F}$ the Newtonian force but we notice that the varying mass m enters into its definition. We will say that the Newtonian force $\mathbf{F}$ is the space component of the four-dimensional force $\mathfrak{F}$.

For the x components of the Newtonian force we can write

$$F_x = \frac{d}{dt} \frac{m_0 v_x}{\sqrt{1 - \dfrac{v^2}{c^2}}}$$

or

$$F_x = \frac{m_0}{\sqrt{1 - \dfrac{v^2}{c^2}}} \frac{dv_x}{dt} + m_0 v_0 \frac{d}{dt} \frac{1}{\sqrt{1 - \dfrac{v^2}{c^2}}} \qquad (18.61)$$

We see that for $v/c \ll 1$,

$$F_x = m_0 \frac{dv_x}{dt}$$

Thus *the laws of dynamics in the four-dimensional space are in agreement with Newton's laws for small velocities.*

18-5 Force

Consider the scalar product of the four-dimensional force and the four-dimensional velocity. For this we can write

$$\mathfrak{F}_x \mathfrak{V}_x + \mathfrak{F}_y \mathfrak{V}_y + \mathfrak{F}_z \mathfrak{V}_z + \mathfrak{F}_w \mathfrak{V}_w = m_0 \frac{d^2 x}{d\tau^2} \frac{dx}{d\tau} + \cdots + m_0 \frac{d^2 w}{d\tau^2} \frac{dw}{d\tau}$$

$$= \tfrac{1}{2} m_0 \frac{d}{d\tau} \left[\left(\frac{dx}{d\tau}\right)^2 + \left(\frac{dy}{d\tau}\right)^2 + \left(\frac{dz}{d\tau}\right)^2 + \left(\frac{dw}{d\tau}\right)^2 \right]$$

$$= \tfrac{1}{2} m_0 \frac{d}{d\tau} \frac{dx^2 + dy^2 + dz^2 + dw^2}{d\tau^2}$$

$$= \tfrac{1}{2} m_0 \frac{d}{d\tau} \left[\frac{-c^2 d\tau^2}{d\tau^2} \right]$$

$$= \tfrac{1}{2} m_0 \frac{d}{d\tau} (-c^2)$$

or
$$\mathfrak{F}_x \mathfrak{V}_x + \mathfrak{F}_y \mathfrak{V}_y + \mathfrak{F}_z \mathfrak{V}_z + \mathfrak{F}_w \mathfrak{V}_w = 0 \qquad (18.62)$$

Now

$$\mathfrak{F}_x = \gamma F_x \qquad \mathfrak{F}_y = \gamma F_y \qquad \mathfrak{F}_z = \gamma F_z$$

$$\mathfrak{V}_x = \gamma v_x \qquad \mathfrak{V}_y = \gamma v_y \qquad \mathfrak{V}_z = \gamma v_z \qquad \mathfrak{V}_w = \gamma ic$$

and
$$\mathfrak{F}_w = \frac{d}{d\tau} (m_0 \mathfrak{V}_w)$$

or
$$\mathfrak{F}_w = \gamma \frac{d}{dt} (m_0 \gamma ic)$$

Substitution of these in Eq. (18.62) yields

$$F_x \frac{dx}{dt} + F_y \frac{dy}{dt} + F_z \frac{dz}{dt} = \frac{d}{dt} (mc^2) \qquad (18.63)$$

The left-hand side of this equation can be written as $\mathbf{F} \cdot \dot{\mathbf{r}}$ and for it we can write

$$\frac{dE}{dt} = \mathbf{F} \cdot \dot{\mathbf{r}} \qquad (18.64)$$

where $E = T + V$ is the total energy.* We have therefore shown that

$$\frac{dE}{dt} = \frac{d}{dt} (mc^2) \qquad (18.65)$$

Let us apply this equation to a system of colliding particles. Let t_1 denote some instant of time before the collision and t_2 that after the collision. Integration between these two instants yields

$$\Delta E = \Delta \left(\sum mc^2 \right) \qquad (18.66)$$

* See Eq. (2.90).

In Section 18–4 we have seen that in a situation like the one we are considering here, the total (relativistic) mass of the system of particles is conserved. We can express this by writing

$$\Delta\left(\sum m\right) = 0$$

From this and from Eq. (18.66) we deduce that also

$$\Delta E = 0 \tag{18.67}$$

Thus, in our case, *the statements of conservation of mass and of conservation of energy are equivalent.*

When the total energy is purely kinetic, Eq. (18.65) becomes

$$\frac{dT}{dt} = \frac{d}{dt}(mc^2) \tag{18.68}$$

Integration yields

$$T = mc^2 + A$$

where A is a constant independent of time. To determine its value we notice that when $v = 0$, then $T = 0$ and $m = m_0$. Thus

$$A = -m_0 c^2$$

Therefore

$$T = (m - m_0)c^2 \tag{18.69}$$

This is the relativistic form of the kinetic energy of a particle of rest mass m_0.

To determine the relation between the relativistic and the Newtonian forms of the kinetic energies we write

$$T = m_0 c^2 \left[\frac{1}{\sqrt{1 - \dfrac{v^2}{c^2}}} - 1 \right]$$

from which we get

$$T = \tfrac{1}{2} m_0 v^2 [1 + o(v^2/c^2)] \tag{18.70}$$

where $o(v^2/c^2)$ denotes terms of order v^2/c^2 and higher.

18–7 The Equivalence of Energy and Mass

We have seen that

$$\Delta E = c^2 \, \Delta m \tag{18.71}$$

is universally true. This equation reads that *an increase in mass leads to a corresponding increase in energy.* As already stated, the conservation of energy and the conservation of mass are two aspects of the same statement. This can be generalized into the principle of equivalence of mass and energy by saying that *any mass M is equivalent to energy Mc^2 and any energy E is equiva-lent to mass E/c^2.* This is the basis for the famous *Einstein relation*

$$E = Mc^2 \qquad (18.72)$$

This relation has been substantiated experimentally on a grandiose scale.

We add the obvious deduction that matter has lost its privileged position and material points are really points of concentrated energy.

PROBLEMS

18.1 (a) Optical engineers claim that they can detect a shift of 10^{-4} of a fringe. If cadmium red light ($\lambda = 6438.4696$ Å) were used to form the fringes, what would be the classical time difference for the two positions of the interferometer in the Michelson-Morley experiment if a shift of 10^{-4} of a fringe were observed?

(b) If it were possible to obtain fringes with x-rays of $\lambda = 1.54$ Å, what would the corresponding time difference be?

18.2 In the Kennedy-Thorndike experiment, what should the fringe shift be in order to obtain $v_\beta = (24 \pm 19)$ km/sec and $v_\alpha = (15 \pm 4)$ km/sec for the two velocity components of the earth discussed in Section 17–4?

18.3 Prove that the temporal sequence of two events p and q, occurring at points P and Q of a frame S, is the same for all frames if, and only if, the time separation between p and q in S is more than it takes light to travel from P to Q.

18.4 The relativistic Lagrangian of a single particle of mass m is

$$L = -mc^2 \sqrt{1 - \left(\frac{v}{c}\right)^2} - V$$

where V is the potential energy. Verify that $L \neq T - V$.

Let $V = V(x, y, z)$ and $L = L(x, y, z, u, v, w)$ where u, v, w are the velocity components of the particle. Using the usual form of Lagrange's equations given by Eqs. (8.76) show that

$$\frac{\partial L}{\partial u} = \frac{mu}{\sqrt{1 - \left(\frac{v}{c}\right)^2}}$$

Similar expressions are valid for the other components.

18.5 Using generalized coordinates q_i, the generalized momentum is defined as

$$p_i = \frac{\partial L}{\partial \dot{q}_i}$$

and the relativistic Hamiltonian is

$$H = \sum_i \dot{q}_i p_i - L$$

Prove that for the form of L given in the previous problem, $H = E$, where $E = T + V$.

18.6 In the Compton effect an incident photon $h\nu$ collides with a stationary electron. After the collision a new photon $h\nu'$ is observed travelling in the direction θ (Fig. 18.4) and the electron moves with velocity $\mathbf{v}$ in the direction

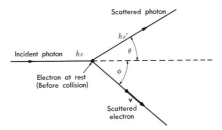

Fig. 18.4
The Compton effect.

making an angle ϕ with the horizontal. Using the law of conservation of four-dimensional momentum and the relativistic expression for the mass of the electron ($m = m_0/\sqrt{1 - (v^2/c^2)}$) show that

$$\lambda' - \lambda = -\frac{h}{m_0 c}(\cos\theta - 1)$$

where $\lambda = c/\nu$ and $\lambda' = c/\nu'$

18.7 One type of amplitude-splitting interferometer consists of one beam splitter and three mirrors as shown in Figure 18.5. (Sometimes it is referred to as the Sagnac interferometer.) If the whole interferometer, together with

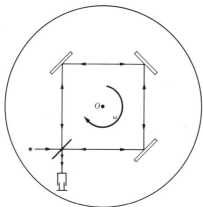

Fig. 18.5
The rotating Sagnac interferometer.

the source and the detector is placed on a platform, then there will be a fringe shift when the platform is set into rotation. The fractional displacement of the fringe is

$$\Delta z = \frac{4A\omega}{c\lambda}$$

where A is the area enclosed by the beams of the light travelling around the interferometer, ω is the angular velocity of the platform, c is the velocity of light and λ is the wavelength of the light used.

(a) Obtain the above expression using purely classical reasoning. You will thus assume that light travels with velocity $c - v$ or $c + v$ where v is the linear velocity of the mirrors travelling in the clockwise or counterclockwise direction.

(b) Apply Lorentz transformations to the infinitesimal element of the path of light travelling around the circuit and to the time element. Integrate around the entire circuit and obtain the same formula as before.

(c) The same formula can be obtained by using methods of the general theory of relativity. Discuss why all the theories give the same results and state which is the "proper" theory to apply.

19

VIBRATIONS IN A STRING

19–1 Heavy String at Rest

Consider a string of linear weight density $\rho(x)$ which is stretched horizontally along the x axis and which is fixed at both ends

Fig. 19.1

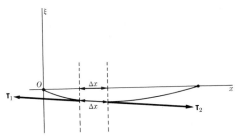

(Fig. 19.1). Because of its weight, every element Δx of the string will actually be below the x axis, but we will assume that the string is tightly stretched and so the length of this element is equal to its projection on the x axis. The string is under tension T which is different in magnitude and direction at various points of the string but we will assume a constant magnitude of the tension throughout the entire length of the string. Thus the element Δx is subjected to two forces T_1 and T_2 of equal magnitude but not lying along the same straight line. The situation is shown more clearly in Figure 19.2, where

Fig. 19.2

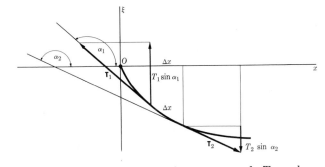

the sagging of the string has been greatly exaggerated; T_1 makes an angle α_1 and T_2 makes an angle α_2, both with the positive x axis. The net restoring force acting on the element Δx is

$$T_1 \sin \alpha_1 \; - \; T_2 \sin \alpha_2 \qquad (19.1)$$

The string is at rest and the restoring force is balanced by the weight of the element. Therefore

$$T_1 \sin \alpha_1 - T_2 \sin \alpha_2 = \rho(x) \, \Delta x \tag{19.2}$$

Both angles α_1 and α_2 are very nearly equal to $180°$ and so

$$\sin \alpha_1 \approx \alpha_1$$

and

$$\sin \alpha_2 \approx \alpha_2$$

Thus

$$T_1 \alpha_1 - T_2 \alpha_2 = \rho(x) \, \Delta x$$

Furthermore, the angles α_1 and α_2 can be replaced by the slopes of the tangents at the two ends of the element of the string, and so we can write

$$T \left(\frac{\partial \xi}{\partial x} \right)_1 - T \left(\frac{\partial \xi}{\partial x} \right)_2 = \rho(x) \, \Delta x$$

or

$$T \left(\frac{\partial \xi}{\partial x} \right)_2 - T \left(\frac{\partial \xi}{\partial x} \right)_1 = -\rho(x) \, \Delta x$$

or

$$\frac{T \left(\frac{\partial \xi}{\partial x} \right)_2 - T \left(\frac{\partial \xi}{\partial x} \right)_1}{\Delta x} = -\rho(x)$$

where we have dropped the subscripts of the tension T. Proceeding to the limit as $\Delta x \to 0$ we obtain

$$T \frac{\partial^2 \xi}{\partial x^2} = -\rho(x) \tag{19.3}$$

This last step really follows from the definition of the second derivative of any function $f(x)$. If its first derivative is denoted by $f'(x)$, then the second derivative is defined as

$$f''(x) = \lim_{\Delta x \to 0} \frac{f'(x + \Delta x) - f'(x)}{\Delta x}$$

Eq. (19.3) is the differential equation for a heavy string in equilibrium.*

19–2 The Vibrating String

Let us suppose that the same string is now vibrating. We again assume that the tension is the same throughout the length of the string, that it does not

* This is as far as we want to go here with our discussion of a string in equilibrium. All that we did is to state the problem of the statics of heavy strings and cables. For detailed solutions, the references listed at the end of this book should be consulted.

change with time, and that the displacements of every element of the string are small. Also, we will assume that the string is light in the sense that the effect of the restoring force acting on an element Δx of the string and caused by the tension, will be much larger than the weight of the element. By Newton's second law we can equate the net force acting on the element to the product of its mass and acceleration; thus

$$T\left\{\left(\frac{\partial \xi}{\partial x}\right)_2 - \left(\frac{\partial \xi}{\partial x}\right)_1\right\} = \rho(x)\,\Delta x\,\frac{\partial^2 \xi}{\partial t^2} \tag{19.4}$$

(If we do not assume that the string is light, then we should add to the left hand side of the equation the weight of the element Δx as one of the forces acting.) From the last equation we obtain

$$\frac{T\left\{\left(\frac{\partial \xi}{\partial x}\right)_2 - \left(\frac{\partial \xi}{\partial x}\right)_1\right\}}{\Delta x} = \rho(x)\,\frac{\partial^2 \xi}{\partial t^2}$$

In the limit when $x \to 0$, we find that

$$T\frac{\partial^2 \xi}{\partial x^2} = \rho\,\frac{\partial^2 \xi}{\partial t^2}$$

or

$$\frac{\partial^2 \xi}{\partial x^2} - \frac{\rho}{T}\frac{\partial^2 \xi}{\partial t^2} = 0 \tag{19.5}$$

It is shown in Appendix C that the differential equation

$$\frac{\partial^2 \xi}{\partial x^2} - \frac{1}{c^2}\frac{\partial^2 \xi}{dt^2} = 0 \tag{19.6}$$

represents a wave travelling along the x direction; therefore, Eq. (19.5) represents a wave travelling along the string with velocity c given by

$$c = \sqrt{\frac{T}{\rho}}$$

We notice that the latter relation gives the velocity of the wave in terms of the physical properties of the medium.

We will now solve the differential equation of the wave, Eq. (19.5), for the case when

$$\rho(x) = \rho_0 = \text{constant} \tag{19.7}$$

We will use the standard method of solving such equations by starting with the assumption that the solution can be written in the form

$$\xi(x, t) = X(x)\Theta(t) \tag{19.8}$$

i.e., that the displacement $\xi(x, t)$ can be expressed as a product of a function X of x only, and another function Θ of t only. Substitution of the assumed solution in the differential equation yields

$$\frac{T}{\rho_0} \frac{1}{X} \frac{d^2X}{dx^2} = \frac{1}{\Theta} \frac{d^2\Theta}{dt^2} \qquad (19.9)$$

We notice that the left hand side is a function of x only and the right hand side a function of t only. Both x and t are independent variables. We can thus vary x, keeping t constant, and at all times both sides must be equal to each other. It is obvious that both sides must be equal to one and the same constant. Call this constant $-\lambda$. Then

$$\frac{T}{\rho_0} \frac{1}{X} \frac{d^2X}{dx^2} = \frac{1}{\Theta} \frac{d^2\Theta}{dt^2} = -\lambda \qquad (19.10)$$

Thus we obtain two equations

$$\frac{d^2X}{dx^2} + \frac{\lambda}{c^2} X = 0 \qquad (19.11)$$

where

$$c^2 = \frac{T}{\rho_0} \qquad (19.12)$$

and

$$\frac{d^2\Theta}{dt^2} + \lambda\Theta = 0 \qquad (19.13)$$

The x equation, Eq. (19.11), will have a solution of the form

$$X(x) = A \cos\frac{\sqrt{\lambda}}{c} x + B \sin\frac{\sqrt{\lambda}}{c} x \qquad (19.14)$$

At this point we may introduce the boundary conditions since we know that the ends of the string are fixed. Thus

$$\xi(0, t) = \xi(\ell, t) = 0$$

which in our case reduce to

$$X(0) = 0$$

and

$$X(\ell) = 0$$

This first condition yields

$$A = 0$$

The second boundary condition gives

$$0 = B \sin\frac{\sqrt{\lambda}}{c} \ell$$

We cannot have $B = 0$, because that would mean that the string is at rest at all times. Thus the second boundary condition requires that

$$\ell \frac{\sqrt{\lambda}}{c} = n\pi$$

or

$$\sqrt{\lambda} = \frac{n\pi c}{\ell} \tag{19.15}$$

or

$$\lambda^2 = \frac{n^2\pi^2 c^2}{\ell^2}$$

The x equation has therefore solutions of the form

$$X(x) = B \sin \frac{n\pi}{\ell} x \tag{19.16}$$

The arbitrary constant B is still present. We can express its value in terms of the length of the string by evaluating the average value of $X^2(x)$ over the range $(0, \ell)$,* and equating it arbitrarily to 1. This process is called normalization.**

Thus

$$B^2 \int_0^\ell \sin^2 \frac{n\pi}{\ell} x \, dx = 1$$

yields

$$B = \sqrt{\frac{2}{\ell}}$$

* The average value of any function $f(x)$ over a range 0 to ℓ, say, is really the height, $\overline{f(x)}$, of a rectangle, the base of which is ℓ, and whose area is equal to the area under the curve $f(x)$, (Fig. 19.3). Thus

$$\ell \times \overline{f(x)} = \int_0^\ell f(x) \, dx$$

or

$$\overline{f(x)} = \frac{1}{\ell} \int_0^\ell f(x) \, dx$$

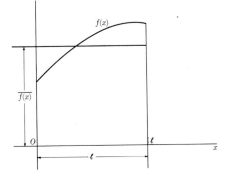

Fig. 19.3

** The process of normalization has no important physical meaning here. Furthermore, as we shall see, when the time solutions are multiplied by the space solution in Eq. (19.19), the constant B merges with the other constants. Nevertheless, when space solutions are used alone, as in Eq. (19.16), these are normalized in cases when such normalization has a physical meaning.

The normalized space solutions of the wave equation are therefore of the form

$$X_n(x) = \sqrt{\frac{2}{\ell}} \sin \frac{n\pi}{\ell} x \qquad n = 0, 1, 2, \ldots \qquad (19.17)$$

Consider now the time equation

$$\frac{d^2\Theta}{dt^2} + \lambda\Theta = 0$$

Its solution is of the form

$$\Theta = C \cos \sqrt{\lambda}\, t + D \sin \sqrt{\lambda}\, t \qquad (19.17a)$$

also written as

$$\Theta = \sqrt{C^2 + D^2} \cos (\sqrt{\lambda}\, t + \epsilon) \qquad (19.17b)$$

We notice that the time variation $\Theta(t)$ of the wave is of the form

$$\Theta = c \cos (\omega t + \epsilon)$$

It is therefore simple harmonic, where

$$\omega = \sqrt{\lambda}$$

The linear frequencies are obtained from

$$2\pi\nu = \sqrt{\lambda}$$

or

$$\nu = \frac{\sqrt{\lambda}}{2\pi}$$

The only permissible values of λ are given by Eq. (19.15). Therefore the only permissible frequencies are

$$\nu_n = \frac{c}{2\ell} n \qquad n = 0, 1, 2, \ldots \qquad (19.18)$$

The fundamental solution of the differential equation of the wave travelling in the string is the product of the space solutions, Eq. (19.17), and the time solutions, Eq. (19.17a or b). Thus

$$\xi(x, t) = \sqrt{\frac{2}{\ell}} \sin \frac{n\pi}{\ell} x \left\{ C \cos \frac{cn\pi}{\ell} t + D \sin \frac{cn\pi}{\ell} t \right\}$$

If we had not introduced the normalization condition which, as we have seen, is arbitrary then the fundamental solution would be of the form

$$\xi(x, t) = B \sin \frac{n\pi}{\ell} x \left\{ C \cos \frac{n\pi c}{\ell} t + D \sin \frac{n\pi c}{\ell} t \right\}$$

which can be written as

$$\xi(x, t) = \sin \frac{n\pi}{\ell} x \left\{ a \cos \frac{n\pi c}{\ell} t + b \sin \frac{n\pi c}{\ell} t \right\} \qquad (19.19)$$

We see that the arbitrary constant B has been incorporated in the new constants a and b without any loss of generality.

The last solution is not unique since it still contains the arbitrary constants a and b. These can be determined from the initial conditions. When we try to meet these initial conditions we will realize that in general there will not be just two constants but a whole series of them. Therefore the most general solution of the wave equation will be made up of the superposition of the solutions with various possible constants a_n, b_n. The general solution will therefore be of the form

$$\xi(x, t) = \sum_{n=1}^{\infty} \left\{ a_n \cos \frac{n \pi c}{\ell} t + b_n \sin \frac{n \pi c}{\ell} t \right\} \sin \frac{n \pi}{\ell} x \qquad (19.20)$$

The initial conditions can now be introduced. These will often be stated in the forms

$$\xi(x, 0) = \xi_0(x)$$

and

$$\frac{\partial \xi(x, 0)}{\partial t} = \xi_1(x)$$

where $\xi_0(x)$ and $\xi_1(x)$ are two given functions of x. (The second initial condition states that the time derivative of $\xi(x, t)$ evaluated at $t = 0$ is equal to the given function $\xi_1(x)$.) Application of the two initial conditions to the last form of the general solution, Eq. (19.20), yields

$$\xi_0(x) = \sum_{n=1}^{\infty} a_n \sin \frac{n \pi}{\ell} x$$

and

$$\xi_1(x) = \sum_{n=1}^{\infty} b_n \frac{n \pi c}{\ell} \sin \frac{n \pi}{\ell} x$$

We see that both $\xi_0(x)$ and $\xi_1(x)$ are expressed as Fourier series, so that every single constant can now be evaluated. Applying the methods of Fourier series we obtain

$$a_n = \frac{2}{\ell} \int_0^\ell \xi_0(x) \sin \frac{n \pi}{\ell} x \, dx$$

and

$$b_n = \frac{2}{n \pi c} \int_0^\ell \xi_1(x) \sin \frac{n \pi}{\ell} x \, dx$$

With these, the most general solution of the differential wave equation takes the form

$$\xi(x, t) = \sum_{n=1}^{\infty} \left\{ \left[\frac{2}{\ell} \int_0^\ell \xi_0(x) \sin \frac{n \pi}{\ell} x \, dx \right] \cos \frac{n \pi c}{\ell} t \right.$$
$$\left. + \left[\frac{2}{n \pi c} \int_0^\ell \xi_1(x) \sin \frac{n \pi}{\ell} x \, dx \right] \sin \frac{n \pi c}{\ell} t \right\} \sin \frac{n \pi}{\ell} x$$

$$(19.21)$$

19–2 The vibrating string

From it, the value of the vertical displacement of the string at any point x and at any time t can be determined to any degree of accuracy.

19-3 Eigenphysics

A differential equation of the form

$$Hu = Eu \qquad (19.22)$$

where H is an operator, u is a function and E is a constant, is called an eigenvalue equation. Thus the basic form of an eigenvalue equation is such that operating on a function u with an operator H yields a product of a constant E and the same function u. In general the constant will not be unique. In some cases a continuous range (E) of constants will satisfy the equation and in other cases a set of discrete constants

$$E_1, E_2, \ldots, E_n$$

will be the only set which will be consistent with the problem stated by the eigenvalue equation. Such a set, either continuous or discrete, constitutes *a set of eigenvalues of the problem. The corresponding set of functions u, which will be the solutions of the eigenvalue equation, are called eigenfunctions.*

In the last section we had examples of eigenvalue equations. One was the differential equation

$$c^2 \frac{d^2}{dx^2} X = -\lambda X$$

We have seen that in the case of a fixed string the eigenvalues form a discrete set, given by Eq. (19.15), and the corresponding eigenfunctions are given by Eq. (19.17).

19-4 The First Order Time Independent Perturbation Theory

The eigenvalue equation cited as an example in the previous section applies to a string of constant density. As we have seen in Section 19-2, this equation could be solved in a straightforward way. The situation changes radically when the density of the string is not constant. For this and similar cases new methods of solutions will have to be derived. Of these, the methods of perturbation theory are the most important ones. We will limit ourselves to the simplest part of this theory.

Consider an eigenvalue equation

$$HX = \lambda X \qquad (19.23)$$

where the operator H can be written in the form

$$H = H^0 + \epsilon H'$$

and where ϵ is a very small number. In this case we say that the operator consists of two parts: the unperturbed (H^0) and the perturbing part $(\epsilon H')$. To solve the eigenvalue equation we assume that both the eigenvalues and the eigenfunctions can be written in the same form as the operator, viz.

$$\lambda = \lambda^0 + \epsilon\lambda'$$

and
$$X = X^0 + \epsilon X'$$

In this case we speak of the unperturbed eigenvalues (λ^0) and eigenfunctions (X^0) and the perturbing parts of the eigenvalues $(\epsilon\lambda')$ and the perturbing eigenfunctions $(\epsilon X')$. Substitution of H, λ and X into the eigenvalue equation yields

$$(H^0 + \epsilon H')(X^0 + \epsilon X') = (\lambda^0 + \epsilon\lambda')(X^0 + \epsilon X') \qquad (19.24)$$

Expanding this expression we obtain

$$H^0X^0 + \epsilon H^0X' + \epsilon H'X^0 + \epsilon^2 H'X' = \lambda^0X^0 + \epsilon\lambda^0X' + \epsilon\lambda'X^0 + \epsilon^2\lambda'X'$$

If ϵ is very small number then ϵ^2 can be neglected and, arranging terms, we are left with

$$H^0X^0 + \epsilon(H^0 - \lambda^0)X' = \lambda^0X^0 + \epsilon(\lambda' - H')X^0 \qquad (19.25)$$

Suppose that we are dealing with some physical problem for which two situations can arise. One of the situations will be simpler than the other in the sense that, in the second case, the system will be slightly disturbed by some physical factors. In the first situation the system will be unperturbed and in the second, the system will be said to be perturbed. Suppose further that the system in the unperturbed state is described by the eigenvalue equation

$$H^0X^0 = \lambda^0X^0 \qquad (19.26)$$

which we were able to solve, thus obtaining the set of unperturbed eigenvalues $(\lambda_n{}^0)$ and the corresponding set of unperturbed eigenfunctions $(X_n{}^0)$. We want to determine the behavior of the perturbed system. The form of the perturbation will have to be given to us or obtained by an appropriate analysis of the problem. This form will be contained in the perturbing part of the operator

$$H = H^0 + \epsilon H'$$

Let us now return to Eq. (19.25). Because the unperturbed eigenvalue equation, Eq. (19.26), is satisfied, Eq. (19.25) takes the form

$$(H^0 - \lambda^0)X' = (\lambda' - H')X^0 \qquad (19.27)$$

Consider the k-th eigenvalue of the set of eigenvalues and the corresponding k-th eigenfunction of the set of eigenfunctions. For these the last equation becomes

$$(H^0 - \lambda_k{}^0)X_k{}' = (\lambda_k{}' - H')X_k{}^0 \qquad (19.28)$$

The set of unperturbed eigenfunctions $(X_n{}^0)$ has special properties. One of them is that this set is *complete*. This means that an arbitrary function can be expressed as a linear combination of the members of the set $(X_n{}^0)$. For this arbitrary function choose X_k', the k-th member of the perturbing part of the eigenfunctions. Thus

$$X_k' = \sum_n a_n X_n{}^0 \tag{19.29}$$

where (a_n) is a set of constant coefficients. Operating on both sides of the last relation with H^0 yields

$$H^0 X_k' = \sum_n a_n H^0 X_n{}^0$$

or

$$H^0 X_k' = \sum_n a_n \lambda_n{}^0 X_n{}^0$$

Eq. (19.28) then becomes

$$\sum_n a_n (\lambda_n{}^0 - \lambda_k{}^0) X_n{}^0 = (\lambda_k' - H') X_k{}^0 \tag{19.30}$$

Multiplying both sides by the complex conjugate of $X_k{}^0$, which will be denoted by $\overline{X_k{}^0}$, and integrating between 0 and ℓ we obtain

$$\int_0^\ell \overline{X_k{}^0}(\lambda_k' - H') X_k{}^0 \, dx = \sum_n a_n \int_0^\ell \overline{X_k{}^0}(\lambda_n{}^0 - \lambda_k{}^0) X_n{}^0 \, dx \tag{19.31}$$

For the right-hand side of this equation we can write

$$\sum_n a_n \int_0^\ell \overline{X_k{}^0}(\lambda_n{}^0 - \lambda_k{}^0) X_n{}^0 \, dx = \sum_n a_n (\lambda_n{}^0 - \lambda_k{}^0) \int_0^\ell \overline{X_k{}^0} X_n{}^0 \, dx$$

We now invoke another property of the set of functions $(X_n{}^0)$, namely its *orthogonality*. By this property the integral of the product $\overline{X_k{}^0} X_n{}^0$ over the range for which the set is defined, is zero, whenever $k \neq n$, and is equal to one when $k = n$. By virtue of this property, therefore, the last integral is zero for $k \neq n$; when $k = n$, it is also zero because then $\lambda_n{}^0 - \lambda_k{}^0 = 0$. Thus Eq. (19.31) becomes

$$\int_0^\ell X_k{}^0 (\lambda_k' - H') X_k{}^0 \, dx = 0$$

or

$$\int_0^\ell \overline{X_k{}^0} \lambda_k' X_k{}^0 \, dx = \int_0^\ell \overline{X_k{}^0} H' X_k{}^0 \, dx$$

which can be written as

$$\lambda_k' \int_0^\ell \overline{X_k{}^0} X_k{}^0 \, dx = \int_0^\ell \overline{X_k{}^0} H' X_k{}^0 \, dx$$

Because of the orthogonality condition,

$$\int_0^\ell \overline{X_k{}^0} X_k{}^0 \, dx = 1$$

and so

$$\lambda_k' = \int_0^\ell \overline{X_k{}^0} H' X_k{}^0 \, dx \qquad (19.32)$$

We have thus obtained an explicit expression from which the perturbing part of the eigenvalues can be evaluated.

19–5 The Perturbed String

We now return to the string considered in one of the previous sections, but now let us suppose that the density of the string is not constant but varies according to the relation

$$\rho(x) = \rho_0 + \epsilon f(x) \qquad (19.33)$$

where ϵ is a small number. As a first step we normally would have to solve the unperturbed string problem but we have already done this and obtained the unperturbed eigenvalues

$$\lambda_n{}^0 = n^2 \frac{\pi^2 c^2}{\ell^2}$$

and the corresponding set of unperturbed eigenfunctions

$$X_n{}^0 = \sqrt{\frac{2}{\ell}} \sin \frac{n\pi}{\ell} x \qquad n = 0, 1, 2, \ldots$$

This latter set $(X_n{}^0)$ constitutes a complete and orthogonal set.

The differential wave equation to be solved is

$$\frac{T}{\rho(x)} \frac{\partial^2 \xi}{\partial x^2} = \frac{\partial^2 \xi}{\partial t^2}$$

where $\rho(x)$ is given by Eq. (19.33). Thus

$$\frac{T}{\rho_0 + \epsilon f(x)} \frac{\partial^2 \xi}{\partial x^2} = \frac{\partial^2 \xi}{\partial t^2}$$

or

$$T[\rho_0 + \epsilon f(x)]^{-1} \frac{\partial^2 \xi}{\partial x^2} = \frac{\partial^2 \xi}{\partial t^2}$$

or

$$\frac{T}{\rho_0} \left[1 + \frac{\epsilon f(x)}{\rho_0}\right]^{-1} \frac{\partial^2 \xi}{\partial x^2} = \frac{\partial^2 \xi}{\partial t^2}$$

By Newton's binomial expansion

$$(1 + x)^n = 1 + nx + \cdots$$

Retaining the first two terms only we obtain

$$\frac{T}{\rho_0}\left[1 - \epsilon \frac{f(x)}{\rho_0}\right]\frac{\partial^2 \xi}{\partial x^2} = \frac{\partial^2 \xi}{\partial t^2}$$

or

$$\left[\frac{T}{\rho_0} - \epsilon \frac{Tf(x)}{\rho_0^2}\right]\frac{\partial^2 \xi}{\partial x^2} = \frac{\partial^2 \xi}{\partial t^2}$$

After the separation of variables we obtain the following perturbed eigenvalue equation

$$\left[\frac{T}{\rho_0}\frac{d^2}{dx^2} - \epsilon \frac{Tf(x)}{\rho_0^2}\frac{d^2}{dx^2}\right]X = \lambda X$$

From this we read off the perturbing part of the operator as

$$H' = - \frac{Tf(x)}{\rho_0^2}\frac{d^2}{dx^2}$$

By Eq. (19.32) the perturbing part of the eigenvalues is obtained from

$$\lambda_n' = - \frac{T}{\rho_0^2}\frac{2}{\ell}\int_0^\ell \sin \frac{n\pi}{\ell} x[f(x)]\frac{d^2}{dx^2}\sin \frac{n\pi}{\ell} x \, dx$$

$$= \frac{T}{\rho_0^2}\frac{2}{\ell}\left(\frac{n\pi}{\ell}\right)^2\int_0^\ell f(x)\sin^2 \frac{n\pi}{\ell} x \, dx$$

The perturbed eigenvalues are given by

$$\lambda_n = \lambda_n^0 + \epsilon \lambda_n'$$

or, in our case,

$$\lambda_n = \frac{n^2\pi^2 c^2}{\ell^2} + \epsilon \frac{2}{T\ell}\frac{T^2}{\rho_0^2}\frac{n^2\pi^2}{\ell^2}\int_0^\ell f(x)\sin^2 \frac{n\pi}{\ell} x \, dx$$

or

$$\lambda_n = \frac{n^2\pi^2 c^2}{\ell^2}\left\{1 + \epsilon \frac{2}{T}\frac{1}{\ell}\int_0^\ell f(x)\sin^2 \frac{n\pi}{\ell} x \, dx\right\} \qquad n = 0, 1, 2, \ldots \qquad (19.34)$$

These are then the possible wavelengths of the waves which will travel in a string, the density of which slightly varies with x.

19–6 Classical and Modern Physics

We have been considering the classical problem of a fixed string first of con-

320

stant density and then of slightly varying density. We have seen that the theory of vibrations of strings reduces to the solution of the differential equation

$$\frac{\partial^2 \xi}{\partial t^2} = a^2 \frac{\partial^2 \xi}{\partial x^2}$$

The realization of this fact dates back to the middle of the 18th century.* Solutions of this problem were attempted by d'Alembert, Euler and Bernoulli. The problem was further clarified by Lagrange and finally completed when Fourier series were introduced and subsequently rigorously treated. All this was done before the advent of the 20th century during which modern physics has been developed.

When methods of solving the string problem were presented in this chapter, a strange sounding jargon of eigenphysics and perturbation theory was used which seemed quite unnatural and perhaps unnecessary. However, the same jargon changed into an esoteric language in modern physics. The eigenvalue problem and perturbation theory are of central importance in quantum mechanics which at the present time furnishes the most accurate description of natural phenomena.

The purpose of introducing the problem of the string was to emphasize the importance of classical mechanics once more. Exactly the same mathematical methods as presented here are used in quantum mechanics. These are extended to more complicated cases such as higher order perturbation theories, time dependent perturbation theories and others, but the roots of their mathematical formulation rest in classical mechanics.

PROBLEM

Solve the equation

$$\frac{1}{c^2} \frac{\partial^2 \phi}{\partial t^2} = \frac{\partial^2 \phi}{\partial x^2}$$

subject to the conditions $\phi_{x=0} = \phi_{x=l} = 0$, and $\phi_{t=0} = \sin^3 (\pi x/l)m$, $(\partial\phi/\partial t)_{t=0} = 0$.

* H. S. Carslaw, *Introduction to the Theory of Fourier Series and Integrals*, 3rd ed., Dover Publications (1930). Read the chapter entitled "Historical Introduction."

20
WAVE MECHANICS

The modern description of nature is given by the theory of relativity and by the quantum theory. We have already discussed certain elements of the special theory of relativity, and we should perhaps also introduce the basic elements of the quantum theory.

We do not intend to present a summary of quantum mechanics, but we have a two-fold purpose in mind: first, to indicate the modern mode of description of natural phenomena, and second, to discuss the relationship between classical mechanics and quantum mechanical theory. The latter discussion will be within the frame of that part of the classical theory which we have discussed in this book. We begin by discussing the classical interpretation of mechanics. Then, after enumerating the instances where classical mechanics was successfully applied, we will discuss certain aspects of some types of motion of a single particle. In this description we will be stressing certain points which to a classical physicist appear obvious and hardly worth discussing. We mention two cases where classical physics was applied successfully to phenomena exhibited in the submicroscopic domain. We then consider the same two physical entities involved in two different physical situations, for which the explanation could not be offered in terms of classical mechanics.

After briefly mentioning the old quantum theory we will discuss the Schrodinger equation, some elementary applications of the Schrodinger equation, the statistical interpretation of the wave functions, and the Heisenberg uncertainty principle. We will show the role and the usefulness of classical mechanics in formulating the procedures in quantum mechanics, and we will finish by outlining the quantum mechanical picture of nature.

20–1   The Classical Interpretation of Mechanics

Physical quantities are described by mathematical functions. Thus a kinematical point, for instance, is a function $f(x, y, z, t)$ in the four-dimensional continuum (x, y, z, t); the most general form of a force is represented by a mathematical function $F(x, y, z, \dot{x}, \dot{y}, \dot{z}, t)$, and so are other quantities. All concepts in classical mechanics are given in terms of mathematical forms, and the interpretation of these concepts is the one used in mathematical analysis applied to points, curves and continuous functions in appropriate spaces. Relations between kinematical and dynamical concepts are stated in mathematical forms; the physical laws are usually in the form of differential equations, and their solutions give functional relationships between the various dynamical and kinematical concepts. Again, all the interpretation is nothing else but that given by the mathematical analysis.

The basic kinematical concepts are the position, velocity, acceleration, angular position, angular velocity and angular acceleration. Their values at some particular instant of time, for a particular system, have unique values. If we consider the position $x = x_0$ of a particle on the x axis, then we understand this to mean a mathematical point on the x axis. Similarly all other kinematical and dynamical variables are point-functions in their respective spaces. In classical mechanics this is the only description of these quantities. The so called physical interpretation of these quantities is identical with the mathematical interpretation.

Troubles may arise when measurements are performed because errors are always present. This does not shake up the undaunted attitude of the classical physicist, and he still assigns point values to all kinematical and dynamical quantities of the system.

In addition to the quantities mentioned above, this applies to concepts of momentum, angular momentum and energy. It is assumed that at any particular time these quantities have precise values, and that in the course of time their values change in a manner exactly dictated by physical laws. It is believed that for any particular system, conditions can be set up such that these values will change in any desired manner.

20–2 Regions of Successful Application of Classical Mechanics

The adherence to the purely mathematical interpretation of the classical phenomena was to a large measure based on the experimental verification of the laws of classical mechanics. The domains in which classical mechanics found successful applications are:

(1) the motion of a single particle (performed on a macroscopic scale) in various force fields, of which we cite as examples the central force field ($\mathbf{F} = \phi(r)\mathbf{r}$) and the harmonic force field ($\mathbf{F} = -K\mathbf{r}$),

(2) rigid body motion, and

(3) several forms of mechanics of continuous media which include wave motion, hydrostatics, and hydrodynamics.

We will review some of the results of classical mechanics for some of the systems. In this review we will stress facts which seem so obvious to us that usually we do not even mention them. And yet—as we will point out later—most of these concepts have undergone a thorough revision in quantum mechanics.

For simplicity let us discuss the motion of a single particle of mass m which has one degree of freedom and which moves in a conservative field. Its Hamiltonian is given by

$$H(q, p) = \frac{p^2}{2m} + V(q) \tag{20.1}$$

and the motion is governed by the equations

$$\frac{\partial H}{\partial q} = -\dot{p} \qquad \frac{\partial H}{\partial p} = \dot{q} \tag{20.2}$$

The positional coordinate q and momentum p related by the above Hamilton equations, are the two canonically conjugate quantities. According to the conviction of the classical physicist, at any time both of these quantities can simultaneously be determined with absolute accuracy. For a particular force field the total energy $E(=H)$ is a constant. When the force field is changed, the total energy changes, and we are assuming that this change can be performed in an arbitrary way consistent with the configuration of the system. It is assumed that the time t and the energy E that the system has at that time, can be determined with absolute accuracy.

If the particle moved in a plane q_1, q_2 and had two degrees of freedom, then, in general, its trajectory would be given by an equation of the form

$$f(q_1, q_2) = 0$$

This of course is an analytical expression for a mathematical curve along which the particle travels. In classical mechanics it is assumed that such a trajectory can in general be evaluated, and the laws of the motion will be such that the position of the particle can be given at any time with absolute accuracy.

20-4 The Simple Harmonic Oscillator*

The motion of a single harmonic oscillator is governed by the differential equation

$$\ddot{q} + 4\pi^2 \nu^2 q = 0$$

or

$$\ddot{q} + (k/m)q = 0$$

where $4\pi^2 \nu^2 = k/m$ is a relation between the frequency, the force constant and the mass of the oscillator. The solution can be written as

$$q = a \cos(\omega t + \delta)$$

* Discussed fully in Chapter 4.

The kinetic energy of the oscillator is

$$T = (1/2)m\dot{q}^2$$
$$= (1/2)m\omega^2(a^2 - q^2)$$

and the potential energy is

$$V = (1/2)kq^2$$

The total energy therefore becomes

$$E = (1/2)m\omega^2 a^2 \qquad (20.3)$$

For a simple harmonic oscillator E is constant. If external influences were acting on the oscillator this energy could be changed. Suppose that at some instant the energy is E_1 and, after the application of an external impulse, the energy changed to E_2. In this process the oscillator has absorbed the amount of energy

$$\Delta E = E_2 - E_1$$

By a suitable process this amount of energy could be extracted from the oscillator.

The amount of energy ΔE which can be absorbed by the oscillator, or which can be extracted from it, can be made arbitrarily small. As a matter of fact, one can imagine experimental arrangements which will permit the energy to be supplied in a continuous manner.

20-5 Motion of a Particle in a Central Force Field*

Let us consider a particle moving in a closed orbit in an inverse square attractive field. We know that this particle will move in an ellipse with its total energy and its total angular momentum conserved. The total energy of the particle is the same for particles moving in ellipses of the same major axes, and is independent of the eccentricity of the ellipse.

The angular momentum of the particle is constant for a particular ellipse but different for ellipses of different eccentricities. The angular momentum $\mathbf{h}_0 (= \mathbf{r} \times m\mathbf{r})$ is perpendicular to the plane of motion. The component of the angular momentum about any direction z in space is also constant.

If the particle is not a mathematical point, but a small sphere for instance, and if it spins about its axis then a spin angular momentum, $\mathbf{h}_s$, is associated with it. If the moment of inertia of the sphere about the axis of rotation is I and the angular velocity is $\boldsymbol{\omega}$, then

$$\mathbf{h}_s = I\boldsymbol{\omega}$$

* Treated in considerable detail in Chapter 5.

The total angular momentum of the particle (in the form of a sphere) is now given by

$$\mathbf{h}_t = \mathbf{h}_0 + \mathbf{h}_s$$

If the system is left alone, the total energy, and the angular momentum will remain constant. However, under the action of external influences the energy and the angular momentum may change. The amount of change will depend on the magnitude of the external impulse but classically this amount of change can be as small as we wish, and could also be brought about in a continuous manner.

If a particle of mass m moves in a *circular* orbit in a gravitational field μ/r^2 then its total energy is

$$E = -\tfrac{1}{2}\mu m/r \tag{20.4}$$

The gravitational force $\mu m/r^2$ balances the centrifugal force $m\omega^2 r$, therefore

$$\mu m/r^2 = m\omega^2 r$$

or

$$\mu m/r = m\omega^2 r^2$$

The angular momentum of the particle is

$$h_0 = mr^2\omega \tag{20.5}$$

Eliminating ω between the last two relations we obtain

$$r = \frac{h_0{}^2}{\mu m^2} \tag{20.6}$$

Now, the angular momentum can be changed by external influences in an arbitrary manner. Thus the radius of the orbit can similarly be changed to any desired value.

Substitution of r from the last expression into the relation for the total energy yields

$$E = -1/2\,\frac{\mu^2 m^3}{h_0{}^2} \tag{20.7}$$

Let us write this as

$$E_1 = -1/2\,\frac{\mu^2 m^3}{h_1{}^2}$$

If by an external impulse the angular momentum is increased to h_2 then the corresponding energy becomes

$$E_2 = -1/2\,\frac{\mu^2 m^2}{h_2{}^2}$$

20–5 Motion of a particle in a central force field

The system has thus absorbed an amount of energy

$$\Delta E = E_2 - E_1$$

or

$$\Delta E = -R_s \left[\frac{1}{h_2{}^2} - \frac{1}{h_1{}^2} \right] \qquad (20.8)$$

where

$$R_s = (1/2)\mu^2 m^3$$

By a suitable process the same amount of energy can be extracted from the system.

According to classical mechanics the change Δh_0 of the angular momentum, and the change ΔE of the total energy caused by external influences can be of arbitrary magnitudes, in particular these changes can be made as small as we wished. Mechanisms can be devised which will perform these changes in a continuous manner.

20-6 The Wave Motion

The macroscopically occurring wave motion is well understood, and can be treated by a rigorous mathematical formalism. The differential equation of an unattenuated wave travelling in the x direction is of the form

$$\frac{\partial^2 \Psi}{\partial x^2} = \frac{1}{c^2} \frac{\partial^2 \Psi}{\partial t^2} \qquad (20.9)$$

where $\Psi(x, t)$ is the vibrating quantity. The general solution of this equation is*

$$\Psi = Af(x - ct) + Bg(x + ct)$$

In a particular case one can have a plane monochromatic wave which can be represented as

$$\Psi = a_0 e^{-i(\omega t - \kappa x + \delta)}$$

or

$$\Psi = a e^{-2\pi i(\nu t - x/\lambda)} \qquad (20.10)$$

where ν is the frequency and λ is the wavelength of the wave. The phenomena which are typical for wave motion are interference, diffraction and polarization of waves. If any of these phenomena are observed, then we say that the radiation exhibiting these phenomena has a wavelike nature.

20-7 The Classical Picture of Nature

According to the classical picture, physical quantities are represented by continuous mathematical functions. In general, the values of any of these

* See Appendix C.

functions can in principle be determined at any point in space and at any instant of time with arbitrary small uncertainties. The kinematical laws of mechanical systems contain the whole past and future history of the motion of the system. When dynamical concepts are introduced, the laws involving the relation between the dynamical and kinematical concepts are usually stated in the form of differential equations. Their solutions predict the behavior of the various systems with mathematical accuracy.

The classical world is divided into discrete and continuous matter. A representative of discrete matter is a particle which we may define as a kinematical point with mass. Its kinematical and dynamical state can be described with mathematical accuracy. Such conjugate quantities as position and momentum or energy and time can be determined simultaneously with arbitrarily small uncertainty. The classical particle has a unique structure which is exhibited uniquely in all circumstances.

Space is capable of transmitting various kinds of waves which can be described mathematically with utmost precision. The nature of a wave is unique and remains so in every circumstance.

The nature of a particle and the nature of a wave are completely distinct. Nevertheless there are certain features common to both of them; for instance, they both carry momentum and energy.

20–8 Successful Applications of Classical Physics to Submicroscopic Quantities. Two Cases

Having met with experimental verification in practically all systems of the macroscopic world, the classical physicist attempted to use classical reasoning to explain submicroscopic phenomena. In several instances he was successful. We shall mention two such instances.

One of the fundamental entities of matter is the electron which classically is pictured as a small sphere of radius about 10^{-13} cm, of mass $m = 9.10 \times 10^{-28}$ gm, and of negative charge $e = 4.80 \times 10^{-10}$ electrostatic units of charge ($=1.60 \times 10^{-19}$ coulombs). The latter two magnitudes have been obtained from experiments, the results of which were explained by classical reasoning.

We should draw attention to the fact that in all the experiments from which the charge e of the electron and the ratio e/m were determined, the electron did not interact with matter.

The concept of the wave motion was successfully applied to light. A monochromatic beam of light is an electromagnetic wave of fixed wavelength and frequency, travelling in vacuum with velocity $c = 3 \times 10^{10}$ cm/sec. When two coherent* light beams are superimposed in some type of an interferometer, interference phenomena will occur. We may consider a Mach-Zehnder interferometer illustrated in Figure 20.1. A beam of light is split by a beam-splitter into two beams which after reflection from two mirrors are reunited

---

* Two beams are coherent when there is a predictable phase relationship between them.

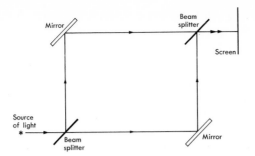

Fig. 20.1
The Mach-Zehnder interferometer.

again. Interference phenomena are observed on the screen. These exhibit themselves as a series of dark and light straight bands or circular rings. Their explanation is offered in terms of the wave theory. This and similar observations, and their theoretical explanations, lead us to the conclusion that light has the wave nature.

As in the case involving the electron, we notice that in experiments involving interference, light is not interacting with matter.*

20–9 Unsuccessful Applications of Classical Physics to Submicroscopic Quantities. The Same Two Physical Entities

We shall now consider the same two entities, viz., an electron and a monochromatic beam of light, involved in two other experiments, the explanation of which could not be found in classical physics.

In one of the experiments a beam of electrons was sent onto a Mach-Zehnder interferometer and interference fringes were observed and photographed.**

Clearly, if we agree that an interference phenomenon can be produced by waves only, then we must attribute a wave nature to the beam of electrons.

In another experiment a beam of light was sent onto a photosensitive surface, and electrons were emitted. The explanation of the dependence of the maximum kinetic energy of the emitted electrons on the frequency of the monochromatic incident light was given by Einstein. Using the results of Planck's early quantum theory, Einstein assumed that a beam of light of frequency ν in the process of interaction with electrons of the photosensitive surface, is equivalent to a stream of photons, each of energy

$$E = h\nu \tag{20.11}$$

where $h(=6.625 \times 10^{-27}$ erg sec) is Planck's constant. The photon was imagined to be localized in space in a similar way as a particle. Thus a beam of monochromatic light appears to have a dual nature, that of a wave, and that of a stream of photons.

* By interaction with matter we mean direct interaction with basic constituents of matter, and not that involving the presence of slits or a beam splitter.
** L. Marton, J. Arol Simpson, and J. A. Suddeth, *Rev. Sci. Instr.* **25**, 1099 (1954). Also in *Phys. Rev.* **90**, 490 (1953).

De Broglie extended this dualism to material particles. A material particle of mass m and velocity v has the linear momentum $p = mv$, and, according to de Broglie, there is a wavelength associated with the particle which is given by

$$\lambda = \frac{h}{p} \tag{20.12}$$

The validity of de Broglie's relation was verified in cases of many elementary particles, in particular for electrons. A beam of monoenergetic electrons of known velocity, and therefore, known linear momentum, was subjected to interference or diffraction. From the resultant pattern, the wavelength associated with the beam of electrons could be evaluated, and thus the de Broglie relation could be verified.

20–10   The Old Quantum Theory

We have already discussed the Bohr theory of the motion of the electron in an hydrogen atom.* It appears that this should have been a case of motion in a central force field for which the results are summarized in Section 20–5. However, we know that Bohr's theory met with considerable experimental success, and thus instead of assigning to the electron the energies given by Eq. (20.7), and the angular momentum given by Eq. (20.5) we should rather assign the energies given by

$$E_n = E_I/n^2 \qquad n = 1, 2, 3, \ldots$$

and the angular momenta

$$h_n = nh/2\pi \qquad n = 1, 2, 3, \ldots$$

Thus the energies and the angular momenta of the electron in the hydrogen atom are both quantized, i.e., they can take on discrete values only.

These and other theoretical developments constituted a definite break with classical mechanics. These results were, however, not quite sufficient and not completely satisfactory. This was so for several reasons. One of them was the lack of agreement with more refined experiments. Other reasons dealt with interpretation of the classical physics and of the results of the old quantum theory. The most disquieting features were the absolute accuracy predicted by the theory and never met by the experiment, and the dual nature of one and the same physical entity. A new quantum theory was thus formulated with the purpose of driving away the shortcomings of both the classical mechanics and of the old quantum theory.

Two forms of the new quantum theory which are most often applied are: the wave mechanics of Schrodinger and the matrix mechanics of Heisenberg. We shall discuss the wave mechanics and try to indicate in what way it modified the classical thinking.

* See Section 5–4.

We shall now introduce an equation which plays the central role in the wave mechanics. This is the Schrodinger equation. The reasoning which led to the development of this equation was based on the assumption that basic phenomena of nature can be represented by wave functions. It was also assumed that relations (20.11) and (20.12) are basic relations of quantum theory.

Let $\Psi = \Psi(x, y, z, t)$ represent a wave function of any form whatsoever. If it represented a plane harmonic and monochromatic wave* then it would be of the form

$$\Psi = a \cos [\omega t - \kappa(\alpha x + \beta y + \gamma z) + \delta)] \tag{20.13}$$

We will write Ψ in exactly the same form as Eq. (20.10) but will make use of the fundamental equations of quantum mechanics, viz., Eqs. (20.11) and (20.12) which we will solve for $1/\lambda$ and ν respectively. Thus, using these experimentally established relations, and the wave equations borrowed from optics, i.e., Eq. (20.10) applied to one-dimensional propagation, we write

$$\Psi = ae^{(2\pi i/h)(px - Et)} \tag{20.14}$$

Making use of Eqs. (12.27) and (12.28) we could also write the wave function as

$$\Psi = ae^{2\pi iS/h} \tag{20.15}$$

where S is Hamilton's principal function.

We can write Eq. (20.14) in the form

$$\Psi = \psi e^{-2\pi iEt/h} \tag{20.16}$$

where

$$\psi = ae^{2\pi ipx/h} \tag{20.17}$$

and where of course ψ is independent of time.

Differentiating Eq. (20.17) twice with respect to x we obtain

$$\frac{\partial^2 \psi}{\partial x^2} + \frac{4\pi^2}{h^2} p^2 \psi = 0 \tag{20.18}$$

This is the differential wave equation in terms of the momentum p. Realizing that

$$\tfrac{1}{2}p^2/m = T$$

or

$$\tfrac{1}{2}p^2m/ = E - V \tag{20.19}$$

* In general, our wave function $\psi(x, y, z, t)$ can be split by Fourier series in sums or integrals of plane harmonic waves, each of the form (20.13). We will concentrate on one component wave of a single frequency ν, wave number k, and amplitude a. Since all components are of the same form and all, in the Fourier sum, make up the actual wave, therefore, our treatment will really be quite general.

where E, T, and V are respectively the total, the kinetic, and the potential energies, we obtain

$$\frac{\partial^2 \psi}{\partial x^2} + \frac{8\pi^2 m}{h^2}(E - V)\psi = 0 \tag{20.20}$$

We are postulating that if $V = V(x)$, this latter equation is still valid.

If we have a plane wave travelling in some general direction, and if $V = V(x, y, z)$, then the last equation takes the form

$$\nabla^2 \psi + \frac{8\pi^2 m}{h^2}[E - V(x, y, z)]\psi = 0 \tag{20.21}$$

This is the time-independent Schrodinger equation; it is also called the *amplitude equation.*

From Eq. (20.14) we get

$$\frac{\partial \Psi}{\partial t} = \frac{-2\pi i E}{h}\Psi \tag{20.22}$$

which can be written as

$$E\Psi = -\frac{h}{2\pi i}\frac{\partial}{\partial t}\Psi \tag{20.23}$$

Now, let us multiply the amplitude equation (20.21) by $\exp(-2\pi i Et/h)$ and make use of Eqs. (20.16) and (20.23). Then

$$-\frac{h^2}{8\pi^2 m}\nabla^2\Psi + V(x, y, z)\Psi = (ih/2\pi)\frac{\partial \Psi}{\partial t} \tag{20.24}$$

This is the time dependent Schrodinger equation.

We notice that this last equation can be obtained by writing the total energy of the particle in the form

$$E = p^2/2m + V \tag{20.25}$$

and identifying the various quantities appearing in this last relation with operators according to the following scheme:

$$E \leftrightarrow -\frac{h}{2\pi i}\frac{\partial}{\partial t} \tag{20.26}$$

$$p \leftrightarrow \frac{hi}{2\pi}\nabla \tag{20.27}$$

The Cartesian coordinates x, y, z appearing in V remain as they were but change their character into operators. Substitution in Eq. (20.25) yields the operator equation

$$-\frac{h}{2\pi i}\frac{\partial}{\partial t} = \frac{-h^2}{8\pi^2 m}\nabla^2 + V(x, y, z) \tag{20.28}$$

If both sides operate on the wave function $\Psi(x, y, z, t)$ then we obtain the time dependent Schrodinger equation (20.24). If we start with time dependent equation, then the amplitude equation is obtained by assuming that the solution of Eq. (20.24) can be written as

$$\Psi = \psi(x,\, y,\, z)f(t) \tag{20.29}$$

(This cannot always be done.) Substitution of this in Eq. (20.24) yields two equations: the ψ equation involving the space coordinates only, i.e., the amplitude equation, and the second equation which will involve time only. The solution of the latter can be given by $\exp(-2\pi i E t/h)$.*

20-12 *Interpretation and Properties of the Wave Function*

The physical interpretation of the wave functions which are the solutions of Schrodinger equation, is dictated by the interpretation of the wave equation used in optics. There the equation of propagation of a monochromatic beam of light can be written as a harmonic wave of the form

$$\xi = a \cos 2\pi k(x - ct)$$

or
$$\xi = ae^{2\pi i k(x-ct)} \tag{20.30}$$

where $k = 1/\lambda$ and c is the speed of the wave. The frequencies associated with visible light are of the order of 10^{15} cycles/sec, and we can never hope to perform experiments which will exhibit the actual value of ξ at some time t and at some particular point in space. We realize that the only observable quantities are a^2 which is proportional to the intensity of light, and the wave number k; the latter would be obtained when λ, the wavelength, is determined from interference or diffraction experiments. Thus, we cannot concern ourselves with the physical meaning of ξ. Since ξ has no equivalent in physical phenomena it can be complex, as given by the second of Eqs. (20.30). Similarly the amplitude a can be complex since in actual phenomena we measure the quantity a^2.

In optics a^2 is proportional to the light intensity; therefore, in wave mechanics we make a^2 proportional to the number of photons per unit volume.

We notice that
$$|\xi|^2 = |\xi\xi^*| \tag{20.31}$$

and
$$|\xi\xi^*| = |aa^*| \tag{20.32}$$

where ξ^* is the complex conjugate of ξ. Therefore

$$|\xi|^2 = |a|^2 \tag{20.33}$$

* As stated above, the time dependent Schrodinger equation (20.24) is a general equation because any wave function can be split up into components of the form

$$\int_{-\infty}^{+\infty} a(\nu)\psi(x,\, y,\, z)e^{-2\pi i E t/h}\, d\nu$$

and all these will satisfy the Schrodinger equation.

Using this relation and the above interpretation we can say that $|\xi|^2\,d\tau$ *is proportional to the probability of finding a particular photon in the element of volume $d\tau$.*

The very same interpretation will be used in the case of the wave functions Ψ which are the solutions of Schrodinger's equation. This interpretation will be included in the following summary of the results obtained thus far which also contain certain additional obvious but basic results.

(i) *The description of a particle is given by the function of the form*

$$\Psi = \Psi(x, y, z, t)$$

(ii) *The quantity $|\Psi\Psi^*|\,d\tau$ is to be interpreted as the probability of finding a particle in the element of volume $d\tau$ at some instant of time t.*

(iii) Ψ *satisfies the time-dependent Schrodinger equation in which $V(x, y, z)$ is the potential energy appropriate to the problem.*

(iv) *The time solutions in many cases can be separated out. Indeed, Ψ can be written as*

$$\Psi = \psi(x, y, z)e^{-2\pi iEt/h}$$

(v) $\psi = \psi(x, y, z)$ *satisfies the amplitude equation and its solution is usually the main task in a particular situation.*

(vi) $|\psi\psi^*| = |\Psi\Psi^*|$.

(vii) *The function Ψ must be single valued, continuous and finite.*

(viii) *The solutions of the wave equation must satisfy the boundary conditions appropriate to the problem.* *

20–13   The Eigenvalue Problem in Quantum Mechanics

In the previous chapter we considered the eigenvalue problem in the classical case of a vibrating string. The same formalism is used in wave mechanics.

Equation (20.21) can be written as

$$\left[-\frac{h^2}{8\pi^2 m}\,\nabla^2 + V(x, y, z)\right]\psi = E\psi \qquad (20.34)$$

which we see has the form $\qquad \alpha\psi = E\psi \qquad (20.35)$

which in turn is an *eigenvalue equation. Operating on ψ with the operator α yields the same function ψ multiplied by a constant.* Here, of course, we are assuming that in a given physical situation the total energy E of the particle is constant.

In general, therefore, a quantum mechanical problem is an eigenvalue problem. In solving such a problem we have to determine a set of eigenvalues

$$E_1, E_2, \ldots, E_n \qquad (20.36)$$

* The type of boundary conditions depends on the particular problem. The second example of Section 20–14 will clarify this statement.

(which sometimes may form a continuous set) and a set of eigenfunctions

$$\psi_1, \psi_2, \ldots, \psi_n \qquad (20.37)$$

To illustrate the procedure we will solve the Schrodinger equation in two simple cases.

20–14   Examples. A Free Particle and a Particle in a One-dimensional Box

(a) The Free Particle

In the case of a free particle moving under no forces the Schrodinger equation is particularly simple because the potential is constant and we may take its value to be zero. The equation therefore becomes

$$-\frac{h^2}{8\pi^2 m} \nabla^2 \psi = E\psi \qquad (20.38)$$

We assume that its solution can be written as

$$\psi = X(x)Y(y)Z(z) \qquad (20.39)$$

Substitution in (20.38) yields

$$\frac{1}{X}\frac{d^2X}{dx^2} + \frac{1}{Y}\frac{d^2Y}{dy^2} + \frac{1}{Z}\frac{d^2Z}{dz^2} = \frac{-8\pi^2 mE}{h^2} \qquad (20.40)$$

The right-hand side is a constant and the left-hand side is a sum of three terms each involving one independent variable only. In such a situation every term on the left-hand side must separately be equal to a constant. Denoting the three constants by

$$\frac{-8\pi^2 mE_x}{h^2} \qquad \frac{-8\pi^2 mE_y}{h^2} \qquad \frac{-8\pi^2 mE_z}{h^2}$$

we get

$$\frac{d^2X}{dx^2} + \frac{8\pi^2 m}{h^2} E_x X = 0$$

$$\frac{d^2Y}{dy^2} + \frac{8\pi^2 m}{h^2} E_y Y = 0 \qquad (20.41)$$

$$\frac{d^2Z}{dz^2} + \frac{8\pi^2 m}{h^2} E_z Z = 0$$

where

$$E = E_x + E_y + E_z$$

The solutions are then given by

$$X = N_x \sin\left[(2\pi/h)\sqrt{2mE_x}\, x + e_x\right]$$

$$Y = N_y \sin\left[(2\pi/h)\sqrt{2mE_y}\, y + e_y\right] \qquad (20.42)$$

$$Z = N_z \sin\left[(2\pi/h)\sqrt{2mE_z}\, z + e_z\right]$$

Substitution of these in Eq. (20.39) gives a solution of the equation.

We notice that the solutions are meaningful for all the positive values of E_x, E_y, E_z. We say therefore that *in the case of a free particle the eigenvalues are continuous and consist of all positive numbers.*

(b) Particle in a One-dimensional Box*

Let us consider a particle m capable of moving along the x axis between two infinite walls. The two infinite vertical lines shown in Figure 20.2 mean that the two barriers at 0 and ℓ are impenetrable.

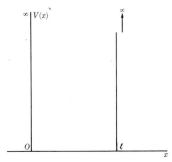

Fig. 20.2
One-dimensional
box with infinite
potential wall.

We will treat this situation as a quantum mechanical problem and will therefore solve the appropriate Schrodinger equation. We will not fail to notice the great similarity between this analytical treatment and that in the classical case considered in the previous chapter.

The one-dimensional Schrodinger amplitude equation is

$$\frac{d^2\psi}{dx^2} + \frac{8\pi^2 m}{h^2}[E - V(x)]\psi = 0$$

Inside the box the potential energy is constant and we will take $V(x) = 0$. The equation then becomes

$$\frac{d^2\psi}{dx^2} + \frac{8\pi^2 m}{h^2} E\psi = 0$$

We recognize it immediately as an eigenvalue equation. Its solution, of course, is

$$\psi = A\cos\beta x + B\sin\beta x$$

where

$$\beta = (2\pi/h)\sqrt{2mE}$$

We will now apply the boundary conditions. Outside the box the probability of finding the particle is zero, therefore, $\psi = 0$ there. Because of the continuity of ψ, $\psi_{x=0} = 0$, and so $A = 0$. Thus

$$\psi = B\sin\beta x$$

* This is a special case of a particle in a three-dimensional box, which in turn is a starting and useful model for actual situations in solid state physics.

Similarly at $x = \ell$ the amplitude is zero, i.e.

$$B \sin \beta \ell = 0$$

and we must put

$$\beta \ell = n\pi$$

or

$$\beta = \frac{n\pi}{\ell}$$

Substituting in $\beta \ell = n\pi$ the value of β and solving for E we get

$$E = \frac{h^2}{8m\ell^2} n^2 \qquad n = 1, 2, \ldots$$

These are the energy eigenvalues of the problem. The integer n, designating the various eigenvalues, is called the *quantum number*. The values of the allowed energies that the particle may possess are shown in Figure 20.3.

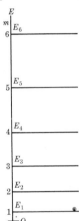

Fig. 20.3
Energy levels of a
particle in a one-
dimensional box.

The corresponding solutions are

$$\psi_n = B \sin \frac{n\pi x}{\ell}$$

These are the eigenfunctions of the problem and they represent a standing wave pattern.

The probability of finding the particle in a certain element dx, say between x and $x + dx$, is proportional to $|\psi\psi^*| \, dx$. In our case

$$|\psi\psi^*| \, dx = B^2 \sin^2 (n\pi/\ell)x \, dx$$

The probability of finding the particles anywhere in the box is†

$$\int_{-\infty}^{+\infty} |\psi\psi^*| \, dx = \int_0^\ell B^2 \sin^2 (n\pi/\ell)x \, dx$$

$$= (1/2)B^2 \ell$$

† The limits of integration can be replaced by infinities because the probability of finding the particle outside the box is zero.

Now, the probability of finding the particle anywhere in the box is unity, i.e.

$$|\psi\psi^*|\, dx = 1$$

or

$$(1/2)B^2\ell = 1$$

from which

$$B = \sqrt{\frac{2}{\ell}}$$

Substitution in the eigenfunctions gives

$$\psi_n = \sqrt{\frac{2}{\ell}}\sin\,(n\pi/\ell)x$$

These are called the *normalized eigenfunctions* of the problem.

Using the normalized eigenfunctions we get

$$\psi\psi^* = \frac{2}{\ell}\sin^2\frac{n\pi x}{\ell}$$

This is plotted for $n = 1$ in Figure 20.4. When the particle is in this state (given by $n = 1$), the probability of finding it between x_0 and $x_0 + \Delta x$ is given by the area of the shaded strip shown in Figure 20.4.

Fig. 20.4

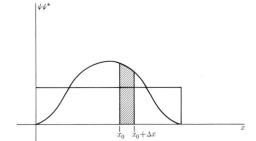

The classical probability represents the smooth average of the wave-mechanical picture and is shown by the rectangle in Figure 20.4.

20–15 *Photons and Matter Waves*

Consider first the case of photons and light waves. Take a monochromatic beam of light moving in an isotropic medium; the medium need not be homogeneous.† As we have seen, there are two ways of looking at this problem. We can look at the light as a beam of photons which all have the same energy $h\nu$. In addition we can also look at the light beam as a wave. In the

---

† A medium is isotropic if its properties at any point do not depend on the direction along which they are being investigated. A homogeneous medium has the same properties at every point.

latter case we will write it in the form

$$\xi = a \cos 2\pi \left[\frac{1}{\lambda} (\alpha x + \beta y + \gamma z) - \nu t \right] \tag{20.43}$$

or

$$\xi = a \cos 2\pi \phi \tag{20.44}$$

where

$$2\pi \phi = 2\pi \left[\frac{1}{\lambda} (\alpha x + \beta y + \gamma z) - \nu t \right] \tag{20.45}$$

is the phase of the wave. As we know, we can also write

$$\xi = a e^{i\phi} \tag{20.46}$$

α, β, γ are the direction cosines of the normal to the plane wavefront.

From Eq. (20.45) we get

$$\frac{\partial \phi}{\partial x} = \frac{\alpha}{\lambda} \qquad \frac{\partial \phi}{\partial y} = \frac{\beta}{\lambda} \qquad \frac{\partial \phi}{\partial z} = \frac{\gamma}{\lambda} \qquad \frac{\partial \phi}{\partial t} = -\nu \tag{20.47}$$

Consider now a beam of material particles all having the same energy. Such a beam can be described by Hamilton's principal function S. From the properties of S given by Eq. (12.28) we can write

$$\frac{\partial S}{\partial x} \mathbf{i} + \frac{\partial S}{\partial y} \mathbf{j} + \frac{\partial S}{\partial z} \mathbf{k} = p_x \mathbf{i} + p_y \mathbf{j} + p_z \mathbf{k} \tag{20.48}$$

i.e.

$$\text{grad } S = \mathbf{p} \tag{20.49}$$

and also

$$\frac{\partial S}{\partial t} = -E \tag{20.50}$$

It follows that $\mathbf{p}$ is perpendicular to the surfaces of constant S.

Let us consider an instant t. At this time two neighboring level surfaces of S pass through two neighboring points A and B (Fig. 20.5). Let the two

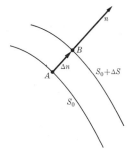

Fig. 20.5

surfaces be denoted by S_0 and $S_0 + \Delta S$. Then

$$\Delta S = S_0 - (S_0 + p\,\Delta n)$$

where $\Delta n = AB$. Thus

$$\Delta S = -p\,\Delta n \tag{20.51}$$

Now consider a later instant of time $t + \Delta t$ and choose Δt in such a way that S takes the value S_0 at B. Then

$$\Delta S = \left(\frac{\Delta S}{\Delta t}\right)\Delta t$$

or

$$\Delta S = -E\,\Delta t \tag{20.52}$$

Comparing Eq. (20.51) with Eq. (20.52) we obtain

$$\frac{\Delta n}{\Delta t} = \frac{E}{p} \tag{20.53}$$

The expression $\Delta n/\Delta t$ gives the velocity u of the S surface. Therefore

$$u = \frac{E}{p} \tag{20.54}$$

Invoking the analogous situation in the case of light we can say that the surfaces S represent the motion of the particles. So far, however, the function S does not exhibit any periodicity. In order for this to be so, S has to be involved in a function similar to that given by Eq. (20.46). Such a function would have to be of the form of Eq. (20.15) viz.

$$\Psi = ae^{\frac{2\pi iS}{h}} \tag{20.55}$$

We notice that h has to be of the dimension of the action in order to render S/h dimensionless.

Using (20.47) we can write

$$\frac{\partial \phi}{\partial x}\mathbf{i} + \frac{\partial \phi}{\partial y}\mathbf{j} + \frac{\partial \phi}{\partial z}\mathbf{k} = k_x\mathbf{i} + k_y\mathbf{j} + k_z\mathbf{k} \tag{20.56}$$

where

$$(k_x,\ k_y,\ k_z) \equiv \left(\frac{\alpha}{\lambda},\ \frac{\beta}{\lambda},\ \frac{\gamma}{\lambda}\right) \tag{20.57}$$

We denote

$$(k_x,\ k_y,\ k_z) = \mathbf{k} \tag{20.58}$$

and recognize it as the wave vector. Thus

$$\operatorname{grad} \phi = \mathbf{k} \tag{20.59}$$

Relations (20.47) also contain

$$\frac{\partial \phi}{\partial t} = -\nu \tag{20.60}$$

Now, instead of Eqs. (20.49) and (20.50) we can write

$$\text{grad } (S/h) = \mathbf{p}/h \tag{20.61}$$

and

$$\frac{\partial (S/h)}{\partial t} = -\frac{E}{h} \tag{20.62}$$

Comparing the last four equations we become more confident about the validity of the form of the function given by Eq. (20.55). The fact that Eq. (20.60) can be made to represent essentially the same thing as Eq. (20.62) is obvious when we realize that the right-hand sides of these two relations are equal, as follows from Planck's relation $E = h\nu$.

The right-hand sides of Eqs. (20.59) and (20.61) are equal because of the de Broglie's relation Eq. (20.12). This relation, however, can also be inferred from the theory of relativity. When considering the relativistic mechanics we have seen that the four-dimensional momentum can be written as*

$$\mathcal{P} \equiv (\mathbf{p}, -E/ic) \tag{20.63}$$

In order to obtain de Broglie's relation we invoke the formal equivalence of space and time dimensions, as suggested by the theory of relativity. Then Planck's relation $E = h\nu$ connecting the energy with the frequency suggests that, in a similar way, we can connect the space component of $\mathcal{P}$ with λ. We write

$$\mathbf{p} = h\mathbf{k} \tag{20.64}$$

In $E = h\nu$, ν is the frequency, i.e., the number of vibrations per second. In $\mathbf{p} = h\mathbf{k}$, k is the number of wavelengths contained in one centimeter. Thus $p = h/\lambda$, which is the de Broglie relation.

20–16 Statistical Interpretation of the Wave Functions**

The previous discussion of the wave mechanical description of natural phenomena will now be presented in a slightly more formal way. To focus our ideas, we will consider a single particle. In classical mechanics its dynamical state is given when its position $\mathbf{q}(x, y, z)$ and its momentum $\mathbf{p}(p_x, p_y, p_z)$ are specified precisely. In wave mechanics, as we have seen, the law of motion

---

* This is Eq. (18.56).
** This and the next three sections follow, in parts, the treatment given in A. Messiah, *Quantum Mechanics*, (Chapter IV, Vol. 1.) North-Holland Publishing Co. Amsterdam (1961).

of the single particle is given in terms of an appropriate Schrodinger equation, and the wave functions (ψ) describe the properties of the particle. The basic difference between classical mechanics and wave mechanics should be stressed. The solutions of a classical differential equation of motion are of the form

$$\mathbf{q} = \mathbf{q}(t)$$

i.e., they give the position coordinate (and momentum coordinates) directly. In wave mechanics, the solutions of the Schrodinger equation yield the wave functions ψ only, and they are functions of position coordinates. Thus for a particular time we obtain the function

$$\psi = \psi(\mathbf{q})$$

(Here we are speaking about an eigenfunction corresponding to some particular eigenvalue.) *This function extends over the whole space in which we are interested* (for instance, a box of given dimensions). Now, from $\psi = \psi(\mathbf{q})$ we want to obtain information about dynamical quantities of interest, in particular the position and the momentum. *All we can do*, however, *is to define the probability of finding the particle in a given volume element when a measurement of position is carried out.* If $P(\mathbf{q}) \, d\mathbf{q}$ denotes the probability of finding the particle in the volume element $\mathbf{q}$ to $\mathbf{q} + d\mathbf{q}$,* then the probability of finding the particle in the volume τ is given by

$$P(\tau) = \iiint_{\tau} P(\mathbf{q}) \, d\mathbf{q} \tag{20.65}$$

Now, consider the wave aspect of the particle. If we associate the plane wave

$$e^{2\pi i \mathbf{k} \cdot \mathbf{q}} \qquad (k = 1/\lambda)$$

with the particle, then, according to de Broglie, it also represents a particle of momentum $\mathbf{p} = h\mathbf{k}$. However, $\psi(\mathbf{q})$, treated as a wave function does not, in general, represent a single wave but a superposition of plane waves of various wave vectors $\mathbf{k}$. *All that we can do is to define the probability of obtaining a particular momentum when an actual measurement is carried out.* We introduce the momentum space (referred to the momentum axes p_x, p_y, p_z), and denote the probability of finding the momentum in the momentum interval $\mathbf{p}$ to $\mathbf{p} + d\mathbf{p}$ by $\mathscr{P}(\mathbf{p}) \, d\mathbf{p}$. The probability of finding the momentum in a finite region D of the momentum space is given by

$$\mathscr{P}(D) = \iiint_{D} \mathscr{P}(\mathbf{p}) \, d\mathbf{p} \tag{20.66}$$

* The volume element $\mathbf{q}$ to $\mathbf{q} + d\mathbf{q}$ signifies an element of volume $dx \, dy \, dz$, for which the position coordinates of one of its corners are x, y, z.

Both probability distributions $P(\mathbf{q})$ and $\mathcal{P}(\mathbf{p})$ satisfy the conditions

$$\iiint P(\mathbf{q})\, d\mathbf{q} = 1$$

and $\hspace{6cm}$ (20.67)

$$\iiint \mathcal{P}(\mathbf{p})\, d\mathbf{p} = 1$$

In the Schrodinger formalism the wave function $\psi(\mathbf{q})$ contains all the available information about the particle. Therefore, *both probability distributions,* $P(\mathbf{q})$ *and* $\mathcal{P}(\mathbf{q})$, *should be defined in terms of* $\psi(\mathbf{q})$. For $P(\mathbf{q})$, as we have already seen, the analogies from optics have led us to the definition

$$P(\mathbf{q}) = \psi^*(\mathbf{q})\psi(\mathbf{q})$$

or $\hspace{6cm}$ (20.68)

$$P(\mathbf{q}) = |\psi(\mathbf{q})|^2$$

Similarly, there is a formal definition of the probability distribution $\mathcal{P}(\mathbf{p})$.*

20–17 The Mean Value of the Position Coordinate and of the Momentum

We now inquire into the problem of determining *the mean value of any function* $f(\mathbf{q})$ *of the position coordinate* $\mathbf{q}$ *of our particle.* We are assuming that we know the probability distribution $P(\mathbf{q})$. The function $f(\mathbf{q})$ is any property of the particle depending on the position of the particle. Using the statistical procedure, we obtain for the average $\langle f(\mathbf{q})\rangle$ of $f(\mathbf{q})$ the following expression

$$\langle f(\mathbf{q})\rangle = \iiint P(\mathbf{q})f(\mathbf{q})\, d\mathbf{q} \hspace{3cm} (20.69)$$

and using the expression for $P(\mathbf{q})$, we have

$$\langle f(\mathbf{q})\rangle = \iiint \psi^*(\mathbf{q})f(\mathbf{q})\psi(\mathbf{q})\, d\mathbf{q} \hspace{2.5cm} (20.70)$$

In particular, the average value of the x coordinate of the particle is given by

$$\langle x\rangle = \iiint \psi^*(\mathbf{q})x\psi(\mathbf{q})\, d\mathbf{q} \hspace{3cm} (20.71)$$

* One first evaluates the Fourier transform $\phi(\mathbf{p})$ of the wave function $\psi(\mathbf{q})$ from

$$\phi(\mathbf{p}) = \frac{1}{h^{3/2}} \iiint \psi(\mathbf{q})e^{-2\pi i \mathbf{p}\cdot\mathbf{q}/h}\, d\mathbf{q}$$

and then defines the probability distribution $\mathcal{P}(\mathbf{p})$ by

$$\mathcal{P}(\mathbf{p}) = \phi^*(\mathbf{p})\phi(\mathbf{p})$$

or

$$\mathcal{P}(\mathbf{p}) = |\phi|(\mathbf{p})|^2$$

Similarly, the average value of any function $g(\mathbf{p})$ of the momentum is given by

$$\langle g(\mathbf{p}) \rangle = \iiint \mathcal{P}(\mathbf{p}) g(\mathbf{p}) \, d\mathbf{p} \qquad (20.72)$$

or, inserting the value of $\mathcal{P}(\mathbf{p})$, defined previously, we obtain

$$\langle g(\mathbf{p}) \rangle = \iiint \phi^*(\mathbf{p}) g(\mathbf{p}) \phi(\mathbf{p}) \, d\mathbf{p} \qquad (20.73)$$

For example, the most probable value of the x component of the momentum is given by

$$\langle p_x \rangle = \iiint \phi^*(\mathbf{p}) p_x \phi(\mathbf{p}) \, d\mathbf{p} \qquad (20.74)$$

20-18 *Heisenberg's Uncertainty Principle*

Every experimentalist knows that he can never determine a value of any physical quantity with absolute accuracy. If the errors attached to the results are to be small then he has to perform many measurements. Some thought about the process of measurement reveals the obvious fact that *the very act of measurement disturbs the system*, and the particular parameter of the system which we want to measure is not the parameter of the system in its closed form but, instead, is a parameter of a disturbed system. Classical physicists believed that the disturbance introduced by the act of measurement can eventually be eliminated from every experiment. A modern physicist does not, at present, share his belief.

As has already been stated, in wave mechanics the laws of motion of a particular system are stated by an appropriate Schrodinger equation, and its solutions, in the form of some wave functions $\psi(\mathbf{q})$, contain all the information about the system. The probability distribution $P(\mathbf{q})$ for the space coordinates, and the probability distribution $\mathcal{P}(\mathbf{p})$ for the momentum coordinates, are both defined in terms of the same wave function $\psi(\mathbf{q})$; these two are therefore not independent of each other. *That there is a correlation between the two probability distributions is characteristic of the quantum theory. This correlation is expressed quantitatively in terms of Heisenberg's uncertainty relations.*[*]

[*] One can arrive at Heisenberg's relation from classical results combined with the de Broglie relation. Suppose we consider the function

$$\psi(\mathbf{q}) = \left(\frac{2}{\pi a^2} \right)^{3/4} e^{-r^2/a^2}$$

or

$$\psi(\mathbf{q}) = N e^{-r^2/a^2} \qquad (r = |q|)$$

This is a type of a wave for which the probability distribution $|\psi(\mathbf{q})|^2$ is Gaussian and is centered at $r = 0$. The condition $\iiint P(\mathbf{q}) d\mathbf{q} = 1$ (stated in Section 20–16) is satisfied for this wave function. The Fourier transform of $\psi(\mathbf{q})$ is

$$\phi(\mathbf{k}) = N \iiint d\mathbf{q} \, e^{-r^2/a^2} e^{-i\mathbf{k} \cdot \mathbf{q}}$$

Mathematically, *Heisenberg's relation expresses the fact that if the wave function* $\psi(\mathbf{q})$ *has a spatial extension* $\Delta\mathbf{q}$, *and the Fourier transform* $\phi(\mathbf{p})$ *extends over the region* $\Delta\mathbf{p}$ *in the momentum space then the product* $\Delta\mathbf{q} \cdot \Delta\mathbf{p}$ *is always greater or at best equal to* $\hbar$ ($= h/2\pi$); *thus*

$$\Delta\mathbf{q} \cdot \Delta\mathbf{p} \geq \hbar$$

Heisenberg's principle has enormous consequences in the interpretation of natural phenomena, and, of course, constitutes a complete break with the classical outlook. To an experimenter it means that if he sets himself a goal of simultaneous determination of the position coordinate x and the linear momentum p_x of a particle, then *there will be uncertainties* Δx *and* Δp_x *inherent in his measurements such that* $\Delta x\, \Delta p_x \geq \hbar$. If he wished to diminish one uncertainty then he can do it at the expense of the other, i.e., he can determine one quantity with greater accuracy and lose some information of the other.

The principle furnishes explanations of some seemingly unexplainable results. As a striking example we shall cite the explanation of the formation of the interference fringes obtained by superposition of two beams of light emitted from two separate lasers.** The diagrammatic representation of the experimental arrangement is shown in Figure 20.6. A fringe pattern is observed on the screen. The phenomenon cannot be explained on classical

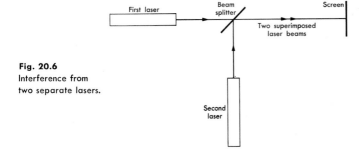

Fig. 20.6
Interference from
two separate lasers.

---

which is evaluated here in terms of the wave number $\mathbf{k}$. This Fourier transform takes the form

$$\phi(\mathbf{k}) = (2\pi a^2)^{3/4} e^{-k^2 a^2/4}$$

We notice that the constant a which characterizes the spread of both functions, in $\psi(\mathbf{q})$ appears in the denominator of the exponent, and in $\phi(\mathbf{k})$ is shifted to the numerator of the exponent. *The narrower the distribution function* $\psi(\mathbf{q})$ *in* $\mathbf{q}$, *the wider the distribution function* $\phi(\mathbf{k})$ *in* $\mathbf{k}$. The half-width $\Delta\mathbf{q}$ of one function is roughly the inverse of the half-width $\Delta\mathbf{k}$ of the other function. Thus we can write $\Delta\mathbf{q} \cdot \Delta\mathbf{k} \approx 1$, or using de Broglie's relation $\mathbf{p} = \hbar\mathbf{k}$ ($\hbar = h/2\pi$, $h =$ Planck's constant), we obtain $\Delta\mathbf{q} \cdot \Delta\mathbf{p} \approx \hbar$. (See J. Mathews and R. L. Walker, *Mathematical Methods of Physics*, W. A. Benjamin, New York (1964), page 101.)

** L. Mandel, "Interference Effects between Independent Photons," 1964 *Annual Meeting Program*, Optical Society of America, 6–9 October, 1964, page 12.

grounds. As is known, two beams of light interfere if they are coherent, i.e., if they bear a constant phase relationship. In all the standard types of interferometers the interfering beams are coherent because they ultimately come from a single source. This is not the case described here. It is true that the light emitted by a laser source is much more monochromatic than that from conventional sources (and this fact is helpful in obtaining the interference), yet there is no phase relationship between the beams emitted from the two separate lasers. The explanation of the formation of the fringes is obtained from the fact that the wave function $\psi(\mathbf{q})$ and its Fourier transform $\phi(\mathbf{p})$ extend considerably in their respective spaces. In this particular case the momentum of the photons is determined quite precisely; therefore, the wave function $\psi(\mathbf{q})$ extends over the space connected with both interferometers, and thus we are in no position to know from which laser a particular photon comes.*

Probably the greatest importance of the Heisenberg uncertainty principle comes from the elucidation of the dualistic and apparently contradictory representation of matter as particles on one hand and as waves on the other.

20–19 *The Principle of Complementarity*

In wave mechanics, the information about a particular system is contained in the eigenvalues and in the eigenfunctions which are the solutions of an appropriate Schrodinger equation. The physical interpretation which one can give to the wave functions is statistical in nature. We have discussed this interpretation in the case of position coordinates and of momentum. Both position and momentum could only be given with a certain probability. This statistical interpretation seems to preclude an exact specification of the state of the particle (or of any other system).

It is, however, still possible to obtain as exact a specification of a system as we wish if we *perform experiments the results of which will be complementary to each other. All the results will combine and point towards a single representation of a given system.* This constitutes the essence of the *principle of complementarity.*

In view of that, the dual aspect of natural phenomena, i.e., the wave nature and the particle nature of basic entities of physics, essentially drops out of consideration. One aspect appears in one series of experiments and the other in some different ones, one making up what was lacking in the other. We see that the Heisenberg principle is at the heart of these considerations. Analyses of experiments leading to the determination of a pair of conjugate quantities, such as position and momentum, will involve both aspects, and will invariably lead to the conclusion that the Heisenberg uncertainty relations must be fulfilled.

---

* This is therefore an interference in Dirac's sense where every photon interferes with itself.

The only mental picture which most of us acquire about the natural phenomena is that obtained from the observation of the external macroscopic world, and most of it, by far, consists of motion of various systems which are governed by the theories of classical mechanics. We have seen, however, that quantum theory must be used in order to explain phenomena in the atomic world. The experimental verifications of the results of quantum theory will involve macroscopic systems and our classical mind will perform the interpretation of these results. This—at least at present—is a necessity. We have seen how in various experimental situations various aspects of nature appear, but these are all unified through the complementarity principle. We therefore see that after going through all the stages of the quantum description of nature, we are forced to return as it were to the classical world.

It should also be pointed out that, as a rule, classical mechanics is the starting point of the formulation of the wave-mechanical theory. As we have already stated several times, in wave mechanics the physical laws are stated by a Schrodinger equation. One of its forms is given by Eq. (20.34). We notice that this equation can be written in the form

$$H\psi = E\psi \qquad (20.75)$$

where H is the Hamiltonian function in which the position and momentum coordinates are replaced by operators. In cases discussed here, the momentum coordinate was replaced by the operator given by Eq. (20.27). Eq. (20.75) is actually a general and starting form of the Schrodinger equation, and the first step to obtain a concrete form of the equation is to formulate the quantum-mechanical Hamiltonian operator appropriate to the system at hand. It would be very hard, if at all possible, to construct such a Hamiltonian operator directly. We must revert to classical mechanics and construct a classical model for the system under consideration. Thus we describe the system by a set (q) of generalized coordinates. The model which we choose will have to be consistent with the special theory of relativity, and we will have to be able to construct a proper action principle for this model. We will therefore formulate a proper action I, and then subject the generalized coordinates q to small variations. The corresponding variation of the action, δI, should be a linear function of the changes δq of the generalized coordinates. From the action principle we will be able to construct the Lagrangian, and from it the Hamiltonian. In simpler cases the generalized velocities will only enter quadratically in the Lagrangian; in that case the generalized momenta will also enter quadratically in the Hamiltonian. However, this quadratic form of the generalized momenta is not a restricting condition to solve the problem. Other forms of the Hamiltonian are capable of mathematical analysis also.

The ultimate result of the adoption of the classical model of the quantum mechanical system is the construction of the Hamiltonian. The next step is the formulation of an appropriate quantum mechanical Hamiltonian from the classical Hamiltonian. There are no guiding rules for this procedure, and it is a matter of ingenuity and luck when a proper quantum mechanical Hamiltonian operator has been obtained. The final test of the choice is the experimental verification of the solutions of the resulting Schrodinger equation. It may so happen that the choice of the Hamiltonian operator was wrong altogether. A new one must then be sought. Notwithstanding such possible failures, the starting point of the whole procedure is the analysis of the classical model of the system.*

20-21 Quantum Mechanical Picture of Nature

We have discussed the classical picture of nature in cases of the motion of a single point. We discussed such simple kinematical concepts as position and velocity. We spoke of the trajectory in some types of motion, such as the motion in an inverse square attractive field. We spoke about energy of the particle moving in a closed orbit, or the energy of a particle executing a simple harmonic motion. We also discussed what on classical grounds is considered a diametrically different phenomenon of nature, namely the wave motion. When dealing with phenomena on the atomic scale we found that in certain cases classical results can be applied successfully, and yield appropriate information. In most other cases, however, classical physics was completely unable to explain certain basic experimental results.

The modern description started with Planck's idea of quantization of energy emitted in the form of radiation from a black body, and with de Broglie's postulate of assigning a wavelength to a material particle. Although introduced as postulates, the two relations $E = h\nu$ and $\lambda = h/p$ were experimentally well founded and had to be accepted. Their mere acceptance has led to many successes including Bohr's theory of the hydrogen atom and Einstein's explanation of the photoelectric effect. However, a general theory was still lacking.

Schrodinger's wave mechanics constitutes one of the forms of such a theory. The law of motion of a particular system is given by an appropriate Schrodinger equation. The amplitude equation is usually an eigenvalue equation. The eigenvalues in most cases form discrete sets, and this leads to various quantizations of energy, of angular momentum, of components of angular momentum along special direction, and of quantization of spin. For instance, the motion of the electron in the hydrogen atom is governed by the Schrodinger equation of the form

$$ -\frac{h^2}{8\pi^2 m}\, \nabla^2\psi - \frac{e^2}{r}\,\psi = E\psi $$

* The discussion given above and concerning the formulation of an appropriate quantum mechanical Hamiltonian follows P. A. M. Dirac's remarks presented at the 1963 New York meeting of the American Physical Society in a paper on "Models of the Electron." (*Bull. Am. Phys. Soc.* 58 (1963). (The reference just quoted contains the title of the paper only.)

in which obviously ∇^2 should be expressed in terms of the spherical polar coordinates. One of the results of investigating the possible eigenvalues is the set of discrete energy eigenvalues which are the same as those obtained by Bohr.* The total energy of the electron is therefore quantized which is contrary to the classical case of motion of a particle in an orbit in an inverse square attractive field where conditions could be varied in such a way that the total energy of the orbiting particle could take on any value. Associated with the transition of the electron from one energy level of the hydrogen atom to another, differing in energy by ΔE, is the emission or absorption of radiation of frequency ν, evaluated from $\Delta E = h\nu$.

A particle executing simple harmonic motion obeys the Schrodinger equation of the form

$$-\frac{h^2}{8\pi^2 m}\frac{d^2\psi}{dx^2} + (1/2)kx^2\psi = E\psi$$

The energy eigenvalues of this particle can be shown to be

$$E_n = (n + 1/2)h\nu$$

and the changes from one energy level to another can, of course, occur in finite steps only.

Corresponding to every eigenvalue obtained for some particular Schrodinger equation, there is an eigenfunction having the nature of a wave function which contains all the other information about the system in question. When, in the case of a single particle, $\psi = \psi(\mathbf{q})$, where $\mathbf{q}$ is the space coordinate, then this wave function $\psi(\mathbf{q})$ and its Fourier transform $\phi(\mathbf{p})$ contain all the information about the functions of the position and the momentum of the particle. The only way we could inquire about the position and the momentum, is through the probability distribution $P(\mathbf{q})$ and $\mathcal{P}(\mathbf{p})$, both obtained from the wave function $\psi(\mathbf{q})$.

The correlation between the two probability distributions leads to Heisenberg's uncertainty principle, the essence of which is that the wave function $\psi(\mathbf{q})$ and the momentum function $\phi(\mathbf{p})$ extend in the configuration space and the momentum space respectively. The end result of the mathematical formulation in the case of position and momentum is expressed by the relation $\Delta p_x \Delta x \geq \hbar$ which means that there are inherent uncertainties if we wish to determine the position and the momentum simultaneously.

The Heisenberg principle can be applied to any pair of conjugate quantities. The quantity which is conjugate to any generalized coordinate q_i is the corresponding generalized momentum p_i. Thus, for instance, the angular position of a body and its angular momentum form a pair of conjugate quantities. Energy and time form a pair of conjugate quantities also. In this latter case, Heisenberg's uncertainty relation takes the form

$$\Delta E \, \Delta t \geq \hbar$$

* See Section 5–4.

which means that if for some system we want to measure the energy E and the time t simultaneously, then we cannot do it with greater accuracy than that dictated by the above relation.

In discussing the classical picture of nature we mentioned the trajectories of particles, which were interpreted as mathematical curves accurately known. According to the quantum mechanical view, if we attempted to determine these trajectories by actual experiments, then we could not achieve the accuracy of the mathematical curve, and this again would be a consequence of Heisenberg's principle.*

We can summarize the importance of the Heisenberg uncertainty principle by saying that on one hand it does away with mathematical accuracies which the classical physics attributed to the values of kinematical and dynamical quantities. On the other hand, however, the principle removed the dualistic aspect of nature, and together with the principle of complementarity permits a unified picture of natural phenomena.

---

* In Wilson's cloud chamber we can actually see and photograph a track of an atomic particle. However, even here, Heisenberg's relation $\Delta q \, \Delta p \geq \hbar$ holds and destroys the accuracy of the classical trajectory.

VECTOR ANALYSIS

A–1 Definition of a Vector

A vector is a quantity which has magnitude, direction, and is added to another vector in the same way as displacements are added. Thus, if a physical quantity is to be a vector it must have all these three properties.* The method of adding displacements is known: the sum of displacements r_1 and r_2 is the resultant displacement r, as shown in Figure A.1.

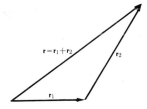

$r = r_1 + r_2$

r_2

r_1

A vector can be free or localized. A free vector is the one mostly discussed in vector analysis. Once its magnitude and direction are specified, it can be moved parallel to itself in any manner. Mathematical vector theorems are true for such a general class of vectors.

Most of the vectors in physics are localized. They may be point-localized or line-localized; for the first type the point of application must be specified and in the latter case the vector can slide along a line without altering its influence on the physical system. Free vectors also exist in physics. Such vectors can be moved parallel to their direction. An example of a free vector is the moment of a couple. This vector describes the turning effect of the couple and it is the same when taken about any axis perpendicular to the plane containing the two forces which form the couple.

Consider a free vector r in the x, y plane and shift it in this plane in such a way that it starts at the origin of a rectangular system of coordinates. Its end point will then have coordinates x, y. It is seen that a free vector in a two-dimensional plane is completely specified by a pair of numbers. The co-

---

* Several books in defining a vector omit the last qualification, which includes, in the definition, the method of adding two vectors. By including this property in the definition of a vector it is implied that there are physical quantities which have both magnitude and direction, and yet they are not vectors.

ordinates x, y of the end point of the vector are equivalent to the lengths of the projections of the vector on the two coordinate axes, and we can write

$$\mathbf{r} = \mathbf{r}_x + \mathbf{r}_y$$

$\mathbf{r}_x$ and $\mathbf{r}_y$ are called rectangular components of the vector. We often write

$$\mathbf{r} \equiv (\mathbf{r}_x, \mathbf{r}_y)$$

or simply

$$\mathbf{r} \equiv (r_x, r_y)$$

Care has to be taken of the sign of the projection. It is the pair of components (r_x, r_y) which is usually taken as the pair of numbers which specify the vector completely.

The rectangular components are not the only type of components of a vector. When the reference axes are oblique, as in Figure A.2, the components

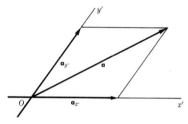

Fig. A.2

are obtained by drawing parallel lines to the coordinate axes. There also exist many types of curvilinear coordinate systems the most popular being spherical polar coordinates.

A–2   The Sum and the Difference of Vectors

The basic mathematical property of a vector in a two-dimensional plane is that it is completely described by two numbers. This fact is utilized quite often. Thus suppose that we want to find the vector sum of two vectors $\mathbf{a}$ and $\mathbf{b}$. We shift the vectors as shown in Figure A.3. We have

$$\mathbf{a} = \mathbf{a}_x + \mathbf{a}_y$$

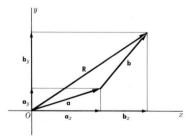

Fig. A.3a

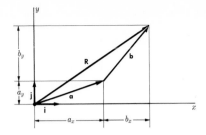

Fig. A.3b

and

$$\mathbf{b} = \mathbf{b}_x + \mathbf{b}_y$$

therefore

$$\mathbf{a} + \mathbf{b} = (\mathbf{a}_x + \mathbf{b}_x) + (\mathbf{a}_y + \mathbf{b}_y)$$

or the sum **a** and **b** is

$$\mathbf{R} = \mathbf{R}_x + \mathbf{R}_y$$

where

$$\mathbf{R}_x = \mathbf{a}_x + \mathbf{b}_x \qquad \mathbf{R}_y = \mathbf{a}_y + \mathbf{b}_y$$

are the x and y components of the sum.

The directions of the reference axes can most conveniently be denoted by unit vectors **i** and **j** along the x and y axes respectively. Then

$$\mathbf{a} = a_x\mathbf{i} + a_y\mathbf{j}$$
$$\mathbf{b} = b_x\mathbf{i} + b_y\mathbf{j}$$

and

$$\mathbf{R} = (a_x + b_x)\mathbf{i} + (a_y + b_y)\mathbf{j}$$

The extension of the summation procedure to any number of vectors is straightforward. The simplest graphical method of adding several vectors is to form a chain of them as shown in Figure A.4. The sum **R** of all the vectors is obtained by joining the beginning of the first to the end of the last vector.

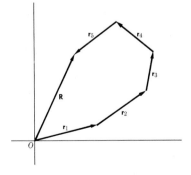

Fig. A.4

The difference of two vectors is contained in the definition of addition, for

$$\mathbf{a} - \mathbf{b} = \mathbf{a} + (-\mathbf{b})$$

The best graphical method to find the difference of two vectors $\mathbf{a}$ and $\mathbf{b}$ is to draw them from a common origin as shown in Figure A.5; the difference

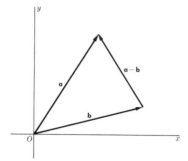

Fig. A.5

$(\mathbf{a} - \mathbf{b})$ is then the vector joining the end points of the two vectors and pointing towards $\mathbf{a}$.

The summation of vectors in the three-dimensional space follows readily.

A–3 The Products of Vectors

There are two types of products of two vectors: the *scalar product* and the *vector product*. Given two vectors $\mathbf{a}$ and $\mathbf{b}$ with an angle θ between them, the scalar product of the two vectors is denoted by $\mathbf{a} \cdot \mathbf{b}$ and defined by

$$\mathbf{a} \cdot \mathbf{b} = ab \cos \theta$$

This product is called the dot product or the inner product and $\mathbf{a} \cdot \mathbf{b}$ is read "a dot b." The scalar product of two vectors is a scalar.

The vector product of two vectors is a vector denoted by $\mathbf{a} \times \mathbf{b}$ ("a cross b"), and is defined as

$$\mathbf{a} \times \mathbf{b} = ab \sin \theta \mathbf{c}_1$$

where $\mathbf{c}_1$ is a unit vector perpendicular to the plane of $\mathbf{a}$ and $\mathbf{b}$; its direction is the same as that into which a right-handed screw would advance if $\mathbf{a}$ were turned towards $\mathbf{b}$ through an angle less than 180°. Thus in Figure A.6(a) θ is

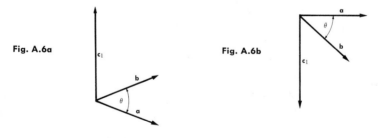

Fig. A.6a   **Fig. A.6b**

354

less than $180°$ and c_1 goes up. In Figure A.6(b) c_1 goes down because rotation of a towards b through the angle θ (which is less than $180°$) would advance a right-handed screw downwards.

It is seen immediately that vector multiplication of two vectors is not commutative, but

$$a \times b = -b \times a$$

If the set of unit vectors i, j, k designates the directions of the rectangular axes, then—referred to these axes—vectors a and b can be written as

$$a = a_x i + a_y j + a_z k$$

and
$$b = b_x i + b_y j + b_z k$$

It is readily verified that

$$j \cdot k = k \cdot i = i \cdot j = 0$$

and
$$i \cdot i = j \cdot j = k \cdot k = 1$$

Also
$$j \times k = i$$
$$k \times i = j$$
$$i \times j = k$$

and
$$i \times i = j \times j = k \times k = 0$$

The scalar product of a and b in terms of the components of the two vectors is

$$a \cdot b = a_x b_x + a_y b_y + a_z b_z$$

This follows when we carry out the multiplication

$$a \cdot b = (a_x i + a_y j + a_z k) \cdot (b_x i + b_y j + b_z k)$$

and make use of the above dot products of unit vectors.

The cross product is slightly more involved. For this product we obtain

$$
\begin{aligned}
a \times b &= (a_x i + a_y j + a_z k) \times (b_x i + b_y j + b_z k) \\
&= a_x b_y i \times j + a_x b_z i \times k + a_y b_x j \times i \\
&\quad + a_y b_z j \times k + a_z b_x k \times i + a_z b_y k \times j \\
&= a_y b_z j \times k - a_z b_y j \times k + a_z b_x k \times i \\
&\quad - a_x b_z k \times i + a_x b_y i \times j - a_y b_x i \times j
\end{aligned}
$$

or $\qquad a \times b = (a_y b_z - a_z b_y)i + (a_z b_x - a_x b_z)j + (a_x b_y - a_y b_x)k$

This can also be written in the determinantal form* as

$$a \times b = \begin{vmatrix} i & j & k \\ a_x & a_y & a_z \\ b_x & b_y & b_z \end{vmatrix}$$

* Section B–6 of the following appendix introduces the determinant.

A-4 Differentiation of Vectors

Let **a** be a variable vector referred to a fixed frame of reference. In that case in the expression

$$\mathbf{a} = a_x\mathbf{i} + a_y\mathbf{j} + a_z\mathbf{k},$$

the components a_x, a_y, a_z are variable and the unit vectors **i**, **j**, **k** are fixed. The time derivative of the vector **a** then becomes

$$\frac{d\mathbf{a}}{dt} = \frac{da_x}{dt}\mathbf{i} + \frac{da_y}{dt}\mathbf{j} + \frac{da_z}{dt}\mathbf{k}$$

When the frame of reference is not fixed, the time variation of the unit vectors has to be considered also,* and so

$$\frac{d\mathbf{a}}{dt} = \frac{da_x}{dt}\mathbf{i} + \frac{da_y}{dt}\mathbf{j} + \frac{da_z}{dt}\mathbf{k} + a_x\frac{d\mathbf{i}}{dt} + a_y\frac{d\mathbf{j}}{dt} + a_z\frac{d\mathbf{k}}{dt}$$

A-5 The Gradient Operator

The equation

$$\phi(x,\, y,\, z) = \phi_0$$

represents a surface referred to the x, y, z coordinate system of axes. A portion of this surface passing through point (x, y, z) is shown in Figure A.7. By

Fig. A.7

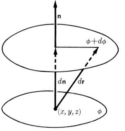

varying ϕ_0 we get various surfaces belonging to a family of surfaces. In Figure A.7 we have drawn a neighboring surface $\phi + d\phi$ belonging to the same family of surfaces. We may investigate the rate of change of ϕ as we move along a particular direction dr. This change is $\dfrac{\partial \phi}{\partial r}$ and its magnitude depends on the direction of dr. The maximum rate of change of ϕ occurs when dr is along the normal to the surface ϕ; this maximum rate of change will thus be denoted by $\dfrac{\partial \phi}{\partial n}$ **n**. We define the gradient of ϕ by

$$\mathbf{grad}\ \phi = \frac{\partial \phi}{\partial n}\,\mathbf{n}$$

* For further development of this case see Chapter 2, Section 2–10.

Grad ϕ is a vector which at any point of space gives the magnitude and direction of the greatest rate of change of the scalar function ϕ. Now, consider the two vectors

$$\mathbf{A} = \frac{\partial \phi}{\partial x} \mathbf{i} + \frac{\partial \phi}{\partial y} \mathbf{j} + \frac{\partial \phi}{\partial z} \mathbf{k}$$

and

$$\mathbf{n} = \frac{dx}{dn} \mathbf{i} + \frac{dy}{dn} \mathbf{j} + \frac{dz}{dn} \mathbf{k}$$

The second vector is a unit vector along the normal to the surface, and $\mathbf{A}$ is a vector which also goes along the same normal, because

$$\frac{\partial \phi}{\partial x} \qquad \frac{\partial \phi}{\partial y} \qquad \frac{\partial \phi}{\partial z}$$

are proportional to the direction cosines of the normal to the surface $\phi(x, y, z)$ at the point (x, y, z). Thus

$$\mathbf{A} \cdot \mathbf{n} = \frac{\partial \phi}{\partial x} \frac{dx}{dn} + \frac{\partial \phi}{\partial y} \frac{dy}{dn} + \frac{\partial \phi}{\partial z} \frac{dz}{dn}$$

or

$$A = \frac{\partial \phi}{\partial n}$$

Thus

$$\mathbf{grad} \; \phi = \frac{\partial \phi}{\partial x} \mathbf{i} + \frac{\partial \phi}{\partial y} \mathbf{j} + \frac{\partial \phi}{\partial z} \mathbf{k}$$

We introduce the vector operator*

$$\nabla \equiv \frac{\partial}{\partial x} \mathbf{i} + \frac{\partial}{\partial y} \mathbf{j} + \frac{\partial}{\partial z} \mathbf{k}$$

In terms of ∇ $$\mathbf{grad} \; \phi = \nabla \phi$$

A–6   The Divergence Operator

Consider an element dS of a surface area S. Such an element of area can be represented by a vector $d\mathbf{S}$, the magnitude of which is equal to the area and the direction is along the normal, Figure A.8. The surface element $d\mathbf{S}$ is

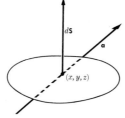

Fig. A.8

* The vector operator ∇ is pronounced "del." We prefer the better sounding name "nabla"; it stems from the name of an Egyptian instrument of the shape ∇.

situated at the point (x, y, z). We imagine that throughout space a vector field $\mathbf{a}(x, y, z)$ is given. This simply means that to every point in space a vector is assigned.* Let the value of the vector field $\mathbf{a}$ at (x, y, z) be given by a vector $\mathbf{a}$ shown in Figure A.8. We define the flux $d\psi$ of the vector $\mathbf{a}$ across the area $d\mathbf{S}$ as

$$d\psi = \mathbf{a} \cdot d\mathbf{S}$$

For a closed surface S the total outgoing flux of the vector $\mathbf{a}$ is given by

$$\psi = \oiint \mathbf{a} \cdot d\mathbf{S}$$

The last integral is an example of a surface integral. As stated in the above expression the value of the vector $\mathbf{a}(x, y, z)$ at a point (x, y, z) is scalar-multiplied into the element $d\mathbf{S}$ of the area at (x, y, z) and then integrated over the surface. In the present case the surface integral is taken over a closed surface. Such an integral can of course also be evaluated over an open surface. Also, surface integrals of scalar functions are used, e.g.,

$$\iint_S f(x, y, z) \, dS.$$

We are now in a position to introduce the definition of the divergence of a vector at a point. It is given by

$$\operatorname{div} \mathbf{a} = \lim_{V \to 0} \frac{\oiint_S \mathbf{a} \cdot d\mathbf{S}}{V}$$

It can be shown** that

$$\operatorname{div} \mathbf{a} = \frac{\partial a_x}{\partial x} + \frac{\partial a_y}{\partial y} + \frac{\partial a_z}{\partial z}$$

It follows that we can write

$$\operatorname{div} \mathbf{a} = \nabla \cdot \mathbf{a}$$

where $\nabla \cdot \mathbf{a}$ represents the scalar product of the vector operator ∇ and the vector $\mathbf{a}$.

We have seen that **grad** ϕ is a vector field. We may therefore operate on it with the divergence operator. Thus

$$\operatorname{div} \mathbf{grad}\, \phi = \nabla \cdot \nabla \phi$$

We find that

$$\operatorname{div} \mathbf{grad}\, \phi = \nabla^2 \phi$$

where

$$\nabla^2 \equiv \frac{\partial^2}{\partial x^2} + \frac{\partial^2}{\partial y^2} + \frac{\partial^2}{\partial z^2}$$

is called the Laplacian operator.

---

* We can easily construct several examples of a vector field. For instance the gravitational attraction on unit mass is an example of a vector field. To every point of space its value and direction can be assigned.
** D. E. Rutherford Vector Methods, 9th ed., Oliver and Boyd, Edinburgh and London, New York: Interscience Publishers (1957).

A-7 The Curl Operator

We have demonstrated above that from every scalar field we can derive a vector field **a** where

$$\mathbf{a} = \mathbf{grad}\ \phi$$

We now inquire whether it is possible to start with a vector field and represent it as a gradient of some scalar field. Let us first investigate the necessary condition that this can be done. We therefore assume that for a given vector field **a** we can write

$$\mathbf{a} = \mathbf{grad}\ \phi$$

In this vector field choose two arbitrary points A and B, Figure A.9, and join

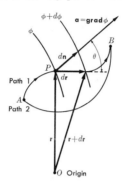

Fig. A.9

them by a path (path 1 in Fig. A.9). Let P be a point on this path, at which we draw an element $d\mathbf{r}$ of the path. The value of the vector field at P is given, and suppose it is as shown in Figure A.9. We see that

$$\mathbf{a} \cdot d\mathbf{r} = \mathbf{grad}\ \phi \cdot d\mathbf{r}$$

$$= \frac{\partial \phi}{\partial n}\ \mathbf{n} \cdot d\mathbf{r}$$

$$= \frac{\partial \phi}{\partial n}\ dr \cos \theta$$

$$= \frac{\partial \phi}{\partial n}\ dn$$

or

$$\mathbf{a} \cdot d\mathbf{r} = d\phi$$

Thus

$$\int_A^B \mathbf{a} \cdot d\mathbf{r} = \int_A^B d\phi$$

or

$$\int_A^B \mathbf{a} \cdot d\mathbf{r} = \phi_B - \phi_A$$

The integral $\int_A^B \mathbf{a} \cdot d\boldsymbol{\ell}$ is an example of a line integral. Again, it does not have to be an integral of a scalar product of a vector function $\mathbf{a}$ and a vector line element $d\boldsymbol{\ell}$, as in this case, but it can be an integral of the form $\int_L f(x, y, z)\, d\ell$. In such a case we are given a curve and a function. At every element $d\ell$ of the curve situated at (x, y, z) we take the value of the function at this point, multiply it by the length of the element $d\ell$ and integrate it between the desired limits.

The last equation states that *the necessary condition that a given vector field be represented as a gradient of a scalar field, is that its line integral between any two points A and B connected by any curve depends on the position of the two points only.*

From Fig. A.9

$$\int_{\substack{A \\ 1}}^B \mathbf{a} \cdot d\boldsymbol{\ell} = \int_{\substack{A \\ 2}}^B \mathbf{a} \cdot d\boldsymbol{\ell}$$

or

$$\int_{\substack{A \\ 1}}^B \mathbf{a} \cdot d\boldsymbol{\ell} - \int_{\substack{A \\ 2}}^B \mathbf{a} \cdot d\boldsymbol{\ell} = 0$$

from which

$$\int_{\substack{A \\ 1}}^B \mathbf{a} \cdot d\boldsymbol{\ell} + \int_{\substack{B \\ 2}}^A \mathbf{a} \cdot d\boldsymbol{\ell} = 0$$

Since both paths are arbitrary therefore

$$\oint_L \mathbf{a} \cdot d\boldsymbol{\ell} = 0$$

where L is any closed path in the field. The last integral is called the circular line integral. Our necessary condition for a vector to be represented as a gradient of a scalar field is that *its circular integral along any closed path in the field is zero.*

Vector fields $\mathbf{a}$ for which the last relation holds are of special type. They are called *conservative fields* and they play an important role in several branches of physics. In general, vector fields are not conservative and for such fields $\oint_L \mathbf{a} \cdot d\boldsymbol{\ell} \neq 0$. Furthermore, upon some exploration it is found that $\oint_L \mathbf{a} \cdot d\boldsymbol{\ell}$ depends on the orientation of the area for which the curve L is the boundary. It is found that for some particular orientation $\oint_L \mathbf{a} \cdot d\boldsymbol{\ell}$ is a maximum. Let S be a flat area bounded by L. We will now define a new vector field, namely that of a **curl** of $\mathbf{a}$, as

$$\mathbf{curl\ a} = \lim_{S \to 0} \frac{\oint_L \mathbf{a} \cdot d\boldsymbol{\ell}}{S}\, \mathbf{c}_1$$

where $\mathbf{c}_1$ is a unit vector normal to S in the position when $\oint_L \mathbf{a} \cdot d\boldsymbol{\ell}$ is a maxi-

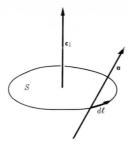

mum. The sense of c_1 is established by the right-handed screw rule, i.e., c_1 points in the direction in which a right-handed screw would move if it were turned in the direction in which the line integration proceeds. (Fig. A.10.) It can be shown* that in terms of components

$$\text{curl } \mathbf{a} = \left(\frac{\partial a_z}{\partial y} - \frac{\partial a_y}{\partial z}\right)\mathbf{i} + \left(\frac{\partial a_x}{\partial z} - \frac{\partial a_z}{\partial x}\right)\mathbf{j} + \left(\frac{\partial a_y}{\partial x} - \frac{\partial a_x}{\partial y}\right)\mathbf{k}$$

It is then readily verified that

$$\text{curl } \mathbf{a} = \nabla \times \mathbf{a}$$

This can be shown by just considering the cross-product of the vector operator ∇ and the vector $\mathbf{a}$.

A–8   Four-dimensional Vectors

We may extend the definition of vectors to spaces of higher dimensions. Thus consider four unit vectors $\mathbf{i}_1$, $\mathbf{i}_2$, $\mathbf{i}_3$, $\mathbf{i}_4$ each mutually orthogonal such that

$$\mathbf{i}_j \cdot \mathbf{i}_k = \delta_{jk}$$

where δ_{jk} is the Kronecker delta, i.e., $\delta_{jk} = 0$ when $j \neq k$ and $\delta_{jk} = 1$ when $j = k$. A position vector in this space will then be of the form

$$\mathfrak{R} = x_1\mathbf{i}_1 + x_2\mathbf{i}_2 + x_3\mathbf{i}_3 + x_4\mathbf{i}_4$$

The algebra of vectors can be extended to the four-dimensional case quite readily.**

A–9   The Components of $\nabla\phi$, $\nabla \cdot \mathbf{a}$ and $\nabla \times \mathbf{a}$ in Generalized Coordinates***

The generalized coordinates were introduced in Chapter 7; we will use some of the results obtained there. We will express the gradient, divergence, curl

---

* See Rutherford, *Vector Methods*, Op. Cit.
** A brief concise treatment can be found in Rutherford's *Vector Methods*, Op. Cit.
*** This section follows quite closely the presentation given in the often cited Rutherford's Vector Methods.

and the Laplacian operator in generalized orthogonal coordinates. The results will then be applied to spherical polar and cylindrical polar coordinates. It goes without saying that these results are quite useful because it is often necessary to be able to express the various operators in different coordinate systems.

(a) The Gradient Operator.

The gradient of a scalar function is a vector which at any point gives the greatest rate of change of the scalar function. Let q_1, q_2, q_3 form an orthogonal set of generalized coordinates. Let $\mathbf{i}_1$, $\mathbf{i}_2$, $\mathbf{i}_3$ be the unit vectors indicating the directions of increase of q_1, q_2, q_3. The components of $\nabla\phi$ in generalized coordinates along $\mathbf{i}_1$, $\mathbf{i}_2$, $\mathbf{i}_3$ are

$$\frac{\partial\phi}{\partial\ell_1} \qquad \frac{\partial\phi}{\partial\ell_2} \qquad \frac{\partial\phi}{\partial\ell_3}$$

where $d\ell_1$ is the element of displacement along the line obtained by the intersection of the surfaces $q_2 = $ const. and $q_3 = $ const.; $d\ell_2$ and $d\ell_3$ are defined in a similar way. We have shown in Chapter 7 that

$$d\ell_1 = h_1\,dq_1 \qquad d\ell_2 = h_2\,dq_2 \qquad d\ell_3 = h_3\,dq_3$$

and so the components of the gradient of ϕ in generalized coordinates are

$$\frac{1}{h_1}\frac{\partial\phi}{\partial q_1} \qquad \frac{1}{h_2}\frac{\partial\phi}{\partial q_2} \qquad \frac{1}{h_3}\frac{\partial\phi}{\partial q_3}$$

(b) The Divergence Operator.

We remember that the divergence of a vector $\mathbf{a}$ is defined as

$$\operatorname{div}\mathbf{a} = \lim_{V\to 0} \frac{\oiint \mathbf{a}\cdot d\mathbf{S}}{V}$$

Let V be the volume bounded by S which is the surface of a box bounded by

$$q_1 \text{ and } q_1 + \delta q_1 \qquad q_2 \text{ and } q_2 + \delta q_2 \qquad q_3 \text{ and } q_3 + \delta q_3$$

Also let a_1, a_2, a_3 be the components of the vector $\mathbf{a}$ along $\mathbf{i}_1$, $\mathbf{i}_2$, $\mathbf{i}_3$.

The integral entering into the definition of div $\mathbf{a}$ represents the total flux out of the volume across the surface S bounding V. In our case we will have to evaluate the total flux across the six faces of the generalized cube. The situation is as shown in Figure A.11.* The outward flux across the bottom

---

* In these and other evaluations we have to remember that we are expressing the elements of length, of surface, and of volume of physical space in terms of generalized coordinates. Thus, e.g., the element of volume is $\delta l_1\,\delta l_2\,\delta l_3$ and not $\delta q_1\,\delta q_2\,\delta q_3$. The whole problem should become clear with the help of a concrete example using spherical polar coordinates. (See Part (e) of Section A–8.)

Fig. A.11

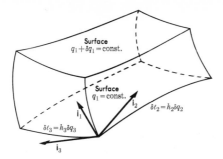

square is

$$\iint_1 \mathbf{a} \cdot d\mathbf{S} = -a_1 h_2 \, \delta q_2 h_3 \, \delta q_3$$

Here a_1 is the component of $\mathbf{a}$ at this bottom square. The flux across the top square is

$$\iint_2 \mathbf{a} \cdot d\mathbf{S} = a_1 h_2 \, \delta q_2 h_3 \, \delta q_3 + \frac{\partial}{\partial q_1} (a_1 h_2 \, \delta q_2 h_3 \, \delta q_3) \, \delta q_1$$

The outgoing flux across the two surfaces becomes

$$\iint_{1,2} \mathbf{a} \cdot d\mathbf{S} = -a_1 h_2 \, \delta q_2 h_3 \, \delta q_3 + a_1 h_2 \, \delta q_2 h_3 \, \delta q_3 + \frac{\partial}{\partial q_1} (a_1 h_2 \, \delta q_2 h_3 \, \delta q_3) \, \delta q_1$$

Similar expressions hold for the flux across the two remaining pairs of surfaces. The outgoing flux across the whole surface is

$$\iint \mathbf{a} \cdot d\mathbf{S} = \left\{ \frac{\partial}{\partial q_1} (a_1 h_2 h_3) + \frac{\partial}{\partial q_2} (a_2 h_3 h_1) + \frac{\partial}{\partial q_3} (a_3 h_1 h_2) \right\} \delta q_1 \, \delta q_2 \, \delta q_3$$

Now, the volume of the generalized cube is

$$V = h_1 h_2 h_3 \, \delta q_1 \, \delta q_2 \, \delta q_3$$

Therefore

$$\text{div } a = \frac{1}{h_1 h_2 h_3} \left\{ \frac{\partial}{\partial q_1} (a_1 h_2 h_3) + \frac{\partial}{\partial q_2} (a_2 h_3 h_1) + \frac{\partial}{\partial q_3} (a_3 h_1 h_2) \right\}$$

(c) *The Laplacian.*

Since

$$\nabla^2 \phi = \text{div } \mathbf{grad} \, \phi$$

therefore combining the results of the two previous sections we obtain

$$\nabla^2 \phi = \frac{1}{h_1 h_2 h_3} \left\{ \frac{\partial}{\partial q_1} \left(\frac{h_2 h_3}{h_1} \frac{\partial \phi}{\partial q_1} \right) + \frac{\partial}{\partial q_2} \left(\frac{h_3 h_1}{h_2} \frac{\partial \phi}{\partial q_2} \right) + \frac{\partial}{\partial q_3} \left(\frac{h_1 h_2}{h_3} \frac{\partial \phi}{\partial q_3} \right) \right\}$$

(d) The Curl Operator.

The definition of the component of the curl of a vector **a** along the direction perpendicular to an area **S** is

$$\lim_{S \to 0} \frac{\oint_L \mathbf{a} \cdot d\boldsymbol{\ell}}{S}$$

Let us first look for the component of **curl a** lying along the unit vector $\mathbf{i}_1$ which gives the direction of increase of q_1. Consider the surface **S** bounded by $q_2 = $ const., $q_2 + \delta q_2 = $ const., $q_3 = $ const. and $q_3 + \delta q_3 = $ const.

Fig. A.12

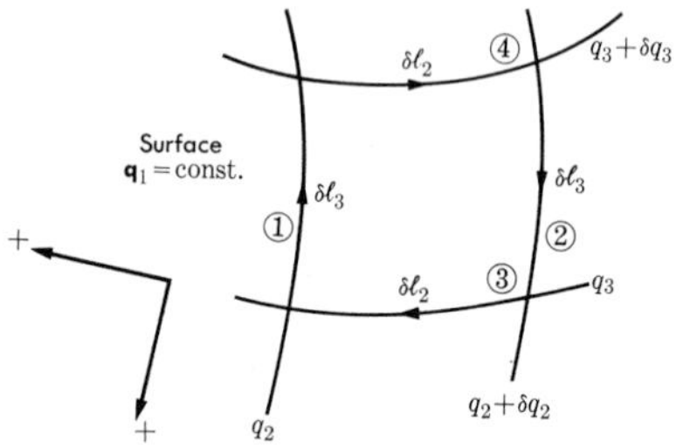

(Fig. A.12). The plane of the paper is the surface $q_1 = $ const. Along $q_2 = $ const.:

$$\int_1 \mathbf{a} \cdot d\boldsymbol{\ell} = -a_3 \, \delta\ell_3$$

or

$$\int_1 \mathbf{a} \cdot d\boldsymbol{\ell} = -a_3 h_3 \, \delta q_3$$

Along $q_2 + \delta q_2 = $ const.:

$$\int_2 \mathbf{a} \cdot d\boldsymbol{\ell} = a_3 h_3 \, \delta q_3 + \frac{\partial}{\partial q_2}(a_3 h_3 \, \delta q_3)\, \delta q_2$$

Along these two portions

$$\int_{1,2} \mathbf{a} \cdot d\boldsymbol{\ell} = \frac{\partial}{\partial q_2}(a_3 h_3 \, \delta q_3)\, \delta q_2$$

Along $q_3 = $ const.: $\qquad \displaystyle\int_3 \mathbf{a} \cdot d\boldsymbol{\ell} = a_2 h_2 \, \delta q_2$

and along $q_3 + \delta q_3 = $ const.:

$$\int_4 \mathbf{a} \cdot d\boldsymbol{\ell} = -a_2 h_2 \, \delta q_2 - \frac{\partial}{\partial q_3}(a_2 h_2 \, \delta q_2)\, \delta q_3$$

Along the two last portions

$$\int_{3,4} \mathbf{a} \cdot d\boldsymbol{\ell} = -\frac{\partial}{\partial q_3}(a_2 h_2)\, \delta q_2 \, \delta q_3$$

A-9 The components of $\nabla\phi$, $\nabla \cdot \mathbf{a}$ and $\nabla \times \mathbf{a}$ in generalized coordinates

The total line integral around the whole loop is

$$\oint \mathbf{a} \cdot d\boldsymbol{\ell} = \left[\frac{\partial}{\partial q_2} (a_3 h_3) - \frac{\partial}{\partial q_3} (a_2 h_2) \right] \delta q_2 \, \delta q_3$$

The area bounded by the loop is given by

$$\delta \ell_2 \, \delta \ell_3 = h_2 h_3 \, \delta q_2 \, \delta q_3$$

Therefore

$$(\nabla \times \mathbf{a}) = \frac{1}{h_2 h_3} \left[\frac{\partial}{\partial q_2} (a_3 h_3) - \frac{\partial}{\partial q_3} (a_2 h_2) \right]$$

Similar components can be obtained for the remaining directions.

(e) *Spherical Polar Coordinates.*

We will now apply the results just obtained to spherical polar coordinates.

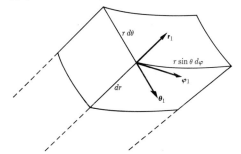

Fig. A.13

In Figure A.13 we have drawn a volume element for the coordinates. We see

that
$$dV = d\ell_1 \, d\ell_2 \, d\ell_3$$
$$= (dr)(r \, d\theta)(r \sin \theta \, d\phi)$$

and from this we find that

$$h_1 = 1 \qquad h_2 = r \qquad h_3 = r \sin \theta$$

Thus the components of $\nabla \phi$ are

$$\frac{\partial \phi}{\partial r} \qquad \frac{1}{r} \frac{\partial \phi}{\partial \theta} \qquad \frac{1}{r \sin \theta} \frac{\partial \phi}{\partial \varphi}$$

We also find that

$$\nabla \cdot \mathbf{a} = \frac{1}{r^2 \sin \theta} \left\{ \frac{\partial}{\partial r} (a_r r^2 \sin \theta) + \frac{\partial}{\partial \theta} (a_\theta r \sin \theta) + \frac{\partial}{\partial \varphi} (a_\varphi r) \right\}$$

and

$$\nabla^2 \phi = \frac{1}{r^2 \sin \theta} \left\{ \frac{\partial}{\partial r} \left(r^2 \sin \theta \frac{\partial \phi}{\partial r} \right) + \frac{\partial}{\partial \theta} \left(\sin \theta \frac{\partial \phi}{\partial \theta} \right) + \frac{\partial}{\partial \varphi} \left(\frac{1}{\sin \theta} \frac{\partial \phi}{\partial \varphi} \right) \right\}$$

or

$$\nabla^2 \phi = \frac{\partial^2 \phi}{\partial r^2} + \frac{2}{r} \frac{\partial \phi}{\partial r} + \frac{1}{r^2} \frac{\partial^2 \phi}{\partial \theta^2} + \frac{\cot \theta}{r^2} \frac{\partial \phi}{\partial \theta} + \frac{1}{r^2 \sin \theta} \frac{\partial^2 \phi}{\partial \varphi^2}$$

The three components of $\nabla \times \mathbf{a}$ are

$$\frac{1}{r^2 \sin \theta} \left[\frac{\partial}{\partial \theta} (a_\varphi r \sin \theta) - \frac{\partial}{\partial \varphi} (a_\theta r) \right]$$

$$\frac{1}{r \sin \theta} \left[\frac{\partial}{\partial \varphi} (a_r) - \frac{\partial}{\partial r} (a_\varphi r \sin \theta) \right]$$

$$\frac{1}{r} \left[\frac{\partial}{\partial r} (a_\theta r) - \frac{\partial}{\partial \theta} (a_r) \right]$$

In the above expressions a_r, a_θ, a_φ are the components of $\mathbf{a}$ in spherical polar coordinates.

(f) *Cylindrical Polar Coordinates.*

The element of length in cylindrical polar coordinates is

$$d\ell^2 = dr^2 + r^2 \, d\theta^2 + dz^2$$

from which we see that

$$h_1 = 1 \qquad h_2 = r \qquad h_3 = 1$$

Thus the components of $\nabla \phi$ are

$$\frac{\partial \phi}{\partial r} \qquad \frac{1}{r} \frac{\partial \phi}{\partial \theta} \qquad \frac{\partial \phi}{\partial z}$$

Also

$$\nabla \cdot \mathbf{a} = \frac{1}{r} \left\{ \frac{\partial}{\partial r} (a_r r) + \frac{\partial}{\partial \theta} (a_\theta) + \frac{\partial}{\partial z} (a_z r) \right\}$$

and

$$\nabla^2 \phi = \frac{1}{r} \left\{ \frac{\partial}{\partial r} \left(r \frac{\partial \phi}{\partial r} \right) + \frac{\partial}{\partial \theta} \left(\frac{1}{r} \frac{\partial \phi}{\partial \theta} \right) + \frac{\partial}{\partial z} \left(r \frac{\partial \phi}{\partial z} \right) \right\}$$

or

The components of $\nabla \times \mathbf{a}$ are

$$\frac{1}{r} \left[\frac{\partial}{\partial \theta} (a_z) - \frac{\partial}{\partial z} (a_\theta z) \right]$$

$$\left[\frac{\partial}{\partial z} (a_r) - \frac{\partial}{\partial r} (a_z) \right]$$

$$\frac{1}{r} \left[\frac{\partial}{\partial r} (a_\theta r) - \frac{\partial}{\partial \theta} (a_r) \right]$$

A-9   The components of $\nabla \phi$, $\nabla \cdot \mathbf{a}$ and $\nabla \times \mathbf{a}$ in generalized coordinates

APPENDIX **B**

MATRICES AND DETERMINANTS

B-1 The Matrix

A matrix is a regular array of detached coefficients, which possesses certain special properties. These properties, to be discussed presently, constitute the algebra of matrices. The array of coefficients which forms the matrix is always rectangular and can consist of various numbers of rows and columns. Thus the array

$$a \quad b \quad c$$
$$d \quad e \quad c$$

has two rows and three columns and for that reason is called a two-by-three matrix. Rarely are different letters used to denote the members of a matrix; a better way to express the same matrix is

$$a_{11} \quad a_{12} \quad a_{13}$$
$$a_{21} \quad a_{22} \quad a_{23}$$

This method has the great advantage that the subscripts give the row and the column in which the particular element is situated. The matrix is usually placed in parentheses or square brackets. We prefer the use of square brackets. The whole matrix can also be denoted by a single capital letter, the same one that is used for the elements. Thus our matrix will be written as

$$\mathbf{A} = \begin{bmatrix} a_{11} & a_{12} & a_{13} \\ a_{21} & a_{22} & a_{23} \end{bmatrix}$$

The same matrix can also be denoted more concisely as

$$\mathbf{A} = [a_{ij}] \qquad i = 1, 2 \qquad j = 1, 2, 3$$

We will now proceed to outline the basic forms of the matrix algebra. The importance of matrices and their applications will be demonstrated later. It should be stated at this point that *a matrix is not an inert quantity*, as it might appear when we study its algebra, *but has an active role as an operator*. In this role, as we will see, it can perform most useful and varied functions.

B-2 Two Equal Matrices

A matrix

$$\mathbf{A} = [a_{ij}]$$

is equal to the matrix

$$\mathbf{B} = [b_{ij}]$$

If every element of $\mathbf{A}$ is equal to the corresponding element of $\mathbf{B}$, i.e., if

$$a_{ij} = b_{ij}$$

for all values of i and j.

It goes without saying that both matrices must be of the same order.

B-3 Matrix Addition

Only matrices of equal order can be added. Given two matrices

$$\mathbf{A} = \begin{bmatrix} a_{11} & a_{12} & a_{13} \\ a_{21} & a_{22} & a_{23} \\ a_{31} & a_{32} & a_{33} \end{bmatrix}$$

and

$$\mathbf{B} = \begin{bmatrix} b_{11} & b_{12} & b_{13} \\ b_{21} & b_{22} & b_{23} \\ b_{31} & b_{32} & b_{33} \end{bmatrix}$$

their sum is the matrix

$$\mathbf{C} = \begin{bmatrix} a_{11} + b_{11} & a_{12} + a_{12} & a_{13} + b_{13} \\ a_{21} + b_{21} & a_{22} + b_{22} & a_{23} + b_{23} \\ a_{31} + b_{31} & a_{32} + b_{32} & a_{33} + b_{33} \end{bmatrix}$$

This definition of addition of matrices can be stated more concisely (and also more generally) in the following way: Given two matrices

$$\mathbf{A} = [a_{ij}] \quad \text{and} \quad \mathbf{B} = [b_{ij}]$$

of equal order, their sum will be a matrix

$$\mathbf{C} = [c_{ij}]$$

such that

$$c_{ij} = a_{ij} + b_{ij}$$

Thus

$$\mathbf{C} = [a_{ij} + b_{ij}]$$

Matrix multiplication is a much more involved process in that there is a specific requirement for orders of the two matrices which are to be multiplied and the sequence of multiplication is unique. To formulate the matrix product

$$\mathbf{C} = \mathbf{AB}$$

in that order, of the two given matrices

$$\mathbf{A} = [a_{ij}] \quad \text{and} \quad \mathbf{B} = [b_{ij}]$$

the order of $\mathbf{A}$ must be $m \times n$ and that of $\mathbf{B}$ $n \times p$, i.e., the number of columns of $\mathbf{A}$ must be equal to the number of rows of $\mathbf{B}$. The i, j-th element of the product matrix is given by

$$c_{ij} = \sum_{l=1}^{l=n} a_{il}b_{lj}$$

Examination of this expression reveals that to obtain an element of the product matrix we must "multiply rows of $\mathbf{A}$ into columns of $\mathbf{B}$." This will best be illustrated by an example. Let

$$\mathbf{A} = \begin{bmatrix} a_{11} & a_{12} \\ a_{21} & a_{22} \\ a_{31} & a_{32} \end{bmatrix}$$

and

$$\mathbf{B} = \begin{bmatrix} b_{11} & b_{12} & b_{13} \\ b_{21} & b_{22} & b_{23} \end{bmatrix}$$

The order of $\mathbf{A}$ is 3×2 and that of $\mathbf{B}$ 2×3. The product matrix will be of the order 3×3, and is given by

$$\mathbf{C} = \begin{bmatrix} \sum_{l=1}^{2} a_{1l}b_{l1} & \sum_{l=1}^{2} a_{1l}b_{l2} & \sum_{l=1}^{2} a_{1l}b_{l3} \\ \sum_{l=1}^{2} a_{2l}b_{l1} & \sum_{l=1}^{2} a_{2l}b_{l2} & \sum_{l=1}^{2} a_{2l}b_{l3} \\ \sum_{l=1}^{2} a_{3l}b_{l1} & \sum_{l=1}^{2} a_{3l}b_{l2} & \sum_{l=1}^{2} a_{3l}b_{l3} \end{bmatrix}$$

or

$$\mathbf{C} = \begin{bmatrix} a_{11}b_{11} + a_{12}b_{21} & a_{11}b_{12} + a_{12}b_{22} & a_{11}b_{13} + a_{12}b_{23} \\ a_{21}b_{11} + a_{22}b_{21} & a_{21}b_{12} + a_{22}b_{22} & a_{21}b_{13} + a_{22}b_{23} \\ a_{31}b_{11} + a_{32}b_{21} & a_{31}b_{12} + a_{32}b_{22} & a_{31}b_{13} + a_{32}b_{23} \end{bmatrix}$$

The row into column multiplication can be represented schematically as shown in Figure B.1

Fig. B.1

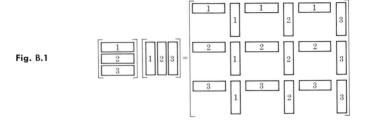

To solve a numerical example let

$$A = \begin{bmatrix} 1 & 1 \\ 0 & 1 \\ 2 & 0 \end{bmatrix}$$

and

$$B = \begin{bmatrix} 0 & 1 & 1 \\ 2 & 1 & 0 \end{bmatrix}$$

Then

$$C = AB$$

$$= \begin{bmatrix} 1 & 1 \\ 0 & 1 \\ 2 & 0 \end{bmatrix} \begin{bmatrix} 0 & 1 & 1 \\ 2 & 1 & 0 \end{bmatrix}$$

$$= \begin{bmatrix} 0+2 & 1+1 & 1+0 \\ 0+2 & 0+1 & 0+0 \\ 0+2 & 2+1 & 2+0 \end{bmatrix}$$

or

$$C = \begin{bmatrix} 2 & 2 & 1 \\ 2 & 1 & 0 \\ 0 & 2 & 2 \end{bmatrix}$$

B–5   Some Types of Matrices

We shall now enumerate a few types of matrices, most of which we will be using later.

A *null matrix* is one with all zero elements. Thus a null matrix will be

370

of the form

$$\mathbf{0} = \begin{bmatrix} 0 & 0 & \cdots & 0 \\ 0 & 0 & \cdots & 0 \\ \vdots & & & \\ 0 & 0 & \cdots & 0 \end{bmatrix}$$

A *diagonal matrix* is one for which all the off-diagonal elements are zero. It is sometimes called a *quasi-scalar matrix*. Such a matrix has the form

$$\mathbf{A} = \begin{bmatrix} a_{11} & 0 & \cdots & 0 \\ 0 & a_{22} & \cdots & 0 \\ \vdots & & & \\ 0 & \cdots\cdots & a_{nn} \end{bmatrix}$$

For the sake of expediency we may represent such a matrix by

$$\mathbf{A} = \begin{bmatrix} a_{11} & & & \mathcal{O} \\ & a_{22} & & \\ & & \ddots & \\ \mathcal{O} & & & a_{nn} \end{bmatrix}$$

A *unit matrix* is one with unit diagonal elements only. It is denoted by **I** and is of the form

$$\mathbf{I} = \begin{bmatrix} 1 & & & \mathcal{O} \\ & 1 & & \\ & & \ddots & \\ \mathcal{O} & & & 1 \end{bmatrix}$$

A *scalar matrix* is a product of a scalar and a unit matrix. In general a product of a scalar λ and a matrix

$$\mathbf{A} = [a_{ij}]$$

is defined by

$$\lambda\mathbf{A} = [\lambda a_{ij}]$$

Thus every element of the matrix is multiplied by the scalar λ, and the scalar matrix is therefore of the form

$$\lambda\mathbf{I} = \begin{bmatrix} \lambda & & & \mathcal{O} \\ & \lambda & & \\ & & \ddots & \\ \mathcal{O} & & & \lambda \end{bmatrix}$$

A *symmetric matrix* is such that

$$a_{ij} = a_{ji}$$

for every i and j.

A *skew symmetric matrix* is one for which

$$a_{ij} = -a_{ji}$$

again for every i and j. Since in this case every diagonal element has to be equal to its negative, therefore all the diagonal elements must be zero.

A *transposed matrix* of a given matrix **A** is formed by interchanging the rows and columns. The transposed matrix is denoted by **A'**. If

$$\mathbf{A} = [a_{ij}]$$

then

$$\mathbf{A'} = [a_{ji}]$$

or

$$A' = \begin{bmatrix} a_{11} & a_{21} & \cdots & a_{n1} \\ a_{12} & a_{22} & \cdots & a_{n2} \\ \vdots & & & \\ a_{1n} & a_{2n} & \cdots & a_{nn} \end{bmatrix}$$

B-6 Determinants

We will now introduce a new mathematical quantity connected with matrices, namely determinants. Whereas the definition of the matrix was simple and straightforward, that of the determinant is not quite so simple.

The determinant of a 2 by 2 square matrix

$$\mathbf{A} = \begin{bmatrix} a_{11} & a_{12} \\ a_{21} & a_{22} \end{bmatrix}$$

is denoted by

$$|\mathbf{A}| = \begin{vmatrix} a_{11} & a_{12} \\ a_{21} & a_{22} \end{vmatrix}$$

and is a number the value of which is

$$|\mathbf{A}| = a_{11}a_{22} - a_{12}a_{21}$$

The manner in which this determinant has been evaluated should be noted: The product of the elements along one diagonal has been subtracted from the product of elements along the other diagonal.

A determinant of a 3 by 3 matrix

$$\mathbf{A} = \begin{bmatrix} a_{11} & a_{12} & a_{13} \\ a_{21} & a_{22} & a_{23} \\ a_{31} & a_{32} & a_{33} \end{bmatrix}$$

372

is defined as a number whose value is

$$|\mathbf{A}| = \begin{vmatrix} a_{11} & a_{12} & a_{13} \\ a_{21} & a_{22} & a_{23} \\ a_{31} & a_{32} & a_{33} \end{vmatrix}$$

$$= a_{11}\begin{vmatrix} a_{22} & a_{23} \\ a_{32} & a_{33} \end{vmatrix} - a_{12}\begin{vmatrix} a_{21} & a_{23} \\ a_{31} & a_{33} \end{vmatrix} + a_{13}\begin{vmatrix} a_{21} & a_{22} \\ a_{31} & a_{32} \end{vmatrix}$$

$$= a_{11}(a_{22}a_{33} - a_{23}a_{32}) - a_{12}(a_{21}a_{33} - a_{23}a_{31})$$
$$+ a_{13}(a_{21}a_{32} - a_{22}a_{31})$$

or

$$|\mathbf{A}| = a_{11}a_{22}a_{33} + a_{12}a_{23}a_{31} + a_{13}a_{21}a_{32}$$
$$- a_{13}a_{22}a_{31} - a_{12}a_{21}a_{33} - a_{11}a_{23}a_{32}$$

Examining this last form of the expansion of the determinant we notice that it can be obtained directly from

$$|\mathbf{A}| = \begin{vmatrix} a_{11} & a_{12} & a_{13} \\ a_{21} & a_{22} & a_{23} \\ a_{31} & a_{32} & a_{33} \end{vmatrix}$$

by first summing three products according to the scheme shown in Figure B.2(a), and then subtracting from this the sum of the three products obtained according to the diagram shown in Figure B.2(b).

Fig. B.2a

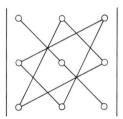

Fig. B.2b

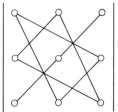

In a similar way the determinant of the matrix

$$\mathbf{A} = \begin{bmatrix} a_{11} & a_{12} & a_{13} & a_{14} \\ a_{21} & a_{22} & a_{23} & a_{24} \\ a_{31} & a_{32} & a_{33} & a_{34} \\ a_{41} & a_{42} & a_{43} & a_{44} \end{bmatrix}$$

is given by

$$|\mathbf{A}| = \begin{vmatrix} a_{11} & a_{12} & a_{13} & a_{14} \\ a_{21} & a_{22} & a_{23} & a_{24} \\ a_{31} & a_{32} & a_{33} & a_{34} \\ a_{41} & a_{42} & a_{43} & a_{44} \end{vmatrix}$$

$$= a_{11} \begin{vmatrix} a_{22} & a_{23} & a_{24} \\ a_{32} & a_{33} & a_{34} \\ a_{42} & a_{43} & a_{44} \end{vmatrix} - a_{12} \begin{vmatrix} a_{21} & a_{23} & a_{24} \\ a_{31} & a_{33} & a_{34} \\ a_{41} & a_{43} & a_{44} \end{vmatrix}$$

$$+ a_{13} \begin{vmatrix} a_{21} & a_{22} & a_{24} \\ a_{31} & a_{32} & a_{34} \\ a_{41} & a_{42} & a_{44} \end{vmatrix} - a_{14} \begin{vmatrix} a_{21} & a_{22} & a_{23} \\ a_{31} & a_{32} & a_{33} \\ a_{41} & a_{42} & a_{43} \end{vmatrix}$$

The rest of the expansion proceeds in the way described above.

We have given an inductive definition of a determinant of a square matrix. The method of evaluation of the determinant given here may be termed "the expansion by the elements of the first row."* As we have seen, every element of the first row is multiplied by a determinant which is one order lower than the original determinant, and is obtained by removing the row and the column in which the element is placed. This lower order determinant is called a minor or a cofactor. The cofactor has a plus or minus sign according to the place of the element. The sign to be given to the cofactors can be read off from the following scheme.

$$\begin{matrix} + & - & + & - & \cdots \\ - & + & - & + & \cdots \\ + & - & + & - & \cdots \\ \vdots & \vdots & \vdots & & \end{matrix}$$

Thus the cofactor of an element a_{ij} of a determinant $|\mathbf{A}|$, denoted by $|\mathbf{A}_{ij}|$ is obtained from $|\mathbf{A}|$ by deleting the i-th row and j-th column from $|\mathbf{A}|$. The sign of the cofactor is $(-1)^{i+j}$.

---

* This method is by no means unique. Any row or any column can be used. In addition, there are other methods of evaluating determinants. (See, for example, Aitken, *Matrices and Determinants*, reference cited at end of book.)

The inductive definition of the determinant is perhaps not too satisfactory but it will suffice for our purpose.*

B-7 Adjoint Matrix. Singular and Nonsingular Matrices. The Reciprocal Matrix

A matrix in which all the elements have been replaced by the cofactors of its determinant, and then transposed, is called the *adjoint (or adjugate) matrix*. Thus for matrix **A**

$$\text{adj } \mathbf{A} = [|\mathbf{A}_{ij}|]'$$

Its determinant $|\text{adj } \mathbf{A}|$ is called the adjugate determinant of **A**.

A matrix **A** for which

$$|\mathbf{A}| = 0$$

is called *singular*. If

$$|\mathbf{A}| \neq 0$$

then the matrix is *nonsingular*.

We are now in position to define the *reciprocal matrix* which may only be defined for a nonsingular matrix. The reciprocal matrix of a nonsingular matrix **A** is defined as

$$\mathbf{A}^{-1} = |\mathbf{A}|^{-1} \text{ adj } \mathbf{A}$$

B-8 Solutions of Linear Equations

The problem of solving a set of linear equations is really a little out of place in a book on mechanics but nevertheless it will be discussed here as a vivid illustration of the power of matrix methods.

Consider the following set of equations

$$a_{11}x_1 + a_{12}x_2 + a_{13}x_3 = h_1$$
$$a_{21}x_1 + a_{22}x_2 + a_{23}x_3 = h_2$$
$$a_{31}x_1 + a_{32}x_2 + a_{33}x_3 = h_3$$

where x_1, x_2, and x_3 are the unknowns and the a_{ij}'s and the h_i's are constants. It can readily be verified that the three expressions on the left hand side form a 3 by 1 matrix which will be the result of multiplying the 3 by 3 matrix

$$\begin{bmatrix} a_{11} & a_{12} & a_{13} \\ a_{21} & a_{22} & a_{23} \\ a_{31} & a_{32} & a_{33} \end{bmatrix}$$

* A more general definition of a determinant can be found for instance in Aitken's book cited in the list of references.

into the 3 by 1 column matrix

$$\begin{bmatrix} x_1 \\ x_2 \\ x_3 \end{bmatrix}$$

i.e.

$$\begin{bmatrix} a_{11} & a_{12} & a_{13} \\ a_{21} & a_{22} & a_{23} \\ a_{31} & a_{32} & a_{33} \end{bmatrix} \begin{bmatrix} x_1 \\ x_2 \\ x_3 \end{bmatrix} = \begin{bmatrix} a_{11}x_1 + a_{12}x_2 + a_{13}x_3 \\ a_{21}x_1 + a_{22}x_2 + a_{23}x_3 \\ a_{31}x_1 + a_{32}x_2 + a_{33}x_3 \end{bmatrix}$$

The right hand side of our original set of equations can be represented as a 3 by 1 column matrix. The whole set of equations can therefore be written in the matrix form as

i.e.

$$\begin{bmatrix} a_{11} & a_{12} & a_{13} \\ a_{21} & a_{22} & a_{23} \\ a_{31} & a_{32} & a_{33} \end{bmatrix} \begin{bmatrix} x_1 \\ x_2 \\ x_3 \end{bmatrix} = \begin{bmatrix} h_1 \\ h_2 \\ h_3 \end{bmatrix}$$

If we denote the three matrices by $\mathbf{A}$, $\mathbf{x}$ and $\mathbf{h}$ respectively then our set of linear equations can be written in the form of the matrix equation

$$\mathbf{Ax} = \mathbf{h}$$

We can immediately appreciate the conciseness of this form. Of couse, the same form can stand for n linear equations with n unknowns. Let the matrix $\mathbf{A}$ be nonsingular. Then the solution can be obtained in one sweep as

$$\mathbf{x} = \mathbf{A}^{-1}\mathbf{h}$$

This can quickly be verified by premultiplying both sides of the matrix equation $\mathbf{Ax} = \mathbf{h}$ by $\mathbf{A}^{-1}$. Then

$$\mathbf{A}^{-1}\mathbf{Ax} = \mathbf{A}^{-1}\mathbf{h}$$

But

$$\mathbf{A}^{-1}\mathbf{A} = \mathbf{I}$$

therefore

$$\mathbf{Ix} = \mathbf{A}^{-1}\mathbf{h}$$

Now

$$\mathbf{Ix} = \mathbf{x}$$

and the result follows.

Obtaining the actual solutions just depends on the ability to construct the inverse matrix. In our case

$$\mathbf{A}^{-1} = \frac{1}{|\mathbf{A}|} \begin{bmatrix} |\mathbf{A}_{11}| & |\mathbf{A}_{21}| & |\mathbf{A}_{31}| \\ |\mathbf{A}_{12}| & |\mathbf{A}_{22}| & |\mathbf{A}_{32}| \\ |\mathbf{A}_{13}| & |\mathbf{A}_{23}| & |\mathbf{A}_{33}| \end{bmatrix}$$

Thus the matrix equation

$$\mathbf{x} = \mathbf{A}^{-1}\mathbf{h}$$

becomes

$$\begin{bmatrix} x_1 \\ x_2 \\ x_3 \end{bmatrix} = \begin{bmatrix} \dfrac{|\mathbf{A}_{11}|}{|\mathbf{A}|} & \dfrac{|\mathbf{A}_{21}|}{|\mathbf{A}|} & \dfrac{|\mathbf{A}_{31}|}{|\mathbf{A}|} \\ \dfrac{|\mathbf{A}_{12}|}{|\mathbf{A}|} & \dfrac{|\mathbf{A}_{22}|}{|\mathbf{A}|} & \dfrac{|\mathbf{A}_{32}|}{|\mathbf{A}|} \\ \dfrac{|\mathbf{A}_{13}|}{|\mathbf{A}|} & \dfrac{|\mathbf{A}_{23}|}{|\mathbf{A}|} & \dfrac{|\mathbf{A}_{33}|}{|\mathbf{A}|} \end{bmatrix} \begin{bmatrix} h_1 \\ h_2 \\ h_3 \end{bmatrix}$$

Upon matrix-multiplying out the right-hand side we get

$$\begin{bmatrix} x_1 \\ x_2 \\ x_3 \end{bmatrix} = \begin{bmatrix} \dfrac{|\mathbf{A}_{11}|}{|\mathbf{A}|} h_1 + \dfrac{|\mathbf{A}_{21}|}{|\mathbf{A}|} h_2 + \dfrac{|\mathbf{A}_{31}|}{|\mathbf{A}|} h_3 \\ \dfrac{|\mathbf{A}_{12}|}{|\mathbf{A}|} h_1 + \dfrac{|\mathbf{A}_{22}|}{|\mathbf{A}|} h_2 + \dfrac{|\mathbf{A}_{32}|}{|\mathbf{A}|} h_3 \\ \dfrac{|\mathbf{A}_{13}|}{|\mathbf{A}|} h_1 + \dfrac{|\mathbf{A}_{23}|}{|\mathbf{A}|} h_2 + \dfrac{|\mathbf{A}_{33}|}{|\mathbf{A}|} h_3 \end{bmatrix}$$

Equating the first element on the left-hand side to the first element on the right-hand side we obtain

$$x_1 = \frac{1}{|\mathbf{A}|} \left(|\mathbf{A}_{11}|h_1 + |\mathbf{A}_{21}|h_2 + |\mathbf{A}_{31}|h_3 \right)$$

Close examination of this expression will reveal that the sum in the parentheses constitutes the expansion of the determinant

$$\begin{vmatrix} h_1 & a_{12} & a_{13} \\ h_2 & a_{22} & a_{23} \\ h_3 & a_{32} & a_{33} \end{vmatrix}$$

according to the elements of the first column. The first unknown is therefore given by

$$x_1 = \frac{\begin{vmatrix} h_1 & a_{12} & a_{13} \\ h_2 & a_{22} & a_{23} \\ h_3 & a_{32} & a_{33} \end{vmatrix}}{\begin{vmatrix} a_{11} & a_{12} & a_{13} \\ a_{21} & a_{22} & a_{23} \\ a_{31} & a_{32} & a_{33} \end{vmatrix}}$$

The other unknowns can be obtained in a similar way.

We have already stated that a matrix is not an inert quantity but plays the active role of an operator. In that role it can perform many varied functions as we shall shortly demonstrate. Actually an example of the usefulness of matrix methods has been demonstrated in the previous section when we were dealing with the solution of a system of linear equations. The entire system of equations could be written as the matrix equation

$$\mathbf{Ax} = \mathbf{h}$$

In this equation the matrix $\mathbf{A}$ stands for the whole scheme of coefficients $[a_{ij}]$. The unknowns, in the case considered, could be represented by a column matrix

$$\begin{bmatrix} x_1 \\ x_2 \\ x_3 \end{bmatrix}$$

Operating on this column matrix by the matrix $\mathbf{A}$ yields the column of constants

$$\begin{bmatrix} h_1 \\ h_2 \\ h_3 \end{bmatrix}$$

As stated above, a matrix may be considered to be an operator, which in different situations may correspond to various physical quantities. Quite often the matrix notation will permit a simple mathematical representation and transformation of complicated mathematical forms.

In most of the cases considered here, the physical quantities will be represented by matrices of three by three order. These quantities are called *tensors*. In elementary physics we have been considering scalar and vector quantities only. To these the tensor quantity has to be added. As an example, we can cite the moment of inertia. For a rotation of a body about a fixed axis the moment of inertia is a scalar quantity. However, for general rotation the moment of inertia becomes a nine component quantity which can be represented by a three by three symmetric matrix. The quantity is the inertia tensor. In the various branches of physics there are a great number of instances where tensor quantities have to be used.

Apart from that, as already mentioned, matrices permit concise and straightforward treatment of complicated mathematical forms. As an example we can cite the quadratic form

$$Q = \sum_i \sum_j a_{ij} x_i x_j \qquad i, j = 1, 2, \ldots, n$$

which for the special case of $i, j = 1, 2, 3$, reads

$$Q = a_{11}x_1x_1 + a_{12}x_1x_2 + a_{13}x_1x_3 + a_{21}x_2x_1 + a_{22}x_2x_2$$
$$+ a_{23}x_2x_3 + a_{31}x_3x_1 + a_{32}x_3x_2 + a_{33}x_3x_3$$

Now, let us introduce the column matrix

$$\mathbf{x} = \begin{bmatrix} x_1 \\ x_2 \\ x_3 \end{bmatrix}$$

Its transpose will be the row matrix

$$\mathbf{x}' = [x_1 \quad x_2 \quad x_3]$$

Next, form the matrix

$$\mathbf{A} = \begin{bmatrix} a_{11} & a_{12} & a_{13} \\ a_{21} & a_{22} & a_{23} \\ a_{31} & a_{32} & a_{33} \end{bmatrix}$$

Then $$Q = \mathbf{x}'\mathbf{A}\mathbf{x}$$

B-10 Linear Transformations in Two- and Three-dimensional Space. Similar Matrices*

It should be clear by now that vectors can be represented by column matrices. Consider a vector $\mathbf{x}$ drawn in the plane Ox_1x_2** (Fig. B.3). Draw unit vectors

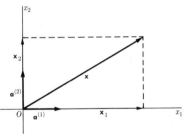

Fig. B.3

$\mathbf{a}^{(1)}$ and $\mathbf{a}^{(2)}$ along the Ox_1 and Ox_2 axes and let x_1 and x_2 be the components of the vector $\mathbf{x}$. Then

$$\mathbf{x} = x_1\mathbf{a}^{(1)} + x_2\mathbf{a}^{(2)}$$

or $$\mathbf{x} = \sum_{j=1}^{2} x_j\mathbf{a}^{(j)}$$

* The next few sections follow in parts the treatment given in I. S. Sokolnikoff, *Tensor Analysis*, Chapter 1, John Wiley, New York (1951).
** The reason for denoting the Cartesian axes by Ox_1 and Ox_2 instead of the conventional Ox, Oy axes is that such a notation can easily be extended to three and more dimensions.

The same vector can be written in the matrix form

$$\mathbf{x} = \begin{bmatrix} x_1 \\ x_2 \end{bmatrix}$$

Now, if we operate on the vector $\mathbf{x}$ by the matrix

$$\mathbf{A} = \begin{bmatrix} a_{11} & a_{12} \\ a_{21} & a_{22} \end{bmatrix}$$

then a new vector $\mathbf{y}$ will be obtained which is given by

$$\begin{bmatrix} y_1 \\ y_2 \end{bmatrix} = \begin{bmatrix} a_{11} & a_{12} \\ a_{21} & a_{22} \end{bmatrix} \begin{bmatrix} x_1 \\ x_2 \end{bmatrix}$$

or briefly

$$\mathbf{y} = \mathbf{Ax}$$

The process of operating on $\mathbf{x}$ by $\mathbf{A}$ may be termed deformation of space. There are many different types of such a deformation. Let us study in detail a particularly simple example.* In the Ox_1x_2 plane draw a line AOB at $45°$ to the Ox_1 axis. Think of this line as the trace of a plane mirror perpendicular to the Ox_1x_2 plane. The deformation of space which we want to consider in this case is the process of reflecting any given vector $\mathbf{x}$ in that plane and obtaining its mirror image $\mathbf{y}$ (Fig. B.4). Let all our vectors $\mathbf{x}$ be drawn from

Fig. B.4

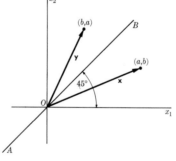

the origin. It can readily be seen that if the coordinates of the end point of $\mathbf{x}$ are $(a\ b)$ then those of the end point of $\mathbf{y}$ will be $(b\ a)$. It should not be too difficult to see that the matrix which will perform this particular deformation of space will be of the form

$$\mathbf{A} = \begin{bmatrix} 0 & 1 \\ 1 & 0 \end{bmatrix}$$

The new vector $\mathbf{y}$, given by

$$\mathbf{y} = \mathbf{Ax}$$

* Taken from Rojansky, cited in list of references.

will in general lie along a direction which is different from the direction of the vector **x**. However, *there are two special lines through the origin such that if the vector* **x** *lies along any of them then the new vector* **Ax** *remains along the same line. Such special lines are called the principal axes of the operator* **A**. In general, the new vector is given by

$$\mathbf{y} = \mathbf{Ax}$$

If, in the special case, the new vector is to lie along the same line as **x** then it will be of the form

$$\mathbf{y} = \lambda\mathbf{x}$$

where λ is a scalar. Combining the last two relations we get

$$\mathbf{Ax} = \lambda\mathbf{x}$$

This type of an equation has a special name; it is called an *eigenvalue equation*.* *The values of λ which make this equation consistent are called eigenvalues of the equation and the vectors* **x** *which satisfy this equation are called the eigenvectors.* The λ's are termed the eigenvalues of **A**; it is also said that the eigenvalue λ of **A** and the eigenvector **x** belong to each other.

Let us determine the eigenvalue of our operator

$$\mathbf{A} = \begin{bmatrix} 0 & 1 \\ 1 & 0 \end{bmatrix}$$

and also its principal axes. In our case the eigenvalue equation is

$$\begin{bmatrix} 0 & 1 \\ 1 & 0 \end{bmatrix}\begin{bmatrix} a \\ b \end{bmatrix} = \lambda\begin{bmatrix} a \\ b \end{bmatrix}$$

or

$$\begin{bmatrix} b \\ a \end{bmatrix} = \begin{bmatrix} \lambda a \\ \lambda b \end{bmatrix}$$

from which

$$\begin{bmatrix} b \\ a \end{bmatrix} - \begin{bmatrix} \lambda a \\ \lambda b \end{bmatrix} = 0$$

and

$$\begin{bmatrix} b - \lambda a \\ a - \lambda b \end{bmatrix} = 0$$

This latter matrix, consisting of two elements, will be zero, only if both of its elements vanish separately. Thus

$$b - \lambda a = 0$$
$$a - \lambda b = 0$$

* See also the section on Eigenphysics in Chapter 19.

or
$$-\lambda a + b = 0$$
$$a - \lambda b = 0$$

We have thus obtained two homogeneous equations in a and b. They are satisfied by the trivial solutions

$$a = b = 0$$

For nontrivial solutions, the determinant of the coefficients of a and b must be equal to zero. This can be seen from the following remarks. Consider the system of nonhomogeneous equations

$$a_{11}x_1 + a_{12}x_2 = h_1$$
$$a_{21}x_1 + a_{22}x_2 = h_2$$

The solutions of these are

$$x_1 = \frac{\begin{vmatrix} h_1 & a_{21} \\ h_2 & a_{22} \end{vmatrix}}{\begin{vmatrix} a_{11} & a_{12} \\ a_{21} & a_{22} \end{vmatrix}} \quad \text{and} \quad x_2 = \frac{\begin{vmatrix} a_{11} & h_1 \\ a_{21} & h_2 \end{vmatrix}}{\begin{vmatrix} a_{11} & a_{12} \\ a_{21} & a_{22} \end{vmatrix}}$$

Now, when

$$h_1 = h_2 = 0$$

then both of the determinants appearing in the numerators are zero. However, if in addition the determinants in the denominators are zero also, then the quotients are indeterminate and there is a possibility of non-zero solutions. In our case therefore the condition for non-zero solutions is

$$\begin{vmatrix} -\lambda & 1 \\ 1 & -\lambda \end{vmatrix} = 0$$

from which

$$\lambda^2 - 1 = 0$$

or

$$\lambda_1 = 1 \qquad \lambda_2 = -1$$

These are the eigenvalues of the operator **A**. Only for these eigenvalues will there exist non-zero solutions for a and b.

To obtain the principal axes of the operator we go back to our system of homogeneous equations

$$-\lambda a + b = 0$$
$$a - \lambda b = 0$$

and substitute in them, in turn, the two eigenvalues. For

$$\lambda_1 = 1$$

the equations become

$$-a + b = 0$$
$$a - b = 0$$

and both yield the result

$$a = b$$

This is the equation of one of the principal axes. As we would expect, this is the trace of the mirror plane, viz., the line AOB. To get the second principal axis we substitute

$$\lambda_2 = -1$$

in the set of homogeneous equations and obtain

$$a = -b$$

which gives the equation of the second principal axis of the operator $\mathbf{A}$.*

Let us perform the same deformation of space as before but now let us refer our vectors to the system of principal axes. Denote these axes as $O\xi_1$ and $O\xi_2$. Any vector will be reflected through the axis $O\xi_1$ and a new vector $\boldsymbol{\eta}$ will be obtained. We seek a matrix $\mathbf{S}$ such that

$$\boldsymbol{\eta} = \mathbf{S}\boldsymbol{\xi}$$

i.e., *we seek a matrix $\mathbf{S}$ which will deform space in the same way as $\mathbf{A}$*; in one case the vectors are referred to the system of principal axes and in the other case to the original system of axes. *Matrix $\mathbf{S}$ is said to be similar to the matrix $\mathbf{A}$.*

It is quite easy to guess the form of the matrix $\mathbf{S}$ similar to our matrix $\mathbf{A}$ but we will first outline the formal mathematical procedure to obtain such a matrix and then apply the procedure to our example. First of all in cases of this nature we will have to know the relation between the two sets of unit vectors defining the two systems of axes. Let the unit vectors in the principal axes be $\boldsymbol{\alpha}^{(1)}$ and $\boldsymbol{\alpha}^{(2)}$. The relation between this set and the set $\mathbf{a}^{(1)}$, $\mathbf{a}^{(2)}$ will be of the form

$$\begin{bmatrix} \boldsymbol{\alpha}^{(1)} \\ \boldsymbol{\alpha}^{(2)} \end{bmatrix} = \mathbf{B} \begin{bmatrix} \mathbf{a}^{(1)} \\ \mathbf{a}^{(2)} \end{bmatrix}$$

or, denoting the two column matrices by $\boldsymbol{\alpha}$ and $\mathbf{a}$ respectively, we can write

$$\boldsymbol{\alpha} = \mathbf{Ba}$$

We are assuming that matrix $\mathbf{B}$ is given. Let us suppose that ξ_1 and ξ_2 are the components of any vector $\mathbf{x}$ referred to the principal axes. Thus we can write

$$\mathbf{x} = \begin{bmatrix} \xi_1 \\ \xi_2 \end{bmatrix}$$

* It is obvious that these results are expected from symmetry arguments. These arguments should be used whenever possible.

Denote this column matrix by ξ. Its transpose is

$$\xi' = [\xi_1 \ \xi_2]$$

The vector **x** can therefore be written as

$$\mathbf{x} = [\xi_1 \quad \xi_2] \begin{bmatrix} \alpha^{(1)} \\ \alpha^{(2)} \end{bmatrix}$$

or briefly

$$\mathbf{x} = \xi'\alpha$$

Substituting for α the value **Ba** we get

$$\mathbf{x} = \xi'\mathbf{Ba}$$

In the original coordinate system the vector **x** can be written as

$$\mathbf{x} = \mathbf{x}'\mathbf{a}$$

where

$$\mathbf{x}' = [x_1 \quad x_2]$$

is the transpose of

$$\begin{bmatrix} x_1 \\ x_2 \end{bmatrix}$$

Comparing the equation $\mathbf{x} = \xi'\mathbf{Ba}$ with $\mathbf{x} = \mathbf{x}'\mathbf{a}$ we see that

$$\mathbf{x}' = \xi'\mathbf{B}$$

Taking the transpose of both sides we obtain

$$(\mathbf{x}')' = (\xi'\mathbf{B})'$$

Now

$$(\mathbf{x}')' = \mathbf{x}$$

and the transpose of a product of two matrices is equal to the reversed product of the two matrices transposed.* Thus

$$(\xi'\mathbf{B})' = \mathbf{B}'\xi$$

Therefore

$$\mathbf{x} = \mathbf{B}'\xi$$

from which

$$\xi = (\mathbf{B}')^{-1}\mathbf{x}$$

Denoting for a moment

$$\mathbf{C} = \mathbf{B}'$$

we have

$$\xi = \mathbf{C}^{-1}\mathbf{x}$$

---

* We will leave the proof of this as an exercise. Take $\mathbf{C} = \mathbf{AB}$ and apply the definition of the product to **AB**. Then apply the definition of the product to $\mathbf{C}' = (\mathbf{AB})'$ and also to $\mathbf{B}'\mathbf{A}'$. You will find that $(\mathbf{AB})' = \mathbf{B}'\mathbf{A}'$.

or

$$\begin{bmatrix} \xi_1 \\ \xi_2 \end{bmatrix} = \mathbf{C}^{-1} \begin{bmatrix} x_1 \\ x_2 \end{bmatrix}$$

This relates the components of one and the same vector referred to the original frame of reference and to the principal axes.

We are considering any vector, so we can also write

$$\eta = \mathbf{C}^{-1}\mathbf{y}$$

Now

$$\mathbf{y} = \mathbf{Ax}$$

therefore

$$\eta = \mathbf{C}^{-1}\mathbf{Ax}$$

From $\xi = \mathbf{C}^{-1}\mathbf{x}$ we obtain

$$\mathbf{x} = \mathbf{C}\xi$$

and substituting this in the last relation we arrive at

$$\eta = \mathbf{C}^{-1}\mathbf{AC}\xi$$

Reintroducing the matrix B, the last relation becomes

$$\eta = (\mathbf{B}')^{-1}\mathbf{AB}'\xi$$

Thus the similar matrix $\mathbf{S}$ which will deform space in the same way as $\mathbf{A}$ is given by

$$\mathbf{S} = (\mathbf{B}')^{-1}\mathbf{AB}'$$

It should perhaps be stated once more that we are deforming one and the same vector space. In the first situation all the vectors are referred to a chosen system of axes x_1, x_2 described by the unit vectors $\mathbf{a}^{(1)}$, $\mathbf{a}^{(2)}$; and we are performing the transformation of space by means of the matrix $\mathbf{A}$. Then, we perform the same deformation of the same space but referred to the system of principal axes ξ_1, ξ_2 described by unit vectors $\boldsymbol{\alpha}^{(1)}$, $\boldsymbol{\alpha}^{(2)}$; the similar matrix $\mathbf{S}$ performs this latter transformation.

Let us now go back to our example. This example is so simple that the form of the similar matrix $\mathbf{S}$ can be guessed immediately. Nevertheless, we will go through the formal procedure. Figure B.5 indicates how the matrix $\mathbf{B}$ relating

Fig. B.5

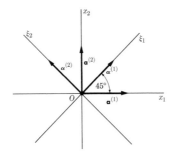

the unit vectors $\boldsymbol{\alpha}^{(1)}$, $\boldsymbol{\alpha}^{(2)}$ to $\mathbf{a}^{(1)}$, $\mathbf{a}^{(2)}$ can be obtained. From the figure we find

$$
\begin{bmatrix} \boldsymbol{\alpha}^{(1)} \\ \\ \boldsymbol{\alpha}^{(2)} \end{bmatrix} = \begin{bmatrix} \dfrac{1}{\sqrt{2}} & \dfrac{1}{\sqrt{2}} \\ \\ \dfrac{-1}{\sqrt{2}} & \dfrac{1}{\sqrt{2}} \end{bmatrix} \begin{bmatrix} \boldsymbol{\alpha}^{(1)} \\ \\ \mathbf{a}^{(2)} \end{bmatrix}
$$

Thus

$$
\mathbf{B} = \begin{bmatrix} \dfrac{1}{\sqrt{2}} & \dfrac{1}{\sqrt{2}} \\ \\ -\dfrac{1}{\sqrt{2}} & \dfrac{1}{\sqrt{2}} \end{bmatrix}
$$

Its transpose is

$$
\mathbf{B}' = \begin{bmatrix} \dfrac{1}{\sqrt{2}} & -\dfrac{1}{\sqrt{2}} \\ \\ \dfrac{1}{\sqrt{2}} & \dfrac{1}{\sqrt{2}} \end{bmatrix}
$$

The determinant of the transpose is

$$
|\mathbf{B}'| = \begin{vmatrix} \dfrac{1}{\sqrt{2}} & -\dfrac{1}{\sqrt{2}} \\ \\ \dfrac{1}{\sqrt{2}} & \dfrac{1}{\sqrt{2}} \end{vmatrix}
$$

or

$$
|\mathbf{B}'| = 1
$$

The inverse of $\mathbf{B}'$ therefore becomes

$$
(\mathbf{B}')^{-1} = \begin{bmatrix} \dfrac{1}{\sqrt{2}} & \dfrac{1}{\sqrt{2}} \\ \\ \dfrac{-1}{\sqrt{2}} & \dfrac{1}{\sqrt{2}} \end{bmatrix}
$$

Now

$$
\mathbf{A}\mathbf{B}' = \begin{bmatrix} 0 & 1 \\ \\ 1 & 0 \end{bmatrix} \begin{bmatrix} \dfrac{1}{\sqrt{2}} & -\dfrac{1}{\sqrt{2}} \\ \\ \dfrac{1}{\sqrt{2}} & \dfrac{1}{\sqrt{2}} \end{bmatrix}
$$

B–10   Linear transformations in two- and three-dimensional space. Similar matrices

or
$$\mathbf{AB'} = \begin{bmatrix} \dfrac{1}{\sqrt{2}} & \dfrac{1}{\sqrt{2}} \\[2ex] \dfrac{1}{\sqrt{2}} & \dfrac{-1}{\sqrt{2}} \end{bmatrix}$$

Finally the similar matrix becomes

$$(\mathbf{B'})^{-1}(\mathbf{AB'}) = \begin{bmatrix} \dfrac{1}{\sqrt{2}} & \dfrac{1}{\sqrt{2}} \\[2ex] \dfrac{-1}{\sqrt{2}} & \dfrac{1}{\sqrt{2}} \end{bmatrix} \begin{bmatrix} \dfrac{1}{\sqrt{2}} & \dfrac{1}{\sqrt{2}} \\[2ex] \dfrac{1}{\sqrt{2}} & \dfrac{-1}{\sqrt{2}} \end{bmatrix}$$

or

$$\mathbf{S} = \begin{bmatrix} 1 & 0 \\ 0 & -1 \end{bmatrix}$$

B–11 Diagonalization of Matrices

The reader will have noticed that the similar matrix $\mathbf{S}$ was diagonal, i.e., of the form

$$\mathbf{S} = \begin{bmatrix} \lambda_1 & 0 \\ 0 & \lambda_2 \end{bmatrix}$$

The resulting transformation

$$\boldsymbol{\eta} = \mathbf{S}\boldsymbol{\xi}$$

was therefore of the special form

$$\eta_1 = \lambda_1\xi_1 \quad \text{and} \quad \eta_2 = \lambda_2\xi_2$$

where in every relation the ξ's and the η's have the same subscripts. The original transformation was of the general form

$$\mathbf{y} = \mathbf{Ax}$$

or

$$y_1 = a_{11}x_1 + a_{12}x_2$$
$$y_2 = a_{21}x_1 + a_{22}x_2$$

We now pose the following general problem: Given a transformation

$$\mathbf{y} = \mathbf{Ax}$$

we wish to find a matrix $\mathbf{C}$ by means of which the diagonal matrix

$$\mathbf{S} = \mathbf{C}^{-1}\mathbf{AC}$$

similar to **A** can be formulated. At the same time we want to determine a set of vectors which will define the principal axes of the operator **A**. We will again work in two dimensions. Consider the required matrix relation

$$\mathbf{C}^{-1}\mathbf{AC} = \mathbf{S}$$

Premultiplying both sides by **C** we get

$$\mathbf{AC} = \mathbf{CS}$$

Written in full, this reads

$$\begin{bmatrix} a_{11} & a_{12} \\ a_{21} & a_{22} \end{bmatrix} \begin{bmatrix} c_{11} & c_{12} \\ c_{21} & c_{22} \end{bmatrix} = \begin{bmatrix} c_{11} & c_{12} \\ c_{21} & c_{22} \end{bmatrix} \begin{bmatrix} \lambda_1 & 0 \\ 0 & \lambda_2 \end{bmatrix}$$

This is a matrix equation in which only the matrix **A** is given. We will have to determine what values of λ make this equation consistent and then determine the matrix **C**. Matrix-multiplying out both sides we get

$$\begin{bmatrix} a_{11}c_{11} + a_{12}c_{21} & a_{11}c_{12} + a_{12}c_{22} \\ a_{21}c_{11} + a_{22}c_{21} & a_{21}c_{12} + a_{22}c_{22} \end{bmatrix} = \begin{bmatrix} c_{11}\lambda_1 & c_{12}\lambda_2 \\ c_{21}\lambda_1 & c_{22}\lambda_2 \end{bmatrix}$$

The matrix on the left will be equal to the matrix on the right if all the corresponding elements will be equal. Thus

$$a_{11}c_{11} + a_{12}c_{21} = c_{11}\lambda_1$$
$$a_{21}c_{11} + a_{22}c_{21} = c_{21}\lambda_1$$

and

$$a_{11}c_{12} + a_{12}c_{22} = c_{12}\lambda_2$$
$$a_{21}c_{12} + a_{22}c_{22} = c_{22}\lambda_2$$

or

$$(a_{11} - \lambda_1)c_{11} + a_{12}c_{21} = 0$$
$$a_{21}c_{11} + (a_{22} - \lambda_1)c_{21} = 0$$

and

$$(a_{11} - \lambda_2)c_{12} + a_{12}c_{22} = 0$$
$$a_{21}c_{12} + (a_{22} - \lambda_2)c_{22} = 0$$

These relations have been paired in order to obtain two sets of homogeneous equations: one for λ_1 with c_{11} and c_{21} as unknowns and the other for λ_2 with c_{12} and c_{22} as unknowns. We notice that c_{11}, c_{21} and c_{12}, c_{22} form the two columns of the matrix **C**. We still have not determined the permissible values of the λ's. Since both sets of equations are homogeneous therefore for nonzero solutions for c_{11}, c_{21} and c_{12}, c_{22} the determinants of the coefficients must be equal to zero. Treating λ as unknown we have

$$\begin{vmatrix} a_{11} - \lambda & a_{12} \\ a_{21} & a_{22} - \lambda \end{vmatrix} = 0$$

388

The solutions of this determinantal equation will furnish the values of λ_1 and λ_2. The two sets of homogeneous equations can now be solved for the column vectors

$$\begin{bmatrix} c_{11} \\ c_{21} \end{bmatrix}$$

and

$$\begin{bmatrix} c_{12} \\ c_{22} \end{bmatrix}$$

of the matrix **C**. In the previous section we had

$$\mathbf{B}' = \mathbf{C}$$

where the matrix **B** related the original system of axes to the principal axes. Therefore the two vectors given by the two above column matrices will determine the principal axes. For this reason they are called the eigenvectors or characteristic vectors. Since the sets of equations written out above are homogeneous, only the ratios c_{11}/c_{21} and c_{12}/c_{22} will be determined. However, for the purpose of determining the directions of the principal axes, these ratios are sufficient.

We now return once more to our previous example and try to diagonalize the matrix

$$\mathbf{A} = \begin{bmatrix} 0 & 1 \\ 1 & 0 \end{bmatrix}$$

and find its principal axes. The determinantal equation

$$\begin{vmatrix} -\lambda & 1 \\ 1 & -\lambda \end{vmatrix} = 0$$

yields

$$\lambda_1 = 1 \quad \text{and} \quad \lambda_2 = -1$$

These are the eigenvalues of the matrix **A**. The first of the above set of homogeneous equations gives

$$(0 - 1)c_{11} + 1 \times c_{21} = 0$$
$$1 \times c_{11} + (0 - 1)c_{21} = 0$$

and both equations yield

$$c_{11} = c_{21}$$

Setting $c_{11} = c_{21} = \alpha$ for a moment, we see that the first eigenvector is

$$\begin{bmatrix} \alpha \\ \alpha \end{bmatrix}$$

This is a vector of equal components and therefore lies along the AOB line of Figure B.4. To make this a unit vector we must choose

$$\alpha = 1/\sqrt{2}$$

for its components. Thus one of the principal axes is specified by the vector

$$\begin{bmatrix} \dfrac{1}{\sqrt{2}} \\ \dfrac{1}{\sqrt{2}} \end{bmatrix}$$

For λ_2 both homogeneous equations yield

$$c_{12} = -c_{22}$$

so, the second principal axis is given by the unit vector

$$\begin{bmatrix} -\dfrac{1}{\sqrt{2}} \\ \dfrac{1}{\sqrt{2}} \end{bmatrix}$$

Therefore the required matrix is

$$\mathbf{C} = \begin{bmatrix} \dfrac{1}{\sqrt{2}} & -\dfrac{1}{\sqrt{2}} \\ \dfrac{1}{\sqrt{2}} & \dfrac{1}{\sqrt{2}} \end{bmatrix}$$

as we obtained previously.

The diagonal matrix $\mathbf{S}$ is immediately determined once λ_1 and λ_2 are found. We can, however, check, using the matrix $\mathbf{C}$ just obtained, that indeed

$$\mathbf{S} = \mathbf{C}^{-1}\mathbf{A}\mathbf{C}$$

B-12 *Orthogonal Transformations*

The length of a vector

$$\mathbf{x} = \begin{bmatrix} x_1 \\ x_2 \end{bmatrix}$$

is given by

$$x^2 = \mathbf{x}'\mathbf{x}$$

where $\mathbf{x}'$ is the transpose of $\mathbf{x}$.

Let a matrix **A** transform the vector **x** into **y**. We thus consider the transformation

$$y = Ax$$

Further, let us require that the length of **y** be the same as that of **x**, i.e.

$$y'y = x'x$$

If **y** = **Ax** then

$$y' = x'A'$$

and

$$y'y = x'A'Ax$$

In order that this last expression be consistent with our requirement of equal lengths for both vectors we must have

$$A'A = I$$

where **I** is the unity matrix. The type of transformation for which the last condition is satisfied is called an *orthogonal transformation*, and the last equation may be called the *orthogonality condition*. Premultiplying this equation by A^{-1} we get

$$A' = A^{-1}$$

which is *another form of the orthogonality condition.*

B–13 Quadratic Forms

Consider the quadratic form

$$Q = x'Ax$$

quoted as an example previously. Let the matrix **A** be symmetric. In general, such a quadratic form consists of squares of the x_i variables as well as mixed terms $x_i x_j$, both with coefficients which are the elements of the matrix **A**.[*] In many instances it is important to represent the same quadratic form as sum of the squares with some coefficients, i.e., we desire the form

$$Q = \lambda_1 \xi_1{}^2 + \lambda_2 \xi_2{}^2 + \cdots + \lambda_n \xi_n{}^2$$

We will show that *the reduction of the quadratic form given by Q* = **x'Ax** *to that given by the last equation is equivalent to reducing the transformation*

$$y = Ax$$

to the form

$$\eta = S\xi$$

*where **S** is a diagonal matrix similar to* **A**. Thus the latter transformation is

[*] Study again the full form of Q given in Section B–9.

of the same type as the reduction of the form

$$Q = \mathbf{x}'\mathbf{A}\mathbf{x}$$

to

$$Q = \xi'\mathbf{\Lambda}\xi$$

where $\mathbf{\Lambda}$ is a diagonal matrix.

We will first show that if the form $Q = \mathbf{x}'\mathbf{A}\mathbf{x}$ is symmetric then a linear transformation

$$\mathbf{x} = \mathbf{C}\xi$$

preserves the symmetry. The transpose of $\mathbf{x}$ is

$$\mathbf{x}' = \xi'\mathbf{C}'$$

Substituting these last relations in $Q = \mathbf{x}'\mathbf{A}\mathbf{x}$ yields

$$Q = \xi'\mathbf{C}'\mathbf{A}\mathbf{C}\xi$$

Now, a matrix is symmetric if it is equal to its transpose. Consider the matrix $\mathbf{C}'\mathbf{A}\mathbf{C}$. Its transpose is*

$$(\mathbf{C}'\mathbf{A}\mathbf{C})' = \mathbf{C}'\mathbf{A}'\mathbf{C}$$

But $\mathbf{A}$ is symmetric, i.e.

$$\mathbf{A}' = \mathbf{A}$$

so that the last relation becomes

$$(\mathbf{C}'\mathbf{A}\mathbf{C})' = \mathbf{C}'\mathbf{A}\mathbf{C}$$

and this proves our assertion.

Let the transformation $\mathbf{x} = \mathbf{C}\xi$ be orthogonal. Then, by the orthogonality condition,

$$\mathbf{C}' = \mathbf{C}^{-1}$$

and

$$\mathbf{C}'\mathbf{A}\mathbf{C} = \mathbf{C}^{-1}\mathbf{A}\mathbf{C}$$

In order to obtain the desired quadratic form we must write

$$\mathbf{\Lambda} = \mathbf{C}^{-1}\mathbf{A}\mathbf{C}$$

where $\mathbf{\Lambda}$ is diagonal. But this is a matrix equation which we have already solved. As we have seen, the diagonal elements of $\mathbf{\Lambda}$ are obtained by solving the determinantal equation

$$|\mathbf{A} - \lambda\mathbf{I}| = 0$$

If every λ is positive, we call the quadratic form positive definite.

* Prove that $(\mathbf{ABC})' = \mathbf{C}'\mathbf{B}'\mathbf{A}'$.

One of the important topics in classical mechanics is the problem of the small oscillations of a system about its position of equilibrium.[*] This problem can be solved in a most elegant and concise way by simultaneously transforming two quadratic forms to sums of squares of the variables. In the problem of small oscillations the two quadratic forms are the kinetic and the potential energies of the system. Here we will consider the purely mathematical aspect of the problem.

Consider the quadratic forms

$$Q_1 = \mathbf{x}'\mathbf{A}\mathbf{x}$$

and

$$Q_2 = \mathbf{x}'\mathbf{B}\mathbf{x}$$

where the matrices $\mathbf{A}$ and $\mathbf{B}$ are symmetric. Let Q_1 be positive definite. Our aim is to reduce the two quadratic forms to

$$Q_1 = \boldsymbol{\eta}'\boldsymbol{\eta}$$

and

$$Q_2 = \boldsymbol{\eta}'\boldsymbol{\Lambda}\boldsymbol{\eta}$$

where the new Q_1 is equal to sum of squares of the new variables and Q_2 is the sum of squares with coefficients λ_i. We will now show that such simultaneous reduction is always possible.

We can always find a transformation

$$\mathbf{x} = \mathbf{C}\boldsymbol{\xi}$$

such that

$$Q_1 = \boldsymbol{\xi}'\boldsymbol{\xi}$$

where $\boldsymbol{\xi}'$ is the transpose of $\boldsymbol{\xi}$. From $\mathbf{x} = \mathbf{C}\boldsymbol{\xi}$ we get

$$\mathbf{x}' = \boldsymbol{\xi}'\mathbf{C}'$$

Substituting $\mathbf{x}$ and $\mathbf{x}'$ in $Q_1 = \mathbf{x}'\mathbf{A}\mathbf{x}$ we obtain

$$Q_1 = \boldsymbol{\xi}'\mathbf{C}'\mathbf{A}\mathbf{C}'\boldsymbol{\xi}$$

In order that Q_1 be of the form $Q_1 = \boldsymbol{\xi}'\boldsymbol{\xi}$ we must have

$$\mathbf{C}'\mathbf{A}\mathbf{C} = \mathbf{I}$$

where $\mathbf{I}$ is the unity matrix. When Q_1 is positive definite the latter matrix equation can always be solved. This we will demonstrate using the techniques which we already know, together with some geometrical arguments. For simplicity we will work with two variables and a concrete example.

[*] See Chapter 16.

Consider the quadratic form

$$Q_1 = \mathbf{x}'\mathbf{A}\mathbf{x}$$

where

$$\mathbf{x} = \begin{bmatrix} x_1 \\ x_2 \end{bmatrix}$$

and

$$\mathbf{A} = \begin{bmatrix} 2 & 1 \\ 1 & 2 \end{bmatrix}$$

The actual form Q_1 is

$$Q_1 = [x_1 \quad x_2] \begin{bmatrix} 2 & 1 \\ 1 & 2 \end{bmatrix} \begin{bmatrix} x_1 \\ x_2 \end{bmatrix}$$

$$= [x_1 \quad x_2] \begin{bmatrix} 2x_1 + x_2 \\ x_1 + 2x_2 \end{bmatrix}$$

$$= 2x_1{}^2 + x_1 x_2 + x_2 x_1 + 2x_2{}^2$$

or

$$Q_1 = 2x_1{}^2 + 2x_1 x_2 + 2x_2{}^2$$

This quadratic form is a positive definite. Such a form can always be transformed to

$$Q_1 = \boldsymbol{\xi}'\boldsymbol{\xi}$$

i.e., to

$$Q_1 = \xi_1{}^2 + \xi_2{}^2$$

The transformation will in general not be an orthogonal one. To show that this can be done, we will first transform $Q_1 = \mathbf{x}'\mathbf{A}\mathbf{x}$ to

$$Q_1 = \boldsymbol{\zeta}'\mathbf{N}\boldsymbol{\zeta}$$

where

$$\mathbf{N} = \begin{bmatrix} \nu_1 & 0 \\ 0 & \nu_2 \end{bmatrix}$$

We can obtain the matrix $\mathbf{N}$ immediately by solving the characteristic determinantal equation of $\mathbf{A}$, viz.

$$\begin{vmatrix} (2 - \nu) & 1 \\ 1 & (2 - \nu) \end{vmatrix} = 0$$

or

$$(2 - \nu - 1)(2 - \nu + 1) = 0$$

Therefore

$$\nu_1 = 1 \quad \text{and} \quad \nu_2 = 3$$

Thus the quadratic form Q_1 becomes

$$Q_1 = \zeta_1{}^2 + 3\zeta_2{}^2$$

We will do away with the determination of the eigenvectors ζ_1 and ζ_2. What we have done so far is to transform the original quadratic form $Q = \mathbf{x'Ax}$ to the system of the principal axes of $\mathbf{A}$. We can see what we are doing, by considering the geometrical interpretation of the quadratic form. For the quadratic form under consideration we can write

$$Q_1 = \mathbf{x'Ax} = c$$

and this represents an ellipse oriented in some way in the x_1, x_2 system of axes (Fig. B.6). The form

$$Q_1 = \zeta_1{}^2 + 3\zeta_2{}^2 = c$$

represents the same ellipse where the coordinate axes $O\zeta_1$ and $O\zeta_2$ run along the axes of the ellipse (Fig. B.6). Now, we can deform the ellipse into a circle.

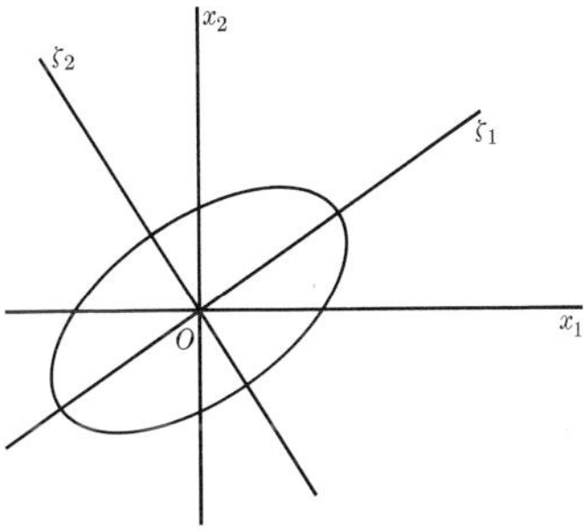

Fig. B.6

The transformation which will perform it will not be orthogonal. This transformation can be found quite easily. In the quadratic form $Q_1 = \zeta_1{}^2 + 3\zeta_2{}^2$ let

$$\xi_1 = \zeta_1 \qquad \text{and} \qquad \xi_2 = \sqrt{3}\,\zeta_2$$

Then the quadratic form transforms to

$$Q_1 = \xi_1{}^2 + \xi_2{}^2$$

Incidentally, this latter transformation of coordinates is

$$\begin{bmatrix} \zeta_1 \\ \zeta_2 \end{bmatrix} = \begin{bmatrix} 1 & 0 \\ 0 & \dfrac{1}{\sqrt{3}} \end{bmatrix} \begin{bmatrix} \xi_1 \\ \xi_2 \end{bmatrix}$$

from which the matrix of the second transformation can be read off.

We have convinced ourselves that some resultant transformation

$$\mathbf{x} = \mathbf{C\xi}$$

will reduce

$$Q_1 = \mathbf{x'Ax}$$

to

$$Q_1 = \mathbf{\xi'\xi}$$

B—14 Simultaneous transformation of two quadratic forms

395

Under the same transformation Q_2 will reduce to

$$Q_2 = \xi' \mathbf{F} \xi$$

where the matrix $\mathbf{F}$ is given by

$$\mathbf{F} = \mathbf{C}' \mathbf{B} \mathbf{C}$$

Next, we will subject the variables ξ to the orthogonal transformation

$$\xi = \mathbf{D} \eta$$

such that Q_2 becomes

$$Q_2 = \eta' \mathbf{\Lambda} \eta$$

where, as we know, the diagonal matrix $\mathbf{\Lambda}$ is given by

$$\mathbf{\Lambda} = \mathbf{D}^{-1} \mathbf{C} \mathbf{D}$$

Since the transformation from the variables ξ to η is orthogonal, therefore

$$\eta' \eta = \xi' \xi$$

and so Q_1 assumes the form

$$Q_1 = \eta' \eta$$

The overall transformation from the variables $\mathbf{x}$ to η will be performed by means of a matrix $\mathbf{S}$ such that

$$\mathbf{x} = \mathbf{S} \eta$$

In this way we have achieved our goal of transforming the quadratic forms

$$Q_1 = \mathbf{x}' \mathbf{A} \mathbf{x}$$

and

$$Q_2 = \mathbf{x}' \mathbf{B} \mathbf{x}$$

to

$$Q_1 = \eta' \eta$$

and

$$Q_2 = \eta' \mathbf{\Lambda} \eta$$

Written in full, the original quadratic forms are

$$Q_1 = a_{11} x_1^2 + a_{12} x_1 x_2 + \cdots + a_{22} x_2^2 + a_{21} x_2 x_1 + \cdots$$

and

$$Q_2 = b_{11} x_1^2 + b_{12} x_1 x_2 + \cdots + b_{22} x_2^2 + b_{21} x_2 x_1 + \cdots$$

and the new ones are

$$Q_1 = \eta_1^2 + \eta_2^2 + \cdots$$

and

$$Q_2 = \lambda_1 \eta_1^2 + \lambda_2 \eta_2^2 + \cdots$$

396   B–14 Simultaneous transformation of two quadratic forms

All that we have shown so far is that such a reduction is possible. We have yet to indicate how to obtain the λ's which in this case can be called the characteristic numbers of Q_2 relative to Q_1.

We notice that if we have any quadratic form

$$Q = \mathbf{x}'\mathbf{A}\mathbf{x}$$

and then transform the variables according to

$$\mathbf{x} = \mathbf{S}\eta$$

then substituting this and

$$\mathbf{x}' = \eta'\mathbf{S}'$$

in Q, we get

$$Q = \eta'\mathbf{S}'\mathbf{A}\mathbf{S}\eta$$

Thus the matrix of the transformation is $\mathbf{S}'\mathbf{A}\mathbf{S}$ and the determinant of this matrix is $|\mathbf{S}|^2|\mathbf{A}|$.*

Now, out of the two quadratic forms Q_1 and Q_2, formulate

$$Q = Q_2 - \lambda Q_1$$

Substituting the original forms we get

$$Q = \mathbf{x}'\mathbf{B}\mathbf{x} - \lambda\mathbf{x}'\mathbf{A}\mathbf{x}$$

or

$$Q = \mathbf{x}'(\mathbf{B} - \lambda\mathbf{A})\mathbf{x}$$

Its determinant is

$$D = |\mathbf{B} - \lambda\mathbf{A}|$$

Inserting in $Q = Q_2 - \lambda Q_1$ the reduced forms we get

$$Q = \eta'\mathbf{\Lambda}\eta - \lambda\eta'\eta$$
$$= \eta'\mathbf{\Lambda}\eta - \eta'\lambda\mathbf{I}\eta$$
$$= \eta'(\mathbf{\Lambda} - \lambda\mathbf{I})\eta$$

and the determinant of this form is

$$\Delta = |\mathbf{\Lambda} - \lambda\mathbf{I}|$$

As in the case just mentioned above the determinant differs from D by $|\mathbf{S}|^2$. Thus

$$|\mathbf{S}|^2|\mathbf{B} - \lambda\mathbf{A}| = |\mathbf{\Lambda} - \lambda\mathbf{I}|$$

Now,

$$|\mathbf{\Lambda} - \lambda\mathbf{I}| = (\lambda_1 - \lambda)(\lambda_2 - \lambda)\cdots(\lambda_n - \lambda)$$

* Here we are making use of two theorems: one states that the determinant of a product of matrices is equal to the product of the determinants of the individual matrices, and the second theorem states that determinants of a matrix and its transpose are equal.

and since S does not contain λ, the λ's must be the roots of the determinantal equation

$$|\mathbf{B} - \lambda\mathbf{A}| = 0*$$

Written in full, this determinantal equation has the form

$$\begin{vmatrix} b_{11} - \lambda a_{11} & b_{12} - \lambda a_{12} & \ldots & b_{1n} - \lambda a_{1n} \\ b_{n1} - \lambda a_{n1} & \ldots\ldots\ldots\ldots\ldots & & b_{nn} - \lambda a_{nn} \end{vmatrix} = 0$$

There still remains the problem of determining the form of the matrix $\mathbf{S}$ in the transformation

$$\mathbf{x} = \mathbf{S}\eta$$

i.e., we still want to determine the relation between the new coordinates η and the old coordinates $\mathbf{x}$. We know that the matrix $\mathbf{S}$ which furnishes this link is the product of successive transformations leading from $\mathbf{x}$ through ξ to η. From the matrices of these successive transformations $\mathbf{S}$ can be determined. The required relation between the η and $\mathbf{x}$ coordinates is then given by

$$\eta = \mathbf{S}^{-1}\mathbf{x}$$

However, when applying the whole procedure to the theory of small oscillations we will see that the relation between the original and the new coordinates is obtained in a simpler manner.**

B–15 *Simultaneous Diagonalization of Two Matrices*

We have demonstrated that two symmetric quadratic forms of which one is positive definite can simultaneously be reduced to sums of squares. We will go through the procedure once more and will show that the problem is really one of simultaneous diagonalization of two matrices. We will show that this can be done by means of a single matrix.

Consider again the two quadratic forms

$$Q_1 = \sum_i \sum_j a_{ij} x_i x_j$$

and

$$Q_2 = \sum_i \sum_j b_{ij} x_i x_j$$

---

* The situation is somewhat similar to the case of, let us say, a quadratic equation. For this equation we can write

$$S(ax^2 + bx + c) = (x - x_1)(x - x_2)$$

If S does not contain the unknowns then x_1 and x_2 are the solutions of the equation

$$ax^2 + bx + c = 0$$

** See Chapter 16.

In matrix form these can be written as

$$Q_1 = \mathbf{x}'\mathbf{Ax}$$

and

$$Q_2 = \mathbf{x}'\mathbf{Bx}$$

If the two matrices $\mathbf{A}$ and $\mathbf{B}$ are symmetric and one of the two quadratic forms, say Q_1 is positive definite, then it is possible to find a transformation

$$\mathbf{x} = \mathbf{C}\boldsymbol{\eta}$$

such that

$$Q_1 = \boldsymbol{\eta}'\boldsymbol{\eta}$$

and

$$Q_2 = \boldsymbol{\eta}'\boldsymbol{\Lambda}\boldsymbol{\eta}$$

where $\boldsymbol{\Lambda}$ is a diagonal matrix.

From $\mathbf{x} = \mathbf{C}\boldsymbol{\eta}$ we get

$$\mathbf{x}' = \boldsymbol{\eta}'\mathbf{C}'$$

Substitution of the expressions for $\mathbf{x}$ and $\mathbf{x}'$ in Q_1 and in Q_2 yields

$$Q_1 = \boldsymbol{\eta}'\mathbf{C}'\mathbf{AC}\boldsymbol{\eta}$$

and

$$Q_2 = \boldsymbol{\eta}'\mathbf{C}'\mathbf{BC}\boldsymbol{\eta}$$

In order that Q_1 and Q_2 reduce to the forms given by $Q_1 = \boldsymbol{\eta}'\boldsymbol{\eta}$ and $Q_2 = \boldsymbol{\eta}'\boldsymbol{\Lambda}\boldsymbol{\eta}$ we must have

$$\mathbf{C}'\mathbf{AC} = \mathbf{I}$$

and

$$\mathbf{C}'\mathbf{BC} = \boldsymbol{\Lambda}$$

where $\mathbf{I}$ is a unit matrix. Premultiplying both last equations by $(\mathbf{C}')^{-1}$ yields

$$\mathbf{AC} = (\mathbf{C}')^{-1}$$

and

$$\mathbf{BC} = (\mathbf{C}')^{-1}\boldsymbol{\Lambda}$$

Therefore

$$\mathbf{BC} = \mathbf{AC}\boldsymbol{\Lambda}$$

Now we will proceed in a similar manner as in the section on diagonalization of matrices. Again, for brevity, let all the matrices be of two-by-two order. Then the last matrix equation written in full becomes

$$\begin{bmatrix} b_{11} & b_{12} \\ b_{21} & b_{22} \end{bmatrix} \begin{bmatrix} c_{11} & c_{12} \\ c_{21} & c_{22} \end{bmatrix} = \begin{bmatrix} a_{11} & a_{12} \\ a_{21} & a_{22} \end{bmatrix} \begin{bmatrix} c_{11} & c_{12} \\ c_{21} & c_{22} \end{bmatrix} \begin{bmatrix} \lambda_1 & 0 \\ 0 & \lambda_2 \end{bmatrix}$$

B–15 Simultaneous diagonalization of two matrices

which after multiplication becomes

$$\begin{bmatrix} b_{11}c_{11} + b_{12}c_{21} & b_{11}c_{12} + b_{12}c_{22} \\ b_{21}c_{11} + b_{22}c_{21} & b_{21}c_{12} + b_{22}c_{22} \end{bmatrix}$$

$$= \begin{bmatrix} (a_{11}c_{11} + a_{12}c_{21})\lambda_1 & (a_{11}c_{12} + a_{12}c_{22})\lambda_2 \\ (a_{21}c_{11} + a_{22}c_{21})\lambda_1 & (a_{21}c_{12} + a_{22}c_{22})\lambda_2 \end{bmatrix}$$

The two matrices will be equal if the corresponding elements on both sides are equal. Thus, after some rearrangement

$$(b_{11} - \lambda_1 a_{11})c_{11} + (b_{12} - \lambda_1 a_{12})c_{21} = 0$$
$$(b_{21} - \lambda_1 a_{21})c_{11} + (b_{22} - \lambda_1 a_{22})c_{21} = 0$$

and

$$(b_{11} - \lambda_2 a_{11})c_{12} + (b_{12} - \lambda_2 a_{12})c_{22} = 0$$
$$(b_{21} - \lambda_2 a_{21})c_{12} + (b_{22} - \lambda_2 a_{22})c_{22} = 0$$

Both sets of equations can be written as

$$\sum_i \sum_j (b_{ij} - \lambda_s a_{ij})c_{is} = 0 \qquad i, j, s = 1, 2$$

These equations have been written on the assumption that the λ's are known. The last two sets of equations are homogeneous equations. In the first set the unknowns are c_{11} and c_{21} which are the elements of the first column of the matrix $\mathbf{C}$. The unknowns of the second set are the elements of the second column of $\mathbf{C}$. These equations will have solutions if the determinant of the coefficients is zero. We see that both λ_1 and λ_2 have to satisfy the determinantal equation

$$\begin{vmatrix} b_{11} - \lambda a_{11} & b_{12} - \lambda a_{12} \\ b_{21} - \lambda a_{21} & b_{22} - \lambda a_{22} \end{vmatrix} = 0$$

This is of the same form as the determinantal equation of the previous section. Once the λ's are known, the above homogeneous equations can be solved for c_{11}, c_{21} and c_{12}, c_{22}, from which the matrix $\mathbf{C}$ may be constructed. Once this matrix is known, the new coordinates are obtained from

$$\boldsymbol{\eta} = \mathbf{C}^{-1}\mathbf{x}$$

In the section on orthogonal transformations we defined the length of a vector as

$$x^2 = \mathbf{x}'\mathbf{x}$$

and the condition for orthogonal transformation was

$$\mathbf{C}'\mathbf{C} = \mathbf{I}$$

where **C** was the transformation matrix and **I** the unity matrix. If a matrix **C** satisfied this condition, then the vector

$$y = Cx$$

was of the same length as **x**. It was understood that the operations were performed in a Cartesian coordinate system.

In the transformations considered here, different conditions are obtained. One is that

$$C'AC = I$$

This may also be looked upon as an orthogonality condition but in a non-Cartesian system, i.e., in a space with inclined axes. In such a space the length of a vector **x** will be given by

$$x'Ax$$

where the matrix **A** characterizes the space.

We can see the situation better if we consider an example. Let a two-dimensional non-Cartesian space be referred to two inclined axes. Draw a vector **x** which has components x_1 and x_2. We notice from Figure B.7 that

Fig. B.7

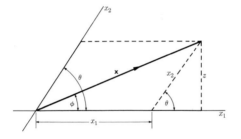

$$z = x_2 \sin \theta = x \sin \phi$$

and

$$x_1 = x \cos \phi - x_2 \cos \theta$$

Therefore

$$x_2 \sin \theta = x \sin \phi$$

and

$$x_1 + x_2 \cos \theta = x \cos \phi$$

From the last two equations, by squaring and adding, we obtain

$$x^2 = x_1{}^2 + \cos \theta x_1 x_2 + \cos \theta x_2 x_1 + x_2{}^2$$

or

$$x^2 = [x_1 \quad x_2] \begin{bmatrix} 1 & \cos \theta \\ \cos \theta & 1 \end{bmatrix} \begin{bmatrix} x_1 \\ x_2 \end{bmatrix}$$

which is of the form

$$x^2 = x'Ax$$

We notice that when $\theta = 90°$

$$x^2 = [x_1 \quad x_2] \begin{bmatrix} 1 & 0 \\ 0 & 1 \end{bmatrix} \begin{bmatrix} x_1 \\ x_2 \end{bmatrix}$$

$$= \mathbf{x'Ix}$$

or

$$x^2 = \mathbf{x'x}$$

WAVE MOTION

C–1 The Wave Equation

Consider a wave of unchanging shape which travels in the positive x direction. Let the medium consist of a one-dimensional continuum, say a string. Under the action of the wave the particles of the medium are displaced up and down in the vertical direction which will be denoted by ξ. We wish to obtain a general expression for the displacement ξ at any time t and at any point x, i.e., we wish to get the general form of the function

$$\xi = f(x, t)$$

which will describe the wave motion. A relation of this form will be called the wave equation. We notice that ξ is a function of the time variable t and the space variable x and as such is more difficult to construct than a function of either variable. We can envisage immediately what happens when one of the variables is held fixed. Thus if $t = t_0$ then

$$\xi = f(x, t_0)$$

will represent the profile of the wave at this time. We may think of it as a snapshot of the wave. It may have a shape such as that shown in Figure C.1.

Fig. C.1

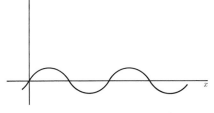

We can also place ourselves at a point $x = x_0$; then

$$\xi = f(x_0, t)$$

We would then examine the time behavior of ξ at this point and plot it as shown in Figure C.2.

Fig. C.2

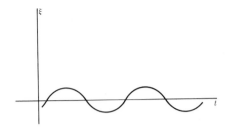

How do we insert in the expression for ξ the combined variation of t and x? We want the whole unchanged profile to move to the right with some speed c. During a time interval t' the profile will have moved a distance

$$x' = ct'$$

We now introduce a coordinate system moving with velocity c. At some time $t = t_0$ let the profile be

$$\xi = f(x)$$

At this instant of time affix to the wave a coordinate system moving with velocity c, and start varying the time. Then at any time t the equation

$$\xi = f(x')$$

will represent the same profile as the previous equation. Now x' and x are related by

$$x' = x - ct$$

therefore

$$\xi = f(x - ct)$$

This is then the general form of the wave equation for a wave moving towards the positive x direction without any change of profile. We can check once more that this is the right form, for an increase t' in time will correspond to an increase ct' in x and

$$f[(x + ct') - c(t + t')] = f(x - ct)$$

Thus we have a method of obtaining the wave equation from the equation of the profile $f(x)$; just replace x by $(x - ct)$. Notice that this applies to a wave of any shape because the nature of the function f has not been specified.

C–2   Differential Equation of the Wave

Differentiate

$$\xi = f(x - ct)$$

partially with respect to x twice; then

$$\frac{\partial^2 \xi}{\partial x^2} = f''$$

where the double prime signifies differentiation with respect to the variable $x' = x - ct$. Next partially differentiate the same expression twice with respect to t and obtain

$$\frac{\partial^2 \xi}{\partial t^2} = c^2 f''$$

Eliminating f'' between the last two expressions we obtain

$$\frac{\partial^2 \xi}{\partial x^2} - \frac{1}{c^2} \frac{\partial^2 \xi}{\partial t^2} = 0$$

which is *the differential equation of a wave travelling along x with the velocity c*. This differential equation is satisfied by any function of the form $f(x - ct)$ and also by any function of the form $g(x + ct)$, the latter representing a wave travelling in the negative x direction. Thus the general solution will have to be written as

$$\xi = Af(x - ct) + Bg(x + ct)$$

We notice that this equation represents two waves: one travelling to the right and the other travelling to the left, both travelling with the same speed. The general solution therefore represents a superposition of two such waves.

C-3   A Simple Harmonic Wave

Consider the wave equation

$$\xi = a \sin [\kappa(x + ct)]$$

This is a relation of the form

$$\xi = f(x, t)$$

or actually of the form

$$\xi = f(x + ct)$$

Therefore it is an equation of a wave propagated along the x direction towards negative x. Both its profile and its time variation at any point in the medium are sinusoidal, as can be checked by first holding t constant and then by fixing the value of x. This wave is therefore both space periodic and time periodic. The space period is called the *wavelength* and is denoted by λ. If λ is to be the space period of the wave then an increase of x by λ should leave ξ unchanged and is therefore equivalent to an increase of the whole argument of the sine function by 2π. Thus

$$\sin \kappa[(x + \lambda) + ct] = \sin [\kappa(x + ct) + 2\pi]$$

Hence

$$\kappa\lambda = 2\pi$$

or

$$\kappa = \frac{2\pi}{\lambda}$$

The constant κ is called the *propagation constant*.

The *time period* will be denoted by τ. An increase of the time by τ should not change the value of ξ and is therefore equivalent to an increase of the whole argument of the sine function by 2π. Therefore

$$\sin \kappa[x + c(t + \tau)] = \sin [\kappa(x + ct) + 2\pi]$$

Thus

$$\kappa c\tau = 2\pi$$

or

$$\frac{2\pi}{\lambda} c\tau = 2\pi$$

from which

$$\tau = \frac{\lambda}{c}$$

In terms of the *linear frequency*

$$c = \lambda\nu$$

Other quantities appearing quite often in the wave equation are the *angular frequency* $\omega = 2\pi\nu$ and the *wave number* $k = 1/\lambda$.

Because of the different quantities characterizing the wave motion, there are several equivalent forms of the wave equation, depending on the quantities used. One of the forms is

$$\xi = a \sin (\omega t + \kappa x)$$

The form of the argument of the sine function used in this expression is the one most often used in discussions of wave motion.

C-4 *The Concept of Phase and Phase Velocity. Definition of the Wave*

Let there be a wave

$$\xi = a \sin (\omega t - \kappa x + \delta)$$

where δ is a constant. This expression can be written as

$$\xi = a \sin \phi$$

where

$$\phi = \omega t - \kappa x + \delta$$

ϕ is the phase of the wave. The quantity δ is the value of the phase at $t = 0$ and $x = 0$, and may therefore be termed the initial phase. For any one wave δ may always be made zero by a suitable choice of coordinate axes. Thus for one wave the initial phase δ is of no particular importance. However, if two (or more) waves are compared then δ is an important quantity. For waves with the same ω and κ, δ may form the only difference between the two waves. It is quite useful to give δ a special name, and the name "epoch angle," often used, will be appropriate.

The all important quantity characterizing a single wave is its phase ϕ. For our simple harmonic wave the phase is also a function of both the space variable x and the time t. However, for fixed x, ϕ is a linear function of t and similarly for fixed t, ϕ is a linear function of x.

Let us write the phase in one of its equivalent forms, namely

$$\phi = \kappa(x - ct) + \delta$$

and go to the moving system of axes introduced before. Substituting

$$x = x' + ct$$

we obtain

$$\phi = \kappa x' + \delta$$

If we place ourselves at some point x_0' fixed in the moving frame of reference, then

$$\phi_0 = \kappa x_0' + \delta = \text{constant}$$

This will be so for any time t. We have placed ourselves in a condition of constant phase. In reality we will be travelling with the velocity c, having attached ourselves, as it were, to some point of the wave.

In studying wave motion for the first time we must ask ourselves the question: What is it that is propagated with the wave? We know that even for matter waves, such as surface water waves, no substance is propagated. We avoid a mathematical analysis by simply stating that *it is the condition of constant phase which is being propagated.* This last statement can be taken as a definition of the monochromatic wave considered here.

To find the velocity of propagation of this single wave we write

$$\omega t - \kappa x + \delta = \phi_0$$

and

$$\omega \, dt - \kappa \, dx = 0$$

or

$$\frac{dx}{dt} = \frac{\omega}{\kappa}$$

which, of course, just confirms our previous results. The velocity obtained is called the *phase velocity* of the wave.

REFERENCES

The list of references given below contains only a fraction of the books published in English on the subject of classical mechanics and related topics. Most of the books cited contain an extensive list of references of their own, and a student of classical mechanics will have no difficulty in compiling his own list.

1. Logical Foundations and Basic Methods of Physics.

Lindsay, R. B. and Morgenau, H., *Foundations of Physics*, J. Wiley and Sons, New York (1936).

This book discusses logical foundations of all branches of physics and carefully develops the concepts and methods used in all the major parts of physics. Classical mechanics is treated generously.

2. Elementary Mechanics.

There is a vast number of books on elementary mechanics, and they all seem to fall into two categories, viz., books for physicists and books on engineering mechanics. The first stress the theory, and the engineering books concentrate more on a great variety of problems. Both types of books have merit, but the physicist often tends to ignore books on engineering mechanics. It might be advisable that the student of physics in his early undergraduate years should pick up a book on engineering mechanics and solve about two hundred problems. He will be amazed to find out what a variety of problems can be solved by the application of elementary principles of mechanics.

Hidgon, A. and Stiles, W. B., *Engineering Mechanics*, Second edition, Prentice-Hall, Englewood Cliffs, N. J. (1955).

The same authors have also written a ''vector edition'' of the same text. A popular book on engineering mechanics; one of its merits is the great variety of problems solved in the text and the great multitude of problems to be solved by the student.

Meriam, J. L., *Mechanics*, Part 1: *Statics*, Part 2: *Dynamics* (in two separate volumes or in one volume), J. Wiley and Sons, New York (1959).

An elegantly written and elegantly edited book on engineering mechanics containing several solved problems.

Stephenson, R. J., *Mechanics and Properties of Matter*, Second edition, J. Wiley and Sons, New York (1960).

In many instances, this book actually goes beyond the elementary level of classical mechanics, but it only briefly introduces Lagrange's equations and does not treat small oscillations at all. This seems to be just the right book for a course in mechanics after elementary physics and before another course in advanced mechanics. Here you will find treated with great care the theories of harmonic motions, elementary elasticity in many of its aspects, hydrostatics, hydrodynamics, viscosity and quite a detailed discussion of wave motion.

3. Books on a Level Roughly the Same as this book.

Ames, J. S. and Murnaghan, F. D., *Theoretical Mechanics*, Ginn and Co., Boston (1929).

A thorough and extensive treatment of all basic branches of classical mechanics with a sound mathematical foundation.

Banach, S., *Mechanics*, Państwowe Towarzystwo Matematyczne, English translation by E. J. Scott of *Mechanika*, Państwowe Wydawnictwo Naukowe, Warszawa (1956).

The author, S. Banach, was a famous mathematician (Banach Spaces). It might seem that a man of his caliber would write a highly mathematical and specialized book. On the contrary, his book is a pedagogical masterpiece, and shows a great insight into the intricacies of mechanics.

Becker, R. A., *Introduction to Theoretical Mechanics*, McGraw-Hill, New York (1954).

This is a fine and quite popular book on mechanics. Only a relatively short part of it deals with the Lagrangian and Hamiltonian formulation, the rigid body motion, and the small oscillations. The student will value the many problems solved in the text.

Fowles, G. R., *Analytical Mechanics*, Holt, Rinehart and Winston, New York (1962).

A book which should be useful to students. Many basic problems are worked out in considerable detail.

Lamb, H., *Dynamics*, University Press, Cambridge, England (1929).

This older book on dynamics has an honored position in the physics library. Advanced topics are only touched upon but such topics as central forces and dissipative forces are covered in great detail with several examples.

McCuskey, S. W., *An Introduction to Advanced Dynamics*, Addison-Wesley, Reading, Mass. (1959).

A clear discussion of all the standard topics in advanced dynamics. Applications to several problems are worked out in detail.

Rutherford, D. E., *Classical Mechanics*, Oliver and Boyd, Edinburgh and London; Interscience Publishers, New York (1951).

A concise book on elementary and some advanced aspects of classical mechanics.

Slater, J. C., and Frank, N. H., *Mechanics*, McGraw-Hill, New York (1947).

The standard topics of classical mechanics are treated in a somewhat condensed but precise manner in the first half of this book. The second half deals with mechanics of continuous media. Here the problems of vibrating strings and membranes and some elements of hydrodynamics are treated quite thoroughly and extensively.

Symon, K. R., *Mechanics*, Addison-Wesley, Reading, Mass. (1953).

A well-written book, containing several applications of classical mechanics to other fields of physics.

Synge, J. L. and Griffith, B. A., *Principles of Mechanics*, McGraw-Hill, New York (1959).

A solid text on the basic principles of elementary and advanced mechanics. The lucid explanation of every part of mechanics is a truly remarkable feature of this book.

Taylor, E. F., *Introductory Mechanics*, J. Wiley, New York (1964).

A highly pedagogical text on the basic aspects of mechanics. The mathematical methods used in mechanics and its logical structure are introduced with utmost care. More than a quarter of this book is reserved for relativistic mechanics, again introduced with great care. Such fashionable topics as rockets and satellites are covered.

4. More Advanced Texts.

Corben, H. C. and Stehle, P., *Classical Mechanics*, J. Wiley and Sons, New York (1960).

An advanced well-written book on classical mechanics with application to various problems of interest in modern physics.

Goldstein, H., *Classical Mechanics*, Addison-Wesley, Reading, Mass. (1959).

An outstanding text on advanced classical mechanics. It is a self-contained treatment of classical mechanics which starts from elementary principles but quickly proceeds to advanced topics which culminate in canonical transformations, Hamilton-Jacobi theory and the Hamiltonian and Lagrangian formulation of continuous fields. One of the many good features of the book deals with the link of classical mechanics to other branches of physics.

Whittaker, E. T., *A Treatise on the Analytical Dynamics of Particles and Rigid Bodies*, 4th edition. Cambridge University Press, Cambridge, England; Dover Publications, New York (1944).

A classic in advanced dynamics and a standard reference for several advanced topics. It should be on every physicist bookshelf.

5. Theory of Wave Motion.

The wave aspect of nature is basic in many branches of physics including modern physics. Some basic aspects of the theory of wave motion are contained in Appendix C. The wave theory is discussed in many books on optics. We will cite only one reference on optics and one small monograph on waves.

Coulson, C. A. *Waves*, Oliver and Boyd, Edinburgh and London; Interscience Publishers, New York (1944).

A small monograph on the theory of wave motion and waves in elastic media, water waves, sound waves and electromagnetic waves.

Ditchburn, R. W., *Light*, 2nd edition, Blackie and Son, London (1963); Interscience Publishers, New York (1963).

Chapter two of this book contains an excellent introduction to the theory of wave motion. Most of the material in Appendix C is very similar to certain parts of this chapter.

6. Relativity.

Practically every modern book on advanced mechanics has a chapter or two on relativity mechanics. Also, several books on modern physics contain treatments of the relativity theory. Here we will only cite two monographs.

Bergmann, P. G., *Introduction to the Theory of Relativity*, Prentice-Hall, New York (1947).

A widely known advanced textbook on special and general theories of relativity including chapters on unified field theories.

Rindler, W. *Special Relativity*, Oliver and Boyd, Edinburgh and London; Interscience Publishers, New York (1960).

It is a self-contained book on the theory of special relativity. The first three chapters could be read with profit without any specialized preparation. The author of this book on relativity claims that these chapters are accessible to a ''casual reader''. The rest requires the formalism of the tensor calculus which is covered in an appendix.

7. Wave Mechanics.

The theory of relativity and quantum mechanics afford the modern description of nature. Whereas there are only a few books on relativity theory, the opposite is true in the case of quantum mechanics. Here we will mention some of them.

Bohm, D., *Quantum Theory*, Prentice-Hall, Englewood Cliffs, N. J. (1951).

The author did not spare any effort to discuss the historical, logical and physical aspects of the quantum theory. This, and the clear mathematical development of quantum theory, makes it a fine textbook for students.

Heitler, W., *Elementary Wave Mechanics*, Clarendon Press, Oxford (1946).

A small elementary book containing the essentials of quantum mechanics with some applications.

Rojansky, V., *Introductory Quantum Mechanics*, Prentice-Hall, New York (1938).

This is a text in which a lot of time is spent on elucidation of the methods used in quantum mechanics. For example, operator algebra is explained in great detail and is illustrated in many examples. The book is rather easy to follow.

Pauling, L. C. and Wilson, B. E. Jr., *Introduction to Quantum Mechanics with Applications to Chemistry*, McGraw-Hill, New York (1935).

This is one of the few books in which the quantum theory of the hydrogen atom is treated in every detail. All basic problems of quantum mechanics are discussed but the treatment of perturbation theory, so basic in quantum theory, is exceptionally clear.

8. Mathematical Background.

The mathematical tools necessary to follow the discussions of mechanics presented here mainly consist of vector and matrix algebras, and some elements of linear algebra. The essentials are given in Appendices A and B. The student will have no difficulty in supplementing this treatment in his course in mathematics or in many existing textbooks. Here we cite two only.

Aitken, A. C. *Determinants and Matrices*, Oliver and Boyd, Edinburgh and London; Interscience Publishers, New York (1944).

Rutherford, D. E., *Vector Methods*, Oliver and Boyd, Edinburgh and London; Interscience Publishers, New York (1957).

A concise treatment of vector algebra with applications to differential geometry, mechanics, and potential theory. The similarity of treatment of some of the topics treated in Appendix A and in Rutherford's book has the origin in the fact that the author had the good fortune of being Rutherford's student at St. Andrew's University in Scotland.

INDEX

1234567890